# MODERN CURRICULUM PRESS
# MATHEMAT[...]

## Teacher's Edition

## Level C

M000303992

**Royce Hargrove**                                **Richard Monnard**

## Acknowledgments

**Content Writers**   Babs Bell Hajdusiewicz
Phyllis Rosner
Laurel Sherman

**Contributors**   Linda Gojak
William Hunt
Christine Bhargava
Jean Laird
Roger Smalley
Erdine Bajbus
Rita Kuhar
Vicki Palisin
Jeanne White
Kathleen M. Becks
Jean Antonelli
Sandra J. Heldman
Susan McKenney
Nancy Toth
Nancy Ross
Connie Gorius
Denise Smith

**Project Director**   Dorothy A. Kirk

**Editors**   Martha Geyen
Phyllis Sibbing

**Editorial Staff**   Sharon M. Marosi
Ann Marie Murray
Patricia Kozak
Ruth Ziccardi

**Design**   John K. Crum
The Remen-Willis
Design Group

Cover Art . . . . . . . © 1993 Adam Peiperl

ISBN 0-8136-3118-1 (Teacher's Edition)        ISBN 0-8136-3111-4 (Pupil's Edition)
13 14 15   07 06 05 04

1-800-321-3106
www.pearsonlearning.com

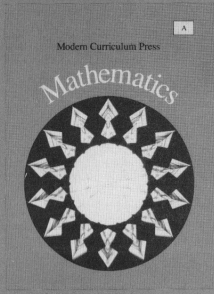

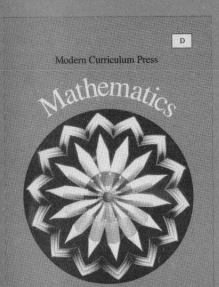

# Introducing
# Modern Curriculum Press Mathematics

## A Complete, Economical Math Series Teaching Problem-Solving Strategies, Critical-Thinking Skills, Estimation, Mental-Math Skills, and All Basic Math Concepts and Skills!

*Modern Curriculum Press Mathematics* is an alternative basal program for students in grades K-6. This unique developmental series is perfect for providing the flexibility teachers need for ability grouping. Its design encourages thinking skills, active participation, and mastery of skills within the context of problem-solving situations, abundant practice to master those skills, developed models students actively work with to solve problems, and reinforcement of problem-solving and strategies. Other features like these provide students with solid math instruction.

- Each lesson begins with a developed model that teaches algorithms and concepts in a problem-solving situation.

- Students are required to interact with the model by gathering data needed to solve the problem.

- A developmental sequence introduces and extends skills taught in the basal curriculum—including statistics, logic, and probability.

- An abundant practice of math skills ensures true mastery of mathematics.

- Estimation and mental math skills are stressed in all computational and problem-solving activities.

- Calculator activities introduce students to basic calculator skills and terms.

- Comprehensive **Teacher's Editions** provide abundant additional help for teachers in features like **Correcting Common Errors, Enrichment,** and **Extra Credit,** and the complete **Table of Common Errors.**

*Modern Curriculum Press Mathematics* is a comprehensive math program that will help students develop a solid mathematics background. This special sampler will show you how:

- **Developed Models** begin each lesson, demonstrate the algorithm and concept in a problem-solving situation, and get students actively involved with the model.

- **Getting Started** provides samples of the concept or skill that is taught and allows the teacher to observe students' understanding.

- **Practice, Apply,** and **Copy and Do** activities develop independent skills where students practice the algorithm and apply what they have learned in the lesson or from a previous lesson. **Excursion** activities extend the math skill and are fun to do.

- **Problem Solving** pages introduce students to the techniques of problem solving using a four-step model. **Apply** activities on these pages allow students to use problem-solving strategies they have learned in everyday situations. The second half of the page focuses on higher-order thinking skills.

- **Chapter Test** pages provide both students and teachers with a checkpoint that tests all the skills taught in the chapter. There are alternative Chapter Tests based on the same objectives at the end of each student book.

- **Cumulative Review** pages maintain skills that have been taught not only in the previous chapter, but all skills taught up to this point. A standardized test format is used beginning at the middle of the second grade text.

- **Calculator** pages teach students the various functions and the basic skills needed to use calculators intelligently.

- **Teacher Edition** pages feature reduced student pages with answers, objectives, suggestions for **Teaching the Lesson, Materials, Correcting Common Errors, Enrichment,** and more.

# A Developed Model Gets Students To Think, Actively Participate, And Understand Math Skills!

The major difference between *Modern Curriculum Press Mathematics* and other math programs is the developed model in which students actively work. Every lesson of *Modern Curriculum Press Mathematics* features concept development based on this developed model. Students are required to interact with this model discriminating what data is needed to solve the problem. This process teaches and reinforces their thinking skills and gets them actively involved providing the motivation to read and understand. The four-step teaching strategy of SEE, PLAN, DO, CHECK successfully increases students' understanding and provides a firm foundation for total math master of skills.

■ One major objective is the focus of every two-page lesson.

■ An algorithm or a model word problem keeps students interested and involved and provides a purpose for learning.

---

### Dividing by 4

Therese is using baskets of flowers to decorate the tables

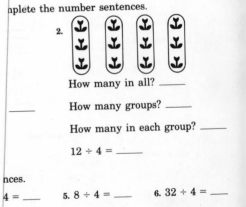

r of flowers that asket.

make up.

the baskets.

rs, we divide

wers into each basket.

mplete the number sentences.

2.

How many in all? _____

How many groups? _____

How many in each group? _____

$12 \div 4 =$ _____

ces.

4 = _____    5. $8 \div 4 =$ _____    6. $32 \div 4 =$ _____

---

### Reviewing Addition Facts

Aaron left home early one morning to walk to the library, before he went to school. How many blocks did he walk on his way to school?

We want to know the number of blocks Aaron walked all together.

We know that he walked _____ blocks from his house to the library.

He walked another _____ blocks from the library to school.
To find the total number of blocks, we add

_____ and _____.

Home ●————————● Library

School

```
0  1  2  3  4  5  6  7  8  9  10  11  12  13  14  15  16  17  18
```

$7 + 6 =$ _____
addends   sum

$\begin{array}{r} 7 \\ + 6 \end{array}$ ←addends
← sum

$7 + 6 = 13$ is called a **number sentence.**

Aaron walked _____ blocks from his home to school.

### Getting Started

Complete the number sentences.

1. $4 + 2 =$ _____    2. $7 + 9 =$ _____    3. $8 + 3 =$ _____

4. $2 + 9 =$ _____    5. $5 + 6 =$ _____    6. $8 + 8 =$ _____

Add.

7. $\begin{array}{r} 8 \\ + 7 \end{array}$    8. $\begin{array}{r} 4 \\ + 1 \end{array}$    9. $\begin{array}{r} 9 \\ + 9 \end{array}$    10. $\begin{array}{r} 5 \\ + 5 \end{array}$    11. $\begin{array}{r} 3 \\ + 6 \end{array}$    12. $\begin{array}{r} 9 \\ + 4 \end{array}$

3

- Students interact with the artwork to gather data needed to solve problems. This interaction helps develop higher-order thinking skills.

- Each objective is introduced in a problem-solving setting developing problem-solving thinking skills.

- The four-step teaching method of SEE, PLAN, DO, CHECK guides students easily through the development of each skill.

- Students SEE the "input" sentences and the artwork and use them to help solve the problems. This allows them to be actively involved in their work.

- Students PLAN how they are going to solve problems using their reasoning skills to determine what operations are needed.

- Students use the model to help DO the problem. Each developed model shows students how to do the algorithm.

- To CHECK understanding of the math skill, a concluding sentence reinforces the problem-solving process.

- Important math vocabulary is bold-faced throughout the text and defined in context and in the glossary.

- A check (√) points out important concepts to which students should give special attention.

## Place Value through Thousands

The government space agency plans to sell used moon buggies to the highest bidders. What did Charley pay for the one he bought?

We want to understand the cost of Charley's moon buggy.

Charley paid exactly _____.
To understand how much money this is, we will look at the place value of each digit in the price.

✔ The numbers 0, 1, 2, 3, 4, 5, 6, 7, 8 and 9 are called **digits**. The position of the digit decides its place value.

| thousands | hundreds | tens | ones |
|-----------|----------|------|------|
| ___ | ___ | ___ | ___ |

In 7,425, the digit 4 represents hundreds, and the digit 7 represents _____.
Numbers can be written in **standard** or **expanded form**.

Standard Form
7,425

Expanded Form
7,000 + 400 + 20 + 5

We say Charley paid **seven thousand, four hundred twenty-five dollars.** We write _____.

### Getting Started

Write in standard form.

1. five thousand, six hundred fifty-eight _____

2. 3,000 + 50 + 8 _____

Write in words.

3. 6,497

4. 823

5. 9,045

_____

_____

_____

Write the place value of the red digits.

6. 3,948

7. 9,603

8. 7,529

9. $5,370

_____

_____

7

## Subtracting Fractions with Unlike

Duncan is feeding the chickens on his uncle's farm. When he started, there were $4\frac{1}{2}$ buckets of chicken feed. How much feed has he used?

We want to know how much chicken feed Duncan has used.

We know that he started with ____ buckets

of feed, and he has ____ buckets left.

To find the amount used, we subtract the amount left from the original amount.

We subtract ____ from ____.

To subtract fractions with unlike denominator follow these steps:

| Rename the fractions as equivalent fractions with the least common denominator |
|---|

$$4\frac{1}{2} = 4\frac{2}{4}$$
$$-1\frac{1}{4} = 1\frac{1}{4}$$

| Subtract the fractions. |
|---|

$$4\frac{1}{2} = 4\frac{2}{4}$$
$$-1\frac{1}{4} = 1\frac{1}{4}$$
$$\frac{1}{4}$$

Duncan has used ____ buckets of feed.

### Getting Started

Subtract.

1. $15\frac{5}{8}$
   $-7\frac{1}{3}$

2. $87\frac{2}{3}$
   $-39\frac{1}{6}$

3.

Copy and subtract.

5. $\frac{7}{8} - \frac{1}{4} =$ ____

6. $\frac{5}{6} - \frac{1}{2} =$ ____

7. $\frac{9}{10} - \frac{6}{15} =$ ____

127

T-5

## TEACHER-GUIDED PRACTICE ACTIVITIES CHECK STUDENTS' UNDERSTANDING OF MATH CONCEPTS!

**G**etting Started activities provide the opportunity for students to try to do what they've just learned and for teachers a chance to check understanding. These activities also allow the teacher to evaluate students' progress in a particular objective before continuing on in the lesson. A complete **Table of Common Errors** can be found in the **Teacher's Editions.** This list helps the teacher diagnose and correct those errors identified by research to be the most common. Lesson plans offer specific suggestions for dealing with each individual error, so the teacher can concentrate on those are where students need help. Showing t teacher ways to keep errors from hap pening by alerting to common mistakes, will make teaching math go more smoothly.

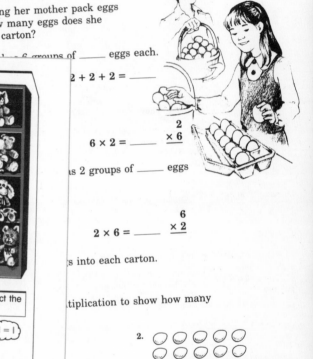

### Multiplying, the Factor 2

Sun Li is helping her mother pack eggs in cartons. How many eggs does she pack into each carton?

_____ 6 groups of _____ eggs each.

$2 + 2 + 2 =$ _____

$6 \times 2 =$ _____ $\begin{array}{r} 2 \\ \times 6 \\ \hline \end{array}$

_____ 2 groups of _____ eggs

$2 \times 6 =$ _____ $\begin{array}{r} 6 \\ \times 2 \\ \hline \end{array}$

_____ into each carton.

_____ multiplication to show how many

2.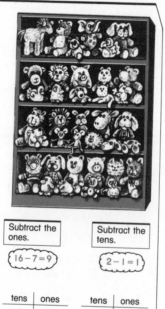

$2 + 2 + 2 + 2 + 2 =$ _____

$5 \times 2 =$ _____

$2 \times 5 =$ _____

4. $2 \times 6 =$ _____    5. $\begin{array}{r} 4 \\ \times 2 \\ \hline \end{array}$    6. $\begin{array}{r} 2 \\ \times 2 \\ \hline \end{array}$

(one hundred nineteen) **119**

---

### Subtracting 2-digit Numbers

Annie collects stuffed animals. She must take 17 of them to school for a display. How many are left at home?

We want to know how many animals she left at home.

Annie has _____ stuffed animals.

She is taking _____ animals to school. To find how many animals she left at home, we subtract _____ from _____.

✔ Subtract the ones first.

| Do you need more ones? | Trade 1 ten to get 10 ones. | Subtract the ones. | Subtract the tens. |
|---|---|---|---|
| $6 - 7 = ?$ Yes, you need more ones. | Now there are 2 tens and 16 ones. | $16 - 7 = 9$ | $2 - 1 = 1$ |

| tens | ones |
|---|---|
| 3 | 6 |
| −1 | 7 |
| | ? |

| tens | ones |
|---|---|
| $\overset{2}{3}$ | $\overset{16}{\cancel{6}}$ |
| −1 | 7 |
| | 9 |

| tens | ones |
|---|---|
| $\overset{2}{3}$ | $\overset{16}{\cancel{6}}$ |
| −1 | 7 |
| 1 | 9 |

Annie left _____ stuffed animals at home.

### Getting Started

Subtract. Trade if needed.

1.
| tens | ones |
|---|---|
| 9 | 3 |
| −5 | 9 |

2.
| tens | ones |
|---|---|
| 6 | 2 |
| −3 | 6 |

3.
| tens | ones |
|---|---|
| 8 | 4 |
| −2 | 9 |

4.
| tens | ones |
|---|---|
| 8 | 8 |
| −1 | 8 |

Subtracting 2-digit numbers, with trading

(one hundred forty-nine) **149**

Samples that the students work allow
e teacher to check students' under-
anding of the skill.

Students gain both confidence and
ompetence in working these prob-
ms.

If the objective is not fully grasped by
e student, the **Table of Common Er-
rs** will help the teacher deal with
ach individual type of error.

■Students gain a deeper understanding
of the basic algorithm introduced in
the developed model.

■New skills are reinforced through the
sample problems students work right
on the spot.

■Teachers observe any typical student
errors before continuing additional
work in the lesson.

■Teacher-guided practice activities
will encourage classroom discussion.

■**Getting Started** activities help the
teacher to single out predictable errors
quickly.

■All samples found in the **Getting
Started** activities prepare students to
work the exercises found in the next
part of the lesson.

---

## Using Customary Units of Length

Robert, Janis and Jonathan are being
measured for band uniforms. What
is Robert's height in inches?

We want to rename Robert's height in inches.

We know that he is ____ feet ____ inches tall.

| |
|---|
| 12 inches (in.) = 1 foot (ft) |
| 3 feet = 1 yard (yd) |
| 36 inches = 1 yard |
| 5,280 feet = 1 mile (mi) |
| 1,760 yards = 1 mile |

____ches as inches, we multiply
____ the number of inches in a
____ extra inches.

____ and add ____.

____ll.

____ber like $5\frac{1}{2}$ feet as inches, we

____ inches

____ as larger units, like 48 inches

____ rename larger units as
____name smaller units as larger ones.

____easurements of length.

| 3 yd 1 ft | |
|---|---|
| − 1 yd 2 ft | 1 yd = 3 ft |
| 1 yd 2 ft | 3 ft + 1 ft = 4 ft |

Add or subtract.

**3.**  6 ft  9 in.
  − 2 ft 11 in.

**4.**  7 yd 2 ft 3 in.
  − 5 yd 1 ft 6 in.

217

---

## Addition and Subtraction Properties

Properties are like special tools. They
make the job of adding and
subtracting much easier.

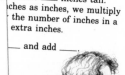

*Twelve minus nine is three.*

*That's right because nine plus three is twelve.*

### Addition

**Order Property**
We can add in any order.

$5 + 2 = 7$     $2 + 5 = 7$

$3 + 6 + 7 = $ ____     $7 + 3 + 6 = $ ____

**Grouping Property**
We can change the grouping.
✔ Remember to add the numbers in
parentheses first.

$(6 + 3) + 5 = 14$     $6 + (3 + 5) = 14$

$(8 + 2) + 4 = $ ____     $8 + (2 + 4) = $ ____

**Zero Property**
Adding zero makes the sum the same
as the other addend.

$5 + 0 = 5$          $0 + 7 = 7$

$0 + 1 = $ ____          $8 + 0 = $ ____

### Subtraction

**Subtracting Zero**
Subtracting zero makes the difference
the same as the minuend.

$9 - 0 = 9$          $7 - 0 = $ ____

**Subtracting a Number
from Itself**
Subtracting a number from itself
leaves zero.

$8 - 8 = 0$          $3 - 3 = $ ____

**Checking Subtraction**
Subtracting is the reverse of adding.

$15 - 9 = 6$ because $6 + 9 = 15$

$12 - 7 = $ ____

because  ____ + ____ = ____

✔ **Solving for *n*** is finding the value for the *n* in
the equation.

### Getting Started

Solve for *n*.

**1.** $0 + 0 = n$

$n = $ ____

**2.** $0 + 6 = n$

$n = $ ____

Subtract. Check by adding.

**3.**   15
   − 9

**4.**   12
   − 7

**5.**   18
   − 9

Add. Check by grouping the addends another way.

**6.**   5
   3
  + 4

**7.**   2
   6
  + 3

**8.**   6
   3
  + 4

**9.** $(5 + 2) + 6 = n$

$n = $ ____

**10.** $3 + (5 + 4) = n$

$n = $ ____

3

T-7

# INDEPENDENT PRACTICE ACTIVITIES PROVIDE PLENTY OF DRILL, PRACTICE, AND EXTENSION IN A VARIETY OF FORMATS!

The purpose of building skills is to ensure that students can use and apply those skills. That goal can only be reached when skills are clearly and systematically taught and then practiced. With *Modern Curriculum Press Mathematics*, the teacher can be as-sured that students will have abundant opportunities to practice their newly-learned math skills. The variety of practice activities allows the teacher to meet the needs of every student. Work-ing independently helps students strengthen new skills, become more confident, and increase their under-standing. Practice helps students le* Some students need more practice t others to help them catch on. *Mode Curriculum Press Mathematics* offer variety of practice situations so that students stay on target with what the are learning.

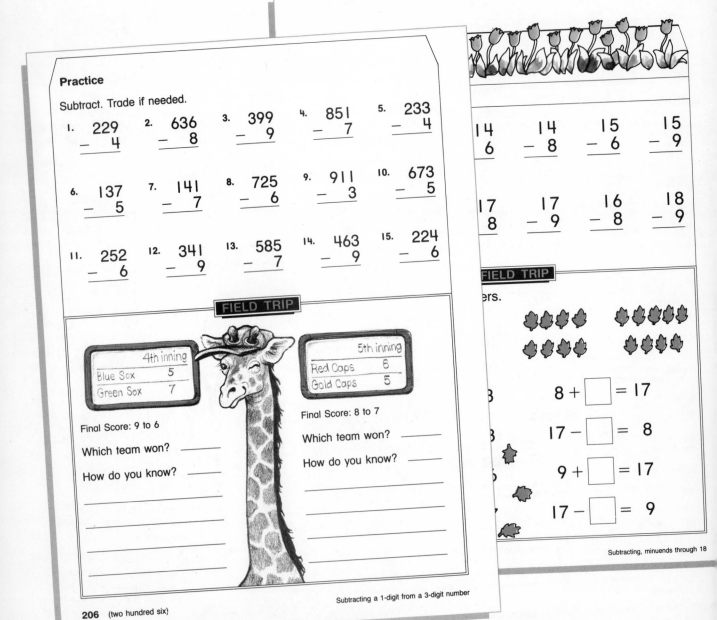

**Practice**

Subtract. Trade if needed.

1. 229 − 4
2. 636 − 8
3. 399 − 9
4. 851 − 7
5. 233 − 4
6. 137 − 5
7. 141 − 7
8. 725 − 6
9. 911 − 3
10. 673 − 5
11. 252 − 6
12. 341 − 9
13. 585 − 7
14. 463 − 9
15. 224 − 6

**FIELD TRIP**

4th inning
Blue Sox — 5
Green Sox — 7

Final Score: 9 to 6

Which team won? _____

How do you know? _____

5th inning
Red Caps — 8
Gold Caps — 5

Final Score: 8 to 7

Which team won? _____

How do you know? _____

206 (two hundred six)

Subtracting a 1-digit from a 3-digit number

14 − 6
14 − 8
15 − 6
15 − 9
17 − 8
17 − 9
16 − 8
18 − 9

**FIELD TRIP**

ers.

8 + ☐ = 17

17 − ☐ = 8

9 + ☐ = 17

17 − ☐ = 9

Subtracting, minuends through 18

T-8

he teacher can begin the process of individual mastery by assigning **Practice** exercises that students can work independently.

*Modern Curriculum Press Mathematics* integrates problem solving into the practice activities with **Apply** problems. Some of these problems relate to the algorithm. However, some require previously-learned skills encouraging students to think and maintain skills.

Both vertical and horizontal forms of problems are used making students more comfortable with forms found in standardized test formats.

■ An emphasis on practical skills encourages learning by applying math to everyday situations.

■ Independent practice provides more opportunities for application and higher-order thinking skills.

■ The variety of practice activities keeps students motivated and interested in learning.

■ **Copy and Do** exercises check students' ability to assemble an algorithm from an equation and gives them practice in transferring information.

■ **Excursion** activities extend the basic skill work and are fun to do. The teacher can challenge the more capable students with these mind-stretching activities.

■ Giving students ample opportunities to practice and strengthen new skills builds solid skill development and helps the teacher more easily measure the results.

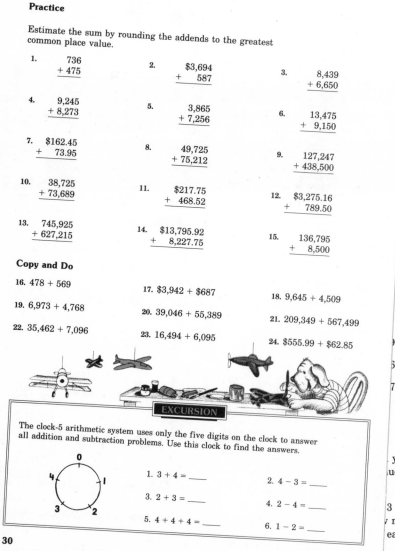

### Practice

Estimate the sum by rounding the addends to the greatest common place value.

| | | | |
|---|---|---|---|
| 1. | 736 <br> + 475 | 2. | $3,694 <br> + 587 | 3. | 8,439 <br> + 6,650 |

4.
9,245
+ 8,273

5.
3,865
+ 7,256

6.
13,475
+ 9,150

7.
$162.45
+ 73.95

8.
49,725
+ 75,212

9.
127,247
+ 438,500

10.
38,725
+ 73,689

11.
$217.75
+ 468.52

12.
$3,275.16
+ 789.50

13.
745,925
+ 627,215

14.
$13,795.92
+ 8,227.75

15.
136,795
+ 8,500

### Copy and Do

16. 478 + 569

17. $3,942 + $687

18. 9,645 + 4,509

19. 6,973 + 4,768

20. 39,046 + 55,389

21. 209,349 + 567,499

22. 35,462 + 7,096

23. 16,494 + 6,095

24. $555.99 + $62.85

EXCURSION

The clock-5 arithmetic system uses only the five digits on the clock to answer all addition and subtraction problems. Use this clock to find the answers.

1. 3 + 4 = _____

2. 4 − 3 = _____

3. 2 + 3 = _____

4. 2 − 4 = _____

5. 4 + 4 + 4 = _____

6. 1 − 2 = _____

30

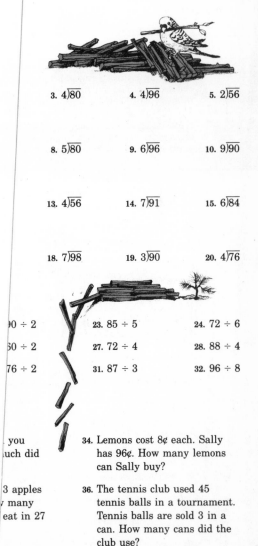

3. 4)80   4. 4)96   5. 2)56

8. 5)80   9. 6)96   10. 9)90

13. 4)56   14. 7)91   15. 6)84

18. 7)98   19. 3)90   20. 4)76

90 ÷ 2   23. 85 ÷ 5   24. 72 ÷ 6

60 ÷ 2   27. 72 ÷ 4   28. 88 ÷ 4

76 ÷ 2   31. 87 ÷ 3   32. 96 ÷ 8

you
uch did

3 apples
y many
eat in 27

34. Lemons cost 8¢ each. Sally has 96¢. How many lemons can Sally buy?

36. The tennis club used 45 tennis balls in a tournament. Tennis balls are sold 3 in a can. How many cans did the club use?

# MATH COMES ALIVE WHEN STUDENTS LEARN TO INTEGRATE COMPUTATION, PROBLEM-SOLVING STRATEGIES, AND REASONING TO MAKE DECISIONS FOR THEMSELVES!

Problem-solving pages present lessons that increase understanding with a four-step teaching strategy: SEE, PLAN, DO, CHECK. *Modern Curriculum Press Mathematics* offers step-by-step instruction in how to understand word problems as well as varied practice in actually using the skills learned. Each lesson focuses on a different problem-solving strategy. These strategies develop students' higher-order thinking skills and help them success-fully solve problems. Step-by-step, students will understand the question, find the information needed, plan a solution, and then check it for accuracy. This develops students' critical-thinking skills and ability to apply what they've learned to solve problems that go beyond basic operations.

■ Word problems utilize high-interest information and focus on everyday situations.

## PROBLEM SOLVING

### Drawing a Picture

A parking lot has 9 rows of 8 parking spaces each. The fourth and fifth spaces in every third row have trees in them. The outside spaces in every row are reserved for the handicapped or for emergency vehicles. How many regular parking spaces are there in the lot?

★ SEE

We want to know how many spaces are left for regular parking.

There are _____ rows of parking spaces.

There are _____ spaces in each row.

In every third row, _____ spaces are lost to trees.

In every row _____ spaces are used for special vehicles.

★ PLAN

We can draw a picture of the parking lot, crossing out the closed parking spaces. Then we can count the regular spaces left.

★ DO

We count _____ spaces left for regular parking.

★ CHECK

We can check by adding the spaces open in each row.

$4 + 6 + 6 + 4 + 6 + 6 + 4 + 6 + 6 =$ _____

ch problem.

2. A Super-Duper ball bounces twice its height when it is dropped. Carl dropped a Super-Duper ball from the roof of a 12-foot garage. How high will the ball bounce after 5 bounces?

4. The distance around a rectangle is 10 centimeters. The length of each of the two longer sides is 3 centimeters. What is the length of each of the two shorter sides?

6. What 7 coins together make 50 cents?

173

**T-10**

Step by step, students learn to understand the question, find the information they need, plan a method of solution, find an answer, and check it for accuracy.

Every step of the process is organized so that students truly understand how to arrive at the solution.

The problem-solving banner alerts students that they are involved in a problem-solving lesson. These focused lessons remind students how to approach problems and how to use skills and specific strategies already learned.

■ Learning to integrate computation, problem-solving strategies, and reasoning makes math come alive for students.

■ Problems incorporate previously taught computational skills—focusing students' minds on the problem-solving process itself.

■ Problem-solving applications appear in every problem-solving lesson. This frequent practice reduces apprehension and builds confidence.

■ Practice in applying the strategies gives students a chance to use skills in routine and non-routine problems.

■ In every chapter, problem-solving strategies and critical-thinking skills are developed, applied, and reinforced.

■ Students choose appropriate strategies to solve problems and are challenged to formulate their own problems and to change the conditions in existing problems.

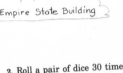
Empire State Building

## PROBLEM SOLVING

### Collecting Data, Determining Missing Data

Which of the following is the tallest structure: Sears Tower in Chicago, CN Tower in Toronto, World Trade Center in New York or the John Hancock Center in Chicago?

Sears Tower

CN Tower

John Hancock Center

World Trade Center

★ SEE

We want to find out which is the tallest structure.
We do not have enough information to solve this problem.

★ PLAN

We need to find the height of each structure. We can

find this information by looking in _____.
Once we have this information we can compare the heights to find the tallest structure.

★ DO

Use a reference book such as an encyclopedia or an almanac to find the height of each structure.

Sears Tower _____

CN Tower _____

World Trade Center _____

John Hancock Center _____

The _____ is the tallest of the four structures.

★ CHECK

We can check by verifying this data in another reference book, and by listing the heights of the four structures in order from largest to smallest.

and
rm the
and
number
number

es in your
k. Explain
s are

assroom
date. Find
of each of
hem in
est.

d sideways,
the distance
ur left hand
right hand.
ht, and
lts. Do this
hat do you
easurements?

2. Roll a pair of dice 30 times and record the number of times each sum appears. Perform the experiment a second time. What sum appears most often? What sum appears least often?

4. Toss a coin 50 times and record the number of heads and tails. Which side of the coin appears most often?

6. Record the dates of the coins available in your classroom. How many years difference exist between the newest and oldest coin?

8. An arithmetic game is created by adding the values of certain U.S. currency. Since a portrait of George Washington appears on a $1 bill and a portrait of Abraham Lincoln appears on the $5 bill, we say that George Washington + Abraham Lincoln = $6. Find the value of Thomas Jefferson + Alexander Hamilton + Woodrow Wilson.

251

## CHAPTER TEST PAGES PROVIDE A VEHICLE FOR STUDENT EVALUATION AND FEEDBACK!

Every chapter in *Modern Curriculum Press Mathematics* concludes with a **Chapter Test.** These tests provide the opportunity for students to demonstrate their mastery of recently acquired skills. **Chapter Test** pages enable the teacher to measure all the basic skills students have practiced in the lesson and evaluate their understanding. The focus of these pages is the assessing of mastery of algorithms. An adequate number of sample problems are provided to accomplish this. This important checkpoint helps the teacher to better meet individual student-computational needs.

■ **Chapter Test** pages are carefully correlated to what has been taught throughout the entire series.

■ **Chapter Test** pages assess students' mastery of all the skills taught in the lesson.

■ All directions are written in an easy-to-follow format.

■ Both vertical and horizontal forms of problems are used making students more comfortable with exercises found in standardized tests.

■ In the back of each student book, there is an alternate **Chapter Test** for each chapter based on the same objectives covered in the first test.

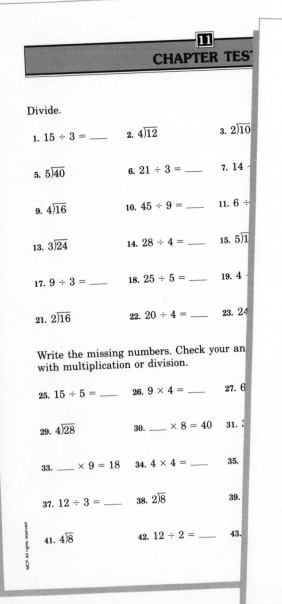

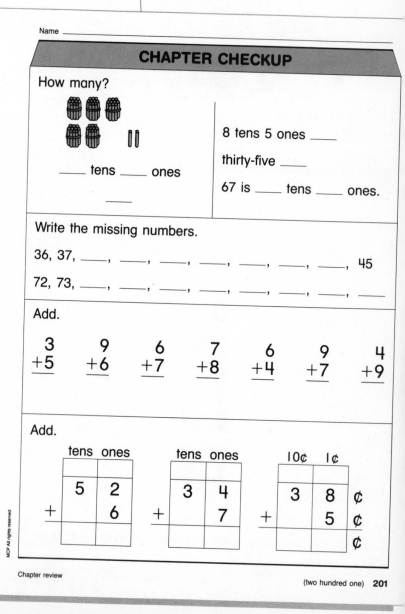

# SYSTEMATIC MAINTENANCE IS PROVIDED AT EVERY LEVEL WITH CUMULATIVE REVIEW PAGES!

Every chapter contains a **Cumulative Review** page that provides an on-going refresher course in basic skills. These pages maintain the skills that have been taught in the chapter plus the skills learned in previous chapters.

**Cumulative Review** pages actually reach back into the text for a total maintenance of skills. **Cumulative Review** pages are progressive instruction because they build on the foundation laid earlier for a thorough and sequential program of review. A standardized test format is used beginning at the middle of the second grade. Students will benefit by gaining experience in dealing with this special test format.

- A variety of problems done in standardized test format give students a better chance to score well on these tests.

- Directions are minimal and easy to understand.

- Design elements on every test are the same found on standardized tests.

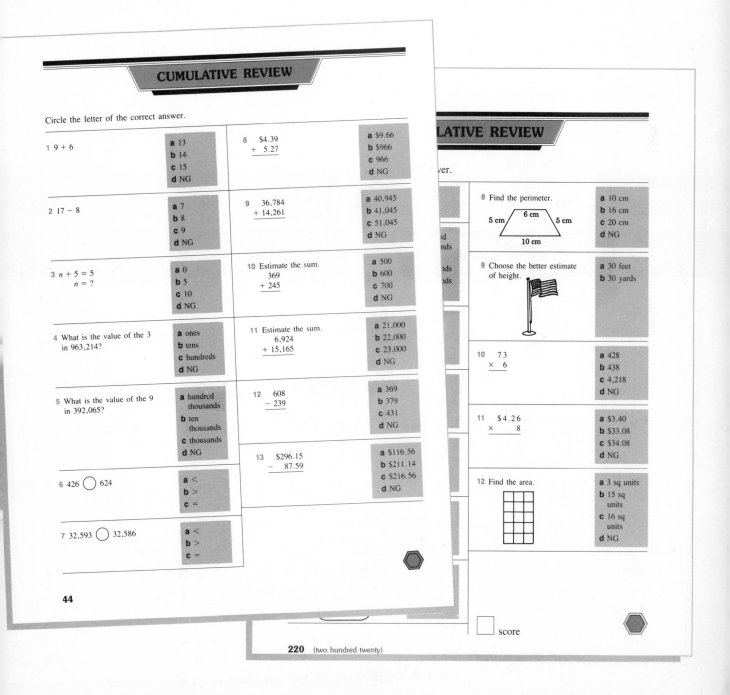

## CUMULATIVE REVIEW

Circle the letter of the correct answer.

1. $9 + 6$
   - **a** 13
   - **b** 14
   - **c** 15
   - **d** NG

2. $17 - 8$
   - **a** 7
   - **b** 8
   - **c** 9
   - **d** NG

3. $n + 5 = 5$
   $n = ?$
   - **a** 0
   - **b** 5
   - **c** 10
   - **d** NG

4. What is the value of the 3 in 963,214?
   - **a** ones
   - **b** tens
   - **c** hundreds
   - **d** NG

5. What is the value of the 9 in 392,065?
   - **a** hundred thousands
   - **b** ten thousands
   - **c** thousands
   - **d** NG

6. 426 ◯ 624
   - **a** <
   - **b** >
   - **c** =

7. 32,593 ◯ 32,586
   - **a** <
   - **b** >
   - **c** =

8. $\begin{array}{r} \$4.39 \\ + \ 5.27 \end{array}$
   - **a** $9.66
   - **b** $966
   - **c** 966
   - **d** NG

9. $\begin{array}{r} 36,784 \\ + 14,261 \end{array}$
   - **a** 40,945
   - **b** 41,045
   - **c** 51,045
   - **d** NG

10. Estimate the sum.
    $\begin{array}{r} 369 \\ + 245 \end{array}$
    - **a** 500
    - **b** 600
    - **c** 700
    - **d** NG

11. Estimate the sum.
    $\begin{array}{r} 6,924 \\ + 15,165 \end{array}$
    - **a** 21,000
    - **b** 22,000
    - **c** 23,000
    - **d** NG

12. $\begin{array}{r} 608 \\ - 239 \end{array}$
    - **a** 369
    - **b** 379
    - **c** 431
    - **d** NG

13. $\begin{array}{r} \$296.15 \\ - \ \ 87.59 \end{array}$
    - **a** $116.56
    - **b** $211.14
    - **c** $216.56
    - **d** NG

44

8. Find the perimeter.
   5 cm / 6 cm / 5 cm / 10 cm
   - **a** 10 cm
   - **b** 16 cm
   - **c** 20 cm
   - **d** NG

9. Choose the better estimate of height.
   - **a** 30 feet
   - **b** 30 yards

10. $\begin{array}{r} 73 \\ \times \ \ 6 \end{array}$
    - **a** 428
    - **b** 438
    - **c** 4,218
    - **d** NG

11. $\begin{array}{r} \$4.26 \\ \times \ \ \ \ 8 \end{array}$
    - **a** $3.40
    - **b** $33.08
    - **c** $34.08
    - **d** NG

12. Find the area.
    - **a** 3 sq units
    - **b** 15 sq units
    - **c** 16 sq units
    - **d** NG

score

# CALCULATOR LESSONS PROVIDE EXCITING LEARNING ACTIVITIES AND ADD INTEREST AND PRACTICALITY TO MATH!

**C**alculator lessons are found throughout *Modern Curriculum Press Mathematics*. The activities are used in many ways—to explore num-ber patterns, to do calculations, to check estimations, and to investigate functions. Each **Calculator** lesson is designed to help students learn to use and operate calculators while they re-inforce and improve their mathematical skills.

■ **Calculator** lessons teach students to use simple calculators while reinforc-ing chapter content.

■ **Calculator** lessons introduce student to basic calculator skills and terms.

■ Practical calculator activities promot student involvement as they take an active part in what they are learning.

■ Students learn, practice, and apply critical-thinking skills as they use cal-culators.

## Practice

Complete these calculator codes.

1. $85 \div 5 =$ ☐

2. $57 \div 3 =$ ☐

4. $96 \div 6 =$ ☐

6. $90 \div 9 =$ ☐

8. $63 \div 7 \times 8 =$ ☐

10. $75 \div 5 \times 6 =$ ☐

12. $216 - 158 \div 2 =$ ☐

14. Nathan can jog 5 miles in 65 minutes. How long will it take Nathan to jog 8 miles?

16. Bananas are on sale at 6 for 96¢. How much do 8 bananas cost?

RCURSION

2. The sum of 2 numbers is 60. Their difference is 12. What are the numbers?

4. Five times one number is three more than six times another number. The difference between the numbers is 1. What are the numbers?

## Calculators, the Division Key

Natalie is packing lunches for a picnic. She needs to buy 5 apples. How much will Natalie pay for the 5 apples?

Apples 3 for 51¢

We want to know the price for 5 apples.

We know that _____ apples cost _____.

To find the cost of 5 apples, we first find the cost of 1 by dividing _____ by _____. Then, we multiply the cost of 1 apple by _____.

This can be done on the calculator in one code.

$\cdot$ $51 \div 3 \times 5 =$ ☐

Natalie will pay _____ for 5 apples.

Complete these calculator codes.

1. $42 \div 7 =$ ☐

3. $96 \div 4 =$ ☐

5. $36 \div 9 \times 7 =$ ☐

7. $72 \div 6 \times 9 =$ ☐

2. $76 \div 2 =$ ☐

4. $52 \div 4 =$ ☐

6. $84 \div 4 \times 3 =$ ☐

8. $75 \div 5 \times 9 =$ ☐

139

## PLAN CLASSROOM-READY MATH LESSONS IN MINUTES WITH COMPREHENSIVE TEACHER'S EDITIONS!

The **Teacher's Editions** of *Modern Curriculum Press Mathematics* are designed and organized with the teacher in mind. The full range of options provides more help than ever before and guarantees efficient use of the teacher's planning time and the most effective results for efforts exerted.

Each **Teacher's Edition** provides an abundance of additional **Enrichment, Correcting Common Errors** and application activities. Plus they contain a complete **Error Pattern Analysis.** The teacher will also find reduced student pages with answers, objectives, suggestions for teaching lessons, materials, **Mental Math** exercises, and more.

■ There's no need for the teacher to struggle with two separate books because student pages are reduced in the **Teacher's Edition.**

■ Clear headings and notes make it easy for the teacher to find what is needed before teaching the lesson.

■ The teacher will be more effective with lesson plans that are always complete in two pages and include everything needed.

■ Student **Objectives** set a clear course for the lesson goal.

---

### Time to the Half-hour
**pages 163-164**

#### Objective
To practice telling time to the hour and half-hour

#### Materials
*Demonstration clock
*Two pencils of different lengths

#### Mental Math
Which is less?
1. 2 dimes or 5 nickels (2 dimes)
2. 14 pennies or 2 nickels (2 nickels)
3. 5 nickels or 4 dimes (5 nickels)
4. 1 quarter or 2 dimes (2 dimes)
5. 6 nickels or 1 quarter (1 quarter)

#### Skill Review
Show times to the hour and half hour on the demonstration clock. Have students write the time on the board. Now have a student set the clock to show an hour or half-hour. Have the student ask another student to write the time on the board. Have a student write a time for the hour or half-hour and invite another student to place the hands on the clock to show the times.

#### Teaching page 163
On the demonstration clock, start at 12:00 and slowly move the minute hand around the clock. Ask students to tell what the hour hand does as the minute hand moves around the clock face. (moves slowly toward the next number) Tell students the minute hand moves around the clock face 60 minutes while the hour hand moves from one number to the next. Tell students there are 60 minutes in 1 hour.

Ask students to tell where the hour hand is on the first clock. (between 5 and 6) Ask where the minute hand is. (on 6) Ask the time. (5:30) Tell students to find 5:30 in the center column and trace the line from the clock to 5:30. Tell students to draw a line from each clock to its time.

Name _____

Match the clocks

Telling time to the hour and half-hour

**163**

---

### Multiplying, the Factor 5
**pages 125-126**

#### Objective
To multiply by the factor 5

#### Materials
none

#### Mental Math
Ask students to multiply 4 by:
1. the number of ears one person has. $(4 \times 2 = 8)$
2. the number of feet two students have. $(4 \times 4 = 16)$
3. the number of noses in a crowd of 7. $(4 \times 7 = 28)$
4. the number of their toes. $(4 \times 10 = 40)$

#### Skill Review
Have students make up a multiplication chart. Tell them to write 2, 3, 4 along the top, 2 through 10 along the side. Tell them to fill in the chart by multiplying each top number by each side number.

#### Teaching the Lesson

**Introducing the Problem** Have students look at the calculator illustrated while you read the problem. Identify the question and explain that there are several ways they could answer it. Have students read the information sentences, filling in the information required. (5 rows, 5 keys) Read each sentence and tell students to do the indicated operation in their text while one student writes it on the board. Read the solution sentence aloud and have a student give the answer while the others complete that sentence in their texts. (30)

**125**

---

**Multiplying, the Factor 5**

Each key on a calculator has a special job to do. How many keys are there on the calculator keyboard?

We need to find the total number of keys on the calculator.

We can see there are ___5___ rows of keys.

Each row has ___5___ keys.

We can add. $5 + 5 + 5 + 5 + 5 =$ ___25___

We can also multiply.

$$5 \times 5 = \underline{25} \quad \begin{array}{r} 5 \\ \times 5 \\ \hline 25 \end{array}$$

There are ___25___ keys on the calculator keyboard.

#### Getting Started
Use both addition and multiplication to show how many are in the picture.

1.  $5 + 5 + 5 + 5 =$ ___20___

    $4 \times 5 =$ ___20___

    $5 \times 4 =$ ___20___

Multiply.

2. $\begin{array}{r} 3 \\ \times 5 \\ \hline 15 \end{array}$
3. $\begin{array}{r} 8 \\ \times 5 \\ \hline 40 \end{array}$
4. $5 \times 6 =$ ___30___
5. $9 \times 5 =$ ___45___

(one hundred twenty-five) **125**

**Developing the Skill** Have students start at 5 and count aloud by five's through 50. Ask a volunteer to continue through 100. Explain that this may seem easy because they are used to counting out nickels. Because five is also half of ten, and when counting by fives, every other number will be a multiple of ten. Now write these addition problems on the board and have students work them: $5 + 5 =$, $5 + 5 + 5 =$, $5 + 5 + 5 + 5 =$. (10, 15, 20) Next to each of these problems write the multiplication problem that corresponds. ($5 \times 2, 5 \times 3, 5 \times 4$) Have volunteers put the rest of the addition and multiplication problems for the factor five on the board, $5 \times 5$ through $5 \times 10$.

- A list of **Materials** helps the teacher reduce class preparation time.

- The **Mental Math** exercise gives the teacher an opportunity to brush-up on skills at the beginning of each day's lesson.

- **Skill Review** bridges new skills with previously-taught skills for total reinforcement.

- The **Teaching the Lesson** section is meant to give practical suggestions for introducing the problem and developing the skill. Specific suggestions for an effective presentation of the model are made in **Introducing the Problem.**

- In **Developing the Skill,** the teacher is given suggestions for presenting and developing the algorithm, skill, and/or concept. Where practical, recommendations are made for the use of manipulatives.

---

## Zeros in Minuend

**pages 69-70**

### Objective

To subtract 4- or 5-digit numbers when minuends have zeros

### Materials

* thousands, hundreds, tens, ones jars
* place value materials

### Mental Math

Tell students to answer true or false:

1. 776 has 77 tens. (T)
2. 10 hundreds < 1,000. (F)
3. 46 is an odd number. (F)
4. 926 can be rounded to 920. (F)
5. 72 hours = 3 days. (T)
6. 42 ÷ 6 > 7 × 1. (F)
7. 1/3 of 18 = 1/2 of 12. (T)
8. perimeter = L × W. (F)

### Skill Review

Write 4 numbers of 3- to 5-digits each on the board. Have students arrange the numbers in order, from the least to the greatest, and then read the numbers as they would appear if written from the greatest to the least. Repeat for more sets of 4 or 5 numbers.

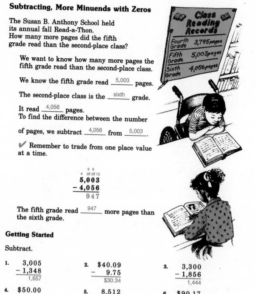

**Subtracting, More Minuends with Zeros**

The Susan B. Anthony School held its annual fall Read-a-Thon. How many more pages did the fifth grade read than the second-place class?

We want to know how many more pages the fifth grade read than the second-place class.

We know the fifth grade read ___5,003___ pages.

The second-place class is the ___sixth___ grade.

It read ___4,056___ pages.
To find the difference between the number of pages, we subtract ___4,056___ from ___5,003___.

✔ Remember to trade from one place value at a time.

$$
\begin{array}{r}
9\ 9 \\
4\ \ \cancel{5}\cancel{3}\cancel{5}\ 13 \\
5,003 \\
-\ 4,056 \\
\hline
947
\end{array}
$$

The fifth grade read ___947___ more pages than the sixth grade.

### Getting Started

Subtract.

| | | |
|---|---|---|
| 1. 3,005<br>− 1,348<br>**1,657** | 2. $40.09<br>− 9.75<br>**$30.34** | 3. 3,300<br>− 1,856<br>**1,444** |
| 4. $50.00<br>− 27.26<br>**$22.74** | 5. 8,512<br>− 7,968<br>**544** | 6. $90.17<br>− 20.87<br>**$69.30** |

Copy and subtract.

7. 26,007 − 18,759  **7,248**

8. 70,026 − 23,576  **46,450**

9. $900.05 − $267.83  **$632.22**

69

---

### Teaching the Lesson

**Introducing the Problem** Have a student read the problem. Ask students what 2 problems are to be solved. (which class read the second-highest number of pages and how many more pages the first-place fifth graders read) Ask students how we can find out which class came in second place. (arrange numbers from the table in order from greatest to least) Ask a student to write the numbers from greatest to least on the board. (5,003, 4,056, 3,795) Have students complete the sentences and work through the model problem with them.

**Developing the Skill** Write **4,000−2,875** vertically on the board. Ask students if a trade is needed to subtract the ones column. (yes) Tell students that since there are no tens and no hundreds, we must trade 1 thousand for 10 hundreds. Show the 3 thousands and 10 hundreds left. Now tell students we can trade 1 hundred for 10 tens. Show the trade with 9 hundreds and 10 tens left. Tell students we can now trade 1 ten for 10 ones. Show the trade so that 9 tens and 10 ones are left. Tell students we can now subtract each column beginning with the ones column and working to the left. Show students the subtraction to a solution of **1,125.** Remind students to add the subtrahend and the difference to check the work. Repeat for more problems with zeros in the minuend.

---

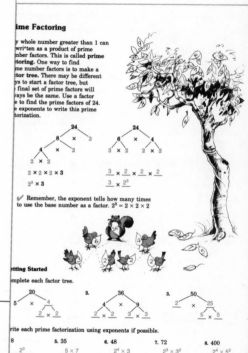

**Prime Factoring**

...y whole number greater than 1 can ...written as a product of prime ...ber factors. This is called **prime ...toring.** One way to find ...me number factors is to make a ...tor tree. There may be different ...ys to start a factor tree, but ...final set of prime factors will ...ways be the same. Use a factor ...e to find the prime factors of 24. ...e exponents to write this prime ...torization.

24 → 8 × 3 → 4 × 2 → 2 × 2
24 → 6 × 4 → 3 × 2 ... 2 × 2

2 × 2 × 2 × 3
$2^3 \times 3$

$\underline{3} \times \underline{2} \times \underline{2} \times \underline{2}$
$\underline{3} \times 2^3$

✔ Remember, the exponent tells how many times to use the base number as a factor. $2^3 = 2 \times 2 \times 2$

**...etting Started**

...omplete each factor tree.

| 1. 20 | 2. 36 | 3. 50 |
|---|---|---|
| 5 × 4<br>2 × 2 | 4 × 9<br>2 × 2  3 × 3 | 2 × 25<br>5 × 5 |

...rite each prime factorization using exponents if possible.

| ...8 | 5. 35 | 6. 48 | 7. 72 | 8. 400 |
|---|---|---|---|---|
| $2^3$ | $5 \times 7$ | $2^4 \times 3$ | $2^3 \times 3^2$ | $2^4 \times 5^2$ |

99

**Developing the Skill** Point out that when a prime number is used more than once in the prime factoring, it can be expressed with an **exponent.** Remind students that $2^3$ is the same as $2 \times 2 \times 2$. Stress that the 3 in $2^3$ is an exponent, and that this exponent tells the number of times 2 is used as a factor. Have students complete each of the following factor trees and then write each prime factorization using exponents:

50 → 2 × 25 → (2) × (5) × (5)   ($2 \times 5^2$)

28 → 7 × 4 → (7) × (2) × (2)   ($7 \times 2^2$)

...composite
...ctors. Tell
...e factor-
...h aloud,
...he tree
...r tree on
...at a num-
...of prime
...d. Have
...f each

s the

# FREQUENT ATTENTION IS GIVEN TO CORRECTING COMMON ERRORS, ENRICHMENT AND OPTIONAL EXTRA-CREDIT ACTIVITIES!

These comprehensive **Teacher's Editions** are intended to provide the teacher with a convenient, well-structured approach to teaching mathematics. From motivating introductory exercises to challenging extension activities, *Modern Curriculum Press*

*Mathematics* **Teacher's Editions** suggest a complete step-by-step plan to insure successful learning. The succinct lesson plans help the teacher provide solid math instruction to students.

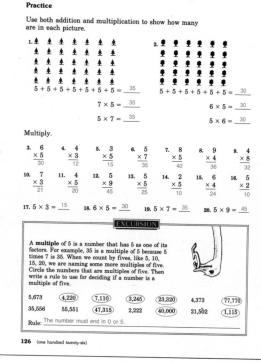

## Practice

Use both addition and multiplication to show how many are in each picture.

1. 5 + 5 + 5 + 5 + 5 + 5 + 5 = __35__

   7 × 5 = __35__

   5 × 7 = __35__

2. 5 + 5 + 5 + 5 + 5 + 5 = __30__

   6 × 5 = __30__

   5 × 6 = __30__

Multiply.

| 3. 6 ×5 = 30 | 4. 4 ×3 = 12 | 5. 3 ×5 = 15 | 6. 5 ×7 = 35 | 7. 8 ×5 = 40 | 8. 9 ×4 = 36 | 9. 4 ×8 = 32 |
| 10. 7 ×3 = 21 | 11. 4 ×5 = 20 | 12. 5 ×9 = 45 | 13. 5 ×5 = 25 | 14. 2 ×5 = 10 | 15. 6 ×4 = 24 | 16. 5 ×2 = 10 |

17. 5 × 3 = __15__     18. 6 × 5 = __30__     19. 5 × 7 = __35__     20. 5 × 9 = __45__

### EXCURSION

A **multiple** of 5 is a number that has 5 as one of its factors. For example, 35 is a multiple of 5 because 5 times 7 is 35. When we count by fives, like 5, 10, 15, 20, we are naming some more multiples of five. Circle the numbers that are multiples of five. Then write a rule to use for deciding if a number is a multiple of five.

5,673   (4,220)   (7,110)   (3,245)   (23,320)   4,373   (77,770)

35,556   55,551   (47,315)   2,222   (40,000)   21,502   (1,115)

Rule: The number must end in 0 or 5.

**126**   (one hundred twenty-six)

### Correcting Common Errors

If students have difficulty learning facts of 5, have them practice with partners. Have them draw a vertical number line from 0 through 50, marking it in intervals of 5. Have one partner write the addition problem to the left of each multiple of five on the number line while the other partner writes the corresponding multiplication problem.

|  |  |  |
|---|---|---|
|  | 0 |  |
| 5 | 5 | (5 × 1) |
| 5 + 5 | 10 | (5 × 2) |
| 5 + 5 + 5 | 15 | (5 × 3) |
| 5 + 5 + 5 + 5 | 20 | (5 × 4) |

### Enrichment

Ask students how many fives are in 55 if, there are 10 fives in 50. (11) Tell them to complete a multiplication table for fives that goes up to the product 150. Have them use the table to figure the number of nickels in $4.00. (80)

---

Write the times.

|  |  |  |
|---|---|---|
| 1:00 | 9:30 | 2:00 |
| 10:30 | 11:00 | 11:30 |
| 8:30 | 9:00 | 12:30 |
| 4:00 | 5:30 | 6:00 |

**164**   (one hundred sixty-four)     Telling time to the hour

---

### Teaching page 164

Ask students to tell the time on the first clock face. (1:00) Tell students to trace the 1:00. Tell students to complete the page by writing the correct time under each clock.

### Practice

Have students do all the problems on the page. Remind the class that they can use addition to figure out any multiplication facts they are not sure of.

### Excursion

Have students write the multiples of 5 through 200. Help students to see that any number that ends in 0 or 5 is a multiple of 5. Have students write the rule. Now write several 4- and 5-digit numbers on the board and ask students to circle the numbers that are multiples of 5.

### Extra Credit   *Logic*

Write the following on the board:

| WOW | TOT | POP | BIB |
|-----|-----|-----|------|
| 525 | 969 | 343 | 5445 |

Ask students what all of these have in common. Explain they are palindromes, or words or numbers which are the same whether they are read forward or backward. Also, explain 302 is not a palindrome, but if you reverse the numbers and add, it will make a palindrome:

302
+203
505

Using this method, ask students what palindrome they can make with these numbers: 36; (99) 342; (585) 4,205; (9,229) 3,406 (9,449). Have students list some other numbers which, when reversed and added, will form a palindrome.

- Follow up activities focus on **Correcting Common Errors, Enrichment,** and **Extra Credit** suggestions.

- In the **Correcting Common Errors** feature, a common error pattern is explored and a method of remediation is recommended. Collectively, all the **Correcting Common Errors** features in any chapter constitute a complete set of the common errors likely to be committed by the students when working in that area of mathematics.

- **Enrichment** activities are a direct extension of the skills being taught. Students can do these activities on their own while the teacher works with those students who need more help.

- **Extra Credits** are challenging independent activities to expand the mathematical experiences of the students. The **Extra Credit** section encompasses a wide variety of activities and project and introduces and extends skills taught in the normal basal curriculum—including statistics, logic, and probability.

---

### Practice

Subtract.

| | | | |
|---|---|---|---|
| 1. 3,004 − 2,356 = 648 | 2. 8,002 − 5,096 = 2,906 | 3. 3,891 − 1,750 = 2,141 | 4. $20.08 − $15.99 = $4.09 |
| 5. 4,020 − 1,865 = 2,155 | 6. $87.00 − 28.59 = $58.41 | 7. 3,007 − 2,090 = 917 | 8. $50.06 − 37.08 = $12.98 |
| 9. 19,006 − 8,275 = 10,731 | 10. 20,006 − 14,758 = 5,248 | 11. $400.26 − 236.58 = $163.68 | 12. $793.42 − 253.87 = $539.55 |

### Copy and Do

13. 4,001 − 2,756  1,245
14. $70.05 − $26.59  $43.46
15. 8,060 − 7,948  112
16. 7,007 − 2,468  4,539
17. 21,316 − 12,479  8,837
18. 14,000 − 8,396  5,604
19. $100.21 − $93.50  $6.71
20. 60,004 − 51,476  8,528
21. 52,006 − 9,037  42,969
22. $800.00 − $275.67  $524.33
23. 34,612 − 29,965  4,647
24. 50,010 − 36,754  13,256

### Apply

Use the chart on page 69 to help solve these problems.

25. How many pages did the three classes read all together? 12,854 pages

26. How many more pages did the sixth grade read than the fourth grade? 261 pages

70

---

### Correcting Common Errors

Some students may bring down the numbers that are being subtracted when there are zeros in the minuend.

| INCORRECT | CORRECT |
|---|---|
| 3,006 − 1,425 = 2,421 | 3,006 − 1,425 = 1,581 |

Have students work in pairs and use play money to model a problem such as $300 − $142, where they see that they must trade 3 hundreds for 2 hundreds, 9 tens, and 10 ones before they can subtract.

### Enrichment

Tell students to find out the year in which each member of their family was born, and make a chart to show how old each will be in the year 2000.

---

3. 28 = 7 × 4, 2 × 2
6. 75 = 3 × 25, 5 × 5

10. 64  $2^6$
11. 66  $2 × 3 × 11$
15. 180  $2^2 × 3^2 × 5$
16. 225  $3^2 × 5^2$

7 are examples of twin
43, 71 and 73
rror primes. 13 and 31 are
9 and 97
f its factors except itself.
f the perfect numbers less

---

### Correcting Common Errors

Some students do not write the prime factorization of a number correctly because they cannot identify prime numbers. Have them work with partners to name all the prime numbers from 1 to 50 and write them on an index card. The students can use these cards as a guide for this work.

### Enrichment

Provide this alternative method of dividing to find prime factorization of a number. Tell students they must always divide by a prime number.

2 | 36    $36 = 2^2 × 3^2$
2 | 18
3 | 9
    3

Have students use this method to find the prime factorization of: 120 ($2^3 × 3 × 5$); 250 ($5^3 × 2$); 1,000 ($2^3 × 5^3$); 72 ($3^2 × 2^3$)

---

### Practice

Remind students to begin with the ones column, work to the left and trade from one place value at a time. Have students complete the page independently.

### Extra Credit   *Biography*

An American inventor, Samuel Morse, struggled for many years before his inventions, the electric telegraph and Morse code were recognized. Morse was born in Massachusetts in 1791, and studied to be an artist. On a trip home from Europe, Morse heard his shipmates discussing the idea of sending electricity over wire. Intrigued, Morse spent the rest of the voyage formulating his ideas about how this could be accomplished. Morse taught at a university in New York City, and used his earnings to continue development of his telegraph. After five years, Morse demonstrated his invention, but found very little support. After years of requests for support, Congress finally granted Morse $30,000 to test his invention. He dramatically strung a telegraph wire from Washington, D.C. to Baltimore, Maryland, and relayed the message, "What hath God wrought" using Morse code. Morse's persistence finally won him wealth and fame. A statue honoring him was unveiled in New York City one year before his death in 1872.

prob-
tly.

enes as
ct num-
o com-

---

### Extra Credit   *Applications*

Have a student write the primary United States time zones across the board. Discuss how this pattern continues around the world. Divide students into groups and provide them with globes or flat maps. Have students choose various cities in the United States and elsewhere in the world, and determine what the time would be in those cities when it is 6:00 AM in their home city. Have students make another list of cities without times indicated to exchange with classmates to figure time comparisons.

100

## Grades K-3

*Bake and Taste*. Tucson, AZ: MindPlay, 1990. (Apple, IBM)

Educators looking for a slightly different program might be interested in *Bake and Taste*. Students are guided through the process of making a dessert of their choosing. In the course of the baking fun, students work on the skills of measuring, counting, and figuring fractions. The desserts can really be baked and eaten. Teacher or parent involvement is necessary for nonreaders.

*Elastic Lines: The Electronic Geoboard*. Education Development Center. Pleasantville, NY: Sunburst Communications, 1989. (Apple, IBM)

This is a simulation of rubber bands being stretched over pegboards of variable size and type. Students can practice the skills of visualizing shapes in space and estimating. Primary students will enjoy the most elementary of the concepts in this program that is recommended for Grades 2 through 8.

*Exploring Measurement, Time, and Money, Level II*. Dayton, NJ: IBM, 1990. (IBM)

This program combines a tutorial with drill and practice focusing on linear measurement, time measurement, and money. Students practice such skills as comparing measurements and making change.

*Hop to It!* Pleasantville, NY: Sunburst Communications, 1990. (Apple)

This program focuses on using problem solving skills to better understand addition, subtraction, and the number line. Students must choose the operation that will help animals capture objects along a number line. The number line can begin anywhere between −10 and 10.

*KidsMath*. Scotts Valley, CA: Great Wave Software, 1989. (Macintosh)

*KidsMath* offers eight games to help students learn basic math skills such as addition, subtraction, multiplication, division, and fractions. Students will be delighted with the attractive graphics and animations.

*Math Rabbit*. Fremont, CA: The Learning Company, 1989. (Apple, IBM, Macintosh)

A colorful program which introduces basic number concepts such as counting, addition, subtraction, and number relationships. Recommended for preschool to Grade 1.

*Math Shop Jr*. Jefferson City, MO: Scholastic, 1989. (Apple, IBM, Mac)

As they pretend to run stores in a mall, students work on real-life situations in which they use addition, subtraction, multiplication, division, odd and even numbers, estimation, and coins.

*New Math Blaster Plus*. Torrance, CA: Davidson & Associates, 1990. (Apple, IBM, Mac)

With its fast-paced, arcade-like games, this program will be a favorite of all students. It includes problems in addition, subtraction, multiplication, division, fractions, decimals, and percents. Teachers can print customized tests.

*Number Munchers*. Minneapolis, MN: MECC, 1986. (Apple, IBM, Mac)

Students control a number-munching monster. If the monster eats the correct answer, the student moves on to the next level. The program drills concepts such as multiples 2–20, factoring of numbers 3–99, prime numbers 1–99, equality and inequality.

*NumberMaze*. Scotts Valley, CA: Great Wave Software, 1988. (Mac)

To travel through the mazes, students must answer questions involving basic math concepts. Some word problems are included.

*Picture Chompers*. Minneapolis, MN: MECC, 1990. (Apple)

Students practice classification skills in this fast-paced game. User guides a pair of teeth around a grid and the teeth eat objects of specified color, pattern, size, or shape.

*Stickybear Math*. Norfolk, CT: Optimum Resource, Inc., 1984. (Apple, IBM)

Students solve simple addition and subtraction problems to get the colorful Stickybear out of sticky situations.

*Super Solvers: Treasure Mountain!* Fremont, CA: The Learning Company, 1990. (IBM)

This program builds problem-solving skills as students try to foil the prankster Morty Maxwell who has stolen the enchanted crown. Math, reading, thinking, and science skills are required.

*Winker's World of Patterns*. Scotts Valley, CA: Wings for Learning, 1990. (Apple, IBM)

Students practice recognizing and remembering patterns involving colors, numbers, and words.

| Scope and Sequence | K | 1 | 2 | 3 | 4 | 5 | 6 |
|---|---|---|---|---|---|---|---|
| **READINESS** | | | | | | | |
| Attributes | ■ | | | | | | |
| Shapes | ■ | ■ | | | | | |
| Colors | ■ | ■ | ■ | | | | |
| **NUMERATION** | | | | | | | |
| On-to-one correspondence | ■ | | | | | | |
| Understanding numbers | ■ | ■ | ■ | | | | |
| Writing numbers | ■ | ■ | | | | | |
| Counting objects | ■ | ■ | ■ | | | | |
| Sequencing numbers | ■ | ■ | ■ | ■ | ■ | | |
| Numbers before and after | ■ | ■ | ■ | ■ | ■ | | |
| Ordering numbers | | | ■ | ■ | ■ | ■ | ■ |
| Comparing numbers | ■ | ■ | ■ | ■ | ■ | ■ | ■ |
| Grouping numbers | ■ | ■ | ■ | ■ | ■ | | |
| Ordinal numbers | ■ | ■ | ■ | ■ | | | |
| Number words | | ■ | ■ | ■ | ■ | ■ | ■ |
| Expanded numbers | | ■ | ■ | ■ | ■ | ■ | ■ |
| Place value | | ■ | ■ | ■ | ■ | ■ | ■ |
| Skip-counting | | ■ | ■ | ■ | ■ | ■ | |
| Roman numerals | | | ■ | ■ | ■ | | |
| Rounding numbers | | | | ■ | ■ | ■ | ■ |
| Squares and square roots | | | | ■ | | | |

## Scope and Sequence

| | K | 1 | 2 | 3 | 4 | 5 | 6 |
|---|---|---|---|---|---|---|---|
| Primes and composites | | | | ■ | ■ | ■ | ■ |
| Multiples | | | | | ■ | ■ | ■ |
| Least common multiples | | | | | | ■ | ■ |
| Greatest common factors | | | | | | ■ | ■ |
| Exponents | | | | | | | ■ |
| **ADDITION** | | | | | | | |
| Addition facts | ■ | ■ | ■ | ■ | ■ | ■ | ■ |
| Fact families | | ■ | ■ | ■ | ■ | ■ | |
| Missing addends | ■ | ■ | ■ | ■ | ■ | | |
| Adding money | ■ | ■ | ■ | ■ | ■ | ■ | ■ |
| Column addition | | ■ | ■ | ■ | ■ | ■ | ■ |
| Two-digit addends | | ■ | ■ | ■ | ■ | ■ | |
| Multidigit addends | | | ■ | ■ | ■ | ■ | ■ |
| Addition with trading | | ■ | ■ | ■ | ■ | ■ | ■ |
| Basic properties of addition | | | | ■ | ■ | ■ | ■ |
| Estimating sums | | | | ■ | ■ | ■ | ■ |
| Addition of fractions | | | | ■ | ■ | ■ | ■ |
| Addition of mixed numbers | | | | ■ | ■ | ■ | ■ |
| Addition of decimals | | | | ■ | ■ | ■ | ■ |
| Rule of order | | | | ■ | ■ | ■ | ■ |
| Addition of customary measures | | | | | | ■ | ■ |

## Scope and Sequence

| | K | 1 | 2 | 3 | 4 | 5 | 6 |
|---|---|---|---|---|---|---|---|
| Addition of integers | | | | | | | ■ |
| **SUBTRACTION** | | | | | | | |
| Subtraction facts | ■ | ■ | ■ | ■ | ■ | ■ | ■ |
| Fact families | | ■ | ■ | ■ | ■ | ■ | |
| Missing subtrahends | | ■ | ■ | | | | |
| Subtracting money | ■ | ■ | ■ | ■ | ■ | ■ | ■ |
| Two-digit numbers | | ■ | ■ | ■ | ■ | ■ | |
| Multidigit numbers | | | ■ | ■ | ■ | ■ | ■ |
| Subtraction with trading | | ■ | ■ | ■ | ■ | ■ | ■ |
| Zeros in the minuend | | | | ■ | ■ | ■ | ■ |
| Basic properties of subtraction | | | | ■ | ■ | ■ | ■ |
| Estimating differences | | | | ■ | ■ | ■ | ■ |
| Subtraction of fractions | | | | ■ | ■ | ■ | ■ |
| Subtraction of mixed numbers | | | | | | ■ | ■ |
| Subtraction of decimals | | | | ■ | ■ | ■ | ■ |
| Rule of order | | | | ■ | ■ | ■ | ■ |
| Subtraction of customary measures | | | | | | ■ | ■ |
| Subtraction of integers | | | | | | | ■ |
| **MULTIPLICATION** | | | | | | | |
| Multiplication facts | | | ■ | ■ | ■ | ■ | ■ |
| Fact families | | | ■ | ■ | ■ | | |

## Scope and Sequence

| | K | 1 | 2 | 3 | 4 | 5 | 6 |
|---|---|---|---|---|---|---|---|
| Missing factors | | | | | ■ | | |
| Multiplying money | | | ■ | ■ | ■ | ■ | ■ |
| Multiplication by powers of ten | | | | ■ | ■ | ■ | ■ |
| Multidigit factors | | | | ■ | ■ | ■ | ■ |
| Multiplication with trading | | | | ■ | ■ | ■ | ■ |
| Basic properties of multiplication | | | ■ | ■ | ■ | ■ | ■ |
| Estimating products | | | | ■ | ■ | ■ | ■ |
| Rule of order | | | | ■ | ■ | ■ | ■ |
| Multiples | | | | | ■ | ■ | ■ |
| Least common multiples | | | | | | ■ | ■ |
| Multiplication of fractions | | | | | | ■ | ■ |
| Factorization | | | | | | ■ | ■ |
| Multiplication of mixed numbers | | | | | | | ■ |
| Multiplication of decimals | | | | | ■ | ■ | ■ |
| Exponents | | | | | | | ■ |
| Multiplication of integers | | | | | | | ■ |
| **DIVISION** | | | | | | | |
| Division facts | | | | ■ | ■ | ■ | ■ |
| Fact families | | | | ■ | ■ | | |
| Divisibility rules | | | | ■ | | ■ | ■ |
| Two-digit quotients | | | | ■ | ■ | ■ | ■ |

## Scope and Sequence

| | K | 1 | 2 | 3 | 4 | 5 | 6 |
|---|---|---|---|---|---|---|---|
| Remainders | | | | ■ | ■ | ■ | ■ |
| Multidigit quotients | | | | | ■ | ■ | ■ |
| Zeros in quotients | | | | | ■ | ■ | ■ |
| Division by multiples of ten | | | | | ■ | ■ | ■ |
| Two-digit divisors | | | | | ■ | ■ | ■ |
| Properties of division | | | | | ■ | ■ | |
| Averages | | | | ■ | ■ | ■ | ■ |
| Greatest common factors | | | | | | ■ | ■ |
| Division of fractions | | | | | | ■ | ■ |
| Division of mixed numbers | | | | | | ■ | ■ |
| Division of decimals | | | | | | ■ | ■ |
| Division by powers of ten | | | | | | ■ | ■ |
| **MONEY** | | | | | | | |
| Counting pennies | ■ | ■ | ■ | ■ | ■ | | |
| Counting nickels | ■ | ■ | ■ | ■ | ■ | | |
| Counting dimes | ■ | ■ | ■ | ■ | ■ | | |
| Counting quarters | | ■ | ■ | ■ | ■ | | |
| Counting half-dollars | | | ■ | ■ | ■ | | |
| Counting dollar bills | | ■ | ■ | ■ | ■ | | |
| Writing dollar and cents signs | | ■ | ■ | ■ | ■ | ■ | ■ |
| Matching money with prices | ■ | ■ | ■ | | | | |

## Scope and Sequence

|  | K | 1 | 2 | 3 | 4 | 5 | 6 |
|---|---|---|---|---|---|---|---|
| Determining amount of change | ■ | ■ | ■ | | | | |
| Determining sufficient amount | | ■ | ■ | | | | |
| Determining which coins to use | | ■ | ■ | | | | |
| Addition | ■ | ■ | ■ | ■ | ■ | ■ | ■ |
| Subtraction | ■ | ■ | ■ | ■ | ■ | ■ | ■ |
| Multiplication | | | ■ | ■ | ■ | ■ | ■ |
| Division | | | | | ■ | ■ | ■ |
| Rounding amounts of money | | | | ■ | ■ | ■ | ■ |
| Finding fractions of amounts | | | | | ■ | ■ | ■ |
| Buying from a menu or ad | | | ■ | ■ | ■ | ■ | ■ |

### FRACTIONS

|  | K | 1 | 2 | 3 | 4 | 5 | 6 |
|---|---|---|---|---|---|---|---|
| Understanding equal parts | ■ | ■ | ■ | ■ | | | |
| One half | ■ | ■ | ■ | ■ | | | |
| One fourth | ■ | ■ | ■ | ■ | | | |
| One third | ■ | ■ | ■ | ■ | | | |
| Identifying fractional parts of figures | | | ■ | ■ | ■ | ■ | ■ |
| Identifying fractional parts of sets | | | ■ | ■ | ■ | ■ | ■ |
| Finding unit fractions of numbers | | | | ■ | ■ | ■ | |
| Equivalent fractions | | | | ■ | ■ | ■ | ■ |
| Comparing fractions | | | | ■ | ■ | ■ | ■ |
| Simplifying fractions | | | | | ■ | ■ | ■ |

## Scope and Sequence

| | K | 1 | 2 | 3 | 4 | 5 | 6 |
|---|---|---|---|---|---|---|---|
| Renaming mixed numbers | | | | | ■ | ■ | ■ |
| Addition of fractions | | | | ■ | ■ | ■ | ■ |
| Subtraction of fractions | | | | ■ | ■ | ■ | ■ |
| Addition of mixed numbers | | | | | ■ | ■ | ■ |
| Subtraction of mixed numbers | | | | | | ■ | ■ |
| Multiplication of fractions | | | | | | ■ | ■ |
| Factorization | | | | | | ■ | ■ |
| Multiplication of mixed numbers | | | | | | ■ | ■ |
| Division of fractions | | | | | | ■ | ■ |
| Division of mixed numbers | | | | | | ■ | ■ |
| Renaming fractions as decimals | | | | | | | ■ |
| Renaming fractions as percents | | | | | | | ■ |
| **DECIMALS** | | | | | | | |
| Place value | | | | ■ | ■ | ■ | ■ |
| Reading decimals | | | | ■ | ■ | ■ | ■ |
| Writing decimals | | | | ■ | ■ | ■ | ■ |
| Converting fractions to decimals | | | | ■ | ■ | ■ | ■ |
| Writing parts of sets as decimals | | | | ■ | ■ | ■ | |
| Comparing decimals | | | | ■ | ■ | ■ | ■ |
| Ordering decimals | | | | | | | ■ |
| Addition of decimals | | | | ■ | ■ | ■ | ■ |

## Scope and Sequence

| | K | 1 | 2 | 3 | 4 | 5 | 6 |
|---|---|---|---|---|---|---|---|
| Subtraction of decimals | | | | ■ | ■ | ■ | ■ |
| Rounding decimals | | | | ■ | | ■ | ■ |
| Multiplication of decimals | | | | | ■ | ■ | ■ |
| Division of decimals | | | | | | ■ | ■ |
| Renaming decimals as percents | | | | | | | ■ |
| **GEOMETRY** | | | | | | | |
| Polygons | ■ | ■ | ■ | ■ | ■ | ■ | ■ |
| Sides and corners of polygons | | | ■ | ■ | ■ | | |
| Lines and line segments | | | | | ■ | ■ | ■ |
| Rays and angles | | | | | ■ | ■ | ■ |
| Measuring angles | | | | | | ■ | ■ |
| Symmetry | | | ■ | | | ■ | ■ |
| Congruency | | | | ■ | ■ | ■ | ■ |
| Similar figures | | | | | ■ | ■ | ■ |
| Circles | | | | | | ■ | ■ |
| **MEASUREMENT** | | | | | | | |
| Non-standard units of measure | ■ | ■ | | | | | |
| Customary units of measure | | ■ | ■ | ■ | ■ | ■ | ■ |
| Metric units of measure | ■ | ■ | ■ | ■ | ■ | ■ | ■ |
| Renaming customary measures | | | | | ■ | ■ | ■ |
| Renaming metric measures | | | | | ■ | ■ | ■ |

## Scope and Sequence

| | K | 1 | 2 | 3 | 4 | 5 | 6 |
|---|---|---|---|---|---|---|---|
| Selecting appropriate units | | | ■ | ■ | ■ | ■ | |
| Estimating measures | | ■ | ■ | ■ | ■ | ■ | |
| Perimeter by counting | ■ | ■ | ■ | | | | |
| Perimeter by formula | | | ■ | ■ | ■ | ■ | ■ |
| Area of polygons by counting | | | ■ | ■ | | | |
| Area of polygons by formula | | | | | ■ | ■ | ■ |
| Volume by counting | | | | ■ | | | |
| Volume by formula | | | | | ■ | ■ | ■ |
| Addition of measures | | | | | | ■ | ■ |
| Subtraction of measures | | | | | | ■ | ■ |
| Circumference of circles | | | | | | | ■ |
| Area of circles | | | | | | | ■ |
| Surface area of space figures | | | | | | | ■ |
| Estimating temperatures | | | | ■ | | | |
| Reading temperature scales | | | ■ | ■ | | | |
| **TIME** | | | | | | | |
| Ordering events | ■ | | | | | | |
| Relative time | ■ | | | | | | |
| Matching values | ■ | ■ | ■ | ■ | ■ | | |
| Calendars | ■ | ■ | ■ | ■ | | | |
| Days of the week | ■ | ■ | ■ | ■ | | | |

## Scope and Sequence

| | K | 1 | 2 | 3 | 4 | 5 | 6 |
|---|---|---|---|---|---|---|---|
| Months of the year | ■ | ■ | ■ | ■ | | | |
| Telling time to the hour | ■ | ■ | ■ | ■ | | | |
| Telling time to the half-hour | | ■ | ■ | ■ | | | |
| Telling time to the five-minutes | | | ■ | ■ | ■ | | |
| Telling time to the minute | | | ■ | ■ | ■ | | |
| Understanding AM and PM | | | | | ■ | | |
| Time zones | | | | | ■ | | |
| **GRAPHING** | | | | | | | |
| Tables | | ■ | ■ | ■ | ■ | ■ | ■ |
| Bar graphs | ■ | ■ | ■ | ■ | ■ | ■ | ■ |
| Picture graphs | | | ■ | ■ | ■ | | ■ |
| Line graphs | | | | | ■ | ■ | ■ |
| Circle graphs | | | | | | ■ | ■ |
| Tree diagrams | | | | | | ■ | |
| Histograms | | | | | | | ■ |
| Ordered pairs | | | | ■ | ■ | ■ | ■ |
| **PROBABILITY** | | | | | | | |
| Understanding probability | | | | | ■ | ■ | ■ |
| Listing outcomes | | | | | ■ | ■ | ■ |
| Means and medians | | | | | | ■ | |
| Circle graphs | | | | | | ■ | ■ |

## Scope and Sequence

| | K | 1 | 2 | 3 | 4 | 5 | 6 |
|---|---|---|---|---|---|---|---|
| Tree diagrams | | | | | | ■ | ■ |
| Histograms | | | | | | | ■ |
| **RATIOS AND PERCENTS** | | | | | | | |
| Understanding ratios | | | | | ■ | ■ | ■ |
| Equal ratios | | | | | | ■ | ■ |
| Proportions | | | | | | | ■ |
| Scale drawings | | | | | | ■ | ■ |
| Ratios as percents | | | | | | ■ | ■ |
| Percents as fractions | | | | | | ■ | ■ |
| Fractions as percents | | | | | | ■ | ■ |
| Finding the percents of numbers | | | | | | ■ | ■ |
| **INTEGERS** | | | | | | | |
| Understanding integers | | | | | | | ■ |
| Addition of integers | | | | | | | ■ |
| Subtraction of integers | | | | | | | ■ |
| Multiplication of integers | | | | | | | ■ |
| Graphing integers on coordinate planes | | | | | | | ■ |
| **PROBLEM SOLVING** | | | | | | | |
| Creating an algorithm from a word problem | | ■ | ■ | ■ | ■ | ■ | ■ |
| Selecting the correct operation | | ■ | ■ | ■ | ■ | ■ | ■ |
| Using data | | | ■ | ■ | ■ | ■ | ■ |

## Scope and Sequence

| | K | 1 | 2 | 3 | 4 | 5 | 6 |
|---|---|---|---|---|---|---|---|
| Reading a chart | | | ■ | ■ | ■ | ■ | ■ |
| Using a four-step plan | | | | ■ | ■ | ■ | ■ |
| Drawing a picture | | | | ■ | ■ | ■ | ■ |
| Acting it out | | | | ■ | ■ | ■ | ■ |
| Making a list | | | | ■ | ■ | ■ | ■ |
| Making a tally | | | | ■ | ■ | ■ | |
| Making a table | | | | ■ | ■ | ■ | ■ |
| Making a graph | | | | ■ | ■ | ■ | |
| Guessing and checking | | | | | ■ | ■ | ■ |
| Looking for a pattern | | | | | ■ | ■ | ■ |
| Making a model | | | | | ■ | | |
| Restating the problem | | | | | ■ | ■ | ■ |
| Selecting notation | | | | | ■ | ■ | ■ |
| Writing an open sentence | | | | | ■ | ■ | ■ |
| Using a formula | | | | | ■ | ■ | ■ |
| Identifying a subgoal | | | | | | ■ | ■ |
| Working backwards | | | | | | ■ | ■ |
| Determining missing data | | | | | | ■ | ■ |
| Collecting data | | | | | | ■ | ■ |
| Solving a simpler but related problem | | | | | | ■ | ■ |
| Making a flow chart | | | | | | | ■ |

# Scope and Sequence for MODERN CURRICULUM PRESS MATHEMATICS

## Scope and Sequence

| | K | 1 | 2 | 3 | 4 | 5 | 6 |
|---|---|---|---|---|---|---|---|
| **CALCULATORS** | | | | | | | |
| Calculator codes | | | | ■ | ■ | ■ | ■ |
| Equal key | | | | ■ | ■ | ■ | ■ |
| Operation keys | | | | ■ | ■ | ■ | ■ |
| Square root key | | | | ■ | | | |
| Clear key | | | | ■ | ■ | ■ | ■ |
| Clear entry key | | | | ■ | ■ | ■ | ■ |
| Money | | | | ■ | ■ | ■ | ■ |
| Unit prices | | | | ■ | ■ | ■ | |
| Fractions | | | | ■ | ■ | | |
| Percents | | | | | ■ | | |
| Banking | | | | ■ | ■ | ■ | |
| Inventories | | | | | ■ | | |
| Averages | | | | | ■ | | |
| Rates | | | | | | ■ | ■ |
| Formulas | | | | | | ■ | ■ |
| Cross multiplication | | | | | | | ■ |
| Functions | | | | | | | ■ |
| Binary numbers | | | | | | | ■ |
| Repeating decimals | | | | | | | ■ |
| Statistics | | | | | | | ■ |

T-32

This **Table of Common Errors** is designed to help the teacher understand the thinking patterns and potential errors that students commonly commit in the course of learning the content in *Modern Curriculum Press Mathematics.* Familiarity with this list can help the teacher forestall errant thinking and save much time used in reteaching.

In the **Correcting Common Errors** feature in each lesson in *Modern Curriculum Press Mathematics,* abundant suggestions are made to remediate situations where students might have misconceptions of other difficulties with a skill. These suggestions make frequent use of manipulatives and cooperative learning.

## Numeration

1. The student transposes digits when writing the number of objects in a picture.

**42**

2. When counting objects in an array, the student counts some objects twice or fails to count each object in the array.

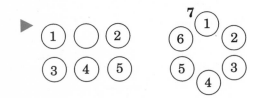

3. The student mistakes one number for another because it has been carelessly written.

4. When writing numerals for a number that is expressed in words, the student fails to write zeros as placeholders where they are needed.

   *Write five hundred four in numerals.*

   ▶ **54**

5. The student confuses the names of place values.

6. The student fails to write the money sign and/or decimal point in an answer involving money.

$$\begin{array}{r} \$3.52 \\ +\quad 2 \\ \hline \mathbf{804} \end{array}$$

7. The student does not relate money to what has been learned about place value.

   For example, the student does not relate dimes to tens place.

8. When ordering whole numbers, the student incorrectly compares single digits regardless of place value.

   For example, the student thinks that ***203 is less than 45*** *because 2 is less than 4 and 3 is less than 5.*

9. The student rounds down when the last significant digit is 5.

   ▶ $75 \approx \mathbf{70}$

10. The student rounds progressively from digit to digit until the designated place value is reached.

    *Round $3.45 to dollars.*

    ▶    $3.45 ≈ **$3.50 ≈ $4**

11. When counting past twenty, the student incorrectly repeats the number pattern between ten and twenty.

    ▶    . . . eighteen, nineteen, twenty, **twenty-eleven, twenty-twelve** . . .

12. The student changes the common interval when skip-counting.

    ▶    2, 4, 6, 8, **11, 14, 17**

13. The student starts off skip-counting but reverts to a counting series after a few numbers.

    ▶    3, 6, 9, **10, 11, 12,** . . .

14. The student fails to count money from the largest bills and coins to the smallest.

15. The student thinks since five pennies equal a nickel, that other coin relationships are also based on a five to one ratio.

    ▶    **5** quarters = 1 dollar

16. The student counts all coins as one cent regardless of their value.

17. The student confuses the greater than and less than signs.

    ▶    56 < 29
    34 > 55

---

## Addition and Subtraction

1. The student is unsure of the basic facts of addition and/or subtraction.

2. The student copies the problem incorrectly.

    *Find the sum of 6, 5, and 9.*

    ▶
    $$\begin{array}{r} 6 \\ 4 \\ +9 \\ \hline \mathbf{19} \end{array}$$

3. The student makes simple addition errors when adding numbers with two or more digits.

    $$\begin{array}{r} 25 \\ +63 \\ \hline \end{array}$$
    ▶    **87**

4. The student thinks that a number plus zero is zero.

    ▶    6 + **0 = 0**

5. The student adds during a subtraction computation, or vice versa.

    $$\begin{array}{rr} 56 & 75 \\ +23 & -28 \\ \hline \end{array}$$
    ▶    **33**      **103**

6. The student computes horizontal equations from left to right regardless of the operation.

    ▶    3 + 2 × 5 = **25**

7. The student adds or subtracts before multiplying or dividing in a horizontal equation.

▶  $3 \times 4 + 6 \times 2 = 60$

8. When doing a computation involving several numbers, the student omits a number.

*Find the sum of 23, 36, 54, and 75.*

▶
$$\begin{array}{r} 23 \\ 36 \\ +75 \\ \hline 134 \end{array}$$

9. The student forgets the partial sum when adding a column of addends.

▶
$$\begin{array}{r} 3 \\ 9 \\ +4 \\ \hline 4 \end{array}$$

10. The student omits the regrouped value.

$$\begin{array}{r} 75 \\ +46 \\ \hline \end{array}$$
▶   111

11. The student fails to rename and places more than one digit in a column in an addition problem.

$$\begin{array}{r} 36 \\ +78 \\ \hline \end{array}$$
▶  1,014

12. In an addition problem, the student writes the tens digit as part of the sum and regroups the ones.

$$\begin{array}{r} 4 \\ 36 \\ +78 \\ \hline \end{array}$$
▶  141

13. The student renames when it is not necessary.

$$\begin{array}{r} 1 \\ 32 \\ +45 \\ \hline \end{array}$$
▶   87

14. In an addition problem with a zero in the first addend, the student aligns the digits of the second addend with the nonzero digits in the first.

*Add 307 and 12.*

▶
$$\begin{array}{r} 307 \\ +1\ 2 \\ \hline 409 \end{array}$$

15. The student does not align the numbers properly when adding or subtracting whole numbers.

▶
$$\begin{array}{r} 62 \\ +39 \\ \hline 659 \end{array}$$

16. The student rounds the answer rather than the components of the problem.

*Estimate the sum of 35 and 49.*

$$\begin{array}{r} 35 \\ +49 \\ \hline \end{array}$$
▶   $84 \approx 80$

17. The student incorrectly adds from left to right.

$$\begin{array}{r} 1 \\ 37 \\ +82 \\ \hline \end{array}$$
▶   110

18. The student confuses addition and subtraction by one with either addition and subtraction of zero or with multiplication by one.

▶  $5 + 1 = 5$
$5 - 1 = 5$

19. The student makes simple subtraction errors when subtracting numbers with two or more digits.

$$\begin{array}{r} 116 \\ \cancel{2}\cancel{6} \\ -19 \\ \hline \end{array}$$
▶    6

20. The student thinks that a number minus zero is zero.

▶ $6 - 0 = 0$

21. The student thinks that zero minus another number is zero.

▶ $0 - 6 = 0$

22. When creating fact families, the student incorrectly applies commutativity to subtraction.

$$8 - 5 = 3$$
$$8 - 3 = 5$$
▶ $5 - 8 = 3$
$3 - 8 = 5$

23. The student brings down the digit in the subtrahend when the corresponding minuend digit is a zero.

$$\begin{array}{r} 50 \\ +36 \\ \hline \end{array}$$
▶ $26$

24. In a multidigit subtraction problem, the student correctly renames the zero in the tens place but does not decrease the digit to the left of the zero.

$$\begin{array}{r} 9\,13 \\ 4\,\cancel{0}\,\cancel{3} \\ -256 \\ \hline 247 \end{array}$$
▶

25. In a multidigit subtraction problem, the student ignores the zero and regroups from the digit to the left of the zero.

$$\begin{array}{r} 3\;\;13 \\ 4\,0\,\cancel{3} \\ -256 \\ \hline 57 \end{array}$$
▶

26. In a multidigit subtraction problem, the student correctly regroups from the digit to the left of the zero and renames the zero as ten, but fails to reduce the ten by one when the second regrouping is done.

$$\begin{array}{r} 1\,10\,14 \\ \cancel{2}\,\cancel{0}\,\cancel{4} \\ -155 \\ \hline 59 \end{array}$$
▶

27. The student does not regroup, but finds the difference between the smaller digit and the larger one regardless of their position and function.

$$\begin{array}{r} 35 \\ -29 \\ \hline 14 \end{array}$$
▶

28. The student does not decrease the digit to the left after regrouping.

$$\begin{array}{r} 15 \\ 3\,\cancel{5} \\ -29 \\ \hline 16 \end{array}$$
▶

29. Instead of regrouping in a subtraction problem, the student incorrectly thinks that if you take a larger digit from a smaller one, there will be nothing left.

$$\begin{array}{r} 35 \\ -29 \\ \hline 10 \end{array}$$
▶

30. In regrouping, the student thinks that the renamed value is found by subtracting the two digits of the same place value.

$$\begin{array}{r} 5\,13 \\ 4\,\cancel{9}\,\cancel{3} \\ -\ \ 45 \\ \hline 418 \end{array}$$
▶

# Multiplication

1. The student does not understand the connection between repeated addition and multiplication.

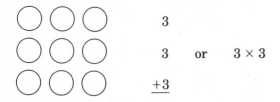

$$3$$
$$3 \quad \text{or} \quad 3 \times 3$$
$$\underline{+3}$$

2. The student is unsure of the basic multiplication facts.

3. The student mistakes a multiplication sign for an addition sign, or vice versa.

▶  $6 \times 3 = \mathbf{9}$
     $6 + 3 = \mathbf{18}$

4. The student thinks that one times any number is one.

▶  $35 \times 1 = \mathbf{1}$

5. The student confuses multiplication by zero with multiplication by one thinking that any number times zero is that number.

▶  $36 \times 0 = \mathbf{36}$

6. The student makes simple multiplication mistakes in multidigit multiplication problems.

$$\begin{array}{r} \$3.46 \\ \times 2 \\ \hline \end{array}$$
▶  $\$6.72$

7. The student is unsure of how many zeros should be in the product when multiplying by a multiple of ten.

$$\begin{array}{r} 20 \\ \times 3 \\ \hline \end{array}$$
▶  $\mathbf{600}$

8. The student multiplies the digits from left to right.

$$\begin{array}{r} 36 \\ \times 3 \\ \hline \end{array}$$
▶  $\mathbf{918}$

9. The student fails to regroup and writes both digits in the product.

$$\begin{array}{r} \mathbf{45} \\ \times \mathbf{3} \\ \hline \end{array}$$
▶  $\mathbf{1,215}$

10. The student writes the tens digit as part of the product and regroups the ones.

$$\begin{array}{r} 2 \\ 36 \\ \times 2 \\ \hline \end{array}$$
▶  $\mathbf{81}$

11. The student does not regroup or fails to add the regrouped value.

$$\begin{array}{r} \mathbf{36} \\ \times \mathbf{2} \\ \hline \end{array}$$
▶  $\mathbf{62}$

12. When multiplying numbers, the student adds the regrouped digit before multiplying.

$$\begin{array}{r} 1 \\ 36 \\ \times 2 \\ \hline \end{array}$$
▶  $82$

# Division

1. The student fails to understand the connection between division and multiplication.

   For example, the student does not see the relationship between the fact $3 \times 2 = 6$ and $6 \div 2 = 3$.

2. The student is unsure of the basic division facts.

3. In a division problem, if either term is one, the student thinks the answer must be one.

   ▶ $6 \div 1 = 1$
   $1 \div 6 = 1$

4. The student confuses division by one with division by the same number.

   ▶ $6 \div 6 = 6$
   $6 \div 1 = 1$

5. The student does not realize that division by zero has no meaning.

   ▶ $6 \div 0 = 6$
   $0 \div 0 = 0$

6. The student places the initial quotient digit over the wrong place value in the dividend.

   ▶
   ```
       77 R1
   2)15
       14
       15
       14
        1
   ```

7. The student ignores initial digits in the dividend that are less than the divisor.

   ▶
   ```
        2 R1
   2)15
        4
        1
   ```

8. The first estimated partial quotient is too low so the student subtracts and divides again and places the extra digit in the quotient.

   ▶
   ```
       1 14
   3)72
       3
       4
       3
      12
      12
   ```

9. The student fails to subtract the last time or fails to record the remainder as part of the quotient.

   ▶
   ```
      1 1
   3)35
      3
      5
      3
   ```

10. The student records the remainder as the last digit of the quotient.

    ▶
    ```
       112
    3)35
       3
       5
       3
       2
    ```

11. The student records a remainder that is larger than the divisor.

    ▶
    ```
       11 R5
    3)38
       3
       8
       3
       5
    ```

12. When checking a division problem, the student fails to add the remainder after multiplying the quotient by the divisor.

```
    15 R1
3)46              15
   3             ×3
  16     ▶       45
  15
   1
```

13. The student incorrectly subtracts in a division problem.

```
     16
3)38
    3
▶  18
   18
```

14. The student fails to subtract before bringing down the next digit in a division problem.

```
    11 R1
3)54
   3
▶   4
    3
    1
```

15. The student incorrectly multiplies in a division problem.

```
     14 R2
3)54
▶   4
   14
   12
    2
```

# Measurement

1. The student is confused about how to read fractional measures on a ruler.

   *Measure the tape to the nearest quarter-inch.*

   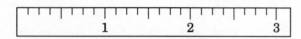

   ▶ **2** inches

2. The student does not properly align the object to be measured with the point that represents zero on the ruler.

   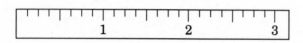

3. The student reads the small hand of a standard clock as minutes and the large hand as hours.

   ▶ **1:15**

4. When the hour hand is between two numbers, the student reads the time for the next hour.

   ▶ **7:50**

5. The student counts the minutes after the hour by starting at the hour hand.

   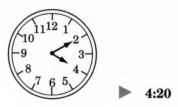

   ▶ **4:20**

6. The student becomes confused about identifying days beyond those in the first week on a calendar.

7. The student uses an incorrect frame of reference when relating temperatures with real-life activities.

8. The student is unfamiliar with the object for which he or she must make an estimate.

# Geometry

1. The student does not understand the concept of a two-dimensional figure.

2. The student does not understand the concept of surface area.

3. The student confuses the names of basic polygons.

4. The student thinks any figure is a square if it has 4 equal sides.

 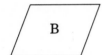

For example, the student thinks that figure A and **B** are both squares.

5. The student does not understand that the relative position of a figure has no effect on the figure's shape.

For example, the student thinks that figure **B** is **not** a square.

6. The student identifies a line as a line of symmetry, even though it does not create two congruent parts.

7. The student thinks that right angles must always have the same orientation.

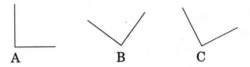

For example, the student thinks that **only** angle A is a right angle.

8. The student omits one or more of the dimensions of a polygon when computing its perimeter.

9. The student confuses the names of basic solid figures.

# Fractions

1. The student counts the wrong number of parts of a picture when naming equivalent fractions.

   *Write a fraction to represent the shaded parts.*

     $\dfrac{3}{4}$

2. The student transposes the numerator and the denominator of a fraction.

3. To find equivalent fractions, the student uses addition or subtraction instead of multiplication or division.

   ▶ $\dfrac{2}{3} + \dfrac{3}{3} = \dfrac{5}{3}$

4. When comparing fractions, the student compares only the numerators.

   ▶ $\dfrac{2}{3} < \dfrac{3}{5}$

5. When comparing fractions with the same numerator, the student compares only the denominators.

   ▶ $\dfrac{1}{4} > \dfrac{1}{3}$

6. When adding fractions, the students add both the numerators and the denominators.

   ▶ $\dfrac{1}{3} + \dfrac{1}{3} = \dfrac{2}{6}$

7. The student fails to multiply by the numerator when finding a fractional part of a number.

   ▶ $\dfrac{2}{5}$ of 15 = 3

# Decimals

1. The student confuses the terms used for place values in decimal numbers with those in whole numbers.

   *Find the place value of the underlined digit in 4.6̲3.*

   ▶ **tens**

2. When writing decimal numbers, the student misplaces the nonzero digit.

   *Write three and four hundredths in numerals.*

   ▶ **3.4**

3. The student omits the decimal point in a decimal number.

   *Write fourteen hundredths in numerals.*

   ▶ **14**

4. When ordering decimal numbers, the student's answer is based on the number of digits rather than their value.

   For example, the student thinks that 0.23 **is larger than** 0.4 because 23 is larger than 4.

5. When rounding decimal numbers, the student replaces values beyond the designated place value with zeros.

   *Round 0.65 to tenths.*

   ▶ **0.60**

6. When adding or subtracting decimal numbers, the student operates on the whole number parts and the decimal parts of the numbers separately.

   $$\begin{array}{r} 4.6 \\ +3.9 \\ \hline \end{array}$$
   ▶ **7.15**

7. The student places the decimal point in the wrong place in a decimal answer.

   $$\begin{array}{r} 4.6 \\ +3.9 \\ \hline \end{array}$$
   ▶ **.715**

# Graphing

1. The student fails to divide by the number of addends when computing the average of a group of numbers.

   *Find the average of 16, 25, 80, 44, and 90.*

   ```
       16
       25
       80
       44
      +90
   ▶  255
   ```

2. The student always divides by 2 or some other constant number when calculating an average.

   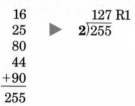

   ```
    16         127 R1
    25    ▶  2)255
    80
    44
   +90
   ───
   255
   ```

3. The student reverses the numbers in an ordered pair.

   For example, the student thinks that (3,2) **is the same as** (2,3).

   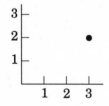

4. The student reads the next larger interval on the scale when reading a bar graph.

   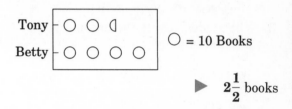

5. The student does not refer to a scale when interpreting a picture graph.

   *How many books does Tony have?*

   Tony ○ ○ ◖

   Betty ○ ○ ○ ○

   ○ = 10 Books

   ▶  $2\frac{1}{2}$ books

# Problem Solving

1. The student's answer is based only on the size of the objects.

   For example, the student thinks a nickel is worth more than a dime.

2. The student uses the wrong operation or operations to solve a problem.

3. The student does not read the problem but chooses the operation based on the relative size of the numbers in the problem.

4. The student does not read the problem carefully, but selects key words to determine the operation or operations.

5. The student thinks that all numbers in a word problem must be used to get the solution.

6. The student does not use all the relevant information given in a problem.

7. When comparing cost, the student does not find the unit cost of each product.

8. The student thinks that a lower cost always means the better buy.

9. The student does not answer the question posed in the problem.

10. The student is confused because the problem contains unfamiliar words or situations.

    For example, the student does not know that there are 52 cards in a standard deck of cards.

11. The student does not find all the possible solutions because he or she does not create a systematic list.

12. The student does not collect enough data to establish a pattern.

13. The student misreads a chart or table used in a problem.

14. The student's diagram does not faithfully depict the situation in the problem.

15. The student does not check if the data that is being tested makes sense in the problem.

16. The student is confused about what to do with a remainder in a real situation involving division.

17. The student does not check to see that the answer is reasonable.

# Calculators

1. The student enters the incorrect codes into the calculator.

2. The student does not enter the codes into the calculator in the correct order.

3. The student does not relate the equal sign on a calculator with the repeated addition function.

4. When entering a subtraction into a calculator, the student enters the subtrahend before the minuend.

5. When entering a division into a calculator, the student enters the divisor before the dividend.

6. The student fails to enter a decimal point at the appropriate place in a calculator code.

# MODERN CURRICULUM PRESS    Level C
# MATHEMATICS

**Richard Monnard**                    **Royce Hargrove**

## Table of Contents

# Sums through 10

## pages 1-2

### Objective

To review addition facts with sums through 10

### Materials

flash cards
ten counters

### Mental Math

Read the following numbers aloud. Tell students to put them in increasing order.

1. 5, 2, 1 (1, 2, 5)
2. 3, 10, 7 (3, 7, 10)
3. 0, 9, 2 (0, 2, 9)
4. 4, 5, 7 (4, 5, 7)
5. 9, 3, 8 (3, 8, 9)

### Skill Review

Read numbers 1 through 10 aloud in random order and have students make the corresponding groups of counters at their desks. Have them write the numbers from one to ten.

Remind students that numbers can be cardinal or ordinal. When they made a group of two counters they used the cardinal number 2. When they describe a position in line as second, they use the ordinal number.

---

### Sums through 10

Patsy walks from home to school along Oak Street and Maple Street. How many blocks does she walk to school?

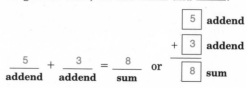

We are looking for the total number of blocks Patsy walks.

Patsy walks __5__ blocks on Oak Street.

She then walks __3__ blocks on Maple.

To get the total, we add __5__ and __3__.

$$\begin{array}{r} 5 \text{ addend} \\ + 3 \text{ addend} \\ \hline 8 \text{ sum} \end{array}$$

$$\underset{\text{addend}}{5} + \underset{\text{addend}}{3} = \underset{\text{sum}}{8}$$ or

Patsy walks __8__ blocks to school.

### Getting Started

Complete the number sentences.

1. $4 + 3 = \underline{7}$
2. $1 + 7 = \underline{8}$
3. $4 + 0 = \underline{4}$
4. $9 + 1 = \underline{10}$
5. $2 + 2 = \underline{4}$
6. $4 + 4 = \underline{8}$
7. $3 + 5 = \underline{8}$
8. $6 + 4 = \underline{10}$

Add.

9. $\begin{array}{r} 3 \\ + 2 \\ \hline 5 \end{array}$
10. $\begin{array}{r} 5 \\ + 5 \\ \hline 10 \end{array}$
11. $\begin{array}{r} 4 \\ + 0 \\ \hline 4 \end{array}$
12. $\begin{array}{r} 2 \\ + 7 \\ \hline 9 \end{array}$
13. $\begin{array}{r} 1 \\ + 5 \\ \hline 6 \end{array}$
14. $\begin{array}{r} 0 \\ + 9 \\ \hline 9 \end{array}$

15. $\begin{array}{r} 6 \\ + 2 \\ \hline 8 \end{array}$
16. $\begin{array}{r} 2 \\ + 3 \\ \hline 5 \end{array}$
17. $\begin{array}{r} 8 \\ + 1 \\ \hline 9 \end{array}$
18. $\begin{array}{r} 7 \\ + 3 \\ \hline 10 \end{array}$
19. $\begin{array}{r} 4 \\ + 5 \\ \hline 9 \end{array}$
20. $\begin{array}{r} 3 \\ + 6 \\ \hline 9 \end{array}$

(one) **1**

---

## Teaching the Lesson

**Introducing the Problem** Have students read the problem at the top of the page and identify what they are looking for. (number of blocks Patsy walks to school) Tell students that to solve the problem, they need to look for information in the problem and the picture. Tell them to find the two important facts in the picture and to fill in the first two blanks. (5 on Oak and 3 on Maple) Have a student read the plan for how to solve the problem aloud, and direct students to fill in the missing numbers. (5 and 3) Tell them that numbers that are added are called addends and that the answer is called a sum. Write the problem horizontally and vertically on the board showing students that either way will give the same sum. Tell students to fill in the addends and the sums in the model and write the answer in the solution sentence. (8)

**Developing the Skill** Have the students use their counters to do similar problems which you dictate. Have students arrange groups of counters horizontally on their desks. Point out that this is the way we write our sentences, and that it is a good way to write out problems that involve one-digit numbers. Give several more problems and direct students to arrange counters vertically on their desks. Ask a student to write each problem horizontally and vertically on the board.

### Getting Started   *Error Pattern Analysis*

errors with zero or one 8, 14; mechanical errors 24, 26, 29; language errors 31

**1**

**Practice**

Complete the number sentences.

1. $6 + 2 = \underline{8}$    2. $0 + 2 = \underline{2}$    3. $1 + 2 = \underline{3}$    4. $8 + 2 = \underline{10}$

5. $4 + 6 = \underline{10}$    6. $3 + 1 = \underline{4}$    7. $4 + 3 = \underline{7}$    8. $3 + 6 = \underline{9}$

9. $3 + 3 = \underline{6}$    10. $0 + 0 = \underline{0}$    11. $2 + 0 = \underline{2}$    12. $7 + 2 = \underline{9}$

Add.

| 13. | 14. | 15. | 16. | 17. | 18. |
|---|---|---|---|---|---|
| 7<br>+ 0<br>7 | 1<br>+ 4<br>5 | 2<br>+ 4<br>6 | 0<br>+ 9<br>9 | 1<br>+ 1<br>2 | 3<br>+ 4<br>7 |
| 19. | 20. | 21. | 22. | 23. | 24. |
| 0<br>+ 3<br>3 | 6<br>+ 3<br>9 | 2<br>+ 2<br>4 | 7<br>+ 1<br>8 | 3<br>+ 2<br>5 | 0<br>+ 6<br>6 |
| 25. | 26. | 27. | 28. | 29. | 30. |
| 4<br>+ 0<br>4 | 2<br>+ 7<br>9 | 4<br>+ 4<br>8 | 2<br>+ 1<br>3 | 2<br>+ 3<br>5 | 9<br>+ 1<br>10 |
| 31. | 32. | 33. | 34. | 35. | 36. |
| 7<br>+ 3<br>10 | 0<br>+ 7<br>7 | 1<br>+ 7<br>8 | 8<br>+ 1<br>9 | 1<br>+ 6<br>7 | 4<br>+ 2<br>6 |

**EXCURSION**

This machine is programmed to add 5. The number 2 goes in and 7 comes out. Write the missing numbers on the In and Out cards.

2 (two)

## Correcting Common Errors

If students have difficulty with sums to 10, have them practice with partners using the "count-on" strategy. For a fact such as $6 + 3$, start with 6 and count on 3 more: 6, 7, 8, 9. The sum is 9. When the first addend is the greater number, have students transpose the addends. For example, if the fact is $3 + 5$, they turn it around to $5 + 3$ and count on.

## Enrichment

Have the students calculate the number of blocks they walk to school or to their bus stop and make a map of the route that they take. Have them compare the maps they have made and see if each student is taking the shortest possible route from home to school or to the bus.

## Practice

Have the students complete the problems on the page. Check to see that they know what it means to complete a number sentence. See that they keep their digits in straight columns.

## Excursion

Tell students that in the first column, they are to write the number that comes out, when 5 is added to the number that went into the machine. Ask students how they will find the number that went into the machine in the second column. (ask what number plus 5 equals the number that comes out, or subtract 5 from the number that comes out) Have students write the missing numbers.

## Extra Credit   *Sets*

Have students identify examples of sets in everyday life. For example, a set of dishes, a set of golf clubs, set of blocks, swing set, set of paints etc. Conduct a discussion about what makes each group a set. Have students make up division problems using the sets using something that happened to them in the past week. For example:

Ed, Laura and Erin are going to play golf. They have one golf set with 12 clubs in it. If they divide the set evenly, how many clubs will each person have? (12 clubs ÷ 3 people = 4 clubs)

# Sums through 18

## Objective

To review addition facts with sums through 18

## Materials

twenty counters
one 25-inch string
* addition flash cards

## Mental Math

Ask students to identify which is larger:

1. (1 + 8) or 7 (1 + 8)
2. (4 + 4) or 5 (4 + 4)
3. (3 + 0) or 4 (4)
4. (7 + 3) or 10 (7 + 3 = 10)
5. (5 + 4) or (6 + 2) (5 + 4)

## Skill Review

Have each student draw a number line, 0 through 20, on paper. Put the same number line on the board. Dictate the following problems and show students how to trace each problem on the line.

1. 3 + 5 = (8)

0 1 2 3 4 5 6 7 8 9 10

2. 7 + 2 = (9)
3. 10 + 1 = (11)
4. 5 + 8 = (13)
5. 14 + 4 = (18)

---

## Sums through 18

Bill earned 7 dimes raking leaves on Monday. His father gave him 6 more on Tuesday when he finished the job. How many dimes did Bill have in all?

We need to find the total number of dimes Bill earned.

Bill earned ___7___ dimes on Monday.

His father paid him ___6___ dimes when he finished the job.

To get the total, we add ___7___ and ___6___.

___7___ + ___6___ = ___13___   or   $\begin{array}{r} 7 \\ + 6 \\ \hline 13 \end{array}$

Bill earned ___13___ dimes in all.

### Getting Started

Complete the number sentences.

1. 3 + 9 = 12      2. 8 + 8 = 16      3. 4 + 7 = 11      4. 9 + 8 = 17

5. 8 + 7 = 15      6. 7 + 7 = 14      7. 6 + 9 = 15      8. 6 + 8 = 14

Add.

| 9. | 10. | 11. | 12. | 13. | 14. |
|---|---|---|---|---|---|
| 7<br>+ 4<br>11 | 9<br>+ 6<br>15 | 8<br>+ 4<br>12 | 9<br>+ 9<br>18 | 7<br>+ 8<br>15 | 3<br>+ 8<br>11 |

| 15. | 16. | 17. | 18. | 19. | 20. |
|---|---|---|---|---|---|
| 8<br>+ 8<br>16 | 7<br>+ 5<br>12 | 8<br>+ 9<br>17 | 9<br>+ 2<br>11 | 7<br>+ 7<br>14 | 4<br>+ 9<br>13 |

(three) **3**

---

## Teaching the Lesson

**Introducing the Problem**   Have students examine the problem and tell what they must find. (number of dimes Bill earned) Tell the class to search for important data in the problem and the picture. As one student reads the facts aloud, the rest can fill in the blanks. (7 on Monday, 6 more when finished) Have a student read the plan as the rest of the class fills in the numbers to be added. (7 and 6) Remind students that these numbers are called addends and that the answer they are looking for is called the sum. Have a student demonstrate on the board the two ways this fact can be written. (horizontally and vertically) Ask students to identify the numbers as "addend" or "sum" as you point to them at random. Finally, have a student read the solution sentence for the class, as all fill in the correct sum.

**Developing the Skill**   Write the following number pairs on the board:

| | |
|---|---|
| 3 and 10 | 5 and 15 |
| 14 and 3 | 7 and 8 |
| 4 and 4 | 12 and 3 |

Starting with the first pair, have students put two groups of counters inside the looped string. Tell them to count all the counters within the string to determine the sum. Ask volunteers to write each problem on the board horizontally and vertically.

## Practice

Complete the number sentences.

1. $9 + 9 = \underline{18}$    2. $4 + 6 = \underline{10}$    3. $7 + 8 = \underline{15}$    4. $6 + 7 = \underline{13}$

5. $7 + 9 = \underline{16}$    6. $8 + 5 = \underline{13}$    7. $7 + 4 = \underline{11}$    8. $8 + 4 = \underline{12}$

9. $5 + 5 = \underline{10}$    10. $2 + 9 = \underline{11}$    11. $4 + 9 = \underline{13}$    12. $8 + 6 = \underline{14}$

13. $3 + 8 = \underline{11}$    14. $8 + 9 = \underline{17}$    15. $7 + 6 = \underline{13}$    16. $5 + 9 = \underline{14}$

Add.

| | | | | | |
|---|---|---|---|---|---|
| 17. $\begin{array}{r}7\\+5\\\hline 12\end{array}$ | 18. $\begin{array}{r}6\\+6\\\hline 12\end{array}$ | 19. $\begin{array}{r}8\\+3\\\hline 11\end{array}$ | 20. $\begin{array}{r}9\\+7\\\hline 16\end{array}$ | 21. $\begin{array}{r}2\\+8\\\hline 10\end{array}$ | 22. $\begin{array}{r}3\\+7\\\hline 10\end{array}$ |
| 23. $\begin{array}{r}9\\+4\\\hline 13\end{array}$ | 24. $\begin{array}{r}6\\+8\\\hline 14\end{array}$ | 25. $\begin{array}{r}9\\+7\\\hline 16\end{array}$ | 26. $\begin{array}{r}5\\+6\\\hline 11\end{array}$ | 27. $\begin{array}{r}9\\+6\\\hline 15\end{array}$ | 28. $\begin{array}{r}4\\+8\\\hline 12\end{array}$ |
| 29. $\begin{array}{r}9\\+3\\\hline 12\end{array}$ | 30. $\begin{array}{r}7\\+7\\\hline 14\end{array}$ | 31. $\begin{array}{r}5\\+8\\\hline 13\end{array}$ | 32. $\begin{array}{r}4\\+7\\\hline 11\end{array}$ | 33. $\begin{array}{r}9\\+5\\\hline 14\end{array}$ | 34. $\begin{array}{r}5\\+7\\\hline 12\end{array}$ |

Complete the tables.

35.

| Add 8 | 6 | 3 | 4 | 7 | 5 | 8 | 0 |
|---|---|---|---|---|---|---|---|
| | 14 | 11 | 12 | 15 | 13 | 16 | 8 |

36.

| Add 9 | 3 | 6 | 2 | 5 | 7 | 4 | 9 |
|---|---|---|---|---|---|---|---|
| | 12 | 15 | 11 | 14 | 16 | 13 | 18 |

## Apply

Solve these problems.

37. Frank has 9 school pennants left to sell. His sister has only three. How many pennants do they have left to sell all together?

12 pennants

38. Dina rode her bike 6 miles on Monday, doing her paper route. On Tuesday she rode 8 miles so she could deliver more papers. How many miles did she ride both days?

14 miles

**4** (four)

# Column Addition

## pages 5-6

## Objective

To review column addition

## Materials

twenty counters
two 25-inch strings
* addition flash cards
* overhead projector

## Mental Math

Have students add 4 to each of the
following numbers:

1. 1 (5)      4. 4 (8)      7. 7 (11)
2. 2 (6)      5. 5 (9)      8. 8 (12)
3. 3 (7)      6. 6 (10)     9. 9 (13)

Have students add 3 and then add 3
again to the numbers 1 through 4.
(4,7; 5,8; 6,9; 7,10)
Have students explain the pattern in
these two sets of problems. (As the
initial addend increases by 1, the sum
increases by 1.)

## Skill Review

Use flash cards to check recognition of
addition facts. Show the card briefly
and have students record the answer
on a piece of paper. Do not give students time to compute an answer.
Have students exchange papers and
show flash cards again.

---

## Column Addition

How many runs did the Greenfield
School baseball team score to
win its final game?

We want to know the total runs Greenfield scored.

The team scored __4__ runs in the first inning.

Then it scored __5__ in the second inning and __2__ in the third.

To find the total runs, we add __4__

and __5__ and __2__.

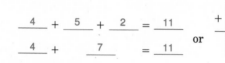

$$\underline{\phantom{0}4\phantom{0}} + \underline{\phantom{0}5\phantom{0}} + \underline{\phantom{0}2\phantom{0}} = \underline{\phantom{0}11\phantom{0}}$$

or

$$\underline{\phantom{00}9\phantom{00}} + \underline{\phantom{0}2\phantom{0}} = \underline{\phantom{0}11\phantom{0}}$$

Greenfield School scored __11__ runs in all.

To check, group the numbers in
a different way.

$$\underline{\phantom{0}4\phantom{0}} + \underline{\phantom{0}5\phantom{0}} + \underline{\phantom{0}2\phantom{0}} = \underline{\phantom{0}11\phantom{0}}$$

or

$$\underline{\phantom{0}4\phantom{0}} + \underline{\phantom{00}7\phantom{00}} = \underline{\phantom{0}11\phantom{0}}$$

## Getting Started

Add and check.

1. 3 + 2 + 4 = __9__

2. 5 + 1 + 4 = __10__

3. 6 + 3 + 2 = __11__

4. 2 + 5 + 1 = __8__

5. 6 + 3 + 6 = __15__

6. 3 + 0 + 3 = __6__

7.  4        8.  3        9.  5       10.  8       11.  7       12.  9
    5            4            4            1            2            0
  + 2          + 2          + 3          + 5          + 7          + 8
  ----         ----         ----         ----         ----         ----
   11            9           12           14           16           17

(five) **5**

---

## Teaching the Lesson

**Introducing the Problem**  Have a student identify the
problem to be solved. (number of runs Greenfield scored)
Ask where the information needed can be found. Direct the
class to fill in the data in the first two spaces. (4 runs and 5
runs). Have a student read the plan for solving the problem.
Have the class fill in the numbers to be added. (4 and 5)
Direct attention to the two ways in which the three numbers
can combined. Have students fill in both combinations on
their own page in both horizontal and vertical forms. Have
one student write this on the board. Ask students if it matters whether they add 4 + 5 and then 2, or if they add 5 +
2 and then 4. (no) Tell students that this is called addition's
**commutative property**.

**Developing the Skill**  Have students make two overlap-
ping loops with their strings. While you demonstrate with
the overhead projector, tell them to put 3 counters in one
area, 4 counters in the intersection of the loops, and 5
counters in the remaining area.

Show them on the board the two ways of adding three
numbers that are illustrated here: (3 + 4) + 5 = 12 and
3 + (4 + 5) = 12. Dictate several problems and have students solve them with their counters and loops. Have students write out the two ways in which the three groups can
be combined in order to reduce the problem to the sum of
two numbers.

## Practice

Add and check.

1. $5 + 1 + 2 = \underline{8}$  2. $2 + 1 + 8 = \underline{11}$  3. $6 + 2 + 4 = \underline{12}$

4. $2 + 5 + 6 = \underline{13}$  5. $7 + 9 + 0 = \underline{16}$  6. $2 + 3 + 4 = \underline{9}$

7. $2 + 1 + 6 = \underline{9}$  8. $5 + 1 + 4 = \underline{10}$  9. $2 + 6 + 9 = \underline{17}$

| 10. | 11. | 12. | 13. | 14. | 15. |
|---|---|---|---|---|---|
| 8 | 1 | 1 | 7 | 1 | 3 |
| 0 | 6 | 3 | 1 | 8 | 4 |
| + 7 | + 8 | + 9 | + 8 | + 9 | + 5 |
| 15 | 15 | 13 | 16 | 18 | 12 |

| 16. | 17. | 18. | 19. | 20. | 21. |
|---|---|---|---|---|---|
| 5 | 3 | 6 | 3 | 2 | 3 |
| 2 | 2 | 3 | 6 | 5 | 5 |
| + 9 | + 9 | + 8 | + 9 | + 8 | + 6 |
| 16 | 14 | 17 | 18 | 15 | 14 |

| 22. | 23. | 24. | 25. | 26. | 27. |
|---|---|---|---|---|---|
| 5 | 2 | 8 | 2 | 6 | 2 |
| 2 | 7 | 1 | 6 | 3 | 7 |
| + 6 | + 6 | + 4 | + 4 | + 6 | + 2 |
| 13 | 15 | 13 | 12 | 15 | 11 |

| 28. | 29. | 30. | 31. | 32. | 33. |
|---|---|---|---|---|---|
| 4 | 7 | 4 | 2 | 3 | 2 |
| 3 | 2 | 4 | 4 | 3 | 5 |
| + 8 | + 3 | + 2 | + 9 | + 6 | + 7 |
| 15 | 12 | 10 | 15 | 12 | 14 |

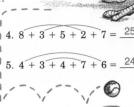

### EXCURSION

In column addition, look for pairs of numbers with sums of ten. Draw a line connecting each pair. Then add the whole column mentally.

| 1. | 2. | 3. |
|---|---|---|
| 4 | 3 | 5 |
| 3 | 2 | 1 |
| 6 | 8 | 4 |
| + 5 | 7 | 9 |
| 18 | + 4 | + 6 |
| | 24 | 25 |

4. $8 + 3 + 5 + 2 + 7 = \underline{25}$

5. $4 + 3 + 4 + 7 + 6 = \underline{24}$

**6** (six)

## Practice

Have students do all the problems. Remind them that they can check their answers by combining the numbers in a different way.

### Correcting Common Errors

Some students may have difficulty finding the sum of three or more numbers because they cannot remember the sum of the first two numbers when they go to add the third number. Have students practice by finding the sum of the first two numbers and writing it just above or beside the next addend. Then have them add this sum to the next addend and write the new sum, continuing in this manner until all the addends have been used.

### Enrichment

Students should complete the following series by filling in 3 more numbers:

1. 1, 3, 5, . . . (7, 9, 11)
2. 1, 4, 7, . . . (11, 14, 17)
3. 0, 1, 3, 6, . . . (10, 15, 21)
4. 1, 1, 2, 3, . . . (5, 8, 13)

## Practice

Have students do all the problems. Remind them that they can check their answers by combining the numbers in a different way.

## Excursion

Tell students that since we can add numbers in any order, we often find column addition easier if we look for sums of 10. Talk through the first problem as students draw a line to connect the 4 and 6. Remind students to add the columns or rows of numbers mentally. Have students complete the problem. Note: Students may choose to combine sums of 10 with one other addend at a time, or with the sum of 2 other addends to find the total sum.

## Extra Credit   *Careers*

Have students make a list of many occupations that use measurements: dressmaker, carpenter, rug layer, wallpaper hanger, baker and others. Tell students to list the types of measurements they think each worker uses, the measuring tools needed, and whether they use the metric or U.S. customary measurements. Assign each student or group of students an occupation and have them make calls, write letters, or interview workers, to obtain the information about how measurement is used in their jobs. Have them report their findings to the class.

# Minuends through 10

pages 7-8

## Objective

To review subtraction facts with minuends through 10

## Materials

ten counters
a 25-inch string

## Mental Math

Dictate the following problems. Direct students to do them by first grouping numbers in tens.

1. $3 + 4 + 7 = (14)$
2. $2 + 8 + 1 = (11)$
3. $1 + 9 + 9 = (19)$
4. $10 + 6 + 1 = (17)$
5. $2 + 7 + 9 + 1 = (19)$

## Skill Review

Remind students that subtraction is the inverse of addition.
Dictate the following problems and have students do them on paper.

1. $3 + 5 = (8)$    5. $4 + 3 = (7)$
2. $4 + 1 = (5)$    6. $6 + 2 = (8)$
3. $7 + 2 = (9)$    7. $3 + 3 = (6)$
4. $5 + 5 = (10)$   8. $9 + 5 = (14)$

Now have them take each sum and subtract one of the addends.
$(8 - 5 = 3$ or $8 - 3 = 5$, etc.$)$

---

### Minuends through 10

If Raoul uses 4 of his stamps to mail letters to his friends, how many stamps will he have left?

We need to find the number of stamps Raoul has left.

Raoul has ___10___ stamps.

He uses ___4___ stamps to mail his letters.

To get the number left, we subtract ___4___ from ___10___.

| 10 | minuend |
| --- | --- |
| − 4 | subtrahend |
| 6 | difference |

$$\underset{\text{minuend}}{10} - \underset{\text{subtrahend}}{4} = \underset{\text{difference}}{6} \quad \text{or}$$

Raoul will have ___6___ stamps left.

### Getting Started

Complete the number sentences.

1. $7 - 3 = \underline{4}$    2. $4 - 2 = \underline{2}$    3. $6 - 5 = \underline{1}$    4. $9 - 7 = \underline{2}$

5. $8 - 2 = \underline{6}$    6. $7 - 1 = \underline{6}$    7. $10 - 3 = \underline{7}$    8. $10 - 5 = \underline{5}$

Subtract.

| 9. $\begin{array}{r} 2 \\ -0 \\ \hline 2 \end{array}$ | 10. $\begin{array}{r} 6 \\ -3 \\ \hline 3 \end{array}$ | 11. $\begin{array}{r} 9 \\ -2 \\ \hline 7 \end{array}$ | 12. $\begin{array}{r} 8 \\ -7 \\ \hline 1 \end{array}$ | 13. $\begin{array}{r} 5 \\ -5 \\ \hline 0 \end{array}$ | 14. $\begin{array}{r} 4 \\ -3 \\ \hline 1 \end{array}$ |
| --- | --- | --- | --- | --- | --- |
| 15. $\begin{array}{r} 9 \\ -4 \\ \hline 5 \end{array}$ | 16. $\begin{array}{r} 3 \\ -1 \\ \hline 2 \end{array}$ | 17. $\begin{array}{r} 8 \\ -3 \\ \hline 5 \end{array}$ | 18. $\begin{array}{r} 7 \\ -0 \\ \hline 7 \end{array}$ | 19. $\begin{array}{r} 6 \\ -2 \\ \hline 4 \end{array}$ | 20. $\begin{array}{r} 2 \\ -2 \\ \hline 0 \end{array}$ |

(seven) **7**

---

## Teaching the Lesson

**Introducing the Problem**   Tell students to examine the problem and explain what operation is meant by the phrase "How many will he have left?" (subtraction) Now direct the class to find the information they will need. Have one student read the information sentences while the others fill in the data they need to answer the problem (10 stamps, 4 stamps). Read the plan for solving the problem, and have students write the number to be subtracted and the number to be subtracted from (4 from 10). Explain that the smaller number is called the **subtrahend** and must always be subtracted from the larger number, which is called the **minuend**. The answer is called the **difference**. Have one student write the problem on the board in its horizontal and vertical forms. Point out the minuend, subtrahend and difference. Have the students fill in the two problems and write their answer in the solution sentence.

**Developing the Skill**   Have students put 6 counters inside their string loops. Direct them to take 4 counters out. Ask how many counters are left. (2) Write the problem on the board in horizontal and vertical form. Ask a student to label the minuend, subtrahend, and difference. To show students that subtraction is not commutative, tell them to put 5 counters in the loop and then to take 7 away. When students object, ask why that particular subtraction is not possible. (7 is greater than 5.)

## Getting Started   *Error Pattern Analysis*

Complete the number sentences.

1. $10 - 5 = \underline{5}$  2. $1 - 0 = \underline{1}$  3. $2 - 2 = \underline{0}$  4. $7 - 4 = \underline{3}$

5. $0 - 0 = \underline{0}$  6. $10 - 9 = \underline{1}$  7. $5 - 1 = \underline{4}$  8. $4 - 3 = \underline{1}$

9. $7 - 3 = \underline{4}$  10. $5 - 5 = \underline{0}$  11. $6 - 0 = \underline{6}$  12. $6 - 3 = \underline{3}$

Subtract.

| 13. $\begin{array}{r} 5 \\ -4 \\ \hline 1 \end{array}$ | 14. $\begin{array}{r} 10 \\ -6 \\ \hline 4 \end{array}$ | 15. $\begin{array}{r} 3 \\ -3 \\ \hline 0 \end{array}$ | 16. $\begin{array}{r} 10 \\ -1 \\ \hline 9 \end{array}$ | 17. $\begin{array}{r} 5 \\ -2 \\ \hline 3 \end{array}$ | 18. $\begin{array}{r} 2 \\ -1 \\ \hline 1 \end{array}$ |

| 19. $\begin{array}{r} 7 \\ -5 \\ \hline 2 \end{array}$ | 20. $\begin{array}{r} 7 \\ -7 \\ \hline 0 \end{array}$ | 21. $\begin{array}{r} 5 \\ -3 \\ \hline 2 \end{array}$ | 22. $\begin{array}{r} 7 \\ -1 \\ \hline 6 \end{array}$ | 23. $\begin{array}{r} 1 \\ -1 \\ \hline 0 \end{array}$ | 24. $\begin{array}{r} 4 \\ -2 \\ \hline 2 \end{array}$ |

| 25. $\begin{array}{r} 6 \\ -4 \\ \hline 2 \end{array}$ | 26. $\begin{array}{r} 7 \\ -6 \\ \hline 1 \end{array}$ | 27. $\begin{array}{r} 4 \\ -4 \\ \hline 0 \end{array}$ | 28. $\begin{array}{r} 10 \\ -3 \\ \hline 7 \end{array}$ | 29. $\begin{array}{r} 4 \\ -1 \\ \hline 3 \end{array}$ | 30. $\begin{array}{r} 6 \\ -1 \\ \hline 5 \end{array}$ |

Complete the wheels.

31.

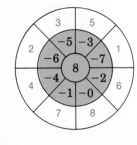

32.

**Apply**

Solve these problems.

33. Kyle's cat had 9 kittens. He left 6 kittens on his uncle's farm. How many does he have left to give away?
3 kittens

34. Nippi walked for 7 miles in the morning. After lunch, she walked another 4 miles. How far did she walk in all?
11 miles

**8** (eight)

# Minuends through 18

pages 9-10

## Objective

To review subtraction facts with minuends through 18

## Materials

twenty counters
* subtraction flash cards

## Mental Math

Tell students to start with 10 and subtract the following:

1. 2, then 3 (5)
2. 1, then 5, then 3 (1)
3. (3 + 4), then 2 (1)
4. (4 + 0), then (5 + 1) (0)
5. (3 + 5 + 1) (1)
6. (8 − 2) (4)

## Skill Review

Use subtraction flash cards with minuends through 10. Look for a quick response from the students, indicating that they are not computing answers. When students have correctly identified the difference, ask them to give an addition problem using the same numbers. For example, given the problem 7 − 3 = 4, the student will respond that 3 + 4 = 7.

---

### Minuends through 18

Ling and Nancy both collect stickers. How many more stickers does Ling have than Nancy?

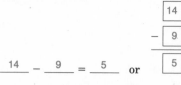

We want to know how many more stickers Ling has than Nancy.

Ling has __14__ stickers.

Nancy has __9__.
To find the difference, we subtract __9__ from __14__.

$$\begin{array}{r} \boxed{14} \\ - \boxed{9} \\ \hline \boxed{5} \end{array}$$

__14__ − __9__ = __5__  or

Ling has __5__ more stickers than Nancy.

Check your subtraction work by addition.

If **14 − 9 = 5**, then **9 + __5__ = 14.**

### Getting Started

Complete the number sentences and check by addition.

1. 16 − 8 = __8__    2. 14 − 5 = __9__    3. 12 − 4 = __8__    4. 18 − 9 = __9__

5. 11 − 7 = __4__    6. 13 − 6 = __7__    7. 15 − 9 = __6__    8. 17 − 8 = __9__

Subtract and check by addition.

| | | | |
|---|---|---|---|
| 9. $\begin{array}{r} 12 \\ -\ 7 \\ \hline 5 \end{array}$ | 10. $\begin{array}{r} 11 \\ -\ 3 \\ \hline 8 \end{array}$ | 11. $\begin{array}{r} 16 \\ -\ 7 \\ \hline 9 \end{array}$ | 12. $\begin{array}{r} 13 \\ -\ 9 \\ \hline 4 \end{array}$ |
| 13. $\begin{array}{r} 11 \\ -\ 5 \\ \hline 6 \end{array}$ | 14. $\begin{array}{r} 12 \\ -\ 3 \\ \hline 9 \end{array}$ | 15. $\begin{array}{r} 15 \\ -\ 6 \\ \hline 9 \end{array}$ | 16. $\begin{array}{r} 12 \\ -\ 6 \\ \hline 6 \end{array}$ |

(nine) **9**

---

## Teaching the Lesson

**Introducing the Problem** Read the problem and have one student explain the phrase "how many more." (indicates subtraction) Ask another to find the data in the picture while the class fills in the information sentences. (14 stickers and 9) Read the plan and tell students to fill in the numbers. (subtract 9 from 14) Ask a student to write the problem in its horizontal and vertical forms on the board, and direct the class to fill in these parts of the problem. Have a student label the minuend, the subtrahend, and the difference. Tell students to complete the solution sentence. Direct their attention to the subtraction check and have them complete the addition problem.

**Developing the Skill** Have students put 13 counters in a horizontal row and a row of 8 counters under it.

XXXXXXXXXXXXX
XXXXXXXX

The difference in the two quantities is represented by the unmatched counters on the left-hand side. Give the class several problems to do in this way. Then have students work together in pairs, checking each of the problems by lining up the counters to show that the sum of the difference and the subtrahend equals the minuend. For example:

$$\begin{array}{r} \text{XXXXXXXXXXXXX} \\ -\ \text{XXXXXXXX} \\ \hline \text{XXXXX} \end{array} \qquad \begin{array}{r} \text{XXXXX} \\ +\ \text{XXXXXXXX} \\ \hline \text{XXXXXXXXXXXXX} \end{array}$$

### Getting Started   *Error Pattern Analysis*

errors with zero or one 8,14; mechanical errors 24,26,29; language errors 31

**9**

## Practice

Complete the number sentences and check by addition.

1. $12 - 8 = \underline{4}$    2. $14 - 7 = \underline{7}$    3. $11 - 2 = \underline{9}$    4. $12 - 7 = \underline{5}$

5. $11 - 9 = \underline{2}$    6. $11 - 4 = \underline{7}$    7. $12 - 3 = \underline{9}$    8. $12 - 6 = \underline{6}$

9. $13 - 6 = \underline{7}$    10. $15 - 9 = \underline{6}$    11. $16 - 8 = \underline{8}$    12. $15 - 6 = \underline{9}$

13. $13 - 4 = \underline{9}$    14. $14 - 6 = \underline{8}$    15. $13 - 5 = \underline{8}$    16. $12 - 5 = \underline{7}$

Subtract and check by addition.

17. $\begin{array}{r} 18 \\ - 9 \\ \hline 9 \end{array}$    18. $\begin{array}{r} 11 \\ - 7 \\ \hline 4 \end{array}$    19. $\begin{array}{r} 15 \\ - 7 \\ \hline 8 \end{array}$    20. $\begin{array}{r} 10 \\ - 3 \\ \hline 7 \end{array}$    21. $\begin{array}{r} 14 \\ - 9 \\ \hline 5 \end{array}$    22. $\begin{array}{r} 17 \\ - 9 \\ \hline 8 \end{array}$

23. $\begin{array}{r} 11 \\ - 3 \\ \hline 8 \end{array}$    24. $\begin{array}{r} 13 \\ - 9 \\ \hline 4 \end{array}$    25. $\begin{array}{r} 13 \\ - 8 \\ \hline 5 \end{array}$    26. $\begin{array}{r} 11 \\ - 5 \\ \hline 6 \end{array}$    27. $\begin{array}{r} 10 \\ - 8 \\ \hline 2 \end{array}$    28. $\begin{array}{r} 13 \\ - 7 \\ \hline 6 \end{array}$

29. $\begin{array}{r} 16 \\ - 9 \\ \hline 7 \end{array}$    30. $\begin{array}{r} 10 \\ - 5 \\ \hline 5 \end{array}$    31. $\begin{array}{r} 14 \\ - 8 \\ \hline 6 \end{array}$    32. $\begin{array}{r} 11 \\ - 8 \\ \hline 3 \end{array}$    33. $\begin{array}{r} 16 \\ - 7 \\ \hline 9 \end{array}$    34. $\begin{array}{r} 17 \\ - 8 \\ \hline 9 \end{array}$

Complete the tables.

35. Subtract 8

| 11 | 14 | 17 | 16 | 12 | 15 |
|----|----|----|----|----|----|
| 3  | 6  | 9  | 8  | 4  | 7  |

36. Subtract 7

| 14 | 11 | 13 | 15 | 12 | 16 |
|----|----|----|----|----|----|
| 7  | 4  | 6  | 8  | 5  | 9  |

## Apply

Solve these problems.

37. Cassie has $13 to spend on a compact disc for her brother's birthday. The disc costs $9. How much money will Cassie have left?
$4

38. Mitch has 5 crickets and 12 grasshoppers in his collection. How many more grasshoppers than crickets does Mitch have?
7 more grasshoppers

**10** (ten)

# Basic Properties

## pages 11-12

### Objective

To review basic properties of addition and subtraction

### Materials

*addition and subtraction flash cards
twenty counters
a 25-inch string

### Mental Math

Ask students which is larger:

1. (9 + 3) or (15 − 1) (15 − 1)
2. (3 + 2 + 1) or (12 − 8) (3 + 2 + 1)
3. (15 − 5 + 1) or (9 + 2) (equal)
4. (19 − 3) or (6 + 8) (19 − 3)
5. (4 + 4 + 4) or
   (3 + 3 + 3 + 3) (equal)
6. (20 − 13) or (10 − 1) (10 − 1)
7. (6 + 3 + 1) or
   (20 − 5 − 3) (20 − 5 − 3)

### Skill Review

Mix addition and subtraction flash cards and quiz students on quick recognition. Take cards they have trouble with and use again. See who in the class can answer without mistakes, in the style of a spelling bee.

---

## Basic Properties

Adding and subtracting are easy if we remember some important ideas.

✔ We can add in any order.

$$\begin{array}{c} 3 \\ +\,4 \\ \hline \boxed{7} \end{array} \qquad \begin{array}{c} 4 \\ +\,3 \\ \hline \boxed{7} \end{array}$$

$3 + 4 = \underline{7}$

$4 + 3 = \underline{7}$

✔ We can group any two addends.

$$\begin{array}{c} \left.\begin{array}{c}2\\4\end{array}\right\}\;\boxed{6} \\ +\,6 \\ \hline \boxed{12} \end{array} \qquad \begin{array}{c} \left.\begin{array}{c}2\\4\\+\,6\end{array}\right\}\;\boxed{10} \\ \hline \boxed{12} \end{array}$$

$(2 + 4) + 6 = ?$

$\underline{6} + 6 = \underline{12}$

$2 + (4 + 6) = ?$

$2 + \underline{10} = \underline{12}$

✔ Adding zero does not affect the answer.

$$\begin{array}{c} 5 \\ +\,0 \\ \hline \boxed{5} \end{array} \qquad \begin{array}{c} 0 \\ +\,5 \\ \hline \boxed{5} \end{array}$$

$5 + 0 = \underline{5}$

$0 + 5 = \underline{5}$

✔ Subtracting zero does not affect the answer.

$$\begin{array}{c} 9 \\ -\,0 \\ \hline \boxed{9} \end{array}$$

$9 − 0 = \underline{9}$

✔ We can check addition by subtracting.

$$\begin{array}{c} 9 \\ +\,6 \\ \hline \boxed{15} \end{array} \qquad \begin{array}{c} 15 \\ -\,6 \\ \hline \boxed{9} \end{array}$$

$9 + 6 = \underline{15}$

$15 − 6 = \underline{9}$

✔ We can check subtraction by adding.

$$\begin{array}{c} 14 \\ -\,6 \\ \hline \boxed{8} \end{array} \qquad \begin{array}{c} 8 \\ +\,6 \\ \hline \boxed{14} \end{array}$$

$14 − 6 = \underline{8}$

$8 + 6 = \underline{14}$

(eleven) **11**

---

## Teaching the Lesson

**Introducing the Problem** Direct students to fill in the spaces on their pages as you read the page aloud. Have a student write each problem on the board. The first section explains that they can add in any order. In the next section help them group the addends to simplify the addition. In sections 3 and 4 show them that when they add or subtract zero, the addend or the minuend remains unchanged. Remind them that they can check addition by subtracting, or subtraction by adding.

**Developing the Skill** Write on the board: **5 + 2 =** , **2 + 5 =** Ask the class to answer each. Tell students we can add numbers in any order and the sum will still be the same. We say that addition is **commutative.** Ask the class if subtraction is commutative. (No, subtraction requires a certain order.)

Write on the board: **6 + 0 =** and **0 + 6 =** Ask what it means to add zero to another number. (Adding zero does not change the value of the number.) Have a student write answers to the problems on the board.

Now write on the board: **8 − 0 =** Ask what it means to subtract zero from a number. (Subtracting zero does not change the value of the original number.) Write the answer.

## Practice

Add in any order.

| | | | | | |
|---|---|---|---|---|---|
| **1.** $\begin{array}{r} 7 \\ +5 \\ \hline 12 \end{array}$ | **2.** $\begin{array}{r} 6 \\ +3 \\ \hline 9 \end{array}$ | **3.** $\begin{array}{r} 2 \\ +7 \\ \hline 9 \end{array}$ | **4.** $\begin{array}{r} 7 \\ +4 \\ \hline 11 \end{array}$ | **5.** $\begin{array}{r} 4 \\ +5 \\ \hline 9 \end{array}$ | **6.** $\begin{array}{r} 9 \\ +6 \\ \hline 15 \end{array}$ |
| **7.** $\begin{array}{r} 6 \\ +7 \\ \hline 13 \end{array}$ | **8.** $\begin{array}{r} 3 \\ +4 \\ \hline 7 \end{array}$ | **9.** $\begin{array}{r} 4 \\ +9 \\ \hline 13 \end{array}$ | **10.** $\begin{array}{r} 7 \\ +7 \\ \hline 14 \end{array}$ | **11.** $\begin{array}{r} 8 \\ +6 \\ \hline 14 \end{array}$ | **12.** $\begin{array}{r} 5 \\ +9 \\ \hline 14 \end{array}$ |

Group any addends.

| | | | | | |
|---|---|---|---|---|---|
| **13.** $\begin{array}{r} 3 \\ 2 \\ +4 \\ \hline 9 \end{array}$ | **14.** $\begin{array}{r} 7 \\ 1 \\ +2 \\ \hline 10 \end{array}$ | **15.** $\begin{array}{r} 6 \\ 3 \\ +4 \\ \hline 13 \end{array}$ | **16.** $\begin{array}{r} 4 \\ 4 \\ +2 \\ \hline 10 \end{array}$ | **17.** $\begin{array}{r} 2 \\ 4 \\ +5 \\ \hline 11 \end{array}$ | **18.** $\begin{array}{r} 7 \\ 4 \\ +3 \\ \hline 14 \end{array}$ |
| **19.** $\begin{array}{r} 5 \\ 4 \\ +5 \\ \hline 14 \end{array}$ | **20.** $\begin{array}{r} 2 \\ 8 \\ +3 \\ \hline 13 \end{array}$ | **21.** $\begin{array}{r} 6 \\ 2 \\ +3 \\ \hline 11 \end{array}$ | **22.** $\begin{array}{r} 3 \\ 5 \\ +4 \\ \hline 12 \end{array}$ | **23.** $\begin{array}{r} 5 \\ 3 \\ +6 \\ \hline 14 \end{array}$ | **24.** $\begin{array}{r} 8 \\ 1 \\ +6 \\ \hline 15 \end{array}$ |

Add or subtract.

| | | | | | |
|---|---|---|---|---|---|
| **25.** $\begin{array}{r} 6 \\ -0 \\ \hline 6 \end{array}$ | **26.** $\begin{array}{r} 7 \\ +0 \\ \hline 7 \end{array}$ | **27.** $\begin{array}{r} 5 \\ -0 \\ \hline 5 \end{array}$ | **28.** $\begin{array}{r} 4 \\ +0 \\ \hline 4 \end{array}$ | **29.** $\begin{array}{r} 9 \\ -0 \\ \hline 9 \end{array}$ | **30.** $\begin{array}{r} 3 \\ +0 \\ \hline 3 \end{array}$ |

Add and check by subtracting.

**31.** $\begin{array}{r} 4 \\ +7 \\ \hline 11 \end{array}$ $\boxed{11} - \boxed{4} \over 7$

**32.** $\begin{array}{r} 5 \\ +8 \\ \hline 13 \end{array}$ $\boxed{13} - \boxed{5} \over 8$

**33.** $\begin{array}{r} 6 \\ +7 \\ \hline 13 \end{array}$ $\boxed{13} - \boxed{6} \over 7$

Subtract and check by adding.

**34.** $\begin{array}{r} 14 \\ -6 \\ \hline 8 \end{array}$ $\boxed{8} + \boxed{6} \over 14$

**35.** $\begin{array}{r} 12 \\ -7 \\ \hline 5 \end{array}$ $\boxed{5} + \boxed{7} \over 12$

**36.** $\begin{array}{r} 16 \\ -9 \\ \hline 7 \end{array}$ $\boxed{7} + \boxed{9} \over 16$

**12** (twelve)

## Practice

Have students do all the problems. Direct their attention to problems 25 through 27, and remind them to check their addition by subtracting. Direct them to subtract one of the addends from the sum. Their answer should be the second addend.

## Correcting Common Errors

Some students may have difficulty believing that three numbers can be added in any order without changing the sum. Have them work in pairs, each with a set of identical addition problems with three addends. Ask one student to find the sum by adding from top to bottom. Ask the other student to find the sum by adding from bottom to top. Then have them compare answers to see that they are the same.

## Enrichment

Have students arrange ten counters so that they have five rows, with four counters in each. (The easiest solution is to put the counters in the shape of a five-pointed star.)

## Extra Credit  *Numeration*

Provide students with a duplicated copy of a 100's chart that has a separate square for each number. Tell students to color every other number on the chart beginning with number 2. Have them use another color for every third number beginning with the 3. Ask them to color in every fifth number beginning with the number 5 using a third color. Discuss the patterns students see developing. Using another 100's chart and other colors, investigate other patterns that might be formed.

# Problem Solving, Choosing the Operation

**pages 13-14**

## Objective

To practice selecting the operation needed to solve a problem

## Materials

9 red objects
6 blue objects

## Mental Math

Have students identify the next two numbers in each series.

1. 2, 4, 6, . . .  (8, 10)
2. 0, 3, 6, . . .  (9, 12)
3. 1, 6, 11, . . .  (16, 21)
4. 20, 15, 10, . . .  (5, 0)
5. 5, 5, 5, . . .  (5, 5)
6. 1, 4, 3, 6, 5, 8, . . .  (7, 10)
7. 1, 2, 4, 7, . . .  (11, 16)

## Skill Review

Have students write out the problem they would use to check the following:

1. $3 + 4 = 7$ $(7 - 4 = 3$ or $7 - 3 = 4)$
2. $11 - 9 = 2$ $(2 + 9 = 11)$
3. $15 + 5 = 20$
4. $19 - 5 = 14$
5. $13 + 3 = 16$
6. $7 - 2 = 5$
7. $19 - 18 = 1$

---

**Choosing the Operation**

To find how many balls altogether,

we __add__ .

To find how many more soccer balls

than basketballs, we __subtract__ .

To find how many bats are left

if we started with 6, we __subtract__ .

### Getting Started

Write the operation.

1. Molly has some marbles. She buys some more. How many does she have in all?
   add

2. Todd is picking strawberries. Jim also picks some. How many more strawberries does Todd pick?
   subtract

Write the operation and solve.

3. Alex took 7 sports pictures. He sent 3 of the pictures to his Aunt Em. How many did he have left?
   subtract    4 pictures

4. Maria had 9 animal pictures. Her brother gives her 8 more animal pictures. How many pictures does she have?
   add    17 pictures

(thirteen) **13**

---

## Teaching the Lesson

**Introducing the Problem**  Have students examine the picture. Ask what operation is indicated by the words "how many altogether." (addition) Have students write in the operation on their page. (add) Ask what operation is needed to find "how many more." (subtract) Have students fill in the blank on their page. (subtract) Ask what words will reveal the operation required. (how many . . . are left) Ask the class what operation is implied in the third problem (subtraction) and have them write that in their text.

**Developing the Skill**  Have students arrange their red objects and blue objects in a row next to each other. Ask the class what they would do if you asked how many red and blue objects there were altogether. (add) Ask what they would do if you asked how many more red objects are there than blue objects. (subtract) Have a student write these three problems on the board: **9 + 6 = 15, 6 + 9 = 15,** and **9 − 6 = 3.** Now ask if it is possible to tell how many more blue objects there are than red objects. (no) Have students take 3 objects away from the group of 9. Ask what operation they have illustrated. (subtraction) Have a student write this problem on the board. (9 − 3 = 6)

Give the students several problems and have them identify the operation before they do the problem.

## Practice

Write the operation.

1. To find how many more cups than saucers, we __subtract__.

2. To find how many dishes in all, we __add__.

3. To find how many fewer saucers than cups, we __subtract__.

4. To find how many cups are left if 2 were broken, we __subtract__.

## Apply

Write the operation and solve.

5. Randy took 6 pictures yesterday. Today he took 5 more pictures. How many pictures did Randy take in all?
add      11 pictures

6. Sally took 4 pictures on Monday, 3 pictures on Tuesday and 5 pictures on Wednesday. How many pictures did Sally take?
add      12 pictures

7. Dawn had 9 shells. Bill gave her 6 more. How many shells does Dawn have now?
add      15 shells

8. Celia had 8 stuffed animals. Betsy had 5. How many more did Celia have?
subtract      3 animals

9. Paul had 9 marbles. Dick had 12 marbles. How many fewer did Paul have?
subtract      3 marbles

10. Elaina bought 7 stamps. Jose bought 8. How many stamps do they have together?
add      15 stamps

11. Ron and Pete are cutting logs. Ron cut 15. Pete cut 9. How many more did Ron cut?
subtract      6 logs

12. Jackie is collecting books. Her mother gave her 7 to start. She bought 4 more. How many does she have now?
add      11 books

**14** (fourteen)

**14**

# Chapter Test

## pages 15-16

### Objective

To review skills learned in Chapter 1

### Materials

### Mental Math

1. 2 + 4 + 11 = (17)
2. 19 + 1 − 5 = (15)
3. 14 + 2 + 0 = (16)
4. 5 + 5 + 2 = (12)
5. 15 − 0 − 3 = (12)
6. 16 − 4 − 5 + 1 = (8)
7. 0 + 5 + 0 = (5)

Add.

| | | | | | | | | | |
|---|---|---|---|---|---|---|---|---|---|
| 0 +8 = 8 | 9 +2 = 11 | 8 +8 = 16 | 7 +4 = 11 | 9 +3 = 12 | 9 +6 = 15 | 5 +3 = 8 | 4 +0 = 4 | 2 +6 = 8 | 5 +4 = 9 |
| 4 +6 = 10 | 2 +5 = 7 | 0 +9 = 9 | 9 +0 = 9 | 7 +2 = 9 | 3 +7 = 10 | 1 +1 = 2 | 2 +4 = 6 | 8 +3 = 11 | 4 +7 = 11 |
| 4 +5 = 9 | 8 +6 = 14 | 1 +8 = 9 | 3 +0 = 3 | 7 +0 = 7 | 2 +3 = 5 | 1 +9 = 10 | 7 +8 = 15 | 4 +4 = 8 | 2 +0 = 2 |
| 7 +6 = 13 | 3 +6 = 9 | 2 +8 = 10 | 4 +3 = 7 | 0 +0 = 0 | 5 +1 = 6 | 0 +3 = 3 | 3 +5 = 8 | 6 +2 = 8 | 5 +6 = 11 |
| 8 +7 = 15 | 1 +7 = 8 | 6 +0 = 6 | 1 +5 = 6 | 0 +4 = 4 | 3 +2 = 5 | 7 +7 = 14 | 3 +1 = 4 | 5 +0 = 5 | 4 +9 = 13 |
| 2 +2 = 4 | 6 +9 = 15 | 6 +3 = 9 | 0 +5 = 5 | 2 +7 = 9 | 9 +4 = 13 | 9 +7 = 16 | 7 +1 = 8 | 6 +5 = 11 | 1 +2 = 3 |
| 0 +6 = 6 | 0 +2 = 2 | 4 +1 = 5 | 6 +1 = 7 | 3 +4 = 7 | 0 +1 = 1 | 4 +2 = 6 | 5 +9 = 14 | 9 +9 = 18 | 2 +1 = 3 |
| 8 +1 = 9 | 7 +5 = 12 | 3 +9 = 12 | 9 +5 = 14 | 1 +6 = 7 | 0 +7 = 7 | 6 +4 = 10 | 8 +2 = 10 | 5 +7 = 12 | 1 +3 = 4 |
| 1 +4 = 5 | 3 +8 = 11 | 8 +5 = 13 | 1 +0 = 1 | 7 +3 = 10 | 3 +3 = 6 | 6 +7 = 13 | 8 +4 = 12 | 5 +2 = 7 | 9 +8 = 17 |
| 8 +0 = 8 | 6 +8 = 14 | 5 +5 = 10 | 2 +9 = 11 | 9 +1 = 10 | 6 +6 = 12 | 7 +9 = 16 | 8 +9 = 17 | 5 +8 = 13 | 4 +8 = 12 |

(fifteen) **15**

## Teaching the Lesson

Explain that the 2-page chapter test is a review of the 100 basic addition facts and subtraction facts; for the numbers 0 through 9. Use these pages as a test, to determine which students need more work with basic facts. Or use the problems as a basis of a timed mastery review, encouraging students to try to work as quickly as possible. Read answers aloud and have students correct each other's papers, also computing the total number correct.

Subtract.

| 12 | 9 | 12 | 3 | 5 | 11 | 10 | 2 | 4 | 6 |
|---|---|---|---|---|---|---|---|---|---|
| − 8 | − 1 | − 4 | − 0 | − 5 | − 5 | − 9 | − 2 | − 0 | − 5 |
| 4 | 8 | 8 | 3 | 0 | 6 | 1 | 0 | 4 | 1 |

| 1 | 4 | 4 | 10 | 9 | 5 | 12 | 7 | 2 | 8 |
|---|---|---|---|---|---|---|---|---|---|
| − 0 | − 3 | − 1 | − 3 | − 4 | − 2 | − 3 | − 6 | − 0 | − 2 |
| 1 | 1 | 3 | 7 | 5 | 3 | 9 | 1 | 2 | 6 |

| 10 | 9 | 11 | 15 | 6 | 7 | 9 | 14 | 8 | 11 |
|---|---|---|---|---|---|---|---|---|---|
| − 6 | − 8 | − 9 | − 7 | − 6 | − 4 | − 5 | − 5 | − 8 | − 4 |
| 4 | 1 | 2 | 8 | 0 | 3 | 4 | 9 | 0 | 7 |

| 10 | 11 | 15 | 8 | 11 | 5 | 8 | 8 | 11 | 13 |
|---|---|---|---|---|---|---|---|---|---|
| − 7 | − 6 | − 6 | − 5 | − 8 | − 1 | − 6 | − 7 | − 3 | − 8 |
| 3 | 5 | 9 | 3 | 3 | 4 | 2 | 1 | 8 | 5 |

| 13 | 16 | 6 | 16 | 6 | 8 | 9 | 6 | 7 | 12 |
|---|---|---|---|---|---|---|---|---|---|
| − 5 | − 7 | − 4 | − 8 | − 0 | − 1 | − 9 | − 3 | − 1 | − 9 |
| 8 | 9 | 2 | 8 | 6 | 7 | 0 | 3 | 6 | 3 |

| 13 | 13 | 10 | 4 | 13 | 7 | 17 | 15 | 12 | 8 |
|---|---|---|---|---|---|---|---|---|---|
| − 4 | − 7 | − 2 | − 2 | − 6 | − 7 | − 9 | − 8 | − 7 | − 4 |
| 9 | 6 | 8 | 2 | 7 | 0 | 8 | 7 | 5 | 4 |

| 6 | 10 | 7 | 9 | 14 | 5 | 10 | 5 | 12 | 15 |
|---|---|---|---|---|---|---|---|---|---|
| − 1 | − 1 | − 3 | − 2 | − 9 | − 3 | − 5 | − 0 | − 6 | − 9 |
| 5 | 9 | 4 | 7 | 5 | 2 | 5 | 5 | 6 | 6 |

| 9 | 8 | 2 | 0 | 13 | 7 | 14 | 7 | 11 | 14 |
|---|---|---|---|---|---|---|---|---|---|
| − 6 | − 3 | − 1 | − 0 | − 9 | − 5 | − 6 | − 2 | − 7 | − 8 |
| 3 | 5 | 1 | 0 | 4 | 2 | 8 | 5 | 4 | 6 |

| 18 | 9 | 10 | 9 | 5 | 7 | 9 | 8 | 14 | 1 |
|---|---|---|---|---|---|---|---|---|---|
| − 9 | − 7 | − 8 | − 0 | − 4 | − 0 | − 3 | − 0 | − 7 | − 1 |
| 9 | 2 | 2 | 9 | 1 | 7 | 6 | 8 | 7 | 0 |

| 16 | 3 | 11 | 3 | 3 | 10 | 6 | 4 | 12 | 17 |
|---|---|---|---|---|---|---|---|---|---|
| − 9 | − 3 | − 2 | − 1 | − 2 | − 4 | − 2 | − 4 | − 5 | − 8 |
| 7 | 0 | 9 | 2 | 1 | 6 | 4 | 0 | 7 | 9 |

**16** (sixteen)

## Practice

Tell students to complete the two pages of problems.

# Tens and Ones

pages 17-18

## Objective

To review place values, tens and ones

## Materials

paper strips, 10 × 1 centimeters
paper singles, 1 × 1 centimeter
2-digit place value charts

## Mental Math

Dictate the following word problems:

1. There are 20 students in a class and 15 of them are buying their lunch today. How many are not buying their lunch? (5)
2. During a kickball game one team scored 5 runs in one inning, 3 runs in another, and no runs in the last. How many runs did they score in those 3 innings? (8)
3. John delivers papers after school. Today 3 of his 19 customers are out of town. How many papers will he deliver? (16)

## Skill Review

Ask students to circle the addends that total 10 and then calculate the sum. Write on board:

1. **2 + 5 + 4 + 3** = (14)
2. **4 + 4 + 1 + 6 + 2** = (17)
3. **5 + 4 + 5 + 6** = (20)
4. **1 + 0 + 2 + 9** = (12)
5. **5 + 4 + 1 + 4** = (14)

### Tens and Ones

Fred and Joel played ten-stick at recess. Fred was taking his turn when the bell rang. What were each of their scores?

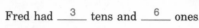

Fred had ___3___ tens and ___6___ ones.

Therefore, he scored ___36___ points. His score was **thirty-six.**

Joel had ___2___ tens and ___8___ ones.

Therefore, he scored ___28___ points.

His score was **twenty-eight.**

### Getting Started

Write the numbers.

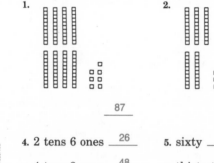

1. _____ 87

2. _____ 56

3. _____ 40

4. 2 tens 6 ones ___26___
5. sixty ___60___
6. 1 ten 9 ones ___19___

7. 4 tens 8 ones ___48___
8. thirty-three ___33___
9. fourteen ___14___

10. 5 tens 0 ones ___50___
11. eighty-one ___81___
12. 7 tens 7 ones ___77___

(seventeen) **17**

## Teaching the Lesson

**Introducing the Problem**  Ask a student to explain how the game ten-stick is played. (Players spin and receive counters totaling the number on the spinner.) Explain that players receive the counters in singles and when they have ten single counters, they trade them for one ten-stick. Ask someone to describe the problem. (to figure each boy's score) Ask how many counters Fred has, while the class fills in blanks. (3 tens and 6 ones) Ask what number is represented by 3 tens and 6 ones and have them write it. (36) Ask how many counters Joel had. (2 tens and 8 ones) Explain that 2 tens and 8 ones means 28 and have students write the total.

**Developing the Skill**  Have students show the number 3 with their 1 × 1 centimeter counters, while you draw three small squares on the board. Now have them show the number 14. Tell them to trade in the first group of 10 1 × 1's for a single 1 × 10 centimeter strip. The total will be one 1 × 10 and four 1 × 1's. Draw this on the board. While you draw a place value chart on the board, have the class fill in their place value charts to show the numbers 3 and 14.

| tens | ones |      | tens | ones |
|------|------|------|------|------|
|      | 3    |      | 1    | 4    |

Dictate several one- and two-digit numbers. Have students show the numbers with counters and then transfer the number to a place value chart.

**17**

## Practice

Write the numbers.

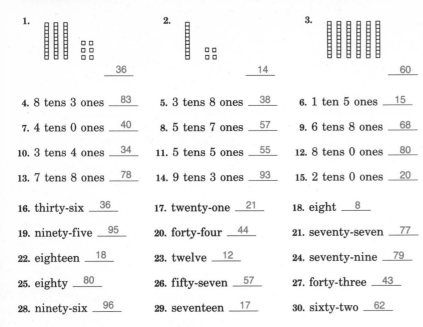

1. _____ 36

2. _____ 14

3. _____ 60

4. 8 tens 3 ones __83__
5. 3 tens 8 ones __38__
6. 1 ten 5 ones __15__

7. 4 tens 0 ones __40__
8. 5 tens 7 ones __57__
9. 6 tens 8 ones __68__

10. 3 tens 4 ones __34__
11. 5 tens 5 ones __55__
12. 8 tens 0 ones __80__

13. 7 tens 8 ones __78__
14. 9 tens 3 ones __93__
15. 2 tens 0 ones __20__

16. thirty-six __36__
17. twenty-one __21__
18. eight __8__

19. ninety-five __95__
20. forty-four __44__
21. seventy-seven __77__

22. eighteen __18__
23. twelve __12__
24. seventy-nine __79__

25. eighty __80__
26. fifty-seven __57__
27. forty-three __43__

28. ninety-six __96__
29. seventeen __17__
30. sixty-two __62__

### EXCURSION

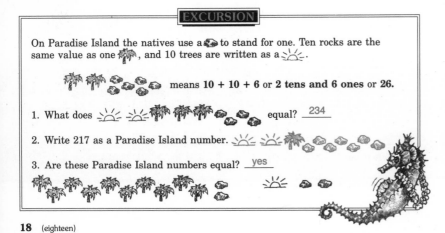

On Paradise Island the natives use a 🪨 to stand for one. Ten rocks are the same value as one 🌴, and 10 trees are written as a ☀️.

🌴🌴🪨🪨🪨 means 10 + 10 + 6 or 2 tens and 6 ones or 26.

1. What does ☀️ ☀️ 🌴🌴🌴 🪨🪨 equal? __234__

2. Write 217 as a Paradise Island number. ☀️ ☀️ 🌴 🪨🪨🪨🪨🪨🪨🪨

3. Are these Paradise Island numbers equal? __yes__

🌴🌴🌴🌴🌴🌴 🪨🪨    ☀️ 🪨🪨

18  (eighteen)

# Hundreds

## pages 19-20

### Objective

To review place values through hundreds

### Materials

*a spinner, numbered 1 through 9
paper sheets, strips, and squares
(10 × 10, 1 × 10, and 1 × 1 centimeters)
3-digit place value charts

### Mental Math

Dictate the following word problems:

1. Sally found 3 dimes and 4 pennies in her bank. How much money did she have? (34¢)
2. Ray wanted to buy a book that costs 45¢. How many dimes and pennies will he need? (4 and 5)
3. Ayesha had 2 dimes and Sam had 1 dime and 6 pennies. Do they have enough to buy pencils that cost 35¢? (yes)

### Skill Review

Tell students to keep track of the class score for each turn of the spinner and illustrate the number with their paper counters. Pass the spinner to at least 10 students and have the class add each new number to the total with their counters. Have them write the final score on a place value chart.

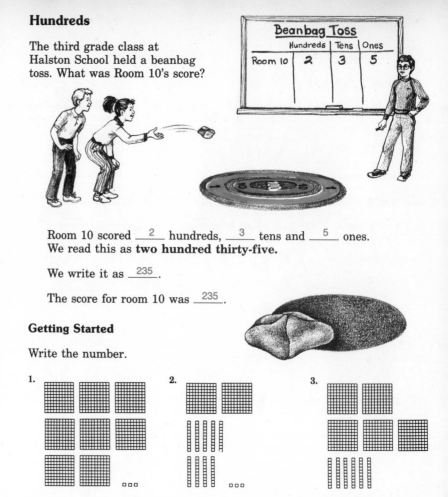

## Hundreds

The third grade class at Halston School held a beanbag toss. What was Room 10's score?

Room 10 scored ___2___ hundreds, ___3___ tens and ___5___ ones.
We read this as **two hundred thirty-five.**

We write it as __235__.

The score for room 10 was __235__.

### Getting Started

Write the number.

1. 803
2. 293
3. 560

4. 3 hundreds 1 ten 5 ones __315__     5. 9 hundreds 2 tens 9 ones __929__

6. two hundred eight __208__     7. four hundred twenty-seven __427__

8. 5 hundreds 3 tens 7 ones __537__     9. seven hundred eleven __711__

(nineteen) **19**

## Teaching the Lesson

**Introducing the Problem**  Ask students to look at illustration and explain how the game is scored. (If they hit the hundred, they score 100 points; if the ten, 10 points, etc.) Ask what question the problem asks. (What was Room 10's score?) and where the information can be found. (in the picture) Read aloud the information from the picture and have a student write it on the board while the others write it in their texts. (2 hundreds, 3 tens, and 5 ones) Have the class read this number together. (two hundred thirty-five) Have a student write the number on the board and tell students to write it on their pages. (235)

**Developing the Skill**  Remind students that ten single counters equal one ten-strip, and that 10 ten-strips equal one 10 × 10 sheet. Ask how many single counters would equal one 10 × 10 sheet. (100) Draw on the board:

| hundreds | tens | ones |
|----------|------|------|
|          |      |      |

Write the number 98 on the chart. Have the class show that number with their counters and then write it on their place value charts. Dictate several two- and three-digit numbers and have students show them with their counters and transfer the number to their charts.

**19**

## Practice

Write the number.

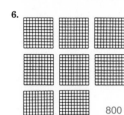

1. 345

2. 157

3. 608

4. 540

5. 275

6. 800

7. 9 hundreds 4 tens 3 ones __943__     8. 6 hundreds 4 tens 3 ones __643__

9. 4 hundreds 0 tens 2 ones __402__     10. 9 hundreds 7 tens 0 ones __970__

11. 8 hundreds 2 tens 6 ones __826__    12. 1 hundred 5 tens 9 ones __159__

13. 5 hundreds 0 tens 0 ones __500__    14. 7 hundreds 6 tens 3 ones __763__

15. 2 hundreds 5 tens 6 ones __256__    16. 4 hundreds 9 tens 1 one __491__

17. 6 hundreds 4 tens 3 ones __643__    18. 3 hundreds 9 tens 0 ones __390__

19. 1 hundred 0 tens 1 one __101__      20. 9 hundreds 0 tens 9 ones __909__

21. one hundred twenty-five __125__     22. six hundred eight __608__

23. four hundred fifty-two __452__      24. nine hundred seventy-five __975__

25. three hundred forty __340__         26. five hundred seventeen __517__

27. two hundred thirty-nine __239__     28. eight hundred ninety-nine __899__

29. three hundred seventy-five __375__  30. one hundred ninety __190__

**20**   (twenty)

**20**

# Money

## pages 21-22

### Objective

To review money and place value

### Materials

*play money

### Mental Math

Write the following numbers on the board for students to read aloud:

1. twenty-three
2. two hundred sixty-seven
3. nine hundred twelve
4. fifty-one
5. three hundred
6. one hundred ten
7. eight hundred eighty-two

### Skill Review

Have students write the numbers represented by the following:

1. 5 tens (50)
2. 25 tens (250)
3. 32 tens and 5 ones (325)
4. 63 tens and 35 ones (665)

Now have a few students make up similar problems for the rest of the class. Have one member of the class write the answers on the board.

---

## Money

During the move to her new house, Wanda's penny bank is broken. She decides to exchange her 123 pennies at the bank. How much has Wanda saved?

Wanda has ___123___ pennies.
She exchanges these pennies for

___1___ dollar, ___2___ dimes and ___3___ pennies.
We read this as **one dollar and twenty-three cents.**

We write it as $1.23.

Wanda has saved $1.23.

✔ Amounts less than one dollar can also be written with a dollar sign.

We can write **53 cents** as **$0.53.**
We can write **5 cents** as **$0.05.**

### Getting Started

Write each amount using the dollar sign.

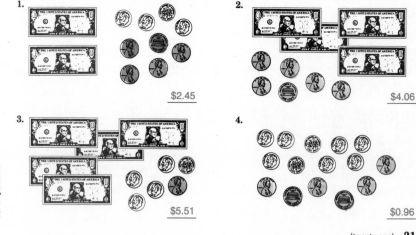

1. $2.45
2. $4.06
3. $5.51
4. $0.96

(twenty-one) **21**

---

## Teaching the Lesson

**Introducing the Problem**  Ask a student to identify the problem. (How much money does Wanda have?) Ask how many pennies Wanda had to begin with. (123) Have a student read the next sentence, filling in the information required from the picture. The rest of the class can complete the sentence in their text. (1 dollar, 2 dimes, and 3 pennies) Explain that we simplify 2 dimes, and 3 pennies and say 23 cents, just as we would simplify 2 tens and 3 ones to 23. Have one student write $1.23 on the board while the others fill it in. Explain that amounts can be written as a part of a whole dollar and call attention to the last section of the model. Read the last two sentences aloud and write **$0.53** and **$0.05** on the board.

**Developing the Skill**  Show the class a pile of 145 pennies and write **145¢** on the board. Place 1 dollar, 4 dimes, and 5 pennies next to the pile. Ask a student to tell you how much money is in the second pile. ($1.45) The two piles represent the same amount of money. Ask the class which pile would be easier to shop with. (dollars, dimes, pennies) Show the class 1 dollar, 6 dimes, and 2 pennies. Ask them to write the total amount on their papers while you write it on the board. ($1.62) Repeat for other sums. Remind the class that amounts less than one dollar can be written in two ways.

## Practice

Write each amount using the dollar sign.

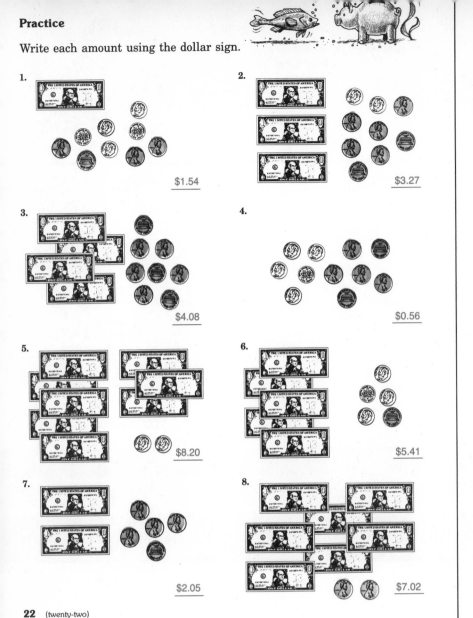

1. $1.54

2. $3.27

3. $4.08

4. $0.56

5. $8.20

6. $5.41

7. $2.05

8. $7.02

**22** (twenty-two)

**22**

# Counting and Ordering Numbers

**pages 23-24**

## Objective

To review ordinal numbers

## Materials

*set of 10 cards labeled first through tenth

## Mental Math

Dictate the following problems:

1. 10 + 10 + 25 = (45)
2. 3 + 7 + 10 = (20)
3. 20 + 11 + 9 = (40)
4. 32 + 8 + 10 = (50)
5. 100 − 50 + 10 = (60)
6. 101 + 9 − 10 = (100)

## Skill Review

Ask the class to look around the room and tell how many students there are. Write the number on the board. Now ask how many are wearing red and write that number. Remind them that these numbers represent a total and that we call them cardinal numbers. Have members of the class suggest other things they might count. Have students volunteer to write the numbers on the board, 28 students, 16 wearing red, etc. Write the word **cardinal** on the board.

---

## Counting and Ordering Numbers

The first six award ribbons are being given in the neighborhood dog show.

__Buttons__ came in first place.

__Spot__ won third place.

__Fluff__ was in second place.

__Pal__ came in fifth.

__Blackie__ was in fourth place.

__Red__ won sixth place.

✔ All numbers are made up of the **digits** 0, 1, 2, 3, 4, 5, 6, 7, 8 and 9. When numbers are given in order, we say they are in a **series**. In the series 2, 3, 4, 5, 6, 7:

2 comes before __3__,

5 comes after __4__,

6 comes between __5__ and __7__.

### Getting Started

Write the number that comes after.

1. 46, __47__    2. 72, __73__    3. 87, __88__    4. 63, __64__    5. 69, __70__

Write the number that comes before.

6. __26__, 27    7. __43__, 44    8. __70__, 71    9. __92__, 93    10. __77__, 78

Complete the series.

11. 1, __2__, 3, __4__, __5__, __6__, __7__, 8    12. 37, __36__, 35, __34__, __33__, 32, __31__

Name the place that comes after.

13. sixth, __seventh__    14. ninth, __tenth__    15. twelfth, __thirteenth__

(twenty-three) **23**

---

## Teaching the Lesson

**Introducing the Problem** Tell students to look at the problem and ask one to describe the illustration. (In a dog show the dogs have been awarded prizes.) Ask someone to explain which dog came in first and have students fill in the name on their pages. (Buttons) Write "first" and "1" on the board. Continue to ask for student input while the class fills in the names of the six winners. Write each ordinal word and number on the board. Read the next two sentences in the model, and write **digits** and **series** on the board. Have a student write the series 2, 3, 4, 5, 6, 7 on the board and ask the class to fill in the blanks while you read each line.

**Developing the Skill** Ask for ten volunteers to stand in front of the class and arrange themselves according to their birthdays. Give the oldest the card labeled "first" and ask the class to explain who should get the second card. (the person born second) Ask for ten more volunteers and have them arrange themselves alphabetically by first name. Give the "first" card to the student whose name begins closest to A, and so on. Explain that they have used the ordinal numbers 1 through 10 to describe the position each student had in line. Introduce the common abbreviations for first, second, and third. (1st, 2nd, and 3rd)

**23**

## Practice

Write the number that comes after.

1. 27, _28_     2. 35, _36_     3. 41, _42_     4. 67, _68_     5. 83, _84_

6. 39, _40_     7. 56, _57_     8. 79, _80_     9. 22, _23_     10. 47, _48_

Write the number that comes before.

11. _30_, 31     12. _24_, 25     13. _48_, 49     14. _52_, 53     15. _45_, 46

16. _59_, 60     17. _71_, 72     18. _33_, 34     19. _79_, 80     20. _70_, 71

Complete the series.

21. 5, 6, _7_, _8_, _9_, 10, _11_          22. 12, _13_, 14, _15_, _16_, 17, _18_

23. 67, _66_, _65_, 64, _63_, _62_, _61_     24. _47_, 48, _49_, 50, _51_, _52_, _53_

25. 70, _71_, _72_, _73_, 74, _75_, 76       26. _57_, 56, _55_, _54_, 53, _52_, _51_

27. 99, _98_, _97_, _96_, 95, _94_, 93       28. _87_, _88_, _89_, 90, _91_, _92_, 93

29. 30, _29_, 28, _27_, _26_, _25_, 24       30. 64, _63_, _62_, 61, _60_, _59_, 58

Name the place that comes after.

31. tenth, ___eleventh___          32. seventh, ___eighth___

33. sixteenth, ___seventeenth___     34. twentieth, ___twenty-first___

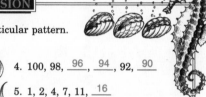

---

**EXCURSION**

In a **sequence**, the numbers follow a particular pattern.
Complete the number sequences.

1. 2, 4, _6_, _8_, 10, _12_          4. 100, 98, _96_, _94_, 92, _90_

2. 15, 12, _9_, 6, _3_, _0_          5. 1, 2, 4, 7, 11, _16_

3. 10, _15_, _20_, 25, 30, _35_     6. 20, _27_, 34, _41_, 48, _55_, _62_

**24**  (twenty-four)

---

---

## Practice

Have students complete the problems on the page. Explain that in the pairs given, the numbers differ from each other by one. In the sequences, the numbers may differ by more than one. Be sure they know how to spell the place names first through twentieth.

## Excursion

Write **3, 5, 7, 9, 11** on the board and ask students to tell the next 3 numbers in this series. (13, 15, 17) Now write **3, 4, 6, 9** on the board and tell students that 1 has been added to 3 to get to 4, and 2 has been added to 4 to get to 6. Ask why 9 is the next number in the series. (3 has been added to 6) Ask students to write the next 2 numbers in the series on the board and tell why. (13 because 4 is added, 18 because 5 is added)

Have students complete the sequences and then name the next 3 numbers in each.

## Extra Credit  *Sets*

Have students list the members of their families. Have them work in pairs and use their combined lists to write the names and number of members of each of these sets:

set P = the set of parents
set M = the set of male children
set F = set of female children
set C = set of children
set G = set of females
set B = set of males

You can extend this activity by changing partners, or by having students work in groups of three or more.

# Counting Money

## pages 25-26

### Objective

To review addition of money

### Materials

*play money

### Mental Math

Ask students to find the following sums and then count up five:

1. 21 + 6 (27, 28, 29, 30, 31, 32)
2. 40 + 4 − 1 (43, 44, 45, 46, 47, 48)
3. 20 − 10 + 3 (13, 14, 15, 16, 17, 18)
4. 59 + 6 (65, 66, 67, 68, 69, 70)
5. 82 − 7 (75, 76, 77, 78, 79, 80)
6. 58 + 2 − 3 (57, 58, 59, 60, 61, 62)

### Skill Review

Write the following problems on the board and have students do them on paper.

1. **10 + 10 + 25 + 5 =** (50)
2. **25 + 25 =** (50)
3. **25 + 5 + 10 =** (40)
4. **25 + 3 =** (28)
5. **10 + 5 + 4 =** (19)
6. **25 + 10 + 3 =** (38)
7. **100 + 25 + 4 =** (129)
8. **100 + 25 + 25 + 2 =** (152)

---

## Counting Money

How much money does Georgio have?

| Money | We count: |
|---|---|
|  | 1 dollar |
|  | 2 dollars |
|  | twenty-five |
|  | fifty |
|  | seventy-five |
|  | eighty |
|  | eighty-five |
|  | eighty-six |
|  | eighty-seven |
| | eighty-eight |

Georgio has ___$2.88___ .

### Getting Started

Write the amount using the dollar sign.

1.

$3.64

2.

$0.34

---

## Teaching the Lesson

**Introducing the Problem**  Explain that in this problem students will learn to count money. Tell them that they are going to count the money with Georgio. Tell them to start with the largest amount, the dollars. Count aloud with the class. (1 dollar, 2 dollars, 25 cents, 50 cents, 75 cents, etc.) Ask individual students to identify each bill or coin while all fill in the value. Write the total **$2.88** on the board and have the students write it in their texts.

**Developing the Skill**  Begin by counting to 100 by fives, by tens, and by twenty-fives. Vary the activity by asking a student to count from 40 to 100 by tens; ask another to count by fives from 35. Give them several more examples.

Now explain that when they count money, they should begin with the largest bill or coin. Hold up 3 dollars, 2 quarters, 1 dime, and a penny and have them count this, starting with the dollars. (1 dollar, 2 dollars, 3 dollars, 25 cents, 50 cents, 60 cents, 61 cents; $3.61) Now have one student make up an item to be bought and its cost. Another student should use the play money and count the cost aloud so that the class can follow. Repeat this with several student pairs.

Write the amount using the dollar sign.

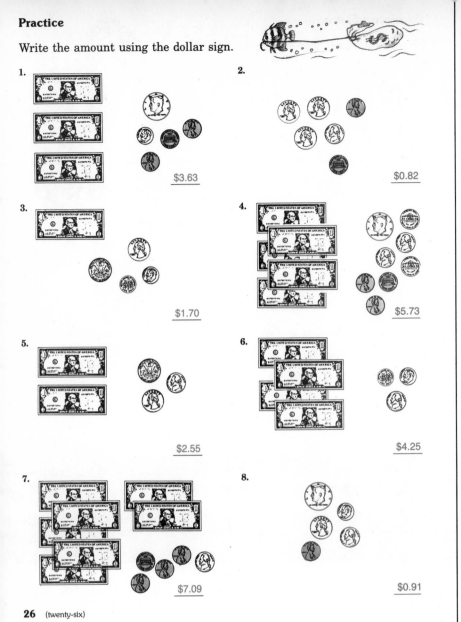

1. $3.63

2. $0.82

3. $1.70

4. $5.73

5. $2.55

6. $4.25

7. $7.09

8. $0.91

## Correcting Common Errors

If students have difficulty counting money, have them write the value of each bill or coin in the group in a column in order from greatest to least. Then they count down the column adding on the value for each new bill or coin.

## Enrichment

1. Explain that **symmetry** means that an object has similarly shaped parts. If if is symmetrical about a line, it means that it is the same on both sides of the line. Explain that if you could fold the object along the line, all points on one side would touch points on the other side. Have the students fold a piece of paper in half. The fold is the line of symmetry. Here is a letter with its line of symmetry. A

2. Have students pick out the letters of the alphabet which have up and down lines of symmetry, and draw those lines in.

   HIMOTWVXY

## Practice

Have students do all the problems on the page. See that they understand that they are to give their answers in dollars and fractions of dollars. Go over the illustrations with the class to be sure they can identify each coin.

## Extra Credit   *Logic*

Give each pair of students 15 bottlecaps, or similar place holders. Tell them to arrange the bottlecaps in three rows: 7 in the first row, 5 in the next and 3 in the third. Tell students the object of the game is to take turns picking up the bottlecaps and forcing your opponent to take the last one. The first player picks up as many caps as he wants to, from one row only. The other player does the same, picking from one row of the remaining bottlecaps. The game continues until the last bottlecap is picked by the losing student. After students play the game several times, have them devise a system for consistent winning.

# Comparing Numbers

## pages 27-28

### Objective

To review concepts of greater than and less than

### Materials

### Mental Math

Have students give as many ways as possible to make the following amounts:

1. $0.13 (1 dime, 3 pennies or 2 nickels, 3 pennies or 13 pennies)
2. $1.02 (1 dollar, 2 pennies or 2 half-dollars, 2 pennies or 4 quarters, 2 pennies or 1 half-dollar, 2 quarters, 2 pennies, etc.)
3. $0.67 (2 quarters, 1 dime, 1 nickel, 2 pennies or 1 quarter, 4 dimes, 2 pennies or 6 dimes, 1 nickel, 2 pennies, etc.)

### Skill Review

Ask students to count to 200 by tens. Ask which is greater, 130 or 150. (150) Repeat this for several number pairs.

---

## Comparing Numbers

Ann and Steve are earning exercise merit badges by riding their bicycles. Who rode more miles?

We want to know which person rode further.

Ann rode ___351___ miles.

Steve rode ___316___ miles.

We need to compare __351__ and __316__. Start with the digits on the left.

| Ann | 351 | 351 |
| Steve | 316 | 316 |

Both have the same number of hundreds.    Ann has more tens.

We write 351 > 316 and say

351 is ___greater___ than 316.

We write 316 < 351 and say

316 is ___less___ than 351.

___Ann___ rode more miles.

### Getting Started

Compare these numbers. Write < or > in the circle.

1. 582 ⊘ 536          2. 118 ⊘ 116          3. 504 ⊘ 540

Write the numbers in order from least to greatest.

4. 651, 647, 663      5. 492, 490, 497      6. 650, 649, 651

__647__, __651__, __663__      __490__, __492__, __497__      __649__, __650__, __651__

Circle the greatest number.

7. 363, (481) 294, 421      8. 752, 749, (767) 755      9. 304, 310, 309, (315)

(twenty-seven) **27**

---

## Teaching the Lesson

**Introducing the Problem**   Have the class examine the problem and ask a student to explain it. (to find out who went farther) Ask what are the numbers on the girls' odometers. (Ann, 351 miles and Steve, 316 miles) Have students write these numbers in the text. Read the plan for the problem aloud and have them fill in the numbers. In the boxed portion of the problem, have them circle the hundreds to see that each rider went the same number of hundreds. Have them circle the tens in the next part of the box to see that Ann has more tens. Explain that the symbol > means greater than, the symbol < less than. Have a student read the comparisons while the class fills in the spaces. Read the solution sentence aloud. (Ann rode farther.)

**Developing the Skill**   Write several 1-digit number pairs on the board and have volunteers put the appropriate symbol, > or < , between each pair. As each symbol is filled in, have a student read the comparison. Write a set of 2-digit number pairs on the board and again call for volunteers to write in the proper symbol. Have each student read the comparison. Write on the board: **236 238.** Tell students to compare these numbers, starting in the hundreds column. Ask the class in which column they find the difference. (ones) Write **236<238** on the board. Give them several more 3-digit pairs and have them compare, starting each time with the hundreds column.

**27**

## Practice

Compare these numbers. Write < or > in the circle.

1. 9 $<$ 11
2. 36 $>$ 29
3. 127 $<$ 138
4. 139 $>$ 136
5. 257 $>$ 243
6. 512 $<$ 675
7. 405 $>$ 403
8. 826 $>$ 806
9. 715 $<$ 725
10. 888 $<$ 999
11. 480 $<$ 481
12. 517 $>$ 516
13. 255 $>$ 156
14. 319 $<$ 320
15. 157 $>$ 148

Write the numbers in order from least to greatest.

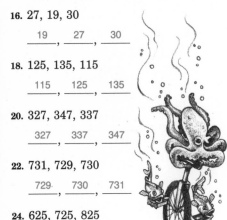

16. 27, 19, 30

   19 , 27 , 30

17. 82, 90, 86

   82 , 86 , 90

18. 125, 135, 115

   115 , 125 , 135

19. 512, 510, 514

   510 , 512 , 514

20. 327, 347, 337

   327 , 337 , 347

21. 926, 916, 925

   916 , 925 , 926

22. 731, 729, 730

   729 , 730 , 731

23. 887, 885, 883

   883 , 885 , 887

24. 625, 725, 825

   625 , 725 , 825

25. 421, 429, 412

   412 , 421 , 429

Circle the greatest number.

26. 245, (376), 151, 236
27. 356, 421, 351, (450)
28. 605, 603, (608), 600
29. (961), 851, 947, 875
30. 400, 425, 475, (500)
31. 871, (878), 787, 788
32. 520, 525, 530, (535)
33. 747, 737, (777), 757
34. 256, 265, (656), 566
35. 180, 185, 183, (188)
36. 321, (371), 301, 312
37. (499), 409, 419, 439

**28** (twenty-eight)

# Rounding to the Nearest Ten

**pages 29-30**

## Objective

To round numbers to the nearest ten

## Materials

## Mental Math

Ask the class to count together to:

1. 50 by fives (5, 10, 15, 20, . . . )
2. 27 by threes (3, 6, 9, 12, 15, . . . )
3. 70 by tens (10, 20, 30, 40, . . . )
4. 20 by twos (2, 4, 6, 8, 10, . . . )
5. 28 by sevens (7, 14, 21, 28)
6. 9 by nines (9)
7. 44 by elevens (11, 22, 33, 44)

## Skill Review

Tell students to draw a number line with numbers from 0 through 20 as you draw one on the board. Write **4, 8,** and **9** on the board. Ask a volunteer to find the numbers, and then explain whether the 8 is closer to 4 or 9. (9) Repeat this exercise with other sets of three numbers.

---

**Rounding to the Nearest Ten**

Beth is using a number line to help round her numbers to the nearest ten.

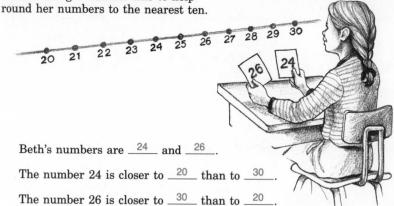

Beth's numbers are __24__ and __26__.

The number 24 is closer to __20__ than to __30__.

The number 26 is closer to __30__ than to __20__.

> To round to the nearest 10, look at the ones digit.

If the ones digit is 0, 1, 2, 3 or 4, the tens digit stays the same, and the ones digit is replaced by zero.

Beth rounds **24** to __20__.

If the ones digit is 5, 6, 7, 8 or 9, the tens digit is raised one, and the ones digit is replaced by zero.

Beth rounds **26** to __30__.

### Getting Started

Circle the ten nearest each red number.

1. (60)  62  70
2. 60¢  66¢  (70¢)
3. (40)  43  50
4. 90  96  (100)
5. (40)  41  50
6. 30¢  35¢  (40¢)

Round to the nearest ten.

7. 77 __80__
8. 19¢ __20¢__
9. 68 __70__
10. 45 __50__
11. 38¢ __40¢__
12. 27 __30__

(twenty-nine) **29**

---

## Teaching the Lesson

**Introducing the Problem**  Have the class examine the illustration in the text and read the problem. Ask what numbers Beth has and have students write these numbers on their pages. (24 and 26) Draw the number line on the board and have a student circle the 24 and the 26. Read the next sentences in the model and have students complete the sentences. (24 is closer to 20 than 30, 26 is closer to 30 than 20.) Explain that when they want to round to the nearest ten they will look at the ones digit. Direct their attention to the flowchart and rules. Reinforce that numbers with 0 through 4 in the ones place will be rounded down and numbers with 5 through 9 in the ones place will be rounded up.

**Developing the Skill**  Have the class count by tens to 100. Explain that it is sometimes convenient to approximate a number by rounding it off to the nearest 10. Tell the class that to do this, they will have to determine which multiple of 10 the number is closest to. Draw a number line on the board from 40 through 50. Point to any number on the line and ask a student to explain whether the number is closer to 40 or to 50. Repeat this for several numbers. Explain that the case of 45, or any number ending with 5, is special because 5 is exactly half-way between one ten and the next. Tell them that the 5 is always rounded up.

**29**

## Practice

Circle the ten nearest each red number.

1. (50)  53  60   2. 40¢  46¢  (50¢)   3. 10  17  (20)

4. 20¢  28¢  (30¢)   5. (80)  81  90   6. (70)  73  80

7. 40  45  (50)   8. (90¢)  93¢  100¢   9. 20  26  (30)

10. 70  77  (80)   11. (40)  42  50   12. 50¢  55¢  (60¢)

Round each number to the nearest ten.

13. 48 __50__     14. 51 __50__     15. 19¢ __20¢__     16. 87¢ __90¢__

17. 62 __60__     18. 35¢ __40¢__     19. 11 __10__     20. 68¢ __70¢__

21. 92¢ __90¢__     22. 33¢ __30¢__     23. 79 __80__     24. 71 __70__

25. 9 __10__     26. 57 __60__     27. 75¢ __80¢__     28. 43 __40__

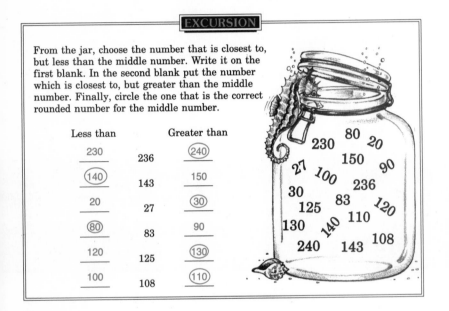

**EXCURSION**

From the jar, choose the number that is closest to, but less than the middle number. Write it on the first blank. In the second blank put the number which is closest to, but greater than the middle number. Finally, circle the one that is the correct rounded number for the middle number.

| Less than | | Greater than |
|---|---|---|
| 230 | 236 | (240) |
| (140) | 143 | 150 |
| 20 | 27 | (30) |
| (80) | 83 | 90 |
| 120 | 125 | (130) |
| 100 | 108 | (110) |

Numbers in jar: 230 80 20 27 150 100 90 30 236 83 125 120 130 140 110 240 143 108

## Correcting Common Errors

Some students may round numbers up when they should be rounded down, or round numbers down when they should be rounded up. When rounding to the nearest ten, have students first write the two tens the number is between. Then have them use a number line to decide which ten the number is nearer to and circle this ten.

## Enrichment

1. Students who have done the last two enrichment activities will be ready to combine what they know about symmetry on a vertical line and on a horizontal line. Ask them to find letters that are symmetric about both vertical and horizontal lines and to draw those lines on the letters. H I O X

2. Ask them to draw at least one other figure which is symmetric on two lines. (Ex. A square)

## Practice

Have students complete the problems on the page. Point out that they will treat the money the same way they do the other numbers.

## Excursion

Tell students to cross out each number in the jar as it is used. Remind students to circle the number that tells what each middle number would be if rounded to the nearest ten.

## Extra Credit  *Biography*

Isaac Newton was enjoying a cup of tea in his garden when he saw an apple drop to the ground from a nearby tree. Suddenly, he realized that the same force that pulled the apple to Earth also held the moon in its orbit and held the whole universe together. Newton's theories of gravity were published in 1687 in his book, *Principia*. Newton was born in 1642 in England to a farming family. He studied and later became a mathematics professor at Trinity College, Cambridge. An absent-minded bachelor, Newton spent almost every waking moment testing his ideas and studying the theories of other mathematicians. Though he has been called one of the greatest mathematicians of all time, the modest Newton once said, "If I have seen farther than most, it is because I have stood on the shoulders of giants."

# Rounding to the Nearest Hundred

**pages 31-32**

## Objective

To round numbers to the nearest hundred

## Materials

## Mental Math

Dictate the following numbers. Ask students to identify the number in the ones place.

| | | |
|---|---|---|
| 1. 53 (3) | 4. 645 (5) | 7. 438 (8) |
| 2. 236 (6) | 5. 6 (6) | 8. 276 (6) |
| 3. 788 (8) | 6. 390 (0) | 9. 84 (4) |

Now ask what number is in the tens place in the following:

| | | |
|---|---|---|
| 1. 542 (4) | 4. 640 (4) | 7. 72 (7) |
| 2. 7 (0) | 5. 968 (6) | 8. 173 (7) |
| 3. 902 (0) | 6. 15 (1) | 9. 881 (8) |

Repeat these numbers and have students identify the hundreds.

## Skill Review

Write the following numbers on the board and ask students to round them to the nearest ten.

| | |
|---|---|
| 1. **23** (20) | 6. **12** (10) |
| 2. **97** (100) | 7. **41** (40) |
| 3. **4** (0) | 8. **65** (70) |
| 4. **67** (70) | 9. **48¢** (50¢) |
| 5. **55** (60) | 10. **5** (10) |

---

### Rounding to the Nearest Hundred

Rinaldo wants to round his numbers to the nearest hundred.

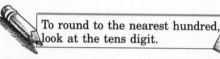

Rinaldo's numbers are __746__ and __769__.

The number 746 is closer to __700__ than to __800__.

The number 769 is closer to __800__ than to __700__.

To round to the nearest hundred, look at the tens digit. **268**

If the tens digit is 0, 1, 2, 3 or 4, the hundreds digit stays the same, and the tens and ones digits are replaced by zeros.

Rinaldo rounds 746 to __700__.

If the tens digit is 5, 6, 7, 8 or 9, the hundreds digit is raised one, and the tens and ones digits are replaced by zeros.

Rinaldo rounds 769 to __800__.

### Getting Started

Circle the hundred or dollar nearest the red number.

| | | | | | | | | |
|---|---|---|---|---|---|---|---|---|
| 1. 500 | 583 | (600) | 2. (900) | 909 | 1,000 | 3. ($6) | $6.30 | $7 |
| 4. (100) | 147 | 200 | 5. 700 | 750 | (800) | 6. (300) | 329 | 400 |
| 7. $1 | $1.96 | ($2) | 8. 500 | 551 | (600) | 9. 900 | 995 | (1,000) |

Round to the nearest hundred or dollar.

| | | |
|---|---|---|
| 10. 429 __400__ | 11. 650 __700__ | 12. $9.81 __$10__ |
| 13. 807 __800__ | 14. 196 __200__ | 15. $5.83 __$6__ |
| 16. 470 __500__ | 17. $2.49 __$2__ | 18. 738 __700__ |

(thirty-one) **31**

---

## Teaching the Lesson

**Introducing the Problem** Ask students to examine the illustration while you read the problem. Ask what Rinaldo wants to do. (round his numbers to the nearest hundred) Ask what numbers Rinaldo has. (746, 769) Ask which hundred 746 is closer to. (700) Direct students to complete that sentence in their books. (closer to 700 than to 800) Read the next sentence aloud and have students name the closest hundred to 769. (closer to 800 than to 700) Now direct their attention to the rules. Write **746** on the board and have a student circle the number in the tens place. Repeat for **769.** Explain that they will look to the tens place when rounding to the nearest hundred. Have a student read the sentence in the left-hand rule while the others fill in the answer. (746 to 700) Repeat for the right-hand rule. (769 to 800)

**Developing the Skill** Have the class count by hundreds to 1,000. Draw a number line on the board from 300 through 400, showing intervals of ten. Explain that they will be rounding numbers as they did in the last lesson. In this case, however, they will look at the tens place in order to determine which hundred a given number is closer to. Write **325** on the board and have a student point to its place on the number line. Ask whether 325 is closer to 300 or to 400. (300) Repeat this for several numbers. Remind them that when a 5 appears in the tens place, they round the number up.

Circle the hundred or dollar nearest the red number.

1. 300    356    (400)
2. (200)    212    300
3. ($6)    $6.28    $7

4. ($1)    $1.07    $2
5. 600    675    (700)
6. 800    850    (900)

7. 200    283    (300)
8. 100    196    (200)
9. $7    $7.57    ($8)

10. ($4)    $4.12    $5
11. 900    985    (1,000)
12. (300)    349    400

Round to the nearest hundred or dollar.

13. 736 __700__
14. $4.27 __$4__
15. 385 __400__

16. 150 __200__
17. 226 __200__
18. $8.57 __$9__

19. $5.35 __$5__
20. 929 __900__
21. 599 __600__

22. $6.09 __$6__
23. $3.15 __$3__
24. 950 __1,000__

25. 468 __500__
26. 815 __800__
27. $2.12 __$2__

28. 777 __800__
29. 286 __300__
30. $7.45 __$7__

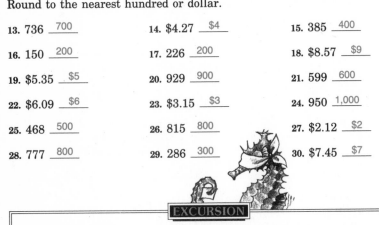

**EXCURSION**

"There are 12 red squares, 12 white and 12 black..."

"I'm going to pick 6 squares. I predict I will pick 2 white, 2 red and 2 black."

Now you try it. Make a prediction before you pick.
Outcomes will vary.

## Correcting Common Errors

Some students may round to the wrong place. Have them first draw an arrow above the place to which they are rounding. Then have them look at the digit to the right to determine whether the digit under the arrow should stay the same or be increased by 1. Then have them replace all the digits to the right of the arrow with zeros.

## Enrichment

Students are familiar with the idea of symmetry about a line. Ask them to write all the numbers 0 through 11 and identify any that are symmetric about a line either horizontal, vertical or both. Have them draw in the lines of symmetry. (0, 1, 3, 8, 10, 11)

## Practice

Have students complete all the problems on the page. Be sure they understand that rounding dollars is the same as rounding other numbers. Tell them they can omit the decimal point.

## Excursion

Read the cartoon strip with the students. Tell students that this activity asks them to make a prediction of what will happen based on what is known. Ask students if they have heard the term **educated guess.** Tell students we make educated guesses or predictions often. Give students the example of guessing what their parents will say when they ask to go to a movie on a school night. Have students suggest other examples. Tell students that the result may be different each time. Have students make their own bag of items and chart their predictions and results.

## Extra Credit    *Numeration*

Begin a calendar unit. Copy several months' calendars on a worksheet for students. Have class list possible questions regarding these months. For example: How many Tuesdays in all the months? How many days until the end of this month? How many weekends until June 20th? How many holidays? Tell students to work individually to find and record the answers.

# Thousands

## pages 33-34

### Objective

To understand thousands

### Materials

1 thousand-cube, 10 hundred-sheets, 10 ten-strips, and 10 single counters 4-digit place value charts

### Mental Math

Ask students to round each number to the nearest ten and then add:

1. 21 + 39 = (20 + 40 = 60)
2. 19 + 55 = (20 + 60 = 80)
3. 72 + 10 = (70 + 10 = 80)
4. 49 + 9 = (50 + 10 = 60)
5. 75 + 2 = (80 + 0 = 80)
6. 15 + 14 = (20 + 10 = 30)

### Skill Review

Have students count by tens to 100. Have them count to 1,000 by hundreds. Ask how many 10's there are in 100 and how many 100's there are in 1,000. (10, 10)

Write the following numbers on the board and have students underline the number in the ones place, circle the number in the tens place, and cross out the number in the hundreds place:

1. **43** (④ 3)    4. **5** (5)
2. **128** (1̸ ② 8)    5. **71** (⑦ 1)
3. **732** (7̸ ③ 2̲)    6. **559** (5̸ ⑤ 9̲)

---

## Thousands

Recess is over and Nadia is putting the game counters away. What is the total value of her counters?

| Thousands | Hundreds | Tens | Ones |
|-----------|----------|------|------|
| 3 | 6 | 4 | 5 |

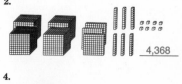

Nadia has __3__ thousands,

__6__ hundreds, __4__ tens and __5__ ones.

We write __3,645__.

We say **three thousand, six hundred forty-five.**

The total value of Nadia's counters is __3,645__.

### Getting Started

Write the numbers.

1.  __1,133__

2. __4,368__

3. __8,061__

4. __3,057__

5. three thousand, six hundred six __3,606__

6. nine thousand, two hundred fifty-five __9,255__

7. six thousand, two hundred twelve __6,212__

8. one thousand, nineteen __1,019__

What is the value of the 3 in each number?

9. 4,329 __hundreds__    10. 3,291 __thousands__    11. 6,430 __tens__

(thirty-three) **33**

---

## Teaching the Lesson

**Introducing the Problem**  Ask a student to read the problem and explain what is needed. (total value of the counters) Ask a volunteer to identify the number of thousands, hundreds, tens, and ones while the class fills in their texts. (3 thousands, 6 hundreds, 4 tens, 5 ones) Explain that in addition to the place values of ones, tens, and hundreds, there is another, thousands. Draw a 4-digit place value chart on the board and label thousands through ones. Ask for a student to fill in the numbers of Nadia's counters on the place value chart and read the number aloud. Have students fill in the number (3,645) on their pages.

**Developing the Skill**  Hold up a single counter and ask students how many it would take to equal a 10-strip. (10) Have each student line up 10 singles and one 10-strip. Hold up the ten-strip and ask how many it would take to make a hundred-sheet. (10) Have them line up 10 ten-strips and one hundred-sheet. Repeat for hundred-sheets in a thousand cube. (10) Draw a 4-digit place value chart on the board and point to each value. Write the number **3,407** on the board and ask a student to transfer the number to the place value chart. Repeat for several other 4-digit numbers. Now have students use their own place value charts. Dictate a series of 1-, 2-, 3-, and 4-digit numbers and have them write them on their own charts.

**33**

## Practice

Write the numbers.

1.     2,903

2.     5,604

3.    6,005

4.    1,875

5. four thousand, five hundred twenty-five   4,525

6. six thousand, two hundred seventy-nine   6,279

7. one thousand, eight hundred four   1,804

8. nine thousand, eighty-three   9,083

9. seven thousand, seven hundred   7,700

10. eight thousand, four hundred ninety   8,490

11. five thousand, one hundred thirty-three   5,133

12. two thousand, six hundred twelve   2,612

13. three thousand, nineteen   3,019

14. six thousand, five hundred ninety-five   6,595

15. four thousand, one   4,001

16. one thousand, one hundred eleven   1,111

What is the value of the 6 in each number?

17. 6,521   thousands

18. 3,621   hundreds

19. 4,006   ones

20. 3,609   hundreds

21. 9,467   tens

22. 6,975   thousands

**34** (thirty-four)

## Correcting Common Errors

Some students may omit zeros or write too many zeros; e.g., for 7,006 they may write 706 or 70,006. Have students first write their numbers on a place-value chart making sure that there is a zero in each place to the right of the left-most digit.

| THOUSANDS | HUNDREDS | TENS | ONES |
|-----------|----------|------|------|
| 7 | 0 | 0 | 6 |

## Enrichment

Have a group of students review what they know about symmetry. Explain that they are to look around the room for as many symmetrical objects as they can find. They should illustrate each one as best they can, and draw the line, or lines, of symmetry in. (for example, the windows, doors, books, pencils, paper, or people)

## Practice

Have students do all the problems on the page. Point to the illustration of the thousand-cube in the text and hold up a thousand cube. Point to the hundred-sheet in the book and the hundred-sheet on their desks. See that they understand all the illustrations. Write the words **hundred** and **thousand** on the board.

## Extra Credit   *Numeration*

Have students keep track of the attendance counts for the class for several days. Ask students to make a bar graph showing how many students were absent and present each day. Have the school secretary visit the class to discuss how she keeps track of absences, etc. and how counting relates to her job.

# Larger Numbers

## pages 35-36

## Objective

To understand numbers larger than one thousand

## Materials

6-digit place value charts

## Mental Math

Have students supply the next three numbers in each series:

1. 340, 360, 370 . . . (380, 390, 400)
2. 225, 230, 235 . . . (240, 245, 250)
3. 90, 80, 70 . . . (60, 50, 40)
4. 5, 15, 10, 20 . . . (15, 25, 20)
5. 125, 150, 175 . . . (200, 225, 250)
6. 400, 350, 300 . . . (250, 200, 150)
7. 0, 5, 15, 30 . . . (50, 75, 105)

## Skill Review

Write these number words on the board and have students write the numbers on their papers.

1. **one thousand two hundred four** (1,204)
2. **three hundred fifty-five** (355)
3. **five thousand forty-six** (5,046)
4. **ninety-two** (92)
5. **eight hundred seventy** (870)
6. **four thousand six hundred seventeen** (4,617)
7. **one hundred thirty-three** (133)
8. **nine thousand nine** (9,009)

---

## Larger Numbers

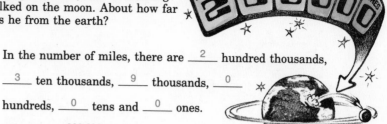

On July 20, 1969, Neil Armstrong walked on the moon. About how far was he from the earth?

In the number of miles, there are __2__ hundred thousands, __3__ ten thousands, __9__ thousands, __0__ hundreds, __0__ tens and __0__ ones.

We write __239,000__.
We say **two hundred thirty-nine thousand.**

Neil Armstrong was about __239,000__ miles from earth.

### Getting Started

Write the numbers.

1. three hundred fifty-nine thousand __359,000__

2. six hundred twenty-three thousand __623,000__

3. seven hundred fifty thousand __750,000__

4. five hundred seventy-six thousand __576,000__

Give the place value of the digit in red.

5. 369,450 __thousands__

6. 692,056 __hundreds__

7. 687,291 __ten thousands__

8. 405,000 __hundred thousands__

9. 37,580 __tens__

10. 209,376 __ten thousands__

Fill in the blanks.

11. 335,921 = __3__ hundred thousands __3__ ten thousands __5__ thousands __9__ hundreds __2__ tens __1__ ones

(thirty-five) **35**

---

## Teaching the Lesson

**Introducing the Problem** Have students examine the illustration and explain what is asked for in the problem. (distance from earth to moon) Explain that the chart in the illustration shows two new place values: ten thousands and hundred thousands. Explain that there are ten thousands in a ten thousand, and ten ten thousands in a hundred thousand. Have a student read the distance from the place value chart. (2 hundred thousands, 3 ten thousands, 9 thousands, 0 hundreds, 0 tens, 0 ones) Have one student write the solution on the board (239,000 miles) and read the number aloud while the others fill in the solution sentence.

**Developing the Skill** Draw a 6-digit place value chart on the board and put the number 9 in the ones column. Ask what the next number will be. (10) Have a student write 10 on the chart. Write the number **99** on the board and ask a volunteer to write the next integer on the board. (100) Ask someone to explain what 100 means. (1 hundred, no tens, no ones) Repeat this process for the number 999. Ask someone to write the number for 9,999+1 on the place value chart. Explain that this is ten thousand and is represented by a one in the ten thousand column. Repeat for the last number, 99,999. Now dictate a variety of 3- to 6-digit numbers and have students write them on their own place value charts.

**35**

**Practice**

Write the numbers.

1. two hundred seven thousand _207,000_

2. eight hundred thousand _800,000_

3. one hundred eleven thousand _111,000_

Write the place value of the digit in red.

4. 156,231 _thousands_

5. 475,300 _hundred thousands_

6. 717,241 _tens_

7. 395,750 _ten thousands_

8. 249,309 _hundred thousands_

9. 525,000 _tens_

Fill in the blanks.

10. 596,015 = _5_ hundred thousands _9_ ten thousands _6_

thousands _0_ hundreds _1_ tens _5_ ones

---

**EXCURSION**

Use these Roman numeral values to help you answer
the questions about this news event in early
Roman times.

I = 1   V = 5   X = 10   L = 50   C = 100   D = 500   M = 1000

Chariot races were held in the Roman Coliseum yesterday.
There were MMDLX seats filled with cheering spectators.
There were XVIII chariots paced against each other.
The winner was awarded CCL gold coins. To share
his good fortune, he tossed XXV of his coins
into the crowd.

How many people watched the races? _2,560_

How many chariots were in the race? _18_

How much money was given to the winner? _250_

How many coins did the winner throw to the crowd? _25_

---

---

**Practice**

Have students complete all the problems. Review any spelling problems the students may have. Write the words **ten thousand** and **hundred thousand** on the board for the class.

**Excursion**

Write **CLII** on the board and help students write an addition problem to tell the value of the number. (100 + 50 + 1 + 1 = 152) Continue for **CCXV** (100 + 100 + 10 + 5 = 215), **MDL** (1,000 + 500 + 50 = 1,550) and **DXXXV.** (500 + 10 + 10 + 10 + 5 = 535)

Tell students to read the paragraph and write and solve addition problems to answer the questions.

**Extra Credit**   *Measurement*

Using a watch with a second hand, have students estimate how long a minute is. Tell students to wait until you say start, and then close their eyes, keeping them closed for exactly one minute. Tell students to open their eyes after they think a minute has passed, and note the actual number of seconds that have gone by. Have them record their score, which is the number of seconds, their estimate was away from 60 seconds. The lower the score, the better. Have students repeat the activity to try to better their scores. As an alternative activity, tell students that they have exactly two minutes to walk across the classroom. They must set their pace accordingly. Their score is the difference between their estimate or time walking and 120 seconds. A score of zero would be best.

# Chapter Test

| Item | Objective |
|------|-----------|
| 1-6 | Read and write numbers and money (See pages 17-22, 25-26, 33-34) |
| 7-10 | Compare and order numbers less than 1,000 (See pages 23-24, 27-28) |
| 11-14 | Round to nearest 10 or 10¢ (See pages 29-30) |
| 15-18 | Round to the nearest 100 or dollar (See pages 31-32) |
| 19-22 | Identify the value of a digit in a number less than 1,000,000 (See pages 33-36) |
| 23-26 | Order numbers less than 100 (See pages 23-24) |

How much?

1.  5,048

2.  $2.62

Write the numbers.

3. six hundred fifty-five __655__

4. seventy-eight __78__

5. four hundred nine __409__

6. two thousand, one __2,001__

Compare these numbers. Write < or > in the circle.

7. 65 ⊘ 56

8. 129 ⊘ 205

9. 634 ⊘ 624

10. 435 ⊘ 453

Round to the nearest ten.

11. 84¢ __80¢__

12. 59 __60__

13. 43 __40__

14. 25¢ __30¢__

Round to the nearest hundred or dollar.

15. 451 __500__

16. 828 __800__

17. $6.07 __$6__

18. 215 __200__

Give the place value of the 2 in each number.

19. 672,591 __thousands__

20. 375,028 __tens__

21. 236,480 __hundred thousands__

22. 826,695 __ten thousands__

Complete the sequences.

23. 32, __34__, 36, __38__, __40__, 42

24. 105, __100__, __95__, 90, __85__, __80__

25. __9__, 12, __15__, __18__, 21, __24__

26. __55__, __60__, __65__, 70, __75__, 80

Circle the letter of the correct answer.

1. $19 + 8$
   - a 16
   - (b) 17
   - c 18
   - d NG

2. $13 - 7$
   - a 9
   - b 8
   - c 7
   - (d) NG

3. $15 - 9$
   - a 8
   - b 7
   - (c) 6
   - d NG

4. $36 \bigcirc 34$
   - (a) >
   - b <

5. $448 \bigcirc 484$
   - a >
   - (b) <

6. $761 \bigcirc 763$
   - a >
   - (b) <

7. Round 52¢ to the nearest ten cents.
   - (a) 50¢
   - b 60¢

8. Round 87 to the nearest ten.
   - a 80
   - (b) 90

9. Round 35¢ to the nearest ten cents.
   - a 30¢
   - (b) 40¢

10. Round 435 to the nearest hundred.
   - (a) 400
   - b 500

11. Round $6.25 to the nearest dollar.
   - (a) $6
   - b $7

12. Round 809 to the nearest hundred.
   - (a) 800
   - b 900

13. What is the value of the 8 in 786,326?
   - (a) ten thousands
   - b hundreds
   - c ones
   - d NG

14. What is the value of the 8 in 420,851?
   - a thousands
   - (b) hundreds
   - c tens
   - d NG

15. In the problem $74 - 29 = 45$, what is the 29 called?
   - a difference
   - (b) subtrahend
   - c minuend
   - d NG

☐ score

⬡

| Item | Objective |
|---|---|
| 1 | Recall addition facts through 18 (See pages 3-4) |
| 2-3 | Recall subtraction facts through 18 (See pages 9-10) |
| 4 | Compare and order numbers less than 100 (See pages 23-24) |
| 5-6 | Compare and order numbers less than 1,000 (See pages 27-28) |
| 7-9 | Round to the nearest 10 or 10¢ (See pages 29-30) |
| 10-12 | Round to the nearest 100 or dollar (See pages 31-32) |
| 13-14 | Identify the value of a digit in a number less than 1,000,000 (See pages 35-36) |
| 15 | Identify the terms in a subtraction problem (See pages 7-10) |

NG stands for "Not Given."

## Alternate Cumulative Review

Circle the letter of the correct answer.

1. $7 + 9 =$
   - a 15
   - (b) 16
   - c 17
   - d NG

2. $15 - 8 =$
   - a 9
   - b 8
   - (c) 7
   - d NG

3. $18 - 9 =$
   - a 6
   - b 7
   - c 8
   - (d) NG

4. $39 \bigcirc 64$
   - a >
   - (b) <
   - c =

5. $329 \bigcirc 392$
   - a >
   - (b) <
   - c =

6. $781 \bigcirc 718$
   - (a) >
   - b <
   - c =

7. Round 18¢ to the nearest ten cents.
   - a 10¢
   - (b) 20¢

8. Round 95 to the nearest ten.
   - a 80
   - b 90
   - (c) 100

9. Round 22¢ to the nearest ten cents.
   - (a) 20¢
   - b 30¢

10. Round 765 to the nearest hundred.
   - a 700
   - (b) 800

11. Round $9.10 to the nearest dollar.
   - (a) $9.00
   - b $10.00

12. Round 531 to the nearest hundred.
   - (a) 500
   - b 600

13. What is the value of the 7 in 967,210?
   - a ten thousands
   - (b) thousands
   - c hundreds
   - d NG

14. What is the value of the 2 in 431,725?
   - a ones
   - (b) tens
   - c hundreds
   - d NG

# Adding 2-digit Numbers, Trading Ones

## pages 39-40

### Objective

To review addition of 2-digit numbers, trading ones for tens

### Materials

ten-strip
single counters

### Mental Math

Read the following, and ask how much money is represented by each:

1. 2 quarters, 1 nickel (55¢)
2. 1 half-dollar, 1 dime, 1 penny (61¢)
3. 2 dimes, 2 nickels, 4 pennies (34¢)
4. 3 nickels, 14 pennies (29¢)
5. 1 quarter, 1 dime, 2 nickels (45¢)

### Skill Review

Write the following problems on the board. Have students do the addition and then circle the number of tens in each sum.

1. **8 + 5** = ( ① 3)
2. **7 + 7** = ( ① 4)
3. **9 + 4** = ( ① 3)
4. **6 + 8** = ( ① 4)
5. **9 + 9** = ( ① 8)
6. **5 + 6** = ( ① 1)
7. **7 + 8** = ( ① 5)

---

## Adding 2-digit Numbers, Trading Ones

Chen's score for the first 9 holes of miniature golf is 37. His score is 26 for the last nine holes. What is his final score?

We want to find Chen's total score.

Chen's two scores are ___37___ and ___26___.

To find the total, we add ___37___ and ___26___.

| Add the ones. | Make a trade. | Add the tens. |
|---|---|---|

| 7 + 6 = 13 ones | 13 ones = 1 ten + 3 ones | 1 + 3 + 2 tens = 6 tens |

| tens | ones | | tens | ones | | tens | ones |
|---|---|---|---|---|---|---|---|
| 3 | 7 | | 3 | 7 | | $\overset{1}{3}$ | 7 |
| +2 | 6 | | +2 | 6 | | +2 | 6 |
| | | | | 3 | | 6 | 3 |

Chen's final score is ___63___.

### Getting Started

Add.

| 1. | 45 | 2. | 53 | 3. | 28 | 4. | 82 |
|---|---|---|---|---|---|---|---|
| | +19 | | +14 | | +63 | | +15 |
| | 64 | | 67 | | 91 | | 97 |

Copy and add.

5. 57 + 23     6. 76 + 20     7. 67 + 28     8. 39 + 46
   80              96              95              85

(thirty-nine) **39**

---

## Teaching the Lesson

**Introducing the Problem**  Ask a student what the problem asks for. (Chen's final score) Ask how the problem can be solved. (by adding the scores) Have a student read the scores while you write them on the board and the class writes them in their texts. (37 and 26) Turn to the counters illustrated. Ask what is seen in the first picture. (5 tens and 13 ones) Have them add the ones. Ask what has happened in the second picture. (13 ones exchanged, 1 ten and 3 ones) Have students write the trade under the illustration. Describe the counters in the final picture. (6 tens and 3 ones) Have them write the addition as it is shown in the picture. Have them fill in the final score.

**Developing the Skill**  Write **25 + 17,** on the board. Have students use counters, putting 2 tens and 5 ones with 1 ten and 7 ones beneath. Direct the class to add the ones first. (5 + 7 = 12) Ask one student to explain the exchange of ones for a ten. (12 ones = 1 ten and 2 ones) Have them add the extra ten above the tens counters, and do the addition. (4 tens and 2 ones) Repeat this procedure for several problems.

**39**

Add.

1.  $\begin{array}{r} 25 \\ +49 \\ \hline 74 \end{array}$
2.  $\begin{array}{r} 37 \\ +56 \\ \hline 93 \end{array}$
3.  $\begin{array}{r} 48 \\ +21 \\ \hline 69 \end{array}$
4.  $\begin{array}{r} 19 \\ +63 \\ \hline 82 \end{array}$
5.  $\begin{array}{r} 66 \\ +14 \\ \hline 80 \end{array}$

6.  $\begin{array}{r} 28 \\ +29 \\ \hline 57 \end{array}$
7.  $\begin{array}{r} 44 \\ +18 \\ \hline 62 \end{array}$
8.  $\begin{array}{r} 85 \\ +14 \\ \hline 99 \end{array}$
9.  $\begin{array}{r} 14 \\ +31 \\ \hline 45 \end{array}$
10. $\begin{array}{r} 83 \\ +\ 9 \\ \hline 92 \end{array}$

11. $\begin{array}{r} 26 \\ +12 \\ \hline 38 \end{array}$
12. $\begin{array}{r} 76 \\ +15 \\ \hline 91 \end{array}$
13. $\begin{array}{r} 28 \\ +37 \\ \hline 65 \end{array}$
14. $\begin{array}{r} 21 \\ +49 \\ \hline 70 \end{array}$
15. $\begin{array}{r} 67 \\ +30 \\ \hline 97 \end{array}$

16. $\begin{array}{r} 9 \\ +46 \\ \hline 55 \end{array}$
17. $\begin{array}{r} 43 \\ +42 \\ \hline 85 \end{array}$
18. $\begin{array}{r} 37 \\ +19 \\ \hline 56 \end{array}$
19. $\begin{array}{r} 72 \\ +18 \\ \hline 90 \end{array}$
20. $\begin{array}{r} 36 \\ +25 \\ \hline 61 \end{array}$

21. $\begin{array}{r} 58 \\ +16 \\ \hline 74 \end{array}$
22. $\begin{array}{r} 38 \\ +42 \\ \hline 80 \end{array}$
23. $\begin{array}{r} 89 \\ +\ 9 \\ \hline 98 \end{array}$
24. $\begin{array}{r} 16 \\ +77 \\ \hline 93 \end{array}$
25. $\begin{array}{r} 39 \\ +52 \\ \hline 91 \end{array}$

**Copy and Do**

26. 48 + 16  64
27. 9 + 36  45
28. 74 + 13  87
29. 67 + 18  85
30. 76 + 15  91
31. 55 + 15  70
32. 57 + 38  95
33. 61 + 28  89
34. 14 + 48  62
35. 75 + 17  92
36. 11 + 29  40
37. 80 + 16  96
38. 52 + 19  71
39. 38 + 39  77
40. 26 + 48  74
41. 87 + 9  96

**Apply**

Solve these problems.

42. Bob has saved $46 for a bike from money he earned washing cars. He needs $39 more. How much does the bike cost?
$85

43. Mr. Ling's food stand sold 58 hot dogs on a sunny day. The next day it rained and he only sold 37. How many hot dogs did Mr. Ling sell both days?
95 hot dogs

## Correcting Common Errors

Some students may add incorrectly because they add each column separately, failing to trade.

INCORRECT
$\begin{array}{r} 27 \\ +56 \\ \hline 713 \end{array}$

CORRECT
$\begin{array}{r} 1 \\ 27 \\ +56 \\ \hline 83 \end{array}$

Correct by having students work with partners, using place-value materials to model the problems.

## Enrichment

Write the following problems on the board and have students fill in the missing numbers.

1. $\begin{array}{r} 47 \\ +\ (44) \\ \hline 91 \end{array}$
2. $\begin{array}{r} 17 \\ +\ (28) \\ \hline 45 \end{array}$
3. $\begin{array}{r} 86 \\ +\ (8) \\ \hline 94 \end{array}$
4. $\begin{array}{r} 28 \\ +\ (24) \\ \hline 52 \end{array}$
5. $\begin{array}{r} 7 \\ +\ (88) \\ \hline 95 \end{array}$
6. $\begin{array}{r} 35 \\ +\ (35) \\ \hline 70 \end{array}$

## Practice

Have students do all the problems on the page. Remind them to work from right to left in each problem to allow them to trade ones for tens. Tell them that when a problem is written horizontally, they are to copy it in its vertical form.

## Mixed Practice

1. 27 + 36 (63)
2. 12 − 6 (6)
3. 9 + 5 + 4 (18)
4. 7 − 2 (5)
5. 42 + 27 (69)
6. 81 + 15 (96)
7. 5 + 8 + 7 (20)
8. 13 − 5 (8)
9. 26 + 42 (68)
10. 2 + 2 + 8 (12)

## Extra Credit  *Probability*

Tell the students to write their guess of how many times a coin will land heads-up out of 100 tries. Tell students to make a chart headed: Guess | Heads | Tails.

Have each student flip a coin 100 times, guessing before each toss whether the coin will show heads or tails. Tell students to record whether the guess was correct and whether the coin showed heads or tails. Have students discuss the following questions:

a. How many times were you correct?
b. How many times did the coin land on heads? How does this compare with your guess?
c. What do you think is meant by something having a 50 - 50 chance?
d. Each time you guess either heads or tails, do you have a 50 - 50 chance of being correct?

# Adding 2-digit Numbers, Two Trades

**pages 41-42**

## Objective

To review addition of 2-digit numbers, trading for tens and hundreds

## Materials

100-sheets, 10-strips, single counters

## Mental Math

1. To win the World Series, a baseball team must win 4 out of 7 games. Team A has won 3 games and Team B, 1 game. How many more games must A win to take the Series? (1) How many more games for B? (3)
2. Amy goes to the store to buy a book. The book costs $1.95; tax is $.15. How much does she owe? ($2.10) How much change will she get from $2.25? ($.15)

## Skill Review

Have students do the following problems on paper. Remind them to trade ones for tens and to show the trade.

| 1. 45 | 2. 74 | 3. 59 | 4. 38 |
|-------|-------|-------|-------|
| +35   | +17   | +32   | +19   |
| (80)  | (91)  | (91)  | (57)  |

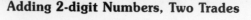

## Adding 2-digit Numbers, Two Trades

A Pony Express rider often had to do double duty. How far did a rider travel if he rode west from Kansas City to the second relay station?

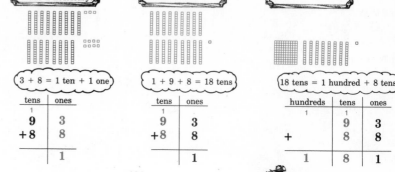

We want the total distance from Kansas City to the second relay station. The distance from Kansas City to the first relay station was __93__ miles. From there to the second relay station was __88__ miles.

To find the total distance, we add __93__ and __88__.

| Add the ones. Trade if necessary. | Add the tens. | Make a trade. |
|---|---|---|

| 3 + 8 = 1 ten + 1 one | 1 + 9 + 8 = 18 tens | 18 tens = 1 hundred + 8 tens |

| tens | ones |
|------|------|
| 1    |      |
| 9    | 3    |
| +8   | 8    |
|      | 1    |

| tens | ones |
|------|------|
| 1    |      |
| 9    | 3    |
| +8   | 8    |
|      | 1    |

| hundreds | tens | ones |
|----------|------|------|
|          | 1    |      |
|          | 9    | 3    |
| +        | 8    | 8    |
| 1        | 8    | 1    |

The rider traveled __181__ miles.

### Getting Started

Add.

| 1. 67 | 2. 49 | 3. 82 | 4. 91 |
|-------|-------|-------|-------|
| +71   | +87   | +59   | +88   |
| 138   | 136   | 141   | 179   |

Copy and add.

5. 66 + 87
153

6. 53 + 97
150

7. 79 + 60
139

8. 59 + 86
145

(forty-one) **41**

## Teaching the Lesson

**Introducing the Problem** Ask a student to explain what the problem asks for, and how to find the answer. (distance to the second station; distances must be added) Have one student read the distances from the illustration. (93 miles, 88 miles) Read the third sentence to the class and have a student write the addition problem on the board while students write in their books. (93 and 88) Direct their attention to the groups of counters and the place value charts. Tell students to add the ones and write the addition in their texts. (3 + 8 = 11) Tell them to trade 10 ones for 1 ten, write it over the tens place, and write the 1 in the ones place. Have them turn to the next section, adding tens. (1 + 9 + 8 = 18 tens) Explain that they will trade 10 tens for 1 hundred and have them look at the final section of the problem. Show the trade on the board and have the class write it. (18 tens = 1 hundred and 8 tens). Have them fill in the solution sentence. (181)

**Developing the Skill** Have students use their counters to do the following problem: 56 + 46. Remind them to start with the ones column (6 + 6) and trade for tens. (12 ones = 1 ten and 2 ones) Now have them add the tens column. (1 + 5 + 6 tens = 12 tens) Ask how many hundreds are in 12 tens. (1 hundred and 2 tens). Illustrate the problem on the board as students write the problem vertically and solve it, showing each trade. Give students several similar problems.

**41**

Add.

| | | | | |
|---|---|---|---|---|
| 1.   97<br> + 48<br>   145 | 2.   67<br> + 75<br>   142 | 3.   38<br> + 29<br>   67 | 4.   77<br> + 63<br>   140 | 5.   57<br> + 82<br>   139 |
| 6.   68<br> + 59<br>   127 | 7.   26<br> + 91<br>   117 | 8.   82<br> + 89<br>   171 | 9.   73<br> + 65<br>   138 | 10.  47<br> + 86<br>   133 |
| 11.  33<br> + 90<br>   123 | 12.   9<br> + 96<br>   105 | 13.  28<br> + 57<br>   85 | 14.  49<br> + 99<br>   148 | 15.  53<br> + 78<br>   131 |
| 16.  68<br> + 54<br>   122 | 17.  37<br> + 88<br>   125 | 18.  58<br> +  8<br>   66 | 19.  47<br> + 73<br>   120 | 20.  67<br> + 82<br>   149 |

**Copy and Do**

21. 78 + 36
114
22. 23 + 98
121
23. 54 + 89
143
24. 33 + 75
108

25. 86 + 49
135
26. 63 + 65
128
27. 55 + 47
102
28. 84 + 97
181

29. 76 + 86
162
30. 52 + 68
120
31. 79 + 86
165
32. 57 + 94
151

**EXCURSION**

In a magic square, every row, column and diagonal has the same sum. Complete these squares using the digits 0 through 9. Do not use the same digit twice in the same square.

| 8 | 1 | 6 |
|---|---|---|
| 3 | 5 | 7 |
| 4 | 9 | 2 |

| 1 | 6 | 5 |
|---|---|---|
| 8 | 4 | 0 |
| 3 | 2 | 7 |

| 7 | 0 | 5 |
|---|---|---|
| 2 | 4 | 6 |
| 3 | 8 | 1 |

**42** (forty-two)

---

## Correcting Common Errors

Some students may rename incorrectly because they simply drop the renamed value.

| INCORRECT | CORRECT |
|---|---|
| | 1 |
| 4 6 | 4 6 |
| + 7 8 | + 7 8 |
| 1 1 4 | 1 2 4 |

Correct by having students work with partners, using place-value materials to model the problems. Encourage students to use small regrouping numbers in the appropriate columns to remind them of the trades.

## Enrichment

Write these problems on the board and have students fill in the missing addends.

1. **145**<br>+<br>**252**<br>(107)
2. **378**<br>+<br>**675**<br>(297)
3. **455**<br>+<br>**603**<br>(148)
4. **589**<br>+<br>**672**<br>( 83)
5. **209**<br>+<br>**341**<br>(132)
6. **945**<br>+<br>**953**<br>( 8)

---

## Practice

Have students complete the page. Remind them that they may have to trade ones for tens and tens for hundreds. Explain that when they are asked to copy the problem they should rewrite it in its vertical form.

## Excursion

Read the paragraph aloud with the students. Remind students to use all digits from 0 through 9 in each magic square. Complete one magic square together. Tell students there are many magic squares which can be made using these numbers. Have students create 2 more magic squares independently. Some students may wish to try to make more.

## Extra Credits   *Sets*

Ask your students to bring in a picture of their favorite food. Briefly discuss the four basic food groups (cereal/bread, meats/protein, vegetable/fruit and milk products). List the four groups on the board and have students place their pictures under the appropriate headings. Ask students to design a symbol for each of the groups. Tell students to make a picture graph using these symbols, to show the number of favorite foods in each of the food groups.

# Adding 3-digit Numbers, One Trade

## pages 43-44

### Objective

To review addition of 3-digit numbers, trading for tens and hundreds

### Materials

3-digit place value charts

### Mental Math

Draw a chest of six drawers and have students point to the:

1. third from the top
2. second from the bottom
3. fourth from the bottom
4. second from the top
5. sixth from the bottom

### Skill Review

Write the following problems on the board. Have students identify whether the trade will be ones for tens or tens for hundreds.

| 1. 340 +178 | 2. 458 +129 | 3. 236 +457 |
|---|---|---|
| (tens/ hundreds) | (ones/ tens) | (tens/ hundreds) |
| 4. 564 +172 | 5. 609 +235 | 6. 248 +291 |
| (tens/ hundreds) | (ones/ tens) | (tens/ hundreds) |

---

## Adding 3-digit Numbers, One Trade

What is the entire length of route I-44 through Oklahoma and Missouri?

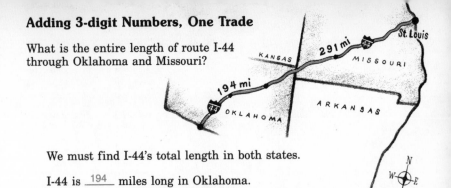

We must find I-44's total length in both states.

I-44 is __194__ miles long in Oklahoma.

It is __291__ miles long in Missouri.

To get the total miles, we add __194__ and __291__.

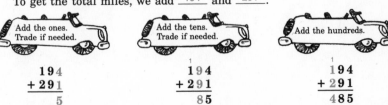

$$\begin{array}{r} 194 \\ +291 \\ \hline 5 \end{array} \qquad \begin{array}{r} {\scriptstyle 1}\phantom{00} \\ 194 \\ +291 \\ \hline 85 \end{array} \qquad \begin{array}{r} {\scriptstyle 1}\phantom{00} \\ 194 \\ +291 \\ \hline 485 \end{array}$$

I-44 is __485__ miles long through Oklahoma and Missouri.

### Getting Started

Add.

| 1. 326 +455 **781** | 2. 675 +183 **858** | 3. 517 + 81 **598** |
|---|---|---|
| 4. 222 +108 **330** | 5. 63 +322 **385** | 6. 449 + 311 **760** |

Copy and add.

7. 359 + 138   **497**
8. 96 + 353   **449**
9. 428 + 139   **567**
10. 518 + 237   **755**
11. 295 + 643   **938**
12. 348 + 536   **884**

(forty-three) **43**

---

## Teaching the Lesson

**Introducing the Problem**  Have one student explain the problem. (to find length of I-44 through Oklahoma and Missouri) Ask what the length of the highway is in Oklahoma. (194 miles) Ask what is the length of I-44 in Missouri. (291 miles) Read the next two sentences aloud and ask students to fill in the missing numbers. (194 and 291) Have them look at the problem worked in three steps. Explain that they must begin in the ones column as in the model. Ask a student to explain how many ones there are after the addition. (5) Repeat for tens (18, or 1 hundred and 8 tens) and the hundreds. (1 + 1 + 2 = 4 hundreds) Ask one student to read the entire answer while the others write the number in the solution sentence.(485)

**Developing the Skill**  Explain that the problems in this lesson require the addition of 3-digit numbers, sometimes trading ones, tens and hundreds. Give students the following problem to work on their place value charts: **463 + 275.** Write the problem on the board and have individuals come up to add each column, starting with the ones. Remind them to trade when the sum of any column is more than 10, and to show any trades on the board. As students do the problem on the board, have others work it at their desks. Give several more problems.

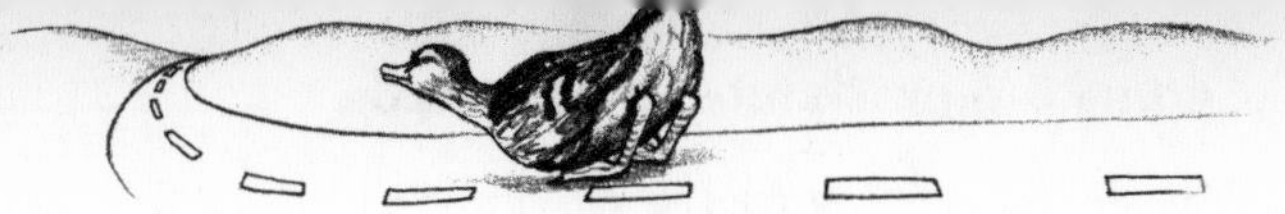

**Practice**

Add.

| | | | |
|---|---|---|---|
| 1. 286<br>+ 542<br>828 | 2. 427<br>+ 358<br>785 | 3. 615<br>+ 239<br>854 | 4. 362<br>+ 18<br>380 |
| 5. 708<br>+ 209<br>917 | 6. 523<br>+ 294<br>817 | 7. 919<br>+ 75<br>994 | 8. 273<br>+ 571<br>844 |
| 9. 426<br>+ 139<br>565 | 10. 96<br>+ 573<br>669 | 11. 377<br>+ 615<br>992 | 12. 517<br>+ 242<br>759 |
| 13. 671<br>+ 186<br>857 | 14. 309<br>+ 83<br>392 | 15. 558<br>+ 170<br>728 | 16. 253<br>+ 638<br>891 |
| 17. 583<br>+ 236<br>819 | 18. 154<br>+ 683<br>837 | 19. 210<br>+ 596<br>806 | 20. 781<br>+ 196<br>977 |

**Copy and Do**

| | | |
|---|---|---|
| 21. 436 + 281<br>717 | 22. 509 + 186<br>695 | 23. 91 + 196<br>287 |
| 24. 321 + 144<br>465 | 25. 883 + 95<br>978 | 26. 565 + 283<br>848 |
| 27. 373 + 445<br>818 | 28. 308 + 154<br>462 | 29. 119 + 453<br>572 |
| 30. 56 + 728<br>784 | 31. 649 + 280<br>929 | 32. 709 + 127<br>836 |

**Apply**

Solve these problems.

33. Mr. Jimeniz drove 384 miles on his delivery route, on Monday. On Tuesday he drove 243 miles. How many miles did he drive both days?
627 miles

34. Daryle collected 129 pounds of old newspapers for the paper drive. Ronald collected 119 pounds. How many pounds of paper did the boys collect?
248 pounds



## Correcting Common Errors

Some students may add incorrectly because they trade incorrectly. Have them work with partners and place-value materials to model the following tens or ones. They then trade to write the ones as tens and ones, and the tens as hundreds and tens.

1. 14 ones (1 ten 4 ones)
2. 25 ones (2 tens 5 ones)
3. 38 ones (3 tens 8 ones)
4. 43 tens (4 hundreds 3 tens)
5. 11 tens (1 hundred 1 ten)

## Enrichment

This activity will require a meter stick. Explain that the distance around a figure is its perimeter. Have the group measure the perimeter of the school in meters. Ask them to explain how they will know the school's perimeter once they know the lengths of each side. (the sum of the lengths of the sides) Have students list the following things: the number of sides the school has, the length of each side, and the total distance around the school.

## Practice

Have students do all the problems on the page. Explain that when they copy problems in the vertical form, they must be careful to keep the columns in line. Tell them to show the trades in the problems.

## Mixed Practice

1. 57 + 28 (85)
2. 12 − 3 (9)
3. 4 + 8 + 7 (19)
4. 39 + 72 (111)
5. 65 + 34 (99)
6. 18 − 9 (9)
7. 37 + 93 (130)
8. 8 + 9 + 7 (24)
9. 48 + 26 (74)
10. 11 − 6 (5)

## Extra Credit *Numeration*

Have students take an inventory of things that are countable in the classroom. Items might include: desks, pieces of chalk, electrical outlets, clocks or blue pencils, etc. Have students work independently, or in small groups, to count and record the number of each item.

Assemble a bulletin board entitled: OUR CLASS HAS. Under the title hang a large poster listing things that have been counted and the number of each. Have the class make a worksheet entitled: MY FAMILY HAS listing countable items in a specified room of their home. Ask students to complete this inventory at home, and make a picture graph of their results.

# Adding 3-digit Numbers, Two Trades

## pages 45-46

### Objective

To review addition of 3-digit numbers, trading for tens and hundreds

### Materials

### Mental Math

Dictate these problems:

1. $25 + 10 - 5 + 2 =$ (32)
2. $50 + 50 - 25 + 10 =$ (85)
3. $40 - 20 - 20 + 2 =$ (2)
4. $14 + 6 + 20 + 0 =$ (40)
5. $35 + 5 - 25 - 15 =$ (0)

### Skill Review

Write these problems on the board. Have students circle the column where trading will take place. Then have volunteers work the problems.

| 1. 245 | 2. 366 | 3. 409 | 4. 562 |
|--------|--------|--------|--------|
| +192 | +319 | +306 | +209 |
| (437) | (685) | (715) | (771) |
| 5. 108 | 6. 145 | 7. 114 | 8. 692 |
| +323 | +161 | +409 | +283 |
| (431) | (306) | (520) | (875) |

### Adding 3-digit Numbers, Two Trades

| DAY | LAPS |
|-----|------|
| Monday | 155 |
| Tuesday | 175 |
| Wednesday | 140 |
| Thursday | 165 |
| Friday | 130 |

Mike was in training for the school swim meet. How many laps did he complete on the first two days?

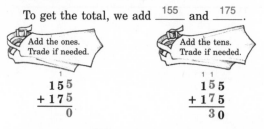

We want to know the total number of laps Mike swam on both days.

Mike swam ___155___ laps on Monday.

He swam ___175___ laps on Tuesday.

To get the total, we add ___155___ and ___175___.

Add the ones. Trade if needed.

$$\begin{array}{r} \overset{1}{1}5\,5 \\ +\ 1\,7\,5 \\ \hline 0 \end{array}$$

Add the tens. Trade if needed.

$$\begin{array}{r} \overset{1\ 1}{1}5\,5 \\ +\ 1\,7\,5 \\ \hline 3\,0 \end{array}$$

Add the hundreds.

$$\begin{array}{r} \overset{1}{1}5\,5 \\ +\ 1\,7\,5 \\ \hline 3\,3\,0 \end{array}$$

Mike swam ___330___ laps on the first two days.

### Getting Started

Add.

| 1. 628 | 2. 427 | 3. 243 |
|--------|--------|--------|
| + 196 | + 96 | + 277 |
| 824 | 523 | 520 |
| 4. 311 | 5. 259 | 6. 155 |
| + 175 | + 442 | + 166 |
| 486 | 701 | 321 |

Copy and add.

7. $85 + 476$ — 561
8. $297 + 684$ — 981
9. $363 + 458$ — 821
10. $463 + 289$ — 752
11. $615 + 96$ — 711
12. $375 + 235$ — 610

(forty-five) **45**

## Teaching the Lesson

**Introducing the Problem**  Ask one student to read the problem aloud and explain what it asks for. (total laps swum Monday and Tuesday) Ask what information is needed. (155 on Monday, 175 on Tuesday) Ask if they will need the other information given to solve the problem. (no) Read the next sentences and have students fill in the plan as you read. (155 and 175) Direct their attention to the three-stage problem. Duplicate the stages on the board and have students complete sections on the board, while the others do them in their books. Point out that in this problem they have to trade both ones for tens and tens for hundreds. Read the solution sentence while students fill in the answer.

**Developing the Skill**  Draw a 3-digit place value chart on the board and write in: **457 + 386.** Ask a student to do the addition in the ones column. Show that the total number of ones, 13, can be rearranged as 1 ten and 3 ones. Have the student write 3 and list the ten over the tens column. Have another student add tens. The total number of tens, $1 + 5 + 8$, exceeds ten. Remind them that 10 tens can be traded for a hundred. Have the student write in the 4 tens and list one hundred above the hundreds column. Have one more student add hundreds. Repeat this for several problems, mixing one trade and two trade problems.

**45**

Add.

| | | | |
|---|---|---|---|
| 1. 583<br>+ 279<br>862 | 2. 285<br>+ 391<br>676 | 3. 673<br>+ 182<br>855 | 4. 296<br>+ 648<br>944 |
| 5. 783<br>+ 139<br>922 | 6. 306<br>+ 147<br>453 | 7. 295<br>+ 476<br>771 | 8. 409<br>+ 391<br>800 |

**Copy and Do**

9. 459 + 473
932

10. 116 + 293
409

11. 346 + 485
831

12. 196 + 547
743

13. 754 + 196
950

14. 236 + 129
365

15. 509 + 366
875

16. 658 + 276
934

**Apply**

Solve these problems.

17. On Monday the lunchroom served 278 cartons of milk. On Tuesday they served 349 cartons. How many cartons were served both days?
627 cartons

18. Mrs. Allen is tiling in her house. She used 458 tiles in the kitchen and 396 tiles in the entry. How many tiles did Mrs. Allen use?
854 tiles

EXCURSION

I was born in November. There are two digits in my birth date.

My birth date is an even number. It is greater than 2 and less than 12.

Can you guess the date?

Answer   November 10

**46**   (forty-six)

## Correcting Common Errors

Some students may rename incorrectly because they reverse the tens and ones or the hundreds and tens, or both.

| INCORRECT | CORRECT |
|---|---|
| 4 2<br>147<br>+ 285<br>711 | 1 1<br>147<br>+ 285<br>432 |

Have students work with partners and place-value materials to model the problems, taking turns explaining how they are trading.

## Enrichment

Select five 3-digit numbers like 536, 438, 963, 758 and 649. Have the students create 3 different addition problems having each of these as a sum. The problems should involve two trades.

## Practice

Have students complete the page. Demonstrate on the board that when they copy and add it is important to list the addends vertically and keep columns straight.

## Excursion

Tell students that we want to know a number that is greater than 16 but less than 24 with both of its digits the same. Ask what we would do first. (list all numbers from 17 through 23) Have a student list the numbers. Ask what additional information we know about the number. (both its digits are the same) Have students tell which number meets all the criteria. (22) Repeat the procedure for the number that is greater than 135, less than 150 and has digits that read the same backwards and forwards. (141)

Tell students to read and then solve the cartoon.

## Extra Credit   *Numeration*

Make several sets of sequencing cards showing multi-digit numbers, as large as your students can work with. Decide on a message for students to decipher. Write one letter or word of the message on the back of each card, so that when the cards are correctly sequenced, they will form a message. Tell students to take a set of cards, and arrange them in a line, from the lowest number to the highest number, left to right. Then tell them to turn the cards over in the same order, and if they have sequenced the numbers correctly, the cards will form a message. If the message doesn't make sense have students correct their sequencing. As an extension, have students make their own set of message, sequencing cards.

# Adding 4-digit Numbers

**pages 47-48**

## Objective

To add 4-digit numbers

## Materials

4-digit place value charts

## Mental Math

Have students count:

1. by hundreds from 300 to 1,000
2. by twenty-fives from 125 to 250
3. by two hundreds from 200 to 1,200
4. by fives from 105 to 175
5. by tens from 550 to 640
6. by tens from 700 to 590

## Skill Review

Write a 4-digit number on the board and have students identify each place value from ones through thousands. Ask for volunteers to explain how many ones in each ten, tens in each hundred, and so on. Have students do the following problems:

1. 354 + 228 = (582)
2. 636 + 98 = (734)
3. 308 + 445 = (753)
4. 460 + 156 = (616)

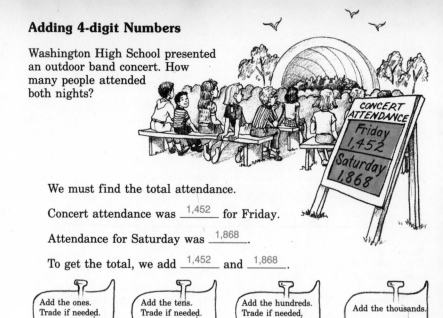

## Adding 4-digit Numbers

Washington High School presented an outdoor band concert. How many people attended both nights?

We must find the total attendance.

Concert attendance was ___1,452___ for Friday.

Attendance for Saturday was ___1,868___.

To get the total, we add ___1,452___ and ___1,868___.

Add the ones. Trade if needed.

Add the tens. Trade if needed.

Add the hundreds. Trade if needed.

Add the thousands.

$$\begin{array}{r} {}^{1}\phantom{0} \\ 1,45 2 \\ +\,1,86 8 \\ \hline 0 \end{array}$$

$$\begin{array}{r} {}^{1\,1}\phantom{0} \\ 1,45 2 \\ +\,1,86 8 \\ \hline 2\,0 \end{array}$$

$$\begin{array}{r} {}^{1\,1}\phantom{0} \\ 1,4 52 \\ +\,1,8 68 \\ \hline 3\,2\,0 \end{array}$$

$$\begin{array}{r} {}^{1}\phantom{0000} \\ 1,452 \\ +\,1,868 \\ \hline 3,3\,2\,0 \end{array}$$

The total concert attendance was ___3,320___.

## Getting Started

Add.

| 1. | 5,136<br>+ 1,597<br>6,733 | 2. | 4,878<br>+ 346<br>5,224 | 3. | 2,819<br>+ 1,504<br>4,323 |

Copy and add.

4. 847 + 7,697
8,544

5. 1,996 + 4,283
6,279

6. 487 + 9,368
9,855

7. 7,621 + 1,596
9,217

8. 2,965 + 5,859
8,824

9. 3,428 + 2,596
6,024

(forty-seven) **47**

## Teaching the Lesson

**Introducing the Problem**   Have students read the problem and say what they need to find. (total number of people attending two concerts) Ask what attendance data they have to work with. (Friday, 1, 452 came; Saturday, 1,868 came.) Read the plan aloud and have students compute the total. Write **1,452** on the board and explain that the comma is written between the thousands place and the hundreds in order to make the number easier to read. Copy each of the four problem stages on the board and add, starting with ones. Students can write each section in their texts. Have students transfer the answer to the solution sentence.

**Developing the Skill**   Write another 4-digit problem on the board. Have students work the problem on their 4-digit place value charts while you do it at the board. Point out that it is easier to do the problem if they leave room at the top to keep track of the trades. Illustrate this on the board:

| thousands | hundreds | tens | ones |
|:---:|:---:|:---:|:---:|
| 5 | 4 | 8 | 4 |
| + 1 | 6 | 1 | 7 |
| 7 | 1 | 0 | 1 |

Dictate several problems for the class to work on paper showing each trade.

**47**

## Practice

Add.

| | | | |
|---|---|---|---|
| **1.** 3,256<br>+ 1,684<br>4,940 | **2.** 2,965<br>+ 4,309<br>7,274 | **3.** 7,059<br>+ 1,827<br>8,886 | **4.** 4,372<br>+ 1,891<br>6,263 |
| **5.** 6,387<br>+ 953<br>7,340 | **6.** 5,806<br>+ 2,759<br>8,565 | **7.** 1,678<br>+ 7,593<br>9,271 | **8.** 3,424<br>+ 2,386<br>5,810 |
| **9.** 5,874<br>+ 3,685<br>9,559 | **10.** 3,651<br>+ 324<br>3,975 | **11.** 6,437<br>+ 2,974<br>9,411 | **12.** 864<br>+ 4,928<br>5,792 |
| **13.** 1,396<br>+ 1,569<br>2,965 | **14.** 2,573<br>+ 6,558<br>9,131 | **15.** 1,987<br>+ 837<br>2,824 | **16.** 2,465<br>+ 4,776<br>7,241 |

### Copy and Do

**17.** 3,826 + 1,947
5,773

**18.** 6,035 + 968
7,003

**19.** 2,456 + 6,817
9,273

**20.** 509 + 7,624
8,133

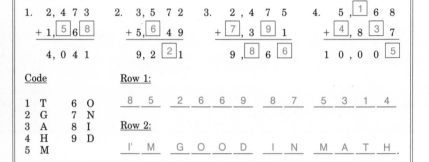

### EXCURSION

Find the missing digits in these addition problems. In the blanks of row 1, list each missing digit as you discover it. Decode these numbers in Row 2 and then discover a secret message.

**1.** 2,4 7 3
+ 1,⑤6⑧
4, 0 4 1

**2.** 3,5 7 2
+ 5,⑥ 4 9
9,2 ②1

**3.** 2, 4 7 5
+ ⑦, 3 ⑨ 1
9 ,⑧ 6 ⑥

**4.** 5 ,①6 8
+ ④, 8 ③ 7
1 0, 0 0 ⑤

| Code | |
|---|---|
| 1 T | 6 O |
| 2 G | 7 N |
| 3 A | 8 I |
| 4 H | 9 D |
| 5 M | |

**Row 1:**
8 5 2 6 6 9 8 7 5 3 1 4

**Row 2:**
I'M  G O O D  I N  M A T H.

# Column Addition

## Objective

To learn column addition of 2- and 3-digit numbers

## Materials

## Mental Math

Dictate the following problems:

1. 40 + 34 = (74)
2. 14 + 52 = (66)
3. 81 + 11 = (92)
4. 30 + 17 = (47)
5. 55 + 25 = (80)
6. 61 + 10 = (71)
7. 23 + 91 = (114)

## Skill Review

Write these problems on the board:

| 1. 4 | 2. 5 | 3. 8 | 4. 1 | 5. 7 |
|------|------|------|------|------|
| 3 | 5 | 1 | 7 | 8 |
| +5 | +4 | +6 | +3 | +3 |
| (12) | (14) | (15) | (11) | (18) |

Direct students to do each problem and then write the answer in a 2-digit place value chart on their papers. Point out that while doing these problems, they automatically trade ones for tens.

## Column Addition

On his first trip to the new world, Columbus landed at San Salvador. He explored the area for 95 days. How long was he gone from Spain?

We want to find the total number of days Columbus was away from Spain.

It took __71__ days for Columbus to reach San Salvador.

He spent __95__ days exploring.

The return trip took __58__ days. To find the total number of days, we add __71__ and __95__ and __58__.

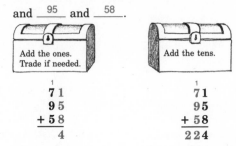

Add the ones. Trade if needed.

```
  1
  7 1
  9 5
+ 5 8
    4
```

Add the tens.

```
  1
  7 1
  9 5
+ 5 8
  2 2 4
```

Columbus was away from Spain for __224__ days.

### Getting Started

Add.

| 1. | 2. | 3. | 4. |
|----|----|----|----|
| 3,926 | 3,516 | 6,213 | 376 |
| 3,151 | 297 | 1,276 | 1,939 |
| + 2,138 | + 385 | 480 | 68 |
| 9,215 | 4,198 | + 1,124 | + 5,432 |
| | | 9,093 | 7,815 |

Copy and add.

5. 2,176 + 159 + 3,641
5,976

6. 4,136 + 25 + 951 + 1,237
6,349

(forty-nine) **49**

## Teaching the Lesson

**Introducing the Problem**    Have students read the problem and identify what is being asked for, (total time Columbus was gone) and where the information can be found. (on the map) Read the data from the map while students write the numbers on their pages. (71 days to San Salvador, 95 days exploring, return trip took 58 days) Point out that the return trip was shorter because the winds blow from the west, and ocean currents there flow southwest to northeast. Ask a student to read the plan for working the problem. (We add 71 and 95 and 58.) Point out the two stages of the problem. Write them on the board and ask the class to add the numbers with you. Have students write the answer in the solution sentence. (224 days)

**Developing the Skill**    Write the following problem on the board. Separate the columns with lines.

| 3 | 4 | 9 |
|---|---|---|
| 4 | 2 | 6 |
| +1 | 8 | 8 |

(963)

Explain that in column addition it is important to keep the columns straight. Ask a student to explain why. (so that we are always adding like numbers) Have a student come to the board and add the ones. Have another add tens and a third, the hundreds. Now dictate a similar problem and have students do it at their desks while you do it on the board. Have them separate columns with lines as you have done.

**Practice**

Add.

| | | | |
|---|---|---|---|
| 1. 4,396<br>2,374<br>+ 653<br>7,423 | 2. 7,286<br>459<br>+ 1,621<br>9,366 | 3. 1,096<br>1,374<br>+ 2,915<br>5,385 | 4. 96<br>475<br>+ 3,826<br>4,397 |
| 5. 1,524<br>2,361<br>+ 4,184<br>8,069 | 6. 1,830<br>916<br>+ 1,385<br>4,131 | 7. 148<br>696<br>+ 4,832<br>5,676 | 8. 2,261<br>4,186<br>+ 2,083<br>8,530 |
| 9. 2,748<br>3,956<br>+ 1,285<br>7,989 | 10. 8,654<br>298<br>+ 845<br>9,797 | 11. 2,295<br>1,876<br>+ 1,381<br>5,552 | 12. 1,003<br>1,659<br>+ 3,288<br>5,950 |
| 13. 4,862<br>937<br>85<br>+ 1,629<br>7,513 | 14. 3,926<br>1,738<br>2,456<br>+ 963<br>9,083 | 15. 2,391<br>1,586<br>2,428<br>+ 1,860<br>8,265 | 16. 985<br>1,821<br>764<br>+ 2,476<br>6,046 |

**Copy and Do**

17. 96 + 128 + 376 + 1,532
2,132

18. 3,219 + 126 + 4,173 + 83
7,601

19. 2,033 + 178 + 332
2,543

20. 5,611 + 44 + 3,123 + 1,111
9,889

21. 3,257 + 2,816 + 1,821 + 1,036
8,930

22. 8,223 + 32 + 439 + 925
9,619

**Apply**

Use the chart to solve these problems.

23. How much does Mr. Ryan spend on rent and food?
$1,295

24. How much does Mr. Ryan spend on rent, auto and other expenses?
$1,707

| Mr. Ryan's Budget | |
|---|---|
| Food | $456 |
| Auto | $358 |
| Rent | $839 |
| Other | $510 |

50 (fifty)

**Practice**

Have students complete the page. Re-emphasize the importance of aligning numbers when they have to copy the problems in a vertical form.

**Mixed Practice**

1. 15 − 8 (7)
2. 328 + 491 (819)
3. 7 + 7 + 7 (21)
4. 15 + 49 (64)
5. 471 + 328 (799)
6. 17 − 9 (8)
7. 35 + 87 (122)
8. 653 + 186 (839)
9. 6 + 4 + 8 (18)
10. 13 − 9 (4)

**Extra Credit**  *Numeration*

Provide students with a local telephone directory. Ask them to find their last name in the phone book. Have them count how many other families have the same name as theirs. Ask them to do the same with the names of five classmates. Tell them to compare the number of times their name appears in the phone book to the number of times their classmates' names appear. Have them use the signs for greater than, less than, and equal to show the comparisons. For example, Grant appears five times and Smith appears 8 times, Grant < Smith.

# Adding Money

## pages 51-52

## Objective

To add amounts of money including 4-digits, and column addition up to 4-digits

## Materials

## Mental Math

Dictate the following:

1. Amy buys her lunch every Monday, Tuesday and Wednesday. In three weeks, how many lunches does she buy? (3 + 3 + 3 = 9)
2. Her lunch costs 90¢ each day. How much does she spend in a week? ($.90 + .90 + .90 = $2.70)
3. Some days she doesn't take milk with her lunch and then the lunch costs only 80¢. What is the price of the milk? (90¢ − 80¢ = 10¢)

## Skill Review

Dictate the following amounts to students and have them write the amount correctly using the dollar sign and decimal point:

1. one dollar, 15 cents ($1.15)
2. three dollars, sixty cents ($3.60)
3. seventy-three cents ($0.73)
4. twenty-four dollars, five cents ($24.05)
5. thirty-nine dollars, fifty-two cents ($39.52)

---

### Adding Money

Rachel was chosen to play on the third grade baseball team. She must earn the money to buy her equipment. How much will she need to buy the glove and ball?

We want to know the cost of both the glove and the ball.
The glove costs $29.98 .

The baseball costs $3.57 .
To find the total cost, we add $29.98 and $3.57 .
✔ Line up the dollars and cents. Don't forget the dollar sign.

$$\begin{array}{r} \$29.98 \\ +\phantom{\$}3.57 \\ \hline \$33.55 \end{array}$$

Rachel must earn $33.55 .

### Getting Started

Add.

1. 
$$\begin{array}{r} \$36.25 \\ +\phantom{\$}5.36 \\ \hline \$41.61 \end{array}$$

2. 
$$\begin{array}{r} \$27.79 \\ +\phantom{\$}8.62 \\ \hline \$36.41 \end{array}$$

3. 
$$\begin{array}{r} \$25.65 \\ 11.36 \\ +\phantom{\$}6.50 \\ \hline \$43.51 \end{array}$$

4. 
$$\begin{array}{r} \$67.45 \\ 14.75 \\ +\phantom{\$}9.55 \\ \hline \$91.75 \end{array}$$

Copy and add.

5. $11.53 + $7.65
   $19.18

6. $32.36 + $29.63 + $12.08
   $74.07

(fifty-one) **51**

---

## Teaching the Lesson

**Introducing the Problem**    Ask the class to read the problem. Have one student explain what the problem requests (how much money she needs all together) and where the information is to be found. (in the picture) Ask a student to read the price of each item while you write them vertically on the board. Read aloud the next two sentences and let a student name the operation and the numbers to be added while others write them in. (add $29.98 and $3.57) Explain that they are to line up money just as they do other numbers, starting from the right. Have a student do the addition on the board while the others write it in their texts. Read the solution sentence and have students write the answer. ($33.55)

**Developing the Skill**    Write these two problems on the board and have students work them.

$$\begin{array}{r} 2{,}575 \\ +\,1{,}525 \end{array} \qquad \begin{array}{r} \$25.75 \\ +\,\$15.25 \end{array}$$

Ask the students how the problems differ. (one represents money, the other doesn't) Explain that the addition of money is the same as any other addition but it requires that they keep the decimal points in line. The answer must indicate that they have added dollars and show the dollar sign and decimal point. Be sure that students understand that numbers to the left of the decimal are the dollars, numbers to the right are cents. Dictate a column addition problem using money and have students work it.

**51**

## Practice

Add.

1.  $5.25
    + 1.36
    $6.61

2.  $3.85
    + 5.75
    $9.60

3.  $9.72
    + 4.53
    $14.25

4.  $5.37
    + 8.94
    $14.31

5.  $23.40
    + 6.56
    $29.96

6.  $ 8.96
    + 37.43
    $46.39

7.  $51.43
    + 12.48
    $63.91

8.  $43.58
    + 29.29
    $72.87

9.  $3.86
    5.48
    + 7.56
    $16.90

10. $25.16
    2.46
    + 1.59
    $29.21

11. $73.28
    19.15
    + 3.50
    $95.93

12. $ 7.80
    19.25
    + 0.35
    $27.40

13. $12.48
    26.85
    + 39.95
    $79.28

14. $71.50
    9.65
    + 4.36
    $85.51

15. $11.09
    14.51
    + 22.66
    $48.26

16. $78.51
    12.85
    + 9.56
    $100.92

### Copy and Do

17. $8.75 + $6.38 + $4.56
    $19.69

18. $11.75 + $0.59 + $28.75
    $41.09

19. $83.61 + $25.76
    $109.37

20. $57.98 + $2.36 + $0.99
    $61.33

21. $35.25 + $16.37 + $29.15 + $8.76
    $89.53

22. $23.45 + $1.75 + $8.50 + $17.25
    $50.95

23. $19.42 + $43.89
    $63.31

24. $36.22 + $0.55 + $21.17
    $57.94

### Apply

Solve these problems.

25. What is the cost of a hat and coat? $89.08

26. What is the cost of a book, a pen and a watch? $98.40

52 (fifty-two)

## Correcting Common Errors

Some students may forget to write the dollar sign and cents point in the sum. Discuss how when they are adding money, writing the dollar sign and cents point shows this. For some students it may be helpful to have them write the dollar sign and cents point first before they add.

## Enrichment

The prices of items we shop for frequently end with a 9. One short-cut to adding all these nines is to round them off to the next ten, add, and then subtract a penny for each item. To add $.49 and $.39 and $.29, for example, they can round each ($.50, $.40, $.30), add ($1.20), and then subtract $.03. ($1.17) Give the group a grocery store ad from the newspaper, and have them choose groups of 3 and 4 items to add using this short-cut.

## Practice

Have students complete the page. Remind them that each answer must be expressed in dollars and that the problems they copy must be carefully aligned.

## Extra Credit    Applications

Discuss with students what it means to comparison shop. Explain that the same item, a 15-oz box of a particular cereal, for example, may have three different prices in three different stores. Ask students why it might be important to compare the prices of things they are going to buy. Tell students to compare the price of some item in at least three different stores. Point out that they have to be careful to compare exactly the same size and brand.

Give students several days to complete the assignment. When they have finished, have volunteers tell the class the results of their comparison shopping. Discuss any conclusions that they might be able to come to. For example, is there one store that consistently has the lowest prices?

# Estimating Sums

**pages 53-54**

## Objective

To estimate amounts, and add

## Materials

None

## Mental Math

Dictate the following problems:

1. two forties (40 + 40 = 80)
2. two nines (9 + 9 = 18)
3. four twos (2 + 2 + 2 + 2 = 8)
4. three sixes (6 + 6 + 6 = 18)
5. three twelves (12 + 12 + 12 = 36)
6. fourteen zeros (0)
7. five threes (3 + 3 + 3 + 3 + 3 = 15)

## Skill Review

Dictate these problems to the class, asking them to round:

1. 43 to the nearest 10 (40)
2. 253 to the nearest 100 (300)
3. 502 to the nearest 100 (500)
4. 1,603 to the nearest 1,000 (2,000)
5. 99 to the nearest 10 (100)
6. 157 to the nearest 10 (160)
7. 157 to the nearest 100 (200)
8. 157 to the nearest 1,000 (0)

---

## Estimating Sums

Farmer Casey weighs his two cows to help set their selling price at market. About how many kilograms of beef does he have to sell?

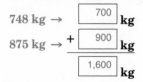

We need to estimate the total weight of both cows.
Bossie weighs 748 kilograms.

Blue weighs ___875___ kilograms.
To estimate the total weight, we round each weight to the nearest hundred, and ___add___.

748 kg → [ 700 ] **kg**

875 kg → + [ 900 ] **kg**

[ 1,600 ] **kg**

Bossie and Blue weigh about ___1,600___ kilograms together.

### Getting Started

Round each addend to the nearest ten and add.

| 1. | 86 | 90 | 2. | 44 | 40 | 3. | 86 | 90 | 4. | 53 | 50 |
|---|---|---|---|---|---|---|---|---|---|---|---|
| | +34 | +30 | | +53 | +50 | | +97 | +100 | | +85 | +90 |
| | | 120 | | | 90 | | | 190 | | | 140 |

Round each addend to the nearest hundred and add.

| 5. | 367 | 400 | 6. | 851 | 900 | 7. | 456 | 500 |
|---|---|---|---|---|---|---|---|---|
| | +186 | +200 | | +365 | +400 | | 238 | 200 |
| | | 600 | | | 1,300 | | +940 | +900 |
| | | | | | | | | 1,600 |

Round each addend to the nearest dollar and add.

| 8. | $9.65 | $10 | 9. | $37.45 | $37 | 10. | $16.57 | $17 |
|---|---|---|---|---|---|---|---|---|
| | + 3.85 | + 4 | | + 16.40 | + 16 | | 23.21 | 23 |
| | | $14 | | | $53 | | + 52.75 | + 53 |
| | | | | | | | | $93 |

(fifty-three) **53**

---

## Teaching the Lesson

**Introducing the Problem**  Have students study the problem and the picture and tell what is being asked. (total weight of both cows) Ask what information is needed. (748 kg, 875 kg) Read the plan to the class and have a volunteer fill in the required operation. (add) Explain that the problem requires estimation, rounding the exact weights to the nearest 100. Have students round each weight and write the rounded numbers (700, 900, 1,600) in the problem as a volunteer writes them on the board. Tell students to fill in the solution sentence. (1,600 kilograms)

**Developing the Skill**  Explain that this method of rounding numbers before addition is useful for estimating a sum and for checking a sum after addition. Now write this problem on the board and have students round to the nearest hundred and estimate the answer without doing any work on paper: **137 + 156 + 378.** (700) Have them copy the problem and do the addition. (681) Ask how close the estimate was to the actual answer. (very close) Give students this problem to copy and work: $45.62 + 58.92 + 32.30 = ($136.74) Next direct them to round each sum to the nearest ten dollars and add again. ($50 + 60 + 30 = $140) Ask them to compare the actual answer with the check.

Round each addend to the nearest ten and add.

| | | | | | | | | | | | |
|---|---|---|---|---|---|---|---|---|---|---|---|
| 1. | 83 | 80 | 2. | 74 | 70 | 3. | 67 | 70 | 4. | 75 | 80 |
| | + 66 | + 70 | | + 29 | + 30 | | + 88 | + 90 | | + 98 | + 100 |
| | | 150 | | | 100 | | | 160 | | | 180 |

| | | | | | | | | | | | |
|---|---|---|---|---|---|---|---|---|---|---|---|
| 5. | 19 | 20 | 6. | 48 | 50 | 7. | 31 | 30 | 8. | 83 | 80 |
| | 38 | 40 | | 72 | 70 | | 47 | 50 | | 39 | 40 |
| | + 26 | + 30 | | + 65 | + 70 | | + 59 | + 60 | | + 78 | + 80 |
| | | 90 | | | 190 | | | 140 | | | 200 |

Round each addend to the nearest hundred and add.

| | | | | | | | | | |
|---|---|---|---|---|---|---|---|---|---|
| 9. | 263 | 300 | 10. | 357 | 400 | 11. | 273 | 300 | |
| | + 129 | + 100 | | + 463 | + 500 | | + 189 | + 200 | |
| | | 400 | | | 900 | | | 500 | |

| | | | | | | | | | |
|---|---|---|---|---|---|---|---|---|---|
| 12. | 675 | 700 | 13. | 426 | 400 | 14. | 621 | 600 | |
| | 286 | 300 | | 538 | 500 | | 845 | 800 | |
| | + 391 | + 400 | | + 780 | + 800 | | + 396 | + 400 | |
| | | 1,400 | | | 1,700 | | | 1,800 | |

Round each addend to the nearest dollar and add.

| | | | | | | | | | |
|---|---|---|---|---|---|---|---|---|---|
| 15. | $8.36 | $8 | 16. | $74.56 | $75 | 17. | $37.51 | $38 | |
| | + 4.56 | + 5 | | + 8.19 | + 8 | | + 22.38 | + 22 | |
| | | $13 | | | $83 | | | $60 | |

| | | | | | | | | | |
|---|---|---|---|---|---|---|---|---|---|
| 18. | $4.75 | $5 | 19. | $16.58 | $17 | 20. | $23.48 | $23 | |
| | 5.36 | 5 | | 7.95 | 8 | | 21.30 | 21 | |
| | + 8.79 | + 9 | | + 11.36 | + 11 | | + 37.89 | + 38 | |
| | | $19 | | | $36 | | | $82 | |

Sometimes, students will find the exact sum first, which they then round to give their estimate. Have students discuss instances where estimates are used as the only answer required, encouraging them to see that, once numbers are rounded, it is much easier to use mental computation to find the answer—the estimate—than to add the original addends.

## Enrichment

Explain that a local merchant is having a half-price sale. Have them estimate the sale prices of the following items, by rounding the original price to the nearest ten dollars and calculating half. Explain that they should do as much calculation in their heads as possible. Television, $89 ($45); lamp, $36 ($20); toaster $19 ($10); and ladder, $59. ($30)

## Practice

Have students do all the problems. Remind them to read directions carefully to know what number they are rounding to.

## Mixed Practice

1. 8 − 4 (4)
2. 279 + 356 (635)
3. 27 + 595 (622)
4. 11 − 7 (4)
5. 3 + 5 + 7 (15)
6. 478 + 356 (834)
7. 49 + 37 (86)
8. 3 + 6 + 9 + 5 (23)
9. 10 − 6 (4)
10. 476 + 387 (863)

## Extra Credit   *Measurement*

Have students write their names in cursive style on a large, manilla paper. Have them estimate the length of yarn in centimeters needed to cover all the letters in their name, and record their estimates. Have them test their guesses by cutting off the estimated length of yarn, and gluing it onto the letters following all curves. If their estimation was too short, have them estimate how much is still needed, record the estimate and repeat the process until all letters are covered. If the estimation was too long, have them cut off the extra yarn, measure it, and subtract its length from the original estimate. When completed, have students label the length of yarn needed to cover their names. Display their yarn names on the bulletin board.

# Problem Solving, Using Estimation

## pages 55-56

### Objective

To learn when to use estimates in solving problems

### Materials

### Mental Math

Have students volunteer several different ways of making each of these sums by addition:

1. 15 (for example, 5 + 5 + 5 or 1 + 14 or 1 + 1 + 1 + 12)
2. 8
3. 100
4. 21

### Skill Review

Explain that in adding tens, the students can work as though they were adding ones. For example, in 30 + 20 + 50, they are adding 3, 2, and 5 tens. The total, 12 tens, is written 120. Ask the class to do the following additions as if they were adding ones:

1. 30 + 50 + 100 = (18 tens, 180)
2. 20 + 10 + 40 = (7 tens, 70)
3. 50 + 60 + 30 = (14 tens, 140)
4. 70 + 70 + 90 = (23 tens, 230)

## Using Estimation

The Sports Club committee sold tickets to their Awards Banquet. Estimate from the bar graph how many tickets the four top sellers sold.

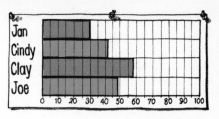

We want the best estimate of the number of tickets sold by all four students.

Jan sold about __30__ tickets.

Cindy sold about __40__ tickets.

Clay sold about __60__ tickets.

Joe sold about __50__ tickets.

To get an estimate of the total we add the rounded addends.

__30__ + __40__ + __60__ + __50__ = __180__

The four top sellers sold about __180__ tickets.

### Getting Started

Round the number of laps for each boy to the nearest hundred, and add.

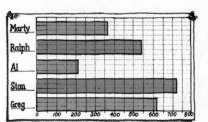

1. Marty and Stan __1,100__

2. Ralph, Al and Greg __1,300__

Circle the best estimate.

3. Betty rode 27 miles. Alice rode 36 miles. Together they rode about

   60 miles.    50 miles.

   (70 miles.)

4. The Bulldogs scored 113 points. The Chicks scored 96 points. Together they scored about

   190 points.    2,000 points.

   (210 points.)

## Teaching the Lesson

**Introducing the Problem** Have students examine the graph. Ask if anyone can tell exactly how many tickets each student sold? (probably not) Ask about how many, to the closest ten, each sold. (Jan, 30; Cindy, 40; Clay, 60; Joe, 50) Have students write these numbers in the sentences in their text. Have a student read the next two sentences, describing the plan for solving the problem. Draw five boxes on the board and have students write ticket sales estimates in each box and add them. (30 + 40 + 60 + 50 = 180) Have them transfer the answer, calculated in this way, to the solution sentence. Ask the class if this is an exact answer. (no, an estimate)

**Developing the Skill** Explain that there are many times when it is convenient to estimate and add instead of calculating an exact answer. When we shop, for example, we frequently estimate the amount we spend on each object and add them all, in order to stay within a budget. Ask the class to think of other times when they might estimate. Remind them that when they add tens or hundreds, they can first treat them like ones. Have them add these amounts as ones:

300 + 500 + 1,000 = (3 + 5 + 10 hundreds, 1,800)
560 + 130 = (56 + 13 tens, 690)
3,200 + 1,200 = (32 + 12 hundreds, 4,400)
50 + 90 + 40 + 10 = (5 + 9 + 4 + 1 tens, 190)

## Apply

Round the numbers on the graph and add.

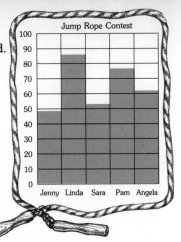

**Jump Rope Contest**

1. Jenny and Pam ___130___

2. Linda and Angela ___150___

3. Pam and Linda ___170___

4. Linda, Sara and Pam ___220___

5. Jenny, Linda and Sara ___190___

6. Linda, Sara, Pam and Angela ___280___

Circle the best estimate.

7. The third grade class scored 86 points. The fourth grade scored 74 points. About how many points were scored altogether?

140 points    150 points    (160 points)

8. A ball costs $7.39. A bat costs $16.59. About how much do they cost together?

$23    ($24)    $25

9. There are 47 boys in the school and 38 girls. About how many children are in the school?

70 children    80 children    (90 children)

10. Katy went to the beach. She collected 134 shells on Monday. She collected 173 shells on Tuesday. About how many shells did she collect?

250 shells    (300 shells)    350 shells

11. The Martins drove 245 miles on Friday. Then they drove 371 miles on Saturday and 316 miles more on Sunday. About how far did the Martins drive in three days?

700 miles    800 miles    (900 miles)

12. A shirt costs $24.56. A pair of pants costs $37.75. A pair of shoes costs $59.15. About how much does all the clothing cost?

($120)    $150    $180

**56** (fifty-six)

## Practice

Have students complete the page. Explain that for some of the problems they will have to refer to the illustration. Point out that the last problems require them to choose the one right answer from a group of three.

## Mixed Practice

1. 12 − 5 (7)
2. 1,295 + 328 (1,623)
3. 157 + 412 (569)
4. 8 + 7 + 3 + 2 (20)
5. 15 − 6 (9)
6. 6,025 + 1,948 (7,973)
7. 752 + 89 (841)
8. 4,307 + 28 (4,335)
9. 7 + 4 + 3 + 6 (20)
10. 8 − 3 (5)

## Extra Credit    *Geometry*

Fold a piece of paper in half and hold it for the class to see. Explain that the folded paper is symmetrical because it is exactly the same on each side of the fold line. Refold the paper and cut out a small square, through both layers of paper. Unfold the paper and hold it up for students to see. Point out that the paper is still symmetric about the fold line.

Give each student a square piece of paper. Tell them to fold the paper in one direction and then in the other. Have them cut out patterns along the fold lines and within the paper to make a paper design. When students are done, ask volunteers to hold up their papers. Explain that their papers are symmetric about both fold lines. Hang up all the students' designs on a bulletin board.

# Calculator Codes

## pages 57-58

### Objective

To use a simple calculator

### Materials

simple calculators with four basic functions

### Mental Math

Have students expand each number into tens and ones, rearrange, and add:

1. 45 + 93   (40 + 5 + 90 + 3 = 40 + 90 + 5 + 3 = 138)
2. 32 + 67   (30 + 2 + 60 + 7 = 30 + 60 + 2 + 7 = 99)
3. 50 + 86   (50 + 0 + 80 + 6 = 50 + 80 + 0 + 6 = 136)
4. 65 + 51   (60 + 5 + 50 + 1 = 60 + 50 + 5 + 1 = 116)
5. 89 + 11   (80 + 9 + 10 + 1 = 80 + 10 + 9 + 1 = 100)

### Skill Review

Have students round to the nearest ten and add:

1. 34 + 59 + 45 = (140)
2. 123 + 52 + 19 = (190)
3. 22 + 89 + 61 = (170)

Now have them round to the nearest hundred and add:

1. 453 + 292 = (500 + 300 = 800)
2. 573 + 443 = (600 + 400 = 1,000)
3. 775 + 123 = (800 + 100 = 900)

---

**Calculator Codes**

A calculator has a screen and a keyboard. The keyboard has an **on/off key**. The keyboard also has **number keys**, **operation keys** and **special keys**. When any of these keys are pressed, an **entry** is made in the calculator.

| Number Keys | Operation Keys | Special Keys |
|:-----------:|:--------------:|:------------:|
|  |  |  |

Turn the calculator on. A zero should appear on the screen. ( 0 )

A **calculator code** tells you in what order to press the keys on the calculator. Follow the codes below and show the results on the screen.

 ( 11 )     ( 79 )

We use a short cut to show calculator numbers. We write 8 as 8 and 8 7 as 87. Show the results of these codes on the screens.

8 [+] 7 [=] ( 15 )    84 [+] 73 [=] ( 157 )

The C key clears the calculator. You must start the problem from the beginning. The CE key cancels only the last number entered. The calculator will still remember earlier entries. Show the results of these codes on the screens.

15 [+] 16 [C] ( 0 )    15 [+] 14 [CE] 16 [=] ( 31 )

---

## Teaching the Lesson

**Introducing the Problem**  Have students look at the illustration and their own calculator while you read the introduction. Have students find the on/off key, each of the number keys, the operations keys, and the special keys. Explain that any time a key is pressed, an entry has been made, and information has been entered into the calculator. The calculator remembers that entry until the machine is turned off. Ask students to turn on their calculators. Point out that the commands for using a calculator are shown in code. The blocks show which key and what order to strike the keys. Have them enter the first problem and write the result in the box. (11) Now they should hit the clear key [C] and do the next problem, writing the answer in the box. (79) Explain that the next line shows similar problems but the numbers to be entered are not shown in boxes. Have students work the problems and write the answers in the boxes. (15, 157) Tell students to clear the first problem with the [C] key before doing the second. Explain that the [C]

key clears the entire problem while the [CE] key is used to clear the last entry. Have students do the last two problems. (0, 31)

**Developing the Skill**  Dictate a number of addition problems to the class to do on the calculator. Point out that the calculator never makes mistakes, but the person using the machine can make a mistake entering the number. Tell them to double-check each entry.

## Practice

Enter these codes. Show the results on the screens.

1. 5 [+] 8 [=] ( 13 )

2. 9 [+] 8 [=] ( 17 )

3. 6 [+] 15 [=] ( 21 )

4. 25 [+] 37 [=] ( 62 )

5. 8 [+] 9 [+] 23 [=] ( 40 )

6. 39 [CE] 6 [+] 42 [=] ( 48 )

7. 14 [+] 39 [+] 64 [C] ( 0 )

8. 129 [+] 64 [+] 4 [=] ( 197 )

Use your calculator to find each sum.
Use estimation to check your answer.

9.    439
  + 225
    664

10.   236
  + 795
  1,031

11.   979
  + 858
  1,837

12.   296
  + 156
   452

13.   921
   365
  + 385
  1,671

14.   986
   750
  + 855
  2,591

Use your calculator to find each sum.

15. 39 + 85 = __124__

16. 256 + 483 + 796 = __1,535__

17. 841 + 650 + 396 = __1,887__

18. 592 + 487 + 936 = __2,015__

Find the sum of each pair of number neighbors.
Write the answer in the box below each pair.

19.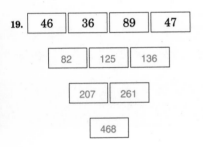

20.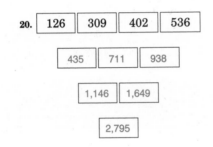

**58** (fifty-eight)

# Chapter Test

page 59

| Item | Objective |
|---|---|
| 1-4 | Add two 2-digit addends with one regrouping (See pages 39-40) |
| 5-8 | Add two 3-digit addends with two regroupings (See pages 41-42) |
| 9-12 | Add two 4-digit addends (See pages 47-48) |
| 13-16 | Add three numbers or amounts of money (See pages 49-52) |
| 17-20 | Round addends to the nearest 10 and add (See pages 53-56) |
| 21-23 | Round addends to the nearest 100 and add (See pages 53-56) |
| 24-29 | Round each addend to the nearest dollar and add (See pages 53-56) |

Add.

1.  $\begin{array}{r} 57 \\ + 38 \\ \hline 95 \end{array}$
2.  $\begin{array}{r} 34 \\ + 23 \\ \hline 57 \end{array}$
3.  $\begin{array}{r} 48 \\ + 37 \\ \hline 85 \end{array}$
4.  $\begin{array}{r} 62 \\ + 29 \\ \hline 91 \end{array}$

5.  $\begin{array}{r} 236 \\ + 175 \\ \hline 411 \end{array}$
6.  $\begin{array}{r} 392 \\ + 568 \\ \hline 960 \end{array}$
7.  $\begin{array}{r} 485 \\ + 296 \\ \hline 781 \end{array}$
8.  $\begin{array}{r} 609 \\ + 257 \\ \hline 866 \end{array}$

9.  $\begin{array}{r} 3,248 \\ + 1,568 \\ \hline 4,816 \end{array}$
10. $\begin{array}{r} 7,586 \\ + 1,798 \\ \hline 9,384 \end{array}$
11. $\begin{array}{r} 5,263 \\ + 1,079 \\ \hline 6,342 \end{array}$
12. $\begin{array}{r} 2,179 \\ + 6,391 \\ \hline 8,570 \end{array}$

13. $\begin{array}{r} 875 \\ 1,321 \\ + \quad 68 \\ \hline 2,264 \end{array}$
14. $\begin{array}{r} 5,729 \\ 175 \\ + \quad 315 \\ \hline 6,219 \end{array}$
15. $\begin{array}{r} \$26.41 \\ 37.85 \\ + \quad 26.91 \\ \hline \$91.17 \end{array}$
16. $\begin{array}{r} \$38.21 \\ 16.58 \\ + \quad 24.17 \\ \hline \$78.96 \end{array}$

Round each addend to the nearest ten and add.

17. $\begin{array}{r} 23 \\ + 47 \end{array}$ $\begin{array}{r} 20 \\ + 50 \\ \hline 70 \end{array}$
18. $\begin{array}{r} 39 \\ + 45 \end{array}$ $\begin{array}{r} 40 \\ + 50 \\ \hline 90 \end{array}$
19. $\begin{array}{r} 22 \\ + 28 \end{array}$ $\begin{array}{r} 20 \\ + 30 \\ \hline 50 \end{array}$
20. $\begin{array}{r} 41 \\ + 37 \end{array}$ $\begin{array}{r} 40 \\ + 40 \\ \hline 80 \end{array}$

Round each addend to the nearest hundred and add.

21. $\begin{array}{r} 237 \\ + 189 \end{array}$ $\begin{array}{r} 200 \\ + 200 \\ \hline 400 \end{array}$
22. $\begin{array}{r} 575 \\ + 386 \end{array}$ $\begin{array}{r} 600 \\ + 400 \\ \hline 1,000 \end{array}$
23. $\begin{array}{r} 453 \\ + 387 \end{array}$ $\begin{array}{r} 500 \\ + 400 \\ \hline 900 \end{array}$

Round each addend to the nearest dollar and add.

24. $\begin{array}{r} \$9.27 \\ + 8.57 \end{array}$ $\begin{array}{r} \$9 \\ + 9 \\ \hline \$18 \end{array}$
25. $\begin{array}{r} \$12.75 \\ + 4.36 \end{array}$ $\begin{array}{r} \$13 \\ + 4 \\ \hline \$17 \end{array}$
26. $\begin{array}{r} \$26.38 \\ + 32.45 \end{array}$ $\begin{array}{r} \$26 \\ + 32 \\ \hline \$58 \end{array}$

27. $\begin{array}{r} \$7.75 \\ + 4.60 \end{array}$ $\begin{array}{r} \$8 \\ + 5 \\ \hline \$13 \end{array}$
28. $\begin{array}{r} \$15.95 \\ + 8.10 \end{array}$ $\begin{array}{r} \$16 \\ + 8 \\ \hline \$24 \end{array}$
29. $\begin{array}{r} \$73.29 \\ + 12.50 \end{array}$ $\begin{array}{r} \$73 \\ + 13 \\ \hline \$86 \end{array}$

Circle the letter of the correct answer.

| 1 6 + 7 | a 12<br>(b) 13<br>c 14<br>d NG |
|---|---|

| 8    136<br>   + 249 | a 375<br>b 387<br>c 485<br>(d) NG |
|---|---|

| 2 15 − 7 | a 7<br>(b) 8<br>c 9<br>d NG |
|---|---|

| 9    357<br>   + 288 | a 545<br>b 635<br>(c) 645<br>d NG |
|---|---|

| 3 367 ◯ 358 | (a) ><br>b < |
|---|---|

| 10   3,256<br>   + 1,847 | a 4,103<br>b 5,093<br>(c) 5,103<br>d NG |
|---|---|

| 4 Round 749 to the nearest hundred. | (a) 700<br>b 800 |
|---|---|

| 11  $27.45<br>   + 10.68 | a $37.03<br>(b) $38.13<br>c $48.13<br>d NG |
|---|---|

| 5 What is the value of the 3 in 357? | a ones<br>b tens<br>(c) hundreds<br>d NG |
|---|---|

| 12  1,496<br>     275<br>   + 3,857 | (a) 5,628<br>b 5,629<br>c 6,628<br>d NG |
|---|---|

| 6 What is the value of the 7 in 372,980? | a hundreds<br>b thousands<br>(c) ten thousands<br>d NG |
|---|---|

| 13 Round each number to the nearest ten and add.<br>   43<br>   + 36 | a 70<br>(b) 80<br>c 90<br>d NG |
|---|---|

| 7 Which digit is out of place in the series: 3, 4, 5, 2, 6, 7? | a 6<br>b 5<br>c 3<br>(d) NG |
|---|---|

☐ score

**60** (sixty)

# Cumulative Review

page 60

| Item | Objective |
|---|---|
| 1 | Recall addition facts through 18 (See pages 3-4) |
| 2 | Recall subtraction facts through 18 (See pages 9-10) |
| 3 | Compare and order numbers less than 1,000 (See pages 27-28) |
| 4 | Round to the nearest 100 (See pages 31-32) |
| 5 | Identify the value of a digit in a number less than 10,000 (See pages 33-34) |
| 6 | Identify the value of a digit in a number less than 1,000,000 (See pages 35-36) |
| 7 | Count and order numbers less than 100 (See pages 23-24) |
| 8 | Add two 3-digit numbers with one regrouping (See pages 43-44) |
| 9 | Add two 3-digit numbers with two regroupings (See pages 45-46) |
| 10 | Add two 4-digit numbers (See pages 47-48) |
| 11 | Add dollars and cents with regrouping (See pages 51-52) |
| 12 | Add three or four numbers (See pages 49-50) |
| 13 | Round to the nearest 10, 100 or dollar and add (See pages 53-56) |

## Alternate Cumulative Review

Circle the letter of the correct answer.

**1** 7 + 8 =
a 13
b 14
(c) 15
d NG

**2** 18 − 6 =
a 8
b 10
(c) 12
d NG

**3** 973 ◯ 937
(a) >
b <
c =

**4** Round 861 to the nearest hundred.
a 800
(b) 900

**5** What is the value of the 9 in 692?
a ones
(b) tens
c hundreds
d NG

**6** What is the value of the 4 in 734,619?
a tens
b hundreds
(c) thousands
d NG

**7** Which number is incorrect in this series?
69, 68, 67, 70, 65
a 67
(b) 70
c 66
d NG

**8**    463
   + 128
a 581
(b) 591
c 681
d NG

**9**    658
   + 283
a 831
b 841
(c) 941
d NG

**10**  4,367
   + 1,744
a 5,101
(b) 6,111
c 6,211
d NG

**11**  $35.47
   + 17.81
a $42.21
b $52.21
(c) $53.28
d NG

**12**  6,387
     671
   + 2,724
a 9,672
b 9,682
c 9,772
(d) NG

**13** Round each number to the nearest ten and add.
   67   a 90
   + 33  (b) 100
         c 110
         d NG

**60**

# Trading Tens for Ones

## pages 61-62

### Objective

To review trading tens for ones

### Materials

ten-strips and single counters
spinner, marked 1–9
paper bag
marbles - 9 black, 5 white

### Mental Math

Dictate these numbers. Have students round each one to the nearest ten, nearest hundred, and nearest thousand.

1. 1,382 (1,380, 1,400, 1,000)
2. 867 (870, 900, 1,000)
3. 4,620 (4,620, 4,600, 5,000)
4. 55 (50, 100, 0)
5. 499 (500, 500, 0)

### Skill Review

In preparation for subtraction, review trading for tens in addition. Write these problems on the board for the students to do on paper:

| 1. 23 | 2. 56 | 3. 75 | 4. 8 |
|---|---|---|---|
| + 18 | +29 | +15 | +38 |
| (41) | (85) | (90) | (46) |
| 5. 37 | 6. 69 | 7. 52 | 8. 67 |
| + 48 | +45 | +29 | +33 |
| (85) | (114) | (81) | (100) |

**Trading Tens for Ones**

How many ten-strips and ones will Rodd have if he trades 1 ten-strip for 10 ones?

Rodd has ___3___ ten-strips and ___4___ ones. We want to make a trade. To find the new number, we trade ___1___ ten for ___10___ ones.

Rodd has ___3___ tens and ___4___ ones.

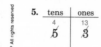

| tens | ones |
|---|---|
| 3 | 4 |

He trades ___1___ ten for ___10___ ones.

| tens | ones |
|---|---|
| 2 | 14 |
| 3 | 4 |

After the trade, Rodd has ___2___ tens and ___14___ ones.

**Getting Started**

Trade 1 ten for 10 ones. Show the number after the trade.

1. 64 = ___5___ tens ___14___ ones
2. 48 = ___3___ tens ___18___ ones
3. 91 = ___8___ tens ___11___ ones
4. 32 = ___2___ tens ___12___ ones

| 5. tens | ones | | 6. tens | ones | | 7. tens | ones | | 8. tens | ones |
|---|---|---|---|---|---|---|---|---|---|---|
| 4 | 13 | | 6 | 15 | | 1 | 14 | | 7 | 11 |
| 5 | 3 | | 7 | 5 | | 2 | 4 | | 8 | 1 |

(sixty-one) **61**

## Teaching the Lesson

**Introducing the Problem** Have students look at the illustration and explain what Rodd needs to do. (trade a ten-strip for 10 single counters) Ask how many tens and ones Rodd has. (3 tens, 4 ones) Then have students write the numbers on the lines. Ask students to read the plan sentences, and then fill in the answers. (1 ten for 10 ones) Direct attention to the counters illustrated below. Have a student draw Rodd's counters on the board while you fill in a place value chart like that in the text. (3 tens, 4 ones) Read the trade sentence aloud and ask students to explain what he must trade in order to get more ones. (1 ten for 10 ones) Have another student come to the board and change the counter drawing to reflect the second illustration. (2 tens, 14 ones) Have students write the information in their texts while you change the place value chart on the board.

**Developing the Skill** Divide class into groups of 5 or 6 students. Appoint a banker in each group to handle trades and collect counters. Give the banker a supply of single counters and give the other students in each group 5 ten-strips. Turn the spinner, explaining that they may get rid of the number of counters indicated by giving them to the banker. Point out that they will have to trade with the banker for singles if they have none. The point of the activity is to get rid of the counters. The group eliminating all of its counters with the fewest spins is the winner.

## Practice

Trade 1 ten for 10 ones. Show the number after the trade.

1. 78 = __6__ tens __18__ ones
2. 43 = __3__ tens __13__ ones
3. 46 = __3__ tens __16__ ones
4. 37 = __2__ tens __17__ ones
5. 21 = __1__ tens __11__ ones
6. 58 = __4__ tens __18__ ones
7. 94 = __8__ tens __14__ ones
8. 29 = __1__ tens __19__ ones
9. 82 = __7__ tens __12__ ones
10. 66 = __5__ tens __16__ ones

11.
| tens | ones |
|---|---|
| 5 / 6 | 13 / 3 |

12.
| tens | ones |
|---|---|
| 6 / 7 | 17 / 7 |

13.
| tens | ones |
|---|---|
| 6 / 7 | 11 / 1 |

14.
| tens | ones |
|---|---|
| 2 / 3 | 14 / 4 |

15.
| tens | ones |
|---|---|
| 4 / 5 | 15 / 5 |

16.
| tens | ones |
|---|---|
| 3 / 4 | 17 / 7 |

17.
| tens | ones |
|---|---|
| 1 / 2 | 18 / 8 |

18.
| tens | ones |
|---|---|
| 4 / 5 | 16 / 6 |

19.
| tens | ones |
|---|---|
| 5 / 6 | 14 / 4 |

20.
| tens | ones |
|---|---|
| 2 / 3 | 13 / 3 |

21.
| tens | ones |
|---|---|
| 8 / 9 | 17 / 7 |

22.
| tens | ones |
|---|---|
| 7 / 8 | 11 / 1 |

23.
| tens | ones |
|---|---|
| 6 / 7 | 12 / 2 |

24.
| tens | ones |
|---|---|
| 3 / 4 | 15 / 5 |

25.
| tens | ones |
|---|---|
| 5 / 6 | 10 / 0 |

26.
| tens | ones |
|---|---|
| 5 / 6 | 15 / 5 |

27.
| tens | ones |
|---|---|
| 1 / 2 | 17 / 7 |

28.
| tens | ones |
|---|---|
| 8 / 9 | 16 / 6 |

**62** (sixty-two)

# Subtracting 2-digit Numbers, One Trade

**pages 63-64**

## Objective

To review subtraction with 2-digit numbers, trading tens for ones

## Materials

ten-strips and single counters
*paper bag
marbles - 1 red, 2 yellow, 8 white, 4 black

## Mental Math

Dictate the following word problems:

1. Leon's birthday is on October 23. Today is October 10. How many days until his birthday? (23 − 10 = 13 days)
2. School starts at 9 o'clock and lunch is served at 12. How many hours between? (12 − 9 = 3 hours)

## Skill Review

Dictate the following problems. Have students change:

1. 24 to 1 ten, ___ ones (14)
2. 3 tens, 15 ones to 4 ___, 5 ones (tens)
3. 152 to ___ tens, 12 ones (14)
4. 76 to 6 tens, ___ ones (16)
5. ___ tens, 13 ones from 63 (5)

---

## Subtracting 2-digit Numbers, One Trade

Helen sells magazines after school and keeps a daily record of her sales. How many magazines did she have left on Wednesday?

We want to find how many magazines Helen had left on Wednesday.

Helen started with __63__ magazines on Wednesday.

She sold __25__ by the end of the day.

To get the number left, we subtract __25__ from __63__.

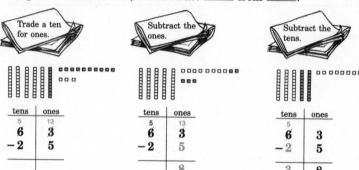

Helen's Magazine Sales

| Day | Start | Sold | Left |
|---|---|---|---|
| Monday | 96 | 18 | 78 |
| Tuesday | 78 | 15 | 63 |
| Wednesday | 63 | 25 | |
| Thursday | | 19 | |
| Friday | | 8 | |

Trade a ten for ones.

Subtract the ones.

Subtract the tens.

| tens | ones | | tens | ones | | tens | ones |
|---|---|---|---|---|---|---|---|
| 5 | 13 | | 5 | 13 | | 5 | |
| 6 | 3 | | 6 | 3 | | 6 | 3 |
| − 2 | 5 | | − 2 | 5 | | − 2 | 5 |
| | | | | 8 | | 3 | 8 |

Helen had __38__ magazines left by the end of Wednesday.

### Getting Started

Subtract. Trade a ten if needed.

1. 73
   − 29
   44

2. 72
   − 64
   8

3. 51
   − 37
   14

4. 26
   − 18
   8

Copy and subtract.

5. 75 − 48
   27

6. 38 − 16
   22

7. 55 − 49
   6

8. 48 − 29
   19

(sixty-three) **63**

---

## Teaching the Lesson

**Introducing the Problem** Have students read the problem and look at the chart. What is being asked? (how many magazines were left on Wednesday) Explain that the number of magazines left on one day becomes the number she starts with the next. Ask how can we find the number left? (subtract number sold from number at the start) Have a volunteer read the data sentences, filling in the number of magazines she started with on Wednesday and the number sold that day. (63 magazines on Wednesday, sold 25) Read the plan sentences aloud while students complete them in their texts. (subtract 25 from 63) Point out the counters which illustrate the problem. Draw 6 tens and 3 ones and write the problem as in the illustration. Have students come to the board to demonstrate each part of the problem. Read the solution sentence while students complete it. (38 left)

**Developing the Skill** Have students put 4 ten-strips and 2 single counters on their desks. Write **42** on the board. Explain that you want to take 26 away from the 42. Ask how they will do it. (exchange 1 ten for 10 ones, then subtract) Have students exchange one of their tens and then take 2 tens and 6 singles away. Ask for the answer. (16) Write the problem on the board and have a student show the subtraction.

Subtract.

1. $\begin{array}{r} 81 \\ -32 \\ \hline 49 \end{array}$  2. $\begin{array}{r} 33 \\ -25 \\ \hline 8 \end{array}$  3. $\begin{array}{r} 51 \\ -29 \\ \hline 22 \end{array}$  4. $\begin{array}{r} 63 \\ -27 \\ \hline 36 \end{array}$  5. $\begin{array}{r} 88 \\ -43 \\ \hline 45 \end{array}$

6. $\begin{array}{r} 82 \\ -9 \\ \hline 73 \end{array}$  7. $\begin{array}{r} 45 \\ -29 \\ \hline 16 \end{array}$  8. $\begin{array}{r} 38 \\ -29 \\ \hline 9 \end{array}$  9. $\begin{array}{r} 90 \\ -13 \\ \hline 77 \end{array}$  10. $\begin{array}{r} 49 \\ -19 \\ \hline 30 \end{array}$

11. $\begin{array}{r} 73 \\ -28 \\ \hline 45 \end{array}$  12. $\begin{array}{r} 72 \\ -35 \\ \hline 37 \end{array}$  13. $\begin{array}{r} 40 \\ -20 \\ \hline 20 \end{array}$  14. $\begin{array}{r} 81 \\ -67 \\ \hline 14 \end{array}$  15. $\begin{array}{r} 97 \\ -93 \\ \hline 4 \end{array}$

16. $\begin{array}{r} 81 \\ -37 \\ \hline 44 \end{array}$  17. $\begin{array}{r} 38 \\ -16 \\ \hline 22 \end{array}$  18. $\begin{array}{r} 91 \\ -36 \\ \hline 55 \end{array}$  19. $\begin{array}{r} 75 \\ -58 \\ \hline 17 \end{array}$  20. $\begin{array}{r} 66 \\ -39 \\ \hline 27 \end{array}$

21. $\begin{array}{r} 29 \\ -15 \\ \hline 14 \end{array}$  22. $\begin{array}{r} 46 \\ -37 \\ \hline 9 \end{array}$  23. $\begin{array}{r} 63 \\ -28 \\ \hline 35 \end{array}$  24. $\begin{array}{r} 35 \\ -12 \\ \hline 23 \end{array}$  25. $\begin{array}{r} 80 \\ -59 \\ \hline 21 \end{array}$

**Copy and Do**

26. 62 − 21   27. 86 − 28   28. 71 − 67   29. 92 − 27
    41           58            4            65

30. 80 − 21   31. 38 − 7    32. 46 − 28   33. 53 − 47
    59           31            18            6

34. 72 − 58   35. 47 − 23   36. 66 − 27   37. 91 − 63
    14           24            39            28

38. 44 − 17   39. 70 − 46   40. 55 − 15   41. 22 − 9
    27           24            40            13

**Apply**

Solve these problems.

42. Danielle packed 63 first aid kits for a service project. Pat packed 47. How many more kits did Danielle pack than Pat?
16 kits

43. Trish earned $60 walking dogs for her neighbors. She spent $47 on school clothes. How much money does she have left?
$13

## Correcting Common Errors

Some students may not trade but subtract the lesser digit from the greater digit in a subtraction problem.

| INCORRECT | CORRECT |
|---|---|
| $\begin{array}{r} 53 \\ -28 \\ \hline 35 \end{array}$ | $\begin{array}{r} 413 \\ \cancel{5}\cancel{3} \\ -28 \\ \hline 25 \end{array}$ |

Correct by having students work in pairs and use place-value materials to model the problem and to demonstrate that the terms of a subtraction problem cannot be transposed without changing the difference.

## Enrichment

Put 1 red marble, 2 yellow marbles, 8 white marbles and 4 black marbles in a paper bag. Have students draw the marbles one at a time, recording the color they get on each draw and replacing the marble in the bag each time. Have them predict the contents of the bag after 10 draws, after 15 draws, and after 25 draws. Then open the bag and verify the actual contents.

## Practice

Have students complete the problems on the page. Remind them to show each trade the way they did in the examples. Also, remind them to keep their columns straight when they copy and subtract.

## Extra Credit   *Counting*

Make several gameboards from 12″ × 18″ posterboard. Draw a path divided into about 50 square sections on each board. Color in some of the squares with various colors. Include a "start" and "finish" square on each end.

Have students help you make a set of direction cards. On each card write orders such as: move ahead 20−13, go back 42−36, or go to nearest red. Divide the class into groups. Provide each group with a gameboard, 4 different colored counters and a set of direction cards.*
*Have groups exchange sets of direction cards after they have finished a game. Keep a chart of "winners" who reach finish first each time.

# Subtracting 3-digit Numbers, One Trade

## pages 65-66

## Objective

To review subtraction with 3-digit numbers, trading tens for ones or hundreds for tens

## Materials

## Mental Math

Dictate these problems:

1. $24 - 12 = (12)$
2. $90 - 3 = (87)$
3. $45 - 5 = (40)$
4. $15 - 8 = (7)$
5. $25 - 16 = (9)$
6. $32 - 3 = (29)$
7. $21 - 11 = (10)$

## Skill Review

Remind students to trade 1 ten for 10 ones when needed. Write these problems on the board and have students do them on paper, showing the trade.

| 1. 45 | 2. 78 | 3. 28 | 4. 154 |
|-------|-------|-------|--------|
| − 18 | −29 | − 9 | −56 |
| (27) | (49) | (19) | (98) |
| 5. 46 | 6. 67 | 7. 351 | 8. 55 |
| − 37 | −23 | −226 | −17 |
| (9) | (44) | (125) | (38) |

## Subtracting 3-digit Numbers, One Trade

Amtrak trains connect major cities in the United States. How many more trains travel the route between New York and Washington, D.C., than the Los Angeles to San Diego route?

<table>
<tr><th colspan="2">TWO-WAY AMTRAK ROUTES</th></tr>
<tr><td>Route</td><td>Monthly Trains</td></tr>
<tr><td>New York City–Washington, D.C.</td><td>952</td></tr>
<tr><td>Philadelphia–Harrisburg</td><td>593</td></tr>
<tr><td>New York City–Philadelphia</td><td>419</td></tr>
<tr><td>New Haven–Springfield</td><td>400</td></tr>
<tr><td>Boston–Washington, D.C.</td><td>377</td></tr>
<tr><td>Los Angeles–San Diego</td><td>362</td></tr>
</table>

We want to know the difference between the number of trains.

In one month, __952__ trains travel between New York and Washington, D.C.

During the same time period, __362__ trains go between Los Angeles and San Diego. To find how many more trains travel one route than the other, we subtract __362__ from __952__.

Subtract the ones. Trade if needed.

Subtract the tens. Trade if needed.

Subtract the hundreds.

$$\begin{array}{r} 952 \\ -362 \\ \hline 0 \end{array} \qquad \begin{array}{r} {}^{8\ 15} \\ 952 \\ -362 \\ \hline 90 \end{array} \qquad \begin{array}{r} {}^{8} \\ 952 \\ -362 \\ \hline 590 \end{array}$$

In one month, __590__ more trains travel the New York to Washington, D.C. route, than between Los Angeles and San Diego.

### Getting Started

Subtract.

| 1. 376 | 2. 827 | 3. 627 | 4. 968 |
|--------|--------|--------|--------|
| − 149 | − 356 | − 253 | − 794 |
| 227 | 471 | 374 | 174 |

Copy and subtract.

5. $473 - 151$  322
6. $727 - 18$  709
7. $947 - 156$  791
8. $590 - 163$  427
9. $635 - 281$  354
10. $656 - 212$  444

(sixty-five) **65**

## Teaching the Lesson

**Introducing the Problem**  Read the problem aloud while students examine the problem and chart. Ask what the problem calls for. (the number of trains on the N.Y.–Washington route exceeding that on the L.A.–San Diego route) Read the data sentences aloud while students find the information needed on their charts (952 trains N.Y. to Washington, 362 trains between L.A. and San Diego) Have one student read the plan sentence while the others write the numbers in the blanks. (subtract 362 from 952) Direct attention to the three steps and write the problem on the board. Ask what trades are needed. (hundreds for tens) Have a student show the trade on the board and subtract while the others follow in their texts. Circle the answer as students write it in their solution sentence. (590 more)

**Developing the Skill**  Write these two problems on the board: **364    582**  (205)  (91)
**−159   −491**

Ask someone to explain where trading will be required in the first problem (tens for ones) and in the second problem. (hundreds for tens) Point out that trading is the same no matter which column they are working in. There are 10 ones in ten and 10 tens in a hundred. Have a volunteer work the first problem at the board, showing the trade. Have another do the second problem showing the trade. Dictate similar problems for the class to do.

Subtract.

1. 436
   − 118
   318

2. 596
   − 358
   238

3. 729
   − 258
   471

4. 651
   − 519
   132

5. 813
   − 290
   523

6. 753
   − 281
   472

7. 381
   − 19
   362

8. 816
   − 132
   684

9. 459
   − 183
   276

10. 915
    − 283
    632

11. 685
    − 527
    158

12. 728
    − 235
    493

13. 185
    − 16
    169

14. 883
    − 628
    255

15. 520
    − 370
    150

16. 327
    − 75
    252

17. 926
    − 861
    65

18. 182
    − 9
    173

19. 761
    − 528
    233

20. 627
    − 190
    437

**Copy and Do**

21. 821 − 318
    503

22. 583 − 238
    345

23. 816 − 753
    63

24. 429 − 150
    279

25. 456 − 275
    181

26. 691 − 385
    306

27. 752 − 28
    724

28. 464 − 392
    72

29. 823 − 560
    263

30. 537 − 228
    309

31. 925 − 809
    116

32. 737 − 281
    456

**Apply**

Solve these problems.

33. Miss Shaw flew 391 miles crop dusting, on Friday. On Saturday, she flew 186 miles. How much farther did Miss Shaw fly on Friday?
    205 miles

34. On opening day, 783 people visited the Science Museum. On the same day, 417 people went to the Aquarium. How many more people visited the museum?
    366 people

## Correcting Common Errors

Some students may always write either ten tens or ten ones when they are trading without adding the trade to the existing number.

INCORRECT

   710          710
   8̷6̷4          9̷8̷2̷
  − 591        − 436
   213          544

Correct by having students work in pairs using place-value materials to model the problems so they see that ten tens or ten ones must be added to the number already in the place.

## Enrichment

Have students flip a penny and record the number of heads and tails they get for 50 tosses. Before they begin, ask if they think heads or tails are more likely. (equally likely) When they finish they should describe the results. (the number of heads, the number of tails)

## Practice

Have students do the problems on the page. Remind them again to show each trade. Explain that when they copy problems they will have to leave room above the problem for that purpose.

## Extra Credit   *Logic*

Write each of these number riddles on the board and tape a large envelope below each. Tell students to solve the riddles, write their solutions on paper and put them in the envelopes. Read the solutions aloud at the end of the day. See if anyone solved all three correctly.

1. If a clock is accurate and both hands point at 12:00, how can you tell whether it is 12:00 noon or 12:00 midnight? (Look outdoors. If the sun is not in the sky, it is midnight)
2. What is it that has two heads, six feet, four ears, and one tail? (a horse and rider)
3. What is it that has only one eye and only one foot, but is a sharp traveller? (a needle)

# Subtracting 3-digit Numbers, Two Trades

## pages 67-68

### Objective

To review 3-digit subtraction, trading tens for ones and hundreds for tens

### Materials

thumb tack
small plastic bottle

### Mental Math

Have students tell which is larger:

1. $(15 - 8)$ or $(5 + 3)$  $(5 + 3)$
2. $(24 + 12)$ or $(50 - 10)$  $(50 - 10)$
3. $(45 - 5)$ or $(29 + 11)$  (equal)
4. $(34 + 7)$ or $(61 - 10)$  $(61 - 10)$
5. $(47 + 0)$ or $(47 - 0)$  (equal)
6. $(56 - 7)$ or $(23 + 23)$  $(56 - 7)$

### Skill Review

Dictate these problems.
Have students circle the column in which a trade is needed and then complete the problem.

1. $345$
   $-126$
   $(219)$

2. $629$
   $-351$
   $(278)$

3. $57$
   $-39$
   $(18)$

4. $422$
   $-408$
   $(14)$

5. $72$
   $-35$
   $(37)$

6. $289$
   $-193$
   $(96)$

7. $426$
   $-231$
   $(195)$

8. $940$
   $-131$
   $(809)$

---

### Subtracting 3-digit Numbers, Two Trades

The Great Lakes form the largest body of fresh water in the world. How much longer is Lake Superior than Lake Ontario?

We need to find how much longer Lake Superior is than Lake Ontario.

Lake Superior is __350__ miles long.

Lake Ontario is only __193__ miles in length.

To find the difference, we subtract __193__ from __350__.

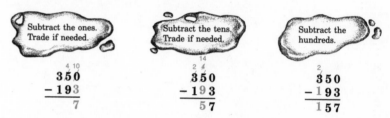

Subtract the ones. Trade if needed.
$$\begin{array}{r} 3\,\overset{4}{\cancel{5}}\,\overset{10}{\cancel{0}} \\ -\,1\,9\,3 \\ \hline 7 \end{array}$$

Subtract the tens. Trade if needed.
$$\begin{array}{r} \overset{2}{\cancel{3}}\,\overset{14}{\cancel{4}}\,0 \\ -\,1\,9\,3 \\ \hline 5\,7 \end{array}$$

Subtract the hundreds.
$$\begin{array}{r} \overset{2}{\cancel{3}}\,5\,0 \\ -\,1\,9\,3 \\ \hline 1\,5\,7 \end{array}$$

Lake Superior is __157__ miles longer than Lake Ontario.

### Getting Started

Subtract.

1. $536$
   $-257$
   $279$

2. $743$
   $-468$
   $275$

3. $637$
   $-258$
   $379$

4. $850$
   $-572$
   $278$

Copy and subtract.

5. $917 - 429$  $488$

6. $385 - 296$  $89$

7. $625 - 177$  $448$

8. $731 - 559$  $172$

9. $858 - 379$  $479$

10. $558 - 144$  $414$

(sixty-seven) **67**

---

## Teaching the Lesson

**Introducing the Problem**  Have students read the problem and identify the question being asked. Have a volunteer locate the information required to find an answer. (lengths of Lake Superior and Lake Ontario) Have students write the lengths. (350 miles-Lake Superior, 193 miles-Lake Ontario) Read the plan sentences aloud and ask a volunteer for the required numbers. (subtract 193 from 350) Draw attention to the problem worked in three steps. Put it on the board and ask if a trade is necessary to subtract ones. (yes) Have a student come to the board and complete the trade and subtract ones. Repeat the procedure for tens. Subtract hundreds and have the class complete the solution sentence. (157 miles)

**Developing the Skill**  Write this problem in a 3-digit place value chart on the board: **635 − 258**. Ask volunteers to identify where trades are needed. (tens for ones, hundreds for tens) Explain that problems of this sort make it important that they start subtraction with ones and work to the left. Make the first trade for the class and have someone do the subtraction. Point out that as they approach the second trade they will be working with numbers they have already written in as trades. In the tens column they now have 2 tens, not the 3 tens there before the trade. When the second trade is made they add 10 more tens, for a total of 12 tens. Complete the subtraction. Dictate several more problems.

## Practice

Subtract.

1.  628
   −139
   _____
    489

2.  535
   −286
   _____
    249

3.  815
   −426
   _____
    389

4.  773
   −396
   _____
    377

5.  351
   − 96
   _____
    255

6.  832
   −686
   _____
    146

7.  925
   −387
   _____
    538

8.  136
   − 88
   _____
     48

9.  714
   −329
   _____
    385

10.  646
    −188
   _____
     458

11.  423
    −175
   _____
     248

12.  821
    −256
   _____
     565

13.  912
    − 87
   _____
     825

14.  630
    −258
   _____
     372

15.  815
    −379
   _____
     436

16.  462
    −185
   _____
     277

### Copy and Do

17. 372 − 96
    276

18. 920 − 387
    533

19. 731 − 285
    446

20. 582 − 369
    213

21. 421 − 259
    162

22. 163 − 78
    85

23. 612 − 224
    388

24. 851 − 273
    578

25. 426 − 387
    39

26. 274 − 198
    76

27. 519 − 258
    261

28. 231 − 138
    93

29. 516 − 278
    238

30. 823 − 258
    565

31. 315 − 98
    217

### Apply

Solve these problems.

32. The Washington Monument is 169 meters tall. The Great Pyramid is 32 meters shorter than the Washington Monument. How tall is the Great Pyramid?
137 meters

33. The Sears Tower is 443 meters tall. The Eiffel Tower is 322 meters tall. How much taller is the Sears Tower?
121 meters

Students may trade but forget to decrease the digit to the left after trading.

INCORRECT       CORRECT

                      13
   14̸12           6̸3̸12
   7̸4̸2̸           7̸4̸2̸
  −185           −185
  _____          _____
   667            557

Have students practice with exercises such as 100 − 14, where they use place-value materials to rename 100 as 10 tens and then rename one of the tens giving them 9 tens 10 ones.

## Enrichment

Put a tack in a small plastic bottle. Shake the bottle several times. Note that the tack lands either point up or point down. Ask if it is equally likely for the tack to land up or down. (It is not.) Give each student a small plastic bottle and a tack. Explain that they are to shake the bottle, recording the number of ups and downs in 50 trials. At the end they should explain whether they think point up or point down is most likely. (up)

## Practice

Have students complete the problems on the page. Remind them that it is very important to write legibly in problems that require several trades, not only when they copy the problem, but for each trade they write in.

## Mixed Practice

1. 65 − 23 (42)
2. $12.95 + 2.98 + 15.36 ($31.29)
3. 197 + 385 (582)
4. 3,278 + 5,929 (9,207)
5. 85 − 27 (58)
6. 23 + 35 + 48 + 63 (169)
7. 60 − 48 (12)
8. 78 − 28 (50)
9. 398 + 275 (673)
10. 43 − 8 (35)

## Extra Credit   *Biography*

Where did Halley's comet get its name? This spectacular ball of fire with a tail was discovered by Edmund Halley, a British scientist and mathematician who was born in 1656, and died in 1742. Halley was England's Astronomer Royal, and the Secretary of the Royal Society. Halley was especially interested in comets, and noted that a comet had appeared in almost the exact place in 1531, 1607 and 1682. He believed that these appearances were all the same comet travelling in an elliptical or oval orbit around the sun, once every seventy-six years. He then predicted that this comet would reappear in 1759. Halley did not live to see the comet's return, but scientists the world over who did, were convinced that his theory was right. Approximately every 76 years, Halley's comet travels close enough to Earth to be seen. When was the comet last seen? When will it visit us next?

# Zeros in Subtraction

**pages 69-70**

## Objective

To subtract, trading zeros in the minu-end

## Materials

hundred-sheets, ten-strips, and single counters
two dice
coin

## Mental Math

Have students supply the missing numbers:

1. 2 + __ +5 + 3 = 12 (2)
2. 4 + 7 + __ +1 = 15 (3)
3. 6 + 1 + 0 + __ =10 (3)
4. 5 + 5 + __ +4 = 14 (0)
5. 9 + 1 + __ +13 = 24 (1)
6. 4 + 3 + 4 + __ =21 (10)

## Skill Review

Have students make the trades:

1. 102 = 10 tens, 2 ones or __ tens, 12 ones (9)
2. 40 = 4 tens or 3 tens and __ ones (10)
3. 308 = 3 hundreds, 0 tens, 8 ones or 2 hundreds, __ tens, 8 ones (10)
4. 600 = 6 hundreds, 0 tens, 0 ones or __ hundreds, 9 tens, 10 ones (5)

---

## Zeros in Subtraction

The states of North and South Carolina both are bounded on the east by the Atlantic Ocean. How much longer is North Carolina's coastline than South Carolina's?

We are looking for how much longer North Carolina's coast is than South Carolina's.

The North Carolina coast is _301_ miles long.

South Carolina's coast is _187_ miles long.

To find the difference, we subtract _187_ from _301_.

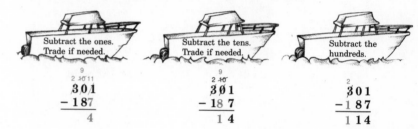

| Subtract the ones. Trade if needed. | Subtract the tens. Trade if needed. | Subtract the hundreds. |
|---|---|---|
| $$\begin{array}{r} 9 \\ 2\ \cancel{10}\ 11 \\ \cancel{3}\cancel{0}1 \\ -\ 1\ 8\ 7 \\ \hline 4 \end{array}$$ | $$\begin{array}{r} 9 \\ 2\ \cancel{10} \\ \cancel{3}\cancel{0}1 \\ -\ 1\ 8\ 7 \\ \hline 1\ 4 \end{array}$$ | $$\begin{array}{r} 2 \\ \cancel{3}\cancel{0}1 \\ -\ 1\ 8\ 7 \\ \hline 1\ 1\ 4 \end{array}$$ |

North Carolina has _114_ more miles of coastline.

### Getting Started

Subtract.

1. $$\begin{array}{r} 603 \\ -258 \\ \hline 345 \end{array}$$
2. $$\begin{array}{r} 700 \\ -217 \\ \hline 483 \end{array}$$
3. $$\begin{array}{r} 201 \\ -\ 83 \\ \hline 118 \end{array}$$
4. $$\begin{array}{r} 909 \\ -435 \\ \hline 474 \end{array}$$

5. $$\begin{array}{r} 509 \\ -318 \\ \hline 191 \end{array}$$
6. $$\begin{array}{r} 903 \\ -605 \\ \hline 298 \end{array}$$
7. $$\begin{array}{r} 820 \\ -299 \\ \hline 521 \end{array}$$
8. $$\begin{array}{r} 405 \\ -376 \\ \hline 29 \end{array}$$

Copy and subtract.

9. 804 − 685
119
10. 200 − 198
2
11. 303 − 172
131
12. 610 − 88
522

(sixty-nine) **69**

---

## Teaching the Lesson

**Introducing the Problem**   Read the problem aloud and ask students to identify the question. (how much longer is N.C's coastline than S.C.'s) Ask a student to read the information required from the map. (301 miles, 187 miles) Read the plan aloud and have volunteers supply the miles. (We subtract 187 from 301.) Write the problem on the board and illustrate the ones subtraction. Draw attention to the fact that when you need to trade for ten ones, you find a zero in the tens column. In this case it is necessary to trade 1 hundred for 10 tens before you trade 1 ten for 10 ones. Read the next stage and have a student show the next trade and subtract tens and hundreds. Have students transfer the answer to the solution sentence.

**Developing the Skill**   The zero presents a special problem because it means students will sometimes have to go over more than one place in order to trade. Write this problem on the board twice:

$$\begin{array}{r} 204 \\ -\ 36 \end{array} \qquad \begin{array}{r} 204 \\ -\ 36 \end{array} \qquad (168)$$

Explain that there are two ways to do this problem. They can treat the 204 like 20 tens and 4 ones as in the first version, or they can treat it like 2 hundreds, 0 tens, 4 ones as in the second example. Work through the trades in both cases on the board.

**69**

## Practice

Subtract.

1. 705 − 158 = 547
2. 302 − 146 = 156
3. 606 − 351 = 255
4. 500 − 396 = 104
5. 903 − 649 = 254
6. 802 − 356 = 446
7. 405 − 138 = 267
8. 603 − 427 = 176

## Copy and Do

9. 502 − 376
126
10. 903 − 658
245
11. 801 − 433
368
12. 700 − 95
605
13. 307 − 140
167
14. 607 − 409
198

## Apply

Solve these problems.

15. Mr. Lewin bought a stereo for $503. He gave the clerk a down payment of $218. How much does Mr. Lewin still owe on the stereo?
$285

16. It is 405 miles from Jim's home to his uncle's farm. It is 167 miles further to his grandfather's. How far does Jim live from his grandfather?
572 miles

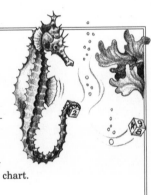

**EXCURSION**

Make two number cubes. Number the first cube from 1 through 6, and the second from 4 through 9. Roll the cubes and add the two numbers showing. This sum is called an **event.**

What is the lowest possible sum you can get? 5

What is the highest possible sum? 15

Make a chart of all the sums possible from rolling the cubes. Roll them 25 times. Record each event by making a tally mark next to the correct sum on the chart.
Answers will vary.

## Correcting Common Errors

Some students may subtract from left to right. Although it gives the correct answer when there is no renaming required, it is not a desirable habit. It will affect their answer when there is renaming. Remind them to operate with the ones first, and then the tens.

## Enrichment

Have students continue experiments concerning probability by flipping other items, as they did the coin, and record which side comes up more often. Ask them to explain why the probability of flipping heads or tails of a coin is equal, whereas point up or down for the tack is not. (The tack is not balanced; its head is heavier.) Extend the discussion to cover additional items they flipped, to see if their conclusion is proven.

## Practice

Have students work all problems on the page. Explain that they can use either of the two methods shown in class to work the problems.

## Excursion

Roll 2 dice and ask students to tell the sum of the 2 numbers. Tell students this sum is called an **event.** Have several students roll the dice and tell their events. Now have 2 students roll and tell who has the lowest and highest events. Ask students to tell the lowest and highest possible sums when rolling 2 dice. (2, 12)
Have students make the number cubes. Cubes can be made by writing numbers on blocks of wood, or by taping numbers over dice. Students should then answer the questions and make the chart. Tell students their answers will vary in their tallies.

## Extra Credit *Applications*

Tell students basketball, which began by a player shooting a ball into a peach basket, has three kinds of regular scores. List these on the board:

**a field goal = 2 points**
**a long field goal = 3 points**
**a free throw = 1 point**

Two teams are tied at 75 points each, with two minutes left in the game. Team one scores 3 regular field goals and two free throws. Team two scores one long field goal, one regular field goal and two free throws.
Which team won the game? (Team one) What was the final score? (83 to 82)

# Checking Subtraction

## pages 71-72

### Objective

To check 2- and 3-digit subtraction by addition

### Materials

hundred-sheets, ten-strips, and single counters

### Mental Math

Have students add 15 to each of these numbers:

1. 5  (20)
2. 21  (36)
3. (10 − 3)  (22)
4. (6 + 4)  (25)
5. (3 + 4 + 7)  (29)
6. (12 − 0)  (27)
7. 43 rounded to the nearest 10  (55)

### Skill Review

To remind students of how addition can be used to check subtraction, ask them to give you the problem to check each of these:

1. 12 − 5 = 7 (7 + 5 = 12)
2. 8 − 3 = 5 (5 + 3 = 8)
3. 40 − 10 = 30 (30 + 10 = 40)
4. 25 − 5 = 20 (20 + 5 = 25)
5. 19 − 8 = 11 (11 + 8 = 19)
6. 100 − 25 = 75 (75 + 25 = 100)
7. 44 − 22 = 22 (22 + 22 = 44)

---

### Checking Subtraction

The movie theater was filled with 585 people. At intermission 362 left, and 223 remained in their seats. The movie started, and everyone returned to their seats. Again there were 585 people in the audience.

There were __585__ people in the theater.

__362__ people went outside for intermission.

All __362__ return to their seats after the

break, so that __585__ people watch the second half of the movie.

We want to use these facts to show how we check a subtraction problem.

$$\begin{array}{r} 585 \\ -\,362 \\ \hline 223 \end{array} \qquad \begin{array}{r} 223 \\ +\,362 \\ \hline 585 \end{array}$$

To check subtraction, we use __addition__.

### Getting Started

Subtract. Check each problem by addition.

| 1. | 396<br>− 158<br>238 | 2. | 705<br>− 653<br>52 | 3. | 976<br>− 457<br>519 |
|---|---|---|---|---|---|
| 4. | 621<br>− 538<br>83 | 5. | 651<br>− 239<br>412 | 6. | 800<br>− 257<br>543 |
| 7. | 413<br>− 291<br>122 | 8. | 534<br>− 396<br>138 | 9. | 403<br>− 87<br>316 |

---

## Teaching the Lesson

**Introducing the Problem**  Have students read the problem. Ask how many people went to the movie (585) and how many left the theater at intermission. (362) Then ask how many people were watching the movie after the intermission. (585) Show them how the problems demonstrate subtraction and an addition check. Point out that to find the number of people remaining in the theater they would subtract the number who left (362) from the original number. (585) In order to find the number in the theater after the intermission, they must add the number who remained in their seats (223), to the number who left. (362) Reproduce these problems on the board and have students work them.

**Developing the Skill**  Have students take one ten-strip and arrange beneath it 4 single counters colored red and 6 singles colored blue. Write on the board: **4 + 6 = 10**. Move the red counters away and write: **10 − 4 = 6.** Explain that addition is the inverse of subtraction. The same set of counters can be used to illustrate either addition or subtraction. Now write **456 − 234** on the board and have a student do the subtraction. (222) Ask how they might check this problem. (by adding) Have a volunteer do the check on the board: 222 + 234. (456) Repeat other examples.

## Practice

Subtract. Check each problem by addition.

1.  583
   −276
   ⎯⎯
    307

2.  409
   −236
   ⎯⎯
    173

3.  755
   −349
   ⎯⎯
    406

4.  821
   −286
   ⎯⎯
    535

5.  726
   −658
   ⎯⎯
     68

6.  800
   −396
   ⎯⎯
    404

7.  637
   −281
   ⎯⎯
    356

8.  853
   −597
   ⎯⎯
    256

9.  795
   −236
   ⎯⎯
    559

10.  804
   −  28
   ⎯⎯
    776

11.  212
   −136
   ⎯⎯
     76

12.  587
   −235
   ⎯⎯
    352

13.  527
   −209
   ⎯⎯
    318

14.  602
   −479
   ⎯⎯
    123

15.  912
   −857
   ⎯⎯
     55

### EXCURSION

To do a quick check of subtraction, add the last two numbers and see if the sum is the same as the first number. Work these problems. Then do a quick check to see if they are right.

    534
   −147
   ⎯⎯
   +387
   ⎯⎯
    534

    536
   −245
   ⎯⎯
    291
   ⎯⎯
    536

    825
   −317
   ⎯⎯
    508
   ⎯⎯
    825

    203
   −172
   ⎯⎯
     31
   ⎯⎯
    203

    947
   −759
   ⎯⎯
    188
   ⎯⎯
    947

    764
   −352
   ⎯⎯
    412
   ⎯⎯
    764

    653
   −574
   ⎯⎯
     79
   ⎯⎯
    653

    425
   −246
   ⎯⎯
    179
   ⎯⎯
    425

    589
   −297
   ⎯⎯
    292
   ⎯⎯
    589

## Correcting Common Errors

Some students may get confused and simply add the minuend and subtrahend to check a subtraction problem. Have students work with partners and place-value materials to model a problem such as 237 − 125. Once they show 112 as the answer, have them add the place-value materials they have removed (125) to those left (112) to get those they started with (237).

## Enrichment

Show the group how they can check their subtraction without writing anything on the problem itself. Explain that they will simply add up. Write:

    672 ↑
   −252
   ⎯⎯
    420

Starting with ones they add 0 + 2 = 2; tens, 2 + 5 = 7; hundreds, 4 + 2 = 6. Let them practice checking without a pencil by doing a number of subtraction problems and checking each other's work.

## Practice

Have students complete the problems on the page. Explain that they are to write the addition check next to each subtraction problem.

## Excursion

Remind students that they have been writing a separate addition problem to check their subtraction. Tell students we can check subtraction quickly by drawing a line under the answer and find the sum of the difference and the subtrahend. Tell students they are to work the subtraction problems and then follow the model to check their work.

## Extra Credit   *Numeration*

Follow these directions, and look for patterns. Start with a single-digit number. Add 9 fifteen times to this number, listing the sum each time. Add the digits of each sum. If that sum is a two-digit number, add the digits again. Now, describe any patterns you discover in: the ones place, the tens place, the hundreds place, and in the sum of the digits of any number you wrote. Try this activity adding 8's or other single-digit addends. Describe the patterns. (the pattern will be counting backward by 1 in the ones column, forward by 1 in the tens column etc.; sum of the digits of the last sum is the beginning number)

# Subtracting 4-digit Numbers

**pages 73-74**

## Objective

To subtract 4-digit numbers

## Materials

## Mental Math

Ask students what the common answer is in two of each set of three problems:

1. $3 + 8$, $19 - 4$, $21 - 10$ (11)
2. $4 + 17$, $21 + 0$, $9 + 13$ (21)
3. $6 + 10$, $20 - 5$, $9 + 6$ (15)
4. $10 + 8$, $4 + 5 + 8$, $21 - 4$ (17)
5. $25 - 0$, $5 + 5 + 5 + 5 + 5$, $19 + 5$ (25)

## Skill Review

Remind students that there are times in subtracting 3-digit numbers that they must trade twice. Sometimes they will cross out a number already traded and substitute a new trade. Give the following problems to do, showing all trades.

1.
$$\begin{array}{r} 3\,9 \\ \cancel{4}\cancel{0}3 \\ -199 \\ \hline (204) \end{array}$$

2.
$$\begin{array}{r} 231 \\ -185 \\ \hline (46) \end{array}$$

3.
$$\begin{array}{r} 568 \\ -289 \\ \hline (279) \end{array}$$

4.
$$\begin{array}{r} 200 \\ -\phantom{0}79 \\ \hline (121) \end{array}$$

---

## Subtracting 4-digit Numbers

Many major cities in the United States have beautiful parks in them. How much larger is Pelham Bay Park than Lincoln Park?

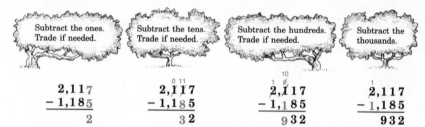

We want to find how much larger. Pelham Bay Park is.

Pelham Bay Park covers __2,117__ acres.

Lincoln Park takes up __1,185__ acres.
We can compare their sizes by using subtraction.

To find the difference, we subtract __1,185__ from __2,117__ .

| Subtract the ones. Trade if needed. | Subtract the tens. Trade if needed. | Subtract the hundreds. Trade if needed. | Subtract the thousands. |
|---|---|---|---|
| $\begin{array}{r} 2,11\overset{}{7} \\ -1,18\underset{}{5} \\ \hline 2 \end{array}$ | $\begin{array}{r} 2,1\overset{0\ 11}{1}7 \\ -1,1\underline{8}5 \\ \hline 3\,2 \end{array}$ | $\begin{array}{r} 2,\overset{1\ \cancel{0}}{1}17 \\ -1,\underline{1}85 \\ \hline 9\,3\,2 \end{array}$ | $\begin{array}{r} \overset{1}{2},117 \\ -1,185 \\ \hline 9\,3\,2 \end{array}$ |

Pelham Bay Park is __932__ acres larger.

### Getting Started

Subtract.

1.
$$\begin{array}{r} 5,438 \\ -2,684 \\ \hline 2,754 \end{array}$$

2.
$$\begin{array}{r} 8,843 \\ -4,578 \\ \hline 4,265 \end{array}$$

3.
$$\begin{array}{r} 9,214 \\ -3,587 \\ \hline 5,627 \end{array}$$

4.
$$\begin{array}{r} 3,276 \\ -1,485 \\ \hline 1,791 \end{array}$$

5.
$$\begin{array}{r} 7,534 \\ -6,657 \\ \hline 877 \end{array}$$

6.
$$\begin{array}{r} 8,264 \\ -1,865 \\ \hline 6,399 \end{array}$$

Copy and subtract.

7. $4,213 - 967$
3,246

8. $5,915 - 5,386$
529

9. $4,655 - 2,849$
1,806

(seventy-three) **73**

---

## Teaching the Lesson

**Introducing the Problem**  Read the problem aloud. Ask a volunteer to explain what the problem asks for and to find the needed information. (Pelham, 2,117 acres; Lincoln, 1,185 acres) Remind them of the comma that separates thousands and hundreds. Read the plan sentences aloud to the class while students complete the sentence. (subtract 1,185 from 2,117) Arrange the numbers on the board as a vertical subtraction problem and work through the problem as illustrated in the text. Ask different students to subtract ones, tens and hundreds, showing all trades. Ask the class to do the thousands subtraction with you $(1 - 1 = 0)$ and then read the answer (932) aloud while students write it in the solution sentence.

**Developing the Skill**  Ask the students to tell you how many ones there are in ten (10), tens in one hundred (10), and hundreds in one thousand (10). Explain that this consistency makes it easy to subtract any number of digits using the same rules that they have applied in 3-digit subtraction. Point out that they must be careful to leave room above each problem so that they can write any trades legibly. Write at least two 4-digit subtraction problems on the board, avoiding zeros in the minuend. Work the problems on the board while the students do them on paper.

Subtract.

| 1. 6,825<br>− 1,384<br>5,441 | 2. 4,326<br>− 1,598<br>2,728 | 3. 8,754<br>− 139<br>8,615 |
| 4. 2,391<br>− 1,836<br>555 | 5. 3,791<br>− 2,118<br>1,673 | 6. 9,213<br>− 3,654<br>5,559 |
| 7. 5,186<br>− 1,392<br>3,794 | 8. 4,528<br>− 4,236<br>292 | 9. 8,286<br>− 6,395<br>1,891 |
| 10. 7,526<br>− 3,867<br>3,659 | 11. 9,215<br>− 1,863<br>7,352 | 12. 1,265<br>− 848<br>417 |

**Copy and Do**

13. 8,275 − 826
7,449
14. 3,216 − 2,148
1,068
15. 7,217 − 4,328
2,889
16. 4,376 − 1,111
3,265
17. 6,370 − 2,342
4,028
18. 5,888 − 1,189
4,699
19. 9,235 − 6,562
2,673
20. 8,256 − 98
8,158
21. 4,324 − 2,875
1,449
22. 3,516 − 3,047
469
23. 7,911 − 4,555
3,356
24. 5,923 − 3,010
2,913
25. 7,296 − 3,468
3,828
26. 5,608 − 1,909
3,699
27. 9,275 − 8,588
687

**Apply**

Use the chart to solve these problems.

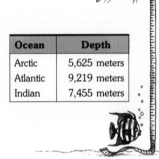

28. How much deeper is the Indian Ocean than the Arctic Ocean?
1,830 meters

29. How much deeper is the Atlantic Ocean than the Arctic Ocean?
3,594 meters

| Ocean | Depth |
|---|---|
| Arctic | 5,625 meters |
| Atlantic | 9,219 meters |
| Indian | 7,455 meters |

**74** (seventy-four)

## Correcting Common Errors

Some students may rename when they do not have to. Remind them to ask each time they subtract; "Do I have enough ones? tens? hundreds? thousands?" Only when the answer is "no" do they rename.

## Enrichment

Tell students to use the subtraction check of adding upwards and doing the trading mentally to check each other's practice problems, doing every other one for numbers 1 through 15. No pencil marks should be made.

## Practice

Have students work all the problems on the page. Remind them to write each trade carefully.

## Mixed Practice

1. 7,258 + 376 + 481 (8,115)
2. 656 − 283 (373)
3. $1.58 + 12.37 + 4.36 ($18.31)
4. 48 − 26 (22)
5. 350 − 160 (190)
6. 865 − 223 (642)
7. 14 + 136 + 395 (545)
8. 4,209 + 3,656 (7,865)
9. 182 − 58 (124)
10. 847 + 353 (1,200)

## Extra Credit  *Numeration*

At the top of the board write from 0 to 9. Below each number write a random symbol. Then write a group of subtraction and addition problems on the board, using the symbols you have chosen in place of the numbers. Have students come to the board and work the problems, also putting their answers in code. Extend the activity by allowing students to make up their own problems for other students to work.

# Subtracting Money

## pages 75-76

## Objective

To subtract money up to 4-digits

## Materials

## Mental Math

Dictate the following word problems:

1. Amy is on page 90 of a library book with 150 pages. The book is due in a week. How many pages does she have to read before she returns the book? (60)
2. If she reads everyday, except Sunday, how many pages does she have to read each day? (60 pages, 6 days, 10 pages/day)
3. Sadly, Amy didn't read fast enough and the book was 3 days overdue. The fine is 5¢ per day. How much did she owe? (15¢)

## Skill Review

Ask students how many pennies there are in a dime (10), dimes in a dollar (10). Ask how money is like the other numbers. (Each place value is a multiple of 10.) Dictate amounts of money and have students write them on paper. Watch for dollar signs and decimal points.

---

## Subtracting Money

Paula was given $20 for her birthday. She plans to use the money to buy a blouse. How much change will she receive?

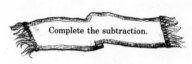

We want to see how much change Paula will receive.

She has <u>$20.00</u> to spend.

The blouse costs <u>$17.59</u>.
To find how much money is left, we subtract

<u>$17.59</u> from <u>$20.00</u>.

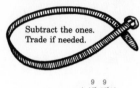

Subtract the ones. Trade if needed.

Complete the subtraction.

$$\begin{array}{r} \overset{9\ \ 9}{1\ \cancel{10}\ \cancel{10}\ 10} \\ \$2\cancel{0}.\cancel{0}0 \\ -\ 17.59 \\ \hline 1 \end{array} \qquad \begin{array}{r} \overset{9\ \ 9}{1\ \cancel{10}\ \cancel{10}} \\ \$2\cancel{0}.\cancel{0}0 \\ -\ 17.59 \\ \hline \$\ 2.41 \end{array}$$

Paula will receive <u>$2.41</u> in change.

## Getting Started

Subtract.

| | | |
|---|---|---|
| 1. $8.05<br>− 3.86<br>$4.19 | 2. $6.00<br>− 4.75<br>$1.25 | 3. $87.00<br>− 19.39<br>$67.61 |
| 4. $27.15<br>− 9.38<br>$17.77 | 5. $36.00<br>− 21.56<br>$14.44 | 6. $10.00<br>− 3.50<br>$6.50 |

Copy and subtract.

7. $25.15 − $13.89
$11.26

8. $75.00 − $29.79
$45.21

9. $86.30 − $29.55
$56.75

(seventy-five) **75**

---

## Teaching the Lesson

**Introducing the Problem**  Have students read and identify the problem. Ask students to locate the needed information. ($20 to spend, blouse costs $17.59) Now read the plan sentences and have students fill in the blanks. (We subtract $17.59 from $20.00.) Have a student copy the problem on the board as it is shown in the text. Explain that subtracting money is the same as subtracting any other 4-digit number. Have volunteers complete the subtraction one column at a time while the class follows in their texts. Read the solution sentence aloud while students fill in the answer. ($2.41)

**Developing the Skill**  Write **$14.99 equals 1,499 pennies** on the board. Tell the class that you want them to subtract 945 pennies from the amount on the board. Let them do the subtraction and have a volunteer write the answer on the board. (554 pennies) Write **554 pennies equals $5.54.** Explain that while students will have to keep track of the decimal point, the decimal point does not affect trading for ones or tens. Write **$37.25 − 9.75** on the board. Help students share another problem with the class, working it first in pennies and then in dollars.

**75**

Subtract.

| | | |
|---|---|---|
| 1. $9.00<br>− 2.37<br>$6.63 | 2. $7.56<br>− 0.29<br>$7.27 | 3. $8.50<br>− 2.78<br>$5.72 |
| 4. $18.39<br>− 6.87<br>$11.52 | 5. $37.68<br>− 9.89<br>$27.79 | 6. $52.00<br>− 8.36<br>$43.64 |
| 7. $39.24<br>− 15.96<br>$23.28 | 8. $42.36<br>− 29.84<br>$12.52 | 9. $85.35<br>− 19.19<br>$66.16 |

### Copy and Do

10. $84.60 − $29.39
$55.21

11. $36.43 − $19.26
$17.17

12. $93.24 − $57.85
$35.39

13. $67.23 − $28.25
$38.98

14. $72.00 − $29.09
$42.91

15. $96.29 − $27.58
$68.71

### Apply

Solve these problems.

16. Devin bought a club sweatshirt for $14.56, and a jacket for $29.85. How much more did Devin spend on the jacket?
$15.29

17. Natalie has saved $20 to buy records. She chooses one record for $7.53 and one for $8.79. How much money does Natalie have left?
$3.68

---

**EXCURSION**

The sum is not correct in each problem. Find the correct sum and write it on the blank below. Then find the addend that was left out and circle it.

| 1. $2.13<br>(1.75)<br>5.23<br>+ 3.40<br>$10.76<br>$12.51 | 2. $3.02<br>1.38<br>(4.27)<br>+ 2.33<br>$6.73<br>$11.00 | 3. ($1.79)<br>2.83<br>0.85<br>+ 1.23<br>$4.91<br>$6.70 |
|---|---|---|

---

## Correcting Common Errors

Some students may forget to write the dollar sign and cents point in the answer. Discuss how when they are subtracting money, writing the dollar sign and cents point shows this. You may wish to ask them to write the dollar sign and cents point first, before they subtract.

## Enrichment

1. The ability to estimate, or guess, is a very important one in mathematics. Have students mentally estimate how many of each of the following things they could buy with $1.00.

1. yogurt cups at 33¢ each (3)
2. tablets at 17¢ each (5)
3. pencils at 4¢ each (25)
4. cartons of milk at 15¢ each (6)
5. pens at 89¢ each (1)
6. gum balls at 3 for 49¢ (6)

---

## Practice

Have students complete the problems on the page. Remind them to keep their decimal points in a straight line and to express their answers with dollar signs.

## Excursion

Ask students how to find which of the addends was left out in the first problem. (add the column again and subtract each amount from it until the incorrect sum is found) Ask students if they can think of a faster way. (subtract the incorrect sum from the correct sum) Have students find and circle the omitted amount in each problem.

## Extra Credit   Logic

Explain that students are going to use the letter W to mean "weighs more than." Ask a volunteer to come to the board and write this sentence in an abbreviated form: the truck weighs more than the dog. (tWd) Ask a third to write a sentence that compares the truck and the cup. (tWc)
Dictate or write these sentences on the board. Ask students to write abbreviated sentences for each:

1. The melon weighs more than the orange. (mWo)
2. The orange weighs more than the strawberry. (oWs)
3. Compare the strawberry and the melon. (mWs)

Have students treat these sentences the same way:

1. The station wagon weighs more than the car. (sWc)
2. The station wagon weighs less than the truck. (tWs)
3. Compare the truck and the car. (tWc)

# Estimating Differences

## Objective

To estimate in subtraction

## Materials

## Mental Math

Dictate these problems to the class:

1. $1,200 - 400 = (800)$
2. $1,000 - 100 - 300 = (600)$
3. $1,500 + 500 + 200 = (2,200)$
4. $300 + 500 - 200 = (600)$
5. $800 - 200 + 500 = (1,100)$
6. $150 + 250 = (400)$
7. $250 + 250 - 100 = (400)$

## Skill Review

Remind students of the way we round numbers to the nearest ten, hundred, or dollar in order to estimate or check our work. Write these numbers on the board and have students round to the

1. nearest ten: **46** (50), **78** (80), **33** (30), and **156** (160)
2. nearest hundred: **449** (400), **358** (400), **821** (800) and **89** (100)
3. nearest dollar: **$23.60** ($24), **$58.91** ($59), and **$33.28** ($33)

---

## Estimating Differences

The goals of the Apollo space project were to orbit the moon, and land a man on it. About how many more orbits around the moon did Apollo 18 make than Apollo 17?

| Apollo–Saturn 7 | 163 orbits |
|---|---|
| Apollo–Saturn 9 | 151 orbits |
| Apollo–Saturn 17 | 75 orbits |
| Apollo–Saturn 18 | 136 orbits |

We need to estimate the difference between the number of orbits.

Apollo 18 made __136__ orbits.

Apollo 17 made __75__ orbits.
To estimate the difference, we round each number to the nearest ten, and subtract.

$$
\begin{array}{rcr}
136 & \to & 140 \\
75 & \to & -\ 80 \\
\hline
& & 60
\end{array}
$$

Apollo 18 made about __60__ more orbits than Apollo 17.

### Getting Started

Estimate the difference by rounding each number to the nearest ten.

| 1. | 78 | 80 | 2. | 53 | 50 | 3. | 41 | 40 | 4. | 85 | 90 |
|---|---|---|---|---|---|---|---|---|---|---|---|
| | − 36 | − 40 | | − 27 | − 30 | | − 19 | − 20 | | − 44 | − 40 |
| | | 40 | | | 20 | | | 20 | | | 50 |

Estimate the difference by rounding each number to the nearest hundred.

| 5. | 768 | 800 | 6. | 478 | 500 | 7. | 750 | 800 |
|---|---|---|---|---|---|---|---|---|
| | − 245 | − 200 | | − 112 | − 100 | | − 325 | − 300 |
| | | 600 | | | 400 | | | 500 |

Estimate the difference by rounding each number to the nearest dollar.

| 8. | $26.45 | $26 | 9. | $56.48 | $56 | 10. | $84.57 | $85 |
|---|---|---|---|---|---|---|---|---|
| | − 13.21 | − 13 | | − 23.75 | − 24 | | − 51.85 | − 52 |
| | | $13 | | | $32 | | | $33 |

(seventy-seven) **77**

---

## Teaching the Lesson

**Introducing the Problem** Have students read the problem and identify the question and locate the necessary information. (Apollo 18, 136; Apollo 17, 75) Read the plan sentences aloud and explain that the use of the word **about** in the text of the problem, requires that they estimate the number of orbits and subtract. Point to the estimations already made in the model and copy them on the board. Subtract the problem and have students write the answer in the solution sentence in their texts.

**Developing the Skill** Ask the class how much change Joel will receive from $20 when he buys a football that costs $14.75? Have a volunteer explain how the problem can be done. (round $14.75 to $15 and subtract from $20) Write the problem on the board and have a student do the subtraction. ($5) Explain that every time they are asked for an approximate answer, they will first round the numbers involved. Point out that they must be careful to round to the number indicated: to tens, or hundreds, or dollars. Remind them that it is possible to round one number in different ways. Have them round 156 to tens (160), to hundreds (200) and to thousands (0). Have students suggest numbers to be rounded to tens, hundreds, and thousands.

Estimate the difference by rounding each number to the nearest ten.

1.  $\begin{array}{r} 59 \\ -26 \\ \hline \end{array}$  $\begin{array}{r} 60 \\ -30 \\ \hline 30 \end{array}$   2.  $\begin{array}{r} 78 \\ -24 \\ \hline \end{array}$  $\begin{array}{r} 80 \\ -20 \\ \hline 60 \end{array}$   3.  $\begin{array}{r} 92 \\ -56 \\ \hline \end{array}$  $\begin{array}{r} 90 \\ -60 \\ \hline 30 \end{array}$   4.  $\begin{array}{r} 57 \\ -23 \\ \hline \end{array}$  $\begin{array}{r} 60 \\ -20 \\ \hline 40 \end{array}$

5.  $\begin{array}{r} 73 \\ -52 \\ \hline \end{array}$  $\begin{array}{r} 70 \\ -50 \\ \hline 20 \end{array}$   6.  $\begin{array}{r} 87 \\ -38 \\ \hline \end{array}$  $\begin{array}{r} 90 \\ -40 \\ \hline 50 \end{array}$   7.  $\begin{array}{r} 42 \\ -29 \\ \hline \end{array}$  $\begin{array}{r} 40 \\ -30 \\ \hline 10 \end{array}$   8.  $\begin{array}{r} 62 \\ -19 \\ \hline \end{array}$  $\begin{array}{r} 60 \\ -20 \\ \hline 40 \end{array}$

Estimate the difference by rounding each number to the nearest hundred.

9.  $\begin{array}{r} 376 \\ -126 \\ \hline \end{array}$  $\begin{array}{r} 400 \\ -100 \\ \hline 300 \end{array}$   10.  $\begin{array}{r} 875 \\ -350 \\ \hline \end{array}$  $\begin{array}{r} 900 \\ -400 \\ \hline 500 \end{array}$   11.  $\begin{array}{r} 625 \\ -516 \\ \hline \end{array}$  $\begin{array}{r} 600 \\ -500 \\ \hline 100 \end{array}$

12.  $\begin{array}{r} 646 \\ -429 \\ \hline \end{array}$  $\begin{array}{r} 600 \\ -400 \\ \hline 200 \end{array}$   13.  $\begin{array}{r} 556 \\ -210 \\ \hline \end{array}$  $\begin{array}{r} 600 \\ -200 \\ \hline 400 \end{array}$   14.  $\begin{array}{r} 889 \\ -846 \\ \hline \end{array}$  $\begin{array}{r} 900 \\ -800 \\ \hline 100 \end{array}$

15.  $\begin{array}{r} 775 \\ -121 \\ \hline \end{array}$  $\begin{array}{r} 800 \\ -100 \\ \hline 700 \end{array}$   16.  $\begin{array}{r} 909 \\ -119 \\ \hline \end{array}$  $\begin{array}{r} 900 \\ -100 \\ \hline 800 \end{array}$   17.  $\begin{array}{r} 529 \\ -383 \\ \hline \end{array}$  $\begin{array}{r} 500 \\ -400 \\ \hline 100 \end{array}$

Estimate the difference by rounding each number to the nearest dollar.

18.  $\begin{array}{r} \$9.86 \\ -6.15 \\ \hline \end{array}$  $\begin{array}{r} \$10 \\ -6 \\ \hline \$4 \end{array}$   19.  $\begin{array}{r} \$42.57 \\ -8.75 \\ \hline \end{array}$  $\begin{array}{r} \$43 \\ -9 \\ \hline \$34 \end{array}$   20.  $\begin{array}{r} \$36.25 \\ -15.18 \\ \hline \end{array}$  $\begin{array}{r} \$36 \\ -15 \\ \hline \$21 \end{array}$

21.  $\begin{array}{r} \$74.39 \\ -55.45 \\ \hline \end{array}$  $\begin{array}{r} \$74 \\ -55 \\ \hline \$19 \end{array}$   22.  $\begin{array}{r} \$86.28 \\ -39.85 \\ \hline \end{array}$  $\begin{array}{r} \$86 \\ -40 \\ \hline \$46 \end{array}$   23.  $\begin{array}{r} \$65.00 \\ -21.38 \\ \hline \end{array}$  $\begin{array}{r} \$65 \\ -21 \\ \hline \$44 \end{array}$

24.  $\begin{array}{r} \$10.81 \\ -9.40 \\ \hline \end{array}$  $\begin{array}{r} \$11 \\ -9 \\ \hline \$2 \end{array}$   25.  $\begin{array}{r} \$87.25 \\ -62.00 \\ \hline \end{array}$  $\begin{array}{r} \$87 \\ -62 \\ \hline \$25 \end{array}$   26.  $\begin{array}{r} \$72.42 \\ -11.27 \\ \hline \end{array}$  $\begin{array}{r} \$72 \\ -11 \\ \hline \$61 \end{array}$

## Correcting Common Errors

Some students may estimate incorrectly because they round incorrectly. Use a number line to estimate the answer to 58 − 32 by rounding. Show 30, 40, 50, and 60 on the number line and have students discuss whether the point for 58 is closer to 50 or 60 and whether the point for 32 is closer to 30 or 40. Then have them use the numbers they chose to estimate the answer: 60 − 30 = 30.

## Enrichment

Have students estimate the following numbers and then check them for accuracy. The school library will be able to help.

1. number of students in each grade level in their school
2. number of students in their school
3. number of students in their school district

## Practice

Have students work the problems on the page. Remind them to read the instructions for each section carefully and not to forget the dollar sign in problems involving money.

## Mixed Practice

1. 608 − 259 (349)
2. 216 + 483 + 207 (906)
3. 1,287 + 6,924 (8,211)
4. 68 − 24 (44)
5. 320 − 176 (144)
6. $15.96 + 0.83 ($16.79)
7. 5 + 8 + 6 + 7 (26)
8. 827 − 763 (64)
9. 653 − 84 (569)
10. $52.27 + 3.98 + 0.42 ($56.67)

## Extra Credit  *Numeration*

Give each student an envelope with small countable objects, such as paper clips. Have them sit on the floor in small groups. Choose one student in each group to be the first counter. Tell the students that when you say start, they are to put as many paper clips in the palm of their hand as they want, and hold it out. Ask the counter to make an immediate estimate of the total number of paper clips shown and write it down. Now ask the counter to add the total number of paper clips actually shown, and find the difference between that total and their estimated total. That is their score. Rotate counters so each student can earn points.

# Problem Solving, Choosing the Operation

**pages 79-80**

## Objective

Choosing the operation to solve a problem

## Materials

## Mental Math

Have students supply the missing numbers:

1. 13 − __ = 8 (5)
2. 5 + __ = 36 (31)
3. __ − 14 = 22 (36)
4. 20 + __ = 45 (25)
5. 21 − __ = 14 (7)
6. __ + 6 = 20 (14)
7. 15 − __ = 0 (15)

## Skill Review

Have students decide what operations the following phrases suggest:

1. how many all together (addition)
2. how many more (subtraction)
3. how much farther (subtraction)
4. how much for both (addition)
5. how many are left (subtraction)
6. how many in all (addition)

---

## Choosing the Operation

The Hanijosa family drove from San Francisco to New York City to attend a family reunion.

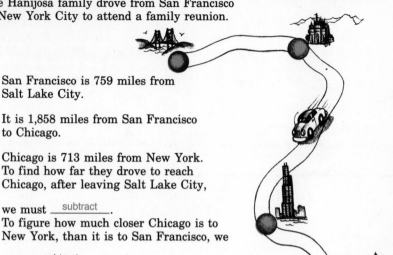

San Francisco is 759 miles from Salt Lake City.

It is 1,858 miles from San Francisco to Chicago.

Chicago is 713 miles from New York. To find how far they drove to reach Chicago, after leaving Salt Lake City,

we must __subtract__.
To figure how much closer Chicago is to New York, than it is to San Francisco, we

must __subtract__.
To find the total distance of the trip from

San Francisco to New York, we must __add__.

### Getting Started

Write the operation.

1. How much higher is Alabama's greatest elevation, than the highest point in Illinois?
   subtract

2. If you know how many merit points the third grade earned in November, and then in January, how do you find the number of points earned in both months together?
   add

Write the operation and solve.

3. Rich had $10.00. He spent $4.75. How much does he have left?
   subtract          $5.25

4. A ball costs $11.59. A bat costs $27.50. How much does it cost to buy the ball and bat?
   add          $39.09

(seventy-nine) **79**

---

## Teaching the Lesson

**Introducing the Problem**  Read the first sentence aloud while the class examines the map. Have students read the next three sentences. Students may insert number of miles on the map. Explain that now they have the information to answer several questions. Read the first one from the text and ask how to solve it. (subtract) Have a student read the second question and tell the operation required. (subtraction) Have another student read the last sentence and pick out the words that indicate the operation (total distance) and identify the operation. (addition) Tell students to write the operations in their books.

**Developing the Skill**  Explain that in doing word problems, it is important to find the words in each problem that give the clue to the operation required. Point out that in this lesson they explain the operation they would use before they actually do a problem. Have students make up problems that use the following phrases, and then explain how they would solve it: how many all together (add), how many more (subtract), how many left (subtract), find the total (add), how many fewer (subtract) and how much further. (subtract)

## Practice

Write the operation.

1. How do you find how much more Pierre weighs than Gary?

subtract

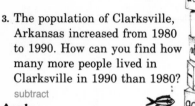

2. If you know how far Lee's mother drove on Monday and Tuesday of their trip, how do you find how far she drove both days?

add

3. The population of Clarksville, Arkansas increased from 1980 to 1990. How can you find how many more people lived in Clarksville in 1990 than 1980?

subtract

4. If Emile bought a shirt with a $20 bill, how can you find how much change he would get back?

subtract

## Apply

Write the operation and solve.

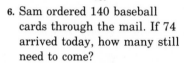

5. Mr. Lance had to pay $2.75 to get into the zoo. His son had to pay only $1.45. How much did they pay all together?

add     $4.20

6. Sam ordered 140 baseball cards through the mail. If 74 arrived today, how many still need to come?

subtract     66 cards

7. Chuck and Sal have babysitting jobs. In one week Chuck earned $10.50, while Sal earned $13.75. How much more did Sal earn?

subtract     $3.25

8. If 1,248 of the 2,000 tickets have been sold, how many still need to be sold?

subtract     752 tickets

9. Carrie dug 38 potatoes at the truck farm. Her sister dug 21 and her mother dug 45. How many potatoes did they harvest all together?

add     104 potatoes

10. Potatoes in the grocery store sell for $1.39 a pound. The potatoes dug at the truck farm sell for $0.68 a pound. How much did Carrie's mother save per pound of potatoes at the truck farm?

subtract     $0.71

**80** (eighty)

## Correcting Common Errors

Some students may have difficulty deciding which operation to use. Have them work with partners, reading each problem and choosing the phrase that tells them what operation to perform. Have them use one sheet of paper to list the phrases that suggest addition and another to list those that suggest subtraction. Next, have them go back and work the problems.

## Enrichment

Write the following numbers and operations on the board. Tell students to write a problem for each set of numbers using the indicated operation.

1. **375, 921, 38**     addition
2. **$42.81, $22.45**     subtraction
3. **845, 241, 345**     addition
4. **5, 10, 6, 8**     addition
5. **$57.90, $42.30**     rounding and addition

## Practice

Have students do the problems on the page. Remind them to look for the word or phrase that describes the operation required. Explain that in some of the problems they are to write the operation only and do not need to actually work the problem.

## Extra Credit   *Applications*

Tell the class their family vacation this year will be to go camping. What things would they need to buy that they don't already have? Using a catalog, tell them to make a list of the necessary equipment, and beside each item, the price. Tell students to add up the prices to find how expensive their camping trip would be. Have students compare costs, because not every family would need to buy the same equipment.

# More Calculator Codes

## pages 81-82

### Objective

To use calculators for subtraction

### Materials

calculators

### Mental Math

Dictate the following word problems:

1. Caroline walks 3 blocks to school. On Tuesdays she goes 2 blocks further to a piano lesson after school. How far does she walk all together on Tuesday? (5 blocks)
2. Gloria is bringing cookies to a school party. She needs 35 cookies and the kind she likes has 18 in each bag. How many bags does she need to bring? (2 bags)

### Skill Review

Have a student draw the calculator number keys on the board. (0 through 9) Have another draw the operation keys. ($+, -, \times, \div, =$) Finally, have a student show the two special keys. (C, CE) Ask what each of the operation keys and special keys does. Then ask how to enter a number with more than one digit. (one digit at a time, reading from left to right)

---

**More Calculator Codes**

Nancy and Zack are doing math activities on the computer. Who has the higher score? How many more points does that person have?

We need to find the total score for each.

We know Nancy has scored __516__ and __296__.

Zack's scores are __345__ and __449__.

Nancy 516 ⊞ 296 ⊟ ( 812 )

Zack   345 ⊞ 449 ⊟ ( 794 )

We want to compare the two scores.

__794__ ⊘ __812__

__Nancy__ has the higher score.

We can also compare their scores by subtraction.

812 ⊟ 794 ⊟ ( 18 )

__Nancy__ has __18__ more points.

Addition and subtraction can be combined on the calculator. Enter this code and write the answer.

652 ⊞ 835 ⊟ 715 ⊟ ( 772 )

Now enter this code and write the answer.

891 ⊟ 348 ⊞ 515 ⊟ ( 1058 )

(eighty-one) **81**

---

## Teaching the Lesson

**Introducing the Problem**  Read the problem and ask students to identify the questions asked. Have students read the information sentences, filling in the data required. (Zack, 345 and 449; Nancy, 516 and 296) Read the plan sentence and draw the addition codes on the board for the class. (**345** ⊞ **449** ⊟ ; **516** ⊞ **296** ⊟) Ask students to do the problems on their calculators. (812, 794) Read the next part of the plan and tell students to fill in the numbers and an inequality sign. (794 < 812) Ask who has the higher score. (Nancy) Have students complete the first solution sentence and now compare the two scores by subtraction. Show the problem as a subtraction code on the board. (**812** ⊟ **794** ⊟) Have students calculate the answer. (18) The models at the bottom show how problems combining addition and subtraction can be done. Have students enter the codes and write the answers. (772, 1,058)

**Developing the Skill**  Write this calculator problem on the board: **34** ⊞ **117** ⊟ **45** ⊟. Ask a student to write the same problem in two steps in the conventional way. (34 + 117 = 151, 151 − 45 = 106) Tell students to do the problem on their calculator and compare the two methods. (Calculator is faster. Written work allows them to check that numbers are correct.) Point out that the calculator can be used to check written work, or a written estimate could be used to check the calculator.

**81**

**Practice**

Enter these codes. Show the results on the screens.

1. 24 $\boxed{-}$ 18 $\boxed{+}$ 7 $\boxed{=}$ ( 13 )

2. 436 $\boxed{+}$ 85 $\boxed{-}$ 278 $\boxed{=}$ ( 243 )

3. 796 $\boxed{-}$ 437 $\boxed{+}$ 496 $\boxed{=}$ ( 855 )

4. 903 $\boxed{+}$ 358 $\boxed{-}$ 876 $\boxed{=}$ ( 385 )

5. 217 $\boxed{+}$ 536 $\boxed{-}$ 391 $\boxed{=}$ ( 362 )

6. 986 $\boxed{+}$ 437 $\boxed{-}$ 286 $\boxed{=}$ ( 1137 )

Use your calculator to find each difference. Use estimation to check your answer.

7.
```
  826
- 415
-----
  411
```

8.
```
  914
- 326
-----
  588
```

9.
```
  750
- 185
-----
  565
```

**Apply**

Use your calculator to solve these problems.

10. Manuela had 312 coins. Her dad gave her 572 from his collection. Then she gave 216 of hers to her brother. How many coins does Manuela have left?
668 coins

11. Ron collected 375 aluminum cans on Monday, 256 on Tuesday, and 196 on Friday. He wants to collect 900 cans altogether. How many more does he need?
73 cans

Use the graph to answer these questions.

12. How many more cans did Mary and Jan collect together, than Tam?
200 more cans

13. How many cans did the three girls collect?
900 cans

**Aluminum Cans**

```
400
350
300
250
200
150
100
 50
    Mary  Jan  Tam
       Collectors
```

Write the operation that makes each code correct.

14. 6 $\boxed{+}$ 4 $\boxed{-}$ 5 $\boxed{+}$ 2 $\boxed{=}$ ( 7 )

15. 45 $\boxed{-}$ 23 $\boxed{+}$ 3 $\boxed{-}$ 15 $\boxed{=}$ ( 10 )

82 (eighty-two)

82

# Chapter Test

page 83

| Item | Objective |
|------|-----------|
| 1-4 | Subtract 2-digit numbers with one regrouping (See pages 63-64) |
| 5-12 | Subtract 3-digit numbers with one or two regroupings (See pages 65-68) |
| 13-16 | Subtract 4-digit numbers (See pages 73-74) |
| 17-20 | Round numbers to the nearest 10 and subtract (See pages 77-78) |
| 21-23 | Round numbers to the nearest 100 and subtract (See pages 77-78) |
| 24-26 | Round addends to the nearest dollar and subtract (See pages 77-78) |

Subtract.

1.  96
   − 23
   ――
    73

2.  85
   − 21
   ――
    64

3.  73
   − 28
   ――
    45

4.  52
   − 19
   ――
    33

5.  526
   − 315
   ―――
    211

6.  826
   − 419
   ―――
    407

7.  621
   − 274
   ―――
    347

8.  924
   − 657
   ―――
    267

9.  509
   − 108
   ―――
    401

10.  804
   − 329
   ―――
    475

11.  700
   − 251
   ―――
    449

12.  905
   − 268
   ―――
    637

13.  6,725
   − 1,319
   ―――――
    5,406

14.  7,215
   − 3,852
   ―――――
    3,363

15.  3,321
   − 1,876
   ―――――
    1,445

16.  9,510
   − 3,854
   ―――――
    5,656

Estimate the difference by rounding each number to the nearest ten.

17.  58    60
   − 26  − 30
   ――  ――
         30

18.  71    70
   − 37  − 40
   ――  ――
         30

19.  45    50
   − 25  − 30
   ――  ――
         20

20.  83    80
   − 19  − 20
   ――  ――
         60

Estimate the difference by rounding each number to the nearest hundred.

21.  523    500
   − 296  − 300
   ―――  ―――
          200

22.  750    800
   − 385  − 400
   ―――  ―――
          400

23.  949    900
   − 527  − 500
   ―――  ―――
          400

Estimate the difference by rounding each number to the nearest dollar.

24.  $27.38    $27
   −  9.75  −  10
   ―――――  ―――
            $17

25.  $38.87    $39
   −  21.50  −  22
   ―――――  ―――
            $17

26.  $57.85    $58
   −  29.35  −  29
   ―――――  ―――
            $29

(eighty-three) **83**

**83**

Circle the letter of the correct answer.

**1** 739 ◯ 736
- ⓐ >
- b <

**2** Round 652 to the nearest hundred.
- a 500
- b 600
- ⓒ NG

**3** What is the value of the 6 in 326,489?
- a tens
- ⓑ thousands
- c ten thousands
- d NG

**4** 76
+ 18
- a 914
- ⓑ 94
- c 84
- d NG

**5** 256
+ 385
- a 741
- b 531
- ⓒ 641
- d NG

**6** $82.96
+ 15.89
- a $98.84
- b $98.86
- c $97.85
- ⓓ NG

**7** 3,250
786
+ 75
- a 4,101
- b 4,011
- ⓒ 4,111
- d NG

**8** Round each number to the nearest hundred and add.
428
+ 367
- ⓐ 800
- b 700
- c 600
- d NG

**9** In the problem 87 + 65 = 152, what is the 152 called?
- a difference
- b addend
- ⓒ sum
- d NG

**10** 723
− 187
- a 664
- b 646
- c 636
- ⓓ NG

**11** 903
− 254
- a 751
- ⓑ 649
- c 559
- d NG

**12** $27.38
− 18.87
- a $18.41
- b $8.41
- c $11.51
- ⓓ NG

**13** Round each number to the nearest ten and subtract.
86
− 27
- ⓐ 60
- b 70
- c 50
- d NG

☐ score

# Cumulative Review
## page 84

| Item | Objective |
|---|---|
| 1 | Compare numbers less than 1,000 (See pages 27-28) |
| 2 | Round to the nearest 100 (See pages 31-32) |
| 3 | Identify the value of a digit in a number less than 1,000,000 (See pages 35-36) |
| 4 | Add two 2-digit addends with one regrouping (See pages 39-40) |
| 5 | Add two 3-digit addends with two regroupings (See pages 45-46) |
| 6 | Add dollars and cents with regrouping (See pages 51-52) |
| 7 | Add three or four numbers (See pages 49-50) |
| 8 | Round addends to the nearest 100 and add (See pages 53-56) |
| 9 | Understand the terms addend and sum (See pages 1-2) |
| 10-11 | Subtract two 3-digit numbers with two regroupings (See pages 67-68) |
| 12 | Subtract dollars and cents with regrouping (See pages 75-76) |
| 13 | Round numbers to the nearest 10 and subtract (See pages 77-78) |

## Alternate Cumulative Review

Circle the letter of the correct answer.

**1** 626 ◯ 627
- a >
- ⓑ <
- c =

**2** Round 727 to the nearest hundred.
- ⓐ 700
- b 800

**3** What is the value of the 5 in 523,687?
- a hundreds
- b thousands
- ⓒ hundred thousands

**4** 89
+ 77
- ⓐ 166
- b 156
- c 167
- d NG

**5** 327
+ 598
- a 935
- ⓑ 925
- c 815
- d NG

**6** $25.73
+ 19.68
- a $34.41
- ⓑ $45.41
- c $44.31
- d NG

**7** 5,683
538
+ 42
- a 5,153
- b 6,163
- c 6,253
- ⓓ NG

**8** Round each number to the nearest hundred and add.
784
+ 259
- a 900
- b 1,000
- ⓒ 1,100
- d NG

**9** In the problem 47 + 82 = 129, what is the 129 called?
- a addend
- b subtrahend
- ⓒ sum
- d NG

**10** 916
− 348
- ⓐ 568
- b 678
- c 632
- d NG

**11** 602
− 478
- ⓐ 124
- b 234
- c 276
- d NG

**12** $38.27
− 29.78
- a $11.51
- b $9.41
- ⓒ $8.49
- d NG

**13** Round each number to the nearest ten and subtract.
95
− 38
- a 70
- b 50
- ⓒ 60
- d NG

# Time to the Quarter-Hour

## pages 85-86

### Objective

To review telling time by the hour, half-hour, and quarter-hour

### Materials

*demonstration clock
cardboard clocks
duplicated clock faces

### Mental Math

Ask students to subtract 10 from:
1. 45 + 5 (40)
2. 23 − 8 (5)
3. 200 + 34 (224)
4. 29 + 0 (19)
5. 86 − 9 (65)
6. 12 + 12 + 12 (26)

### Skill Review

Using demonstration clock, review clock fundamentals. Ask how many hours are shown on the clock. (12) Ask how many hours in a day. (24) How many times does the hour hand go around in a day? (twice) Ask students to explain how many minutes there are in an hour (60) and how the minutes are marked on the clock. (in five minute intervals, indicated by numbers 1 through 12)

---

### Time to the Quarter-hour

Janet will eat dinner in a half-hour.
Show on the clocks what time that will be.

We want to show what time it will be in a half-hour.

The time now is ___7:00___ .

One half-hour and ___30___ minutes are the same.

7:30

Janet will eat at ___7:30___ . We read this as **seven thirty**.

Study the clock times.

| 8:00 | 8:15 | 8:30 | 8:45 |
|------|------|------|------|
| eight o'clock | eight fifteen | eight thirty | eight forty-five |

#### Getting Started

Write the time as you would see it on a digital clock.

Write the time as you would say it.

1.  4:45

2.  _____ six fifty

---

## Teaching the Lesson

**Introducing the Problem**   Read the problem and have a volunteer explain what the problem asks for. (what time will it be in half an hour) Ask students to identify the two types of clocks shown. (standard and digital) Ask what time is shown on the clock in the picture. (7:00) Write this time on the board. Explain that time is written with the hour on the left separated from the minutes by a colon. Ask students how many minutes there are in half an hour (30) and have them write this in the information sentence. Direct their attention to the two clocks in the model, and tell them to draw the faces as they will appear half an hour after the time shown above. Reproduce the illustration on the board. Have students complete the solution sentence. (7:30)

**Developing the Skill**   Draw attention to the difference between the standard clock and the digital clock. Explain that in half an hour, the minute hand moves around half a circle. On the digital clock, however, they must think of parts of an hour in terms of minutes. Ask how many minutes are in half an hour, quarter of an hour, and three quarters of an hour. (30, 15, 45) Give the students practice on both standard and digital clocks, by dictating random times, and having them show the times on their duplicated clocks. Illustrate each on the board.

**85**

## Practice

Write the time as you would see it on a digital clock.

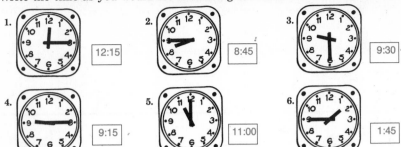

1. `12:15`
2. `8:45`
3. `9:30`

4. `9:15`
5. `11:00`
6. `1:45`

Write the time as you would say it.

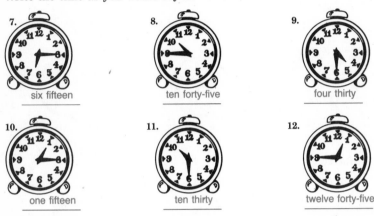

7. six fifteen
8. ten forty-five
9. four thirty

10. one fifteen
11. ten thirty
12. twelve forty-five

## Apply

Solve each problem by writing the correct digital clock time.

13. It takes 15 minutes to walk one mile. If it is 3:15, what time will it be after Tim walks one mile?
3:30

14. A roast takes 3 hours to cook. Mrs. Maguire put her roast on at 4:15. When will the roast be ready?
7:15

**86** (eighty-six)

## Correcting Common Errors

Watch for students who read the next hour instead of the hour the short hand has just passed; e.g., 2:20 instead of 1:20 for twenty minutes after one. Work with these students with a model of a clock to show them that the hour does not change until the short hand moves all the way to 2. When it is between two numbers, they should always use the number that the small hand has passed for the hour.

## Enrichment

In the military and in astronomical observatories the day is described by 24 hours, instead of two rounds of 12. Military time starts at midnight. Write these times on the board and tell them noon becomes 1200 or 1200 hours and 3 PM would be 1500, or 1500 hours. Have students convert these times to military time:

1. 4:30 PM (1630 hours)
2. 11:15 AM (1115 hours)
3. 6:00 PM (1800 hours)
4. 11:45 PM (2345 hours)

## Practice

Have students do all the problems on the page. Before they begin, write the number words **one through twelve, fifteen, thirty,** and **forty-five** on the board.

## Mixed Practice

1. 1,295 + 3,656 (4,951)
2. 18 + 25 + 169 (212)
3. 500 − 157 (343)
4. 14 − 8 (6)
5. 308 − 49 (259)
6. 578 + 6,755 (7,333)
7. 3,175 + 2,672 + 1,196 (7,043)
8. 97 − 25 (72)
9. 478 + 753 (1,231)
10. 750 − 478 (272)

## Extra Credit   *Numeration*

Tell students they can discover their own "lucky" numbers by translating their birth date into a series of numbers. For example, a person born April 4, 1978, would write his birth date as 4/4/1978. Next, he would add these numbers together to reach a single sum, and then add the two digits of that sum to get his "lucky" number. Thus, 4 + 4 + 1 + 9 + 7 + 8 = 33 and 3 + 3 = 6, his lucky number. Have students calculate their own lucky number, using this pattern. After students have completed their calculations, have them find the "lucky" number for each member of their family.

# Time to One Minute

## pages 87-88

### Objective

To tell time by five and one minute intervals

### Materials

*demonstration clock
cardboard clocks
duplicated clock faces

### Mental Math

Have students tell you what time, either AM or PM they:

1. get up in the morning.
2. have breakfast.
3. leave for school.
4. get home in the afternoon.
5. eat dinner.
6. go to bed.

### Skill Review

Have students tell you what time it will be in half an hour after the following:

1. 12:00 (12:30)
2. 3:45 (4:15)
3. 6:30 (7:00)
4. 2:15 (2:45)
5. 5:00 (5:30)
6. quarter to three (3:15)

---

## Time to One Minute

It takes Manuel 20 minutes to walk home from soccer practice. Show on the clocks what time Manuel will arrive home.

We want to know what time Manuel will get home.
He leaves practice at __4:15__.

It takes him __20__ minutes to walk home.
✔ The minute hand moves from one number to the next in 5 minutes.

  4:35

Manuel will get home at __4:35__. We read this as **four thirty-five**.

Study the clock times.

 9:03
**three minutes after nine**

9:28
**nine twenty-eight**

9:47
**nine forty-seven**

### Getting Started

Write the time as you would see it on a digital clock.

1.  2:20

2.  2:05

3.  10:35

Write the time as you would say it.

4.  five twenty-five

5. eleven forty

(eighty-seven) **87**

---

## Teaching the Lesson

**Introducing the Problem**  Read the problem aloud while students examine the illustration. Have them identify what question is being asked. (what time Manuel gets home) Ask them to tell what time the clock indicates. (4:15) Have a student read the information sentences, filling in the data requested. (4:15, 20 minutes) Remind the class that each of the numbers on the clock represents 5 minutes. Have them count together from 4:15 to 4:35 by fives. Draw a clock face on the board and show 4:35 while students draw the face in their books. Ask what the face of the digital clock will say. (4:35) Read the solution sentence aloud while students write the answer. (4:35)

**Developing the Skill**  Explain that the 60 minutes are delineated by 12 hours on a round clock face. Ask how many minutes between one digit and the next. (5 minutes) Count around the clock by fives with the class, pointing to each digit on the demonstration clock as you count. Draw a number line from 0 through 60 on the board, marked off by fives. Have students point to these numbers on the number line: 23, 17, 45, 59. Explain that a standard clock is a number line wrapped around a circle. On duplicated clocks have them indicate these times: 3:23, 4:17, 1:45, 9:59. Point out how the representation of these times is quite easy on a digital clock. Dictate random times for them to write on duplicated digital clocks.

## Practice

Write the time as you would see it on a digital clock.

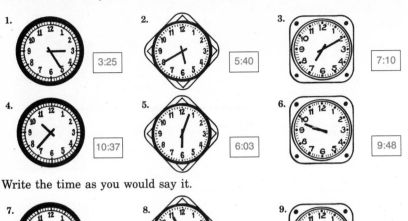

1. 3:25

2. 5:40

3. 7:10

4. 10:37

5. 6:03

6. 9:48

Write the time as you would say it.

7.

two seventeen

8. 

six fifty-five

9. 

seven minutes after five

10. 

eleven fifty-one

11. 

three thirty-six

12. 

seven fifty-eight

### Apply

Solve each problem by writing the correct digital clock time.

13. It takes 15 minutes for water to boil. If it is put on the stove at 4:25, when will the water boil?

    4:40

14. It took Carol 42 minutes to get ready for the school Halloween party. She finished at 2:48. When did she start?

    2:06

**88** (eighty-eight)

## Correcting Common Errors

Some students may read the minutes incorrectly on a standard clock. They might write a time such as 2:21 as 2:11 because they are counting the minutes by starting at 2, the hour number, instead of 12. Remind students that minutes are always counted from the 12. Have each student work with a partner to use a model of a clock. One student sets a time on the clock and the partner writes down the time. Both check the answer to make sure it is correct. They then trade roles to set another time on the clock and write the time.

## Enrichment

One of the hardest things about adding times is figuring time when the clock moves past one hour marking, and into the next hour. Instead of working in multiples of 100, the students have to remember multiples of 60. Explain the difficulty to the group. Have them write these.

1. 45 minutes after 3:35 (4:40)
2. 70 minutes after 1:15 (2:25)
3. 23 minutes after 8:52 (9:15)

## Practice

Have students complete the page. Explain that when they are asked to write out the time as they would say it, they are to write the words.

## Mixed Practice

1. $6.00 − 3.43 ($2.57)
2. 27 + 36 + 153 + 24 (240)
3. 3,256 + 2,052 (5,308)
4. $95.20 − 38.79 ($56.41)
5. 758 − 273 (485)
6. 8,347 − 2,628 (5,719)
7. $17.53 + 0.76 + 7.93 ($26.04)
8. 800 − 657 (143)
9. 6,084 − 3,276 (2,808)
10. 638 + 1,425 (2,063)

## Extra Credit   *Sets*

Put the following number grid on the board and give each pair of students one die.

| 16 | 9 | 18 | 25 | 2 |
|----|----|----|----|----|
| 20 | 6 | 4 | 12 | 24 |
| 5 | 15 | 10 | 8 | 3 |

Have students take turns rolling the cube. Have them find the set of multiples for the number rolled on the grid. For example, if the number 4 is rolled, then the set would be (4, 8, 12, 16, 20 and 24)

Score one point for each number in the set that they can find on the grid. The first person to score 30 points wins the game.

**88**

# Understanding a Calendar

pages 89-90

## Objective

To review reading a calendar

## Materials

calendar of the current month
*overhead projector

## Mental Math

Dictate these problems. Ask students if they have to trade in order to do the subtraction.

1. 98 − 23 (no)
2. 54 − 29 (yes)
3. 80 − 17 (yes)
4. 49 − 12 (no)
5. 109 − 35 (yes)
6. 22 − 10 (no)

## Skill Review

Have students together recite the months of the year and the days of the week. Ask students how many days there are in a month. (varies from 28 to 31) Ask if any students have a device for remembering how many days in each month. (Answers will vary.) Remind them that February has 28 days until every fourth year, or leap year, when it has 29.

## Understanding a Calendar

### November School Calendar

| SUNDAY | MONDAY | TUESDAY | WEDNESDAY | THURSDAY | FRIDAY | SATURDAY |
|--------|--------|---------|-----------|----------|--------|----------|
| | | | | | **1** | **2** |
| **3** Mary's Birthday | **4** | **5** | **6** Class Play | **7** | **8** Report Cards | **9** |
| **10** | **11** No School Veteran's Day | **12** | **13** Bill's Birthday | **14** | **15** Class Trip | **16** |
| **17** | **18** | **19** Cookie Sale | **20** | **21** | **22** | **23** Tony's Birthday |
| **24** | **25** Basketball Lincoln | **26** | **27** Basketball King | **28** No School Thanksgiving | **29** No School | **30** |

November is a busy month for Mr. Turner's third grade class. On what days and dates will the class be on vacation? Give the reason school is closed on these days.

The third grade does not go to school on:

| Day and Date | Reason |
|--------------|--------|
| Monday, November 11 | Veteran's Day |
| Thursday, November 28 | Thanksgiving |
| Friday, November 29 | Thanksgiving |

### Getting Started

Answer the questions about November.

1. How many days in November? _____30_____
2. When is Mary's birthday? _____November 3_____
3. What is happening on Tuesday, November 19? _____Cookie sale_____
4. What team is played on the fourth Monday? _____Lincoln_____
5. How many Fridays in this November? _____5_____
6. When are report cards given out? _____November 8_____

(eighty-nine) **89**

---

## Teaching the Lesson

**Introducing the Problem** Ask the class to look at the calendar in the text while you read the problem aloud. Have students identify what is being asked. Use an overhead projector to demonstrate reading the calendar for the class. Ask students to point out various elements, such as what day the month begins, the column for Fridays, etc. Ask the class how they can identify the days when school will be closed. (by reading the notations on the days of the calendar) Ask volunteers to point out the vacation days. Write each one on the board giving day, date, and reason as students write in their books.

**Developing the Skill** Hand out calendars for the current or specified month to the class and use the overhead projector to display the month. Point to the first day of the month and ask a student to tell what day of the week it is. Ask them to fill in any holidays that fall within that month. Ask students to volunteer their birthdays, if they are in the sample month. Ask if there are any school vacations that should be filled in. Now ask for a volunteer to write out the day, date, and event for one of those marked on their calendar. Review the spelling of the days of the week if necessary. You will also want to explain how they can find with a calendar what date it will be in a week. (read down one row on the calendar) Ask how they could find a date two weeks from now. (read down two rows)

**89**

## Practice

Answer the questions about December.

**December School Calendar**

| SUNDAY | MONDAY | TUESDAY | WEDNESDAY | THURSDAY | FRIDAY | SATURDAY |
|---|---|---|---|---|---|---|
| 1 | 2 | 3 Basketball Carver | 4 | 5 Basketball Clay | 6 Parent Conference | 7 |
| 8 Pete's Birthday | 9 Cookie Sale | 10 Rosa's Birthday | 11 | 12 Basketball Rogers | 13 Dress Up Day | 14 |
| 15 | 16 | 17 Basketball Erhard | 18 Pet Show | 19 | 20 Class Party | 21 Basketball Tourney |
| 22 | 23 No School | 24 No School | 25 No School Christmas | 26 No School Dan's Birthday | 27 No School | 28 |
| 29 | 30 No School | 31 No School | | | | |

1. How many days in December?

   31

2. How many Mondays in this December?

   5

3. What is the day and date of Rosa's birthday?

   Tuesday, December 10

4. When is the parent conference?

   Friday, December 6

5. On what day does the basketball team play Clay?

   Thursday

6. What is the date of the Pet Show?

   December 18

7. On what day is Christmas?

   Wednesday

8. What happens on Friday, December 20?

   Class party

9. When is the basketball tourney played?

   Saturday, December 21

10. What happens on the second Friday?

   Dress up day

**90** (ninety)

# Measuring to the Quarter-inch

pages 91-92

## Objective

To measure to the nearest quarter-inch

## Materials

12-inch rulers with quarter-inch markings

## Mental Math

Dictate the following:

1. Mary Beth wants to buy a pen that costs 95¢. The tax on the pen is 6¢. She has a dollar and a nickel. Will that be enough to buy it? (yes)
2. Jonathan gets an allowance of $1.50 a week. He wants to buy a mechanical toy that costs $4.99. How many weeks will he have to save? (4)

## Skill Review

Draw a picture of a 6-inch ruler, marked in quarter inches, on the board. Ask students to point to the following positions on it:

1. 2 1/2 inches
2. 5 inches
3. 1/2 inches
4. 6 inches
5. 0 inches

### Measuring to the Nearest Quarter-inch

Richard bought a new pencil box that is 6 inches long. Help him measure his pencil to see if it will fit.

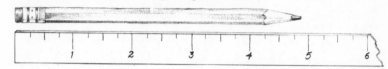

We need to find the length of Richard's pencil to the nearest quarter-inch.

The pencil box is __6__ inches long.

✔ Remember when the end of the object you are measuring falls halfway between quarter lines, round to the next higher quarter-inch.

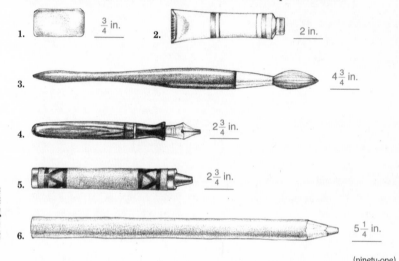

Richard's pencil is about __5__ inches long.

### Getting Started

Measure the length of each item to the nearest quarter-inch.

1.  $\frac{3}{4}$ in.   2.  2 in.

3.  $4\frac{3}{4}$ in.

4.  $2\frac{3}{4}$ in.

5.  $2\frac{3}{4}$ in.

6.  $5\frac{1}{4}$ in.

(ninety-one) **91**

## Teaching the Lesson

**Introducing the Problem**  Have a student read the problem aloud and identify what is being asked. Ask a student to complete the information sentence. (6 inches) Have another student read the rule. Ask a volunteer to read the length of the pencil illustrated. Remind them that lengths are to be rounded to the nearest quarter-inch. If an item seems to fall exactly half-way between two marks it is to be rounded to the higher one. Have students write the rounded length of the pencil (5 inches) in the solution sentence. Ask if Richard will be able to get the pencil in his new box. (yes)

**Developing the Skill**  In measuring, students must be able to read the numbers and intervals on the ruler, and they must be able to line the ruler up along the object properly. This means aligning the zero edge at one side and reading from the other end of the ruler. Use your overhead projector to demonstrate the way a ruler must be lined up on an object. Explain that when an inch is divided in half, each of the two parts is a half-inch. Demonstrate several half-inch points on your projected ruler. Now explain that when an inch is divided into quarters, each of the four parts is a quarter-inch. Start from zero and have the class say together the points on the ruler as you move along by quarter-inches: 1/4, 1/2, 3/4, 1, 1 1/4, 1 1/2 and so on.

**Practice**

Measure the length of each item to the nearest quarter-inch.

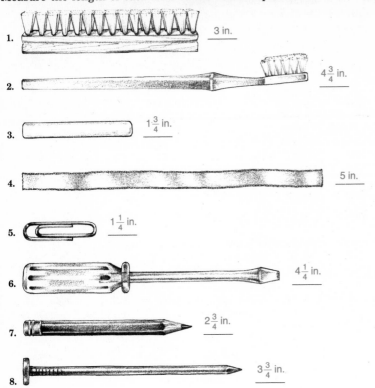

1. 3 in.

2. $4\frac{3}{4}$ in.

3. $1\frac{3}{4}$ in.

4. 5 in.

5. $1\frac{1}{4}$ in.

6. $4\frac{1}{4}$ in.

7. $2\frac{3}{4}$ in.

8. $3\frac{3}{4}$ in.

**Apply**

Solve these problems.

9. Yoko made a paper chain that was 145 inches long. Liz made one 96 inches long. If they joined them together, how long would the chain be?
241 in.

10. Sherry bought 108 inches of ribbon to use on a school project. She only needs 79 inches for the project. How many inches of ribbon were left over?
29 in.

## Practice

Have students complete all the problems on the page. Explain that they are to use their rulers to measure the items. Remind them to round any length that is not an exact quarter-inch.

## Extra Credits   *Applications*

Write the following list on the board:

| | |
|---|---|
| **Nature Study** | 7:15 AM |
| **Butterfly Collecting** | 8:45 AM |
| **Exploring Caves** | 10:45 AM |
| **Field Hockey** | 11:00 AM |
| **Softball** | 1:30 PM |
| **Swimming** | 2:15 PM |
| **Hiking** | 3:45 PM |
| **Canoeing** | 4:15 PM |

Brenda Backpack and her friends go to Camp Poison Ivy. Have students use the schedule to answer these questions: 1. If the softball game lasts 1 hour and 45 minutes, what activities could Homer Hitter take part in after the game? (Hiking, Canoeing) 2. If Marsha Mellow wants to go swimming and hiking, how long can she swim? (1½ hours) 3. If each morning class lasts 1½ hours, can Sally Spelunker go to Nature Study and Cave Exploring? (No)

# Estimating Length

## Objective

To estimate lengths using inches, feet, yards and miles

## Materials

12-inch ruler
yardstick

## Mental Math

Have students tell you the date:

1. one week from April 3. (April 10)
2. ten days from December 15. (December 25)
3. two weeks from August 10. (August 24)
4. one day after September 30. (October 1)

## Skill Review

Remind students there are 12 inches in a foot. Have them add the following and rewrite the totals in feet and inches:

1. 5 inches + 8 inches (13 inches = 1 foot, 1 inch)
2. 14 inches + 6 inches (20 inches = 1 foot, 8 inches)
3. 4 inches + 6 inches (10 inches)
4. 11 inches + 5 inches (16 inches = 1 foot, 4 inches)
5. 6 inches + 6 inches (12 inches = 1 foot)

---

### Estimating Length

Bert is measuring the flagpole at the center of Birch Park playground. Would you guess it to be about 30 feet, 30 yards or 30 miles high?

We want to know if Bert is measuring feet, yards or miles.

We know:

| 1 foot = 12 inches | 1 yard = 3 feet | 1 mile = 5,280 feet |
|---|---|---|
| 1 ft = __12__ in. | 1 yd = __3__ ft | 1 mi = __5,280__ ft |
|  | 1 yd = __36__ in. |  |

The flagpole is probably about 30 __feet__ high.

### Getting Started

Would you measure these in inches, feet, yards or miles?

1. height of a house __feet__
2. width of a desk __inches__
3. height of the Empire State Building __feet__
4. length of a paper clip __inches__
5. length of a freight train __yards__
6. length of your foot __inches__
7. length of a soccer field __yards__
8. distance to the moon __miles__

Circle the better estimate.

9. basketball player's height
   2 ft   (2 yd)
10. length of the Mississippi River
   2,300 ft   (2,300 mi)
11. width of a book
   11 ft   (11 in.)
12. length of a football field
   (100 yd)   100 ft

(ninety-three) **93**

---

## Teaching the Lesson

**Introducing the Problem**   Have a student read the problem and identify what is being asked. Have different students read the equivalents. Write each abbreviation on the board, **foot = ft, yard = yd, mile = mi** as students write each in their texts. Ask a volunteer to estimate the height of the flagpole in the problem. (30 feet) Have students put this estimate in the solution sentence.

**Developing the Skill**   Explain they will be using what they know about inches, feet, yards, and miles to guess how big things are. Ask volunteers to come to the board and write these equivalents: the number of inches in a foot (12) and in a yard (36); the number of feet in a yard (3) and in a mile. (5,280) Ask why we need so many different units for measuring length. Hold up the 12-inch ruler and ask the class to name some things they might measure in inches, and then in feet. Now hold up the yardstick and ask for things easily measured in yards. Explain to the class that to measure miles, we need more than a ruler or yardstick. Ask if anyone knows how to measure miles. Suggest that they can be measured with a wheel, the odometer in a car for example. Ask the class to name distances that are best measured in miles.

## Practice

Would you measure these in inches, feet, yards or miles?

1. length of an Olympic swimming pool
   yards
2. length of your fingernail
   inches
3. distance from Houston to New Orleans
   miles
4. height of the Sears Tower
   feet
5. length of a bicycle
   inches
6. width of your classroom
   feet
7. distance from home plate to first base
   feet
8. length of a pencil
   inches
9. width of your bed
   inches
10. length of a note pad
    inches
11. height of orbiting spacecraft
    miles
12. length of your nose
    inches

Circle the better estimate.

13. width of your foot
    4 ft (4 in.)
14. distance from Chicago to St. Louis
    260 yd (260 mi)
15. distance traveled by a well-hit baseball
    300 in. (300 ft)
16. distance traveled on a bicycle in one hour
    15 yd (15 mi)
17. height of a tree
    10 mi (10 yd)
18. size of your waist
    (23 in.) 23 ft



## Correcting Common Errors

Some students may have difficulty choosing the appropriate unit of measure. Have them work in groups to find and list items in the classroom that measure an inch, a foot, and a yard. Have them use these items as models to estimate the measures of other objects in the classroom. This provides students with everyday-life models for estimating and comparing.

## Enrichment

1. Have students list five objects in the classroom, and their estimate of the height of each. Make sure they use the appropriate unit of measure. Then have students measure the objects, and compare that to their estimates.
2. As an extension, specify five objects students are to both estimate and measure the height of. Select objects of various sizes not found in the classroom.

## Practice

Have students complete the page. Write on the board: **inches, feet, yards, miles.** Explain that in these problems they are asked to give the unit of measure that is most likely to be used. Point out that the word **estimate** means a reasonable guess.

## Extra Credit *Applications*

Ask the students to bring in any variety store catalogs. Tell them to make 5 columns on their papers with the headings: $5.00, $10.00, $20.00, $50.00 and $100.00. Have them cut pictures of the things they would buy if they were limited to each of these amounts. Have the students paste the pictures of their purchases in the proper column and write the prices below each. Ask them to calculate how much change they would receive from each purchase they make, according to each limit.

# Perimeter

**pages 95-96**

## Objective

To measure and calculate perimeters

## Materials

*a set of wooden blocks
a 12-inch piece of yarn
cardboard shapes
12-inch ruler

## Mental Math

Dictate the following problems:

1. 3 feet + 29 feet = (32 feet)
2. 18 inches + 5 inches = (23 inches)
3. 42 miles + 8 miles = (50 miles)
4. 4 inches + 10 inches + 7 inches = (21 inches)

## Skill Review

Have students write all the length equivalents they can remember on the board: inches in a foot (12), feet in a yard (3), inches in a yard (36) and feet in a mile (5,280). Ask what units they would use to measure the height of the classroom door. (feet and inches) Then ask them to estimate the height. Finally have one student measure it and see who made the closest estimate.

---

## Perimeter

The Jablonskis are fencing in their side yard. How many feet of fencing will they need to buy?

We need to find the total distance around the yard to be fenced.

The four sides of the yard measure __65__ feet, __40__ feet, __65__ feet and __40__ feet. The distance around a figure is called the **perimeter.** To find the perimeter, we add all the sides.

```
  65  ft
  40  ft
  65  ft
+ 40  ft
 210  ft
```

The perimeter is __210__ feet.

The Jablonskis must buy __210__ feet of fencing.

### Getting Started

Find the perimeter of each figure.

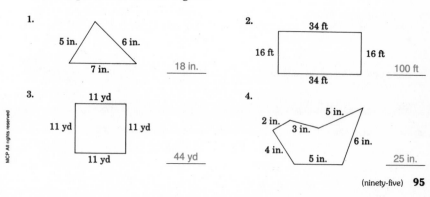

1. 5 in. 6 in. 7 in.    18 in.

2. 34 ft, 16 ft, 16 ft, 34 ft    100 ft

3. 11 yd, 11 yd, 11 yd, 11 yd    44 yd

4. 2 in. 5 in. 3 in. 4 in. 6 in. 5 in.    25 in.

---

## Teaching the Lesson

**Introducing the Problem** Have students examine the picture while you read the problem aloud. Ask what the problem is looking for. Ask a student to read the information sentence, filling in the data. (65 feet, 40 feet, 65 feet, 40 feet) Explain that the total distance around an object is called the object's perimeter. Have a volunteer write the lengths on the board as a column addition problem. While the volunteer does the addition, have the others work the problem in their texts. Ask what is the length of the perimeter. (210 feet) Ask how much fencing is needed. (210 feet) Have students fill in solution sentences.

**Developing the Skill** Ask students to explain what the perimeter of their desk top would be (the distance around the edges of the top), the perimeter of a baseball diamond (the distance from home plate to first, second, third, and back again), the perimeter of the school. (the total distance around the outside of the building) Have each student take a block and a piece of yarn. Tell them to find one perimeter for the block. Some blocks will have as many as three different perimeters. They should wrap the yarn around the block, mark the point where the end touches, lay the yarn along the ruler and measure it. Explain that they could also measure each side individually and add the four measurements to get the perimeter. Have them check their yarn measures by this method.

## Practice

Find the perimeter of each figure.

1.
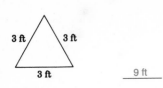
9 ft

2.
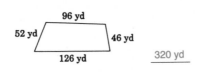
8 mi

3.
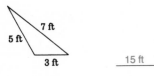
15 ft

4.
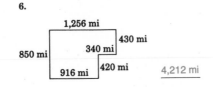
320 yd

5.
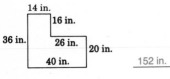
152 in.

6.
1,256 mi
430 mi
850 mi    340 mi
916 mi    420 mi
4,212 mi

---

**EXCURSION**

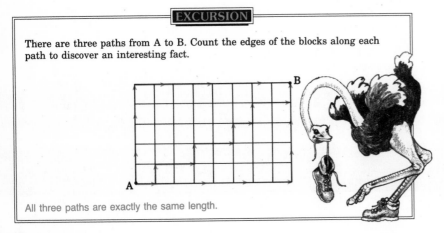

There are three paths from A to B. Count the edges of the blocks along each path to discover an interesting fact.

All three paths are exactly the same length.

# Estimating Volume

**pages 97-98**

## Objective

To estimate and measure volume using cups, pints, quarts and gallons

## Materials

*cup, pint, quart and gallon containers

## Mental Math

Explain to the class that in these problems, the letter **n** stands for the number 10. Have them give you the sum:

1. n + 14 = (24)
2. n + 99 = (109)
3. 3 + 8 + n = (21)
4. 5 + 13 + n = (28)
5. 245 + n = (255)
6. n + n = (20)

## Skill Review

Ask students to give you the following equivalents:

1. minutes in an hour (60)
2. inches in a foot (12)
3. pennies in a dime (10)
4. feet in a yard (3)
5. quarters in a dollar (4)
6. days in a year (365)
7. feet in a mile (5,280)

---

### Estimating Volume

Miss Herrara needs to fill her lawn mower with gas. Will she probably buy 5 gallons, 5 quarts or 5 pints?

We want to know if Miss Herrara buys gallons, quarts or pints of gas.

We know:

**1 gallon = 4 quarts**   **1 quart = 2 pints**   **1 pint = 2 cups**

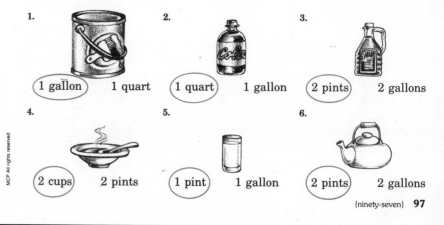

1 gal = __4__ qt     1 qt = __2__ pt     1 pt = __2__ c

Miss Herrara will probably buy 5 ___gallons___ of fuel.

### Getting Started

Circle the better estimate.

1. (1 gallon)   1 quart
2. (1 quart)   1 gallon
3. (2 pints)   2 gallons
4. (2 cups)   2 pints
5. (1 pint)   1 gallon
6. (2 pints)   2 gallons

---

## Teaching the Lesson

**Introducing the Problem**  Ask the class to read through the problem and look at the picture. Have students identify the question. Point out the equivalents. Write on the board while students write in their books: **1 gal = 4 qt, 1 qt = 2 pt, 1 pt = 2 c**. Ask students to tell you something usually measured in gallons, something measured in quarts, in pints and in cups. Ask how many children have stopped with their parents to buy gasoline for the car. Ask what units gasoline is sold in. (gallons) Have students complete the solution sentence. (12 gallons)

**Developing the Skill**  Fill the gallon container with water and hold it up. Ask how many quart containers they think you can fill from the gallon. After they have guessed, empty the gallon, quart by quart. Have students count with you as you fill each quart to see that each gallon is made up of 4 quarts. Now ask how many pints they think the quart contains. Empty the quart into the pint and have students keep track. (two pints) Now ask how many cups they think are in each pint. Repeat the procedure. (two cups in each pint) Fill the quart again and ask a student to demonstrate how many cups are in a quart. (4)

**Practice**

Circle the better estimate.

1.

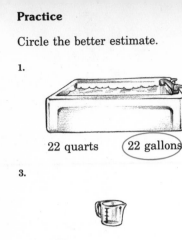

22 quarts    (22 gallons)

2.

(2 cups)    2 quarts

3.

(1 cup)    1 pint

4.

3 pints    (3 gallons)

5.

6 gallons    (6 quarts)

6.

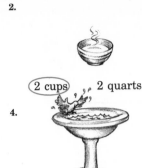

1 pint    (1 gallon)

7.

4 cups    (4 gallons)

8.

16 pints    (16 gallons)

9.

(3 pints)    3 gallons

10.

20 pints    (20 quarts)

## Correcting Common Errors

Some students may have difficulty choosing the appropriate unit. Have them work in cooperative-learning groups with models of a cup, pint, quart, and gallon. Have them use water or sand to see how many of each unit it takes to fill the next larger unit. Then encourage students to compare the standard measures to the capacity of nonstandard containers, such as cups, glasses, and pails. This provides everyday-life models of estimating and comparing capacities.

## Enrichment

Fill a gallon container with puffed rice. Ask students to explain how they could tell how many pieces of cereal there are without counting the entire gallon. Give them the other containers to work with and see which group comes up with a reasonable solution. One tactic would be to fill one cup with rice, count the pieces in that cup, and then figure out how many such cups there would be in a gallon. (16)

## Practice

Have students complete the page. Point out that in each case their answers will be an estimate and not an exact measurement.

## Mixed Practice

1. 873 − 490 (383)
2. $62.00 − 48.79 ($13.21)
3. 27 + 43 + 92 + 48 (210)
4. 3,607 + 2,005 (5,612)
5. 875 + 846 + 227 (1,948)
6. 300 − 105 (195)
7. 7,026 − 3,254 (3,772)
8. 578 + 2,349 (2,927)
9. 483 − 250 (233)
10. $15.95 + 12.13 ($28.08)

## Extra Credit    *Numeration*

Ask students to draw and cut out 2 large birds, or similar objects they might find in the sky, such as: stars, clouds, balloons, satellites etc. Have students write a multi-digit subtraction or addition equation on each bird, making one of the equations correct and one incorrect. Tape the birds high on the walls, or ceiling around the room. Allow students two days to examine the problems. Have them make a list of the correct equations that they discovered, and another of the incorrect equations, that they must have corrected.

# Estimating Weights

## Objective

To estimate and measure weights using pounds and ounces

## Materials

*items weighing 1-5 pounds
*items weighing 1-5 ounces
*postage scale
*scale for weighing pounds
*pan balance

## Mental Math

Tell students to solve the following. Explain that in each problem, the letter n stands for the number 6.

1. n¢ + 25 = (31¢)
2. 13 mi + n mi = (19 mi)
3. 5¢ + n = (11¢)
4. 20 apples + n apples = (26 apples)
5. 7 inches + n inches = (13 inches)

## Skill Review

Ask students to tell if each of these conversions is possible:

1. inches to cups (no)
2. feet to miles (yes)
3. miles to inches (yes)
4. months to miles (no)
5. hours to days (yes)
6. minutes to pints (no)
7. cups to gallons (yes)

---

### Estimating Weight

Laura's puppy made his first trip to the veterinarian to get a checkup. Did the puppy weigh about 5 ounces or 5 pounds?

We want to know if the puppy's weight will be in ounces or pounds.

We know:
**1 pound = 16 ounces**

1 lb = __16__ oz

The puppy weighs about 5 __pounds__.

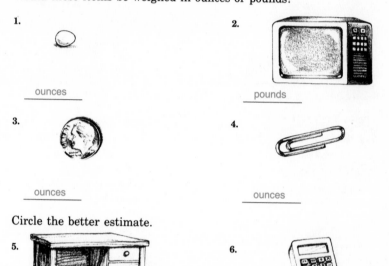

### Getting Started

Would these items be weighed in ounces or pounds?

1. __ounces__

2. __pounds__

3. __ounces__

4. __ounces__

Circle the better estimate.

5. 50 oz  (50 lb)

6. (10 oz)  10 lb

(ninety-nine) **99**

---

## Teaching the Lesson

**Introducing the Problem**   Read the problem aloud and have students identify the question being asked. Explain that a standard bag of flour or sugar weighs five pounds; while a stack of five letters each several pages long, would weigh 5 ounces. Read the equivalent in the text and explain that we abbreviate **pound** with the symbol **lb** and **ounce** with the symbol **oz**. Ask if a puppy is more likely to weigh as much as a bag of sugar or as much as five letters. (bag of sugar) Have them complete the solution sentence. (5 pounds)

**Developing the Skill**   Hold up items that can be weighed in ounces on the postal scale. Have students guess the weight of each and then weigh each. Have a volunteer write each estimate and each actual weight on the board. Now hold up objects that can be weighed in pounds. Repeat the procedure. Keep track of the estimates and the actual weights on the board, using the abbreviation, lb. Ask students to find some combination of small objects that equal one pound by putting an object weighing about a pound on one side of the pan balance, and filling the other side with smaller objects until it balances. There are two confusing aspects to pounds and ounces. One of these is the existence of **fluid ounces**, which is used to measure volume, not weight. (8 fl oz in 1 cup) The other is the unlikely abbreviation for pound (lb) which comes from the Latin word **libra**, which meant pound.

### Getting Started   *Error Pattern Analysis*

mechanical errors 24, 29; language errors 30, 31; measurement and geometry errors 75, 77

Would these items be weighed in ounces or pounds?

1.

<u>    ounces    </u>

2.

<u>    pounds    </u>

3.

<u>    pounds    </u>

4.

<u>    ounces    </u>

5.

<u>    pounds    </u>

6.

<u>    ounces    </u>

Circle the better estimate.

7.

7 oz    (7 lb)

8.

(14 oz)    14 lb

9.

25 oz    (25 lb)

10.

(18 oz)    18 lb

**100**    (one hundred)

# Understanding the Fahrenheit Scale

## pages 101-102

### Objective

To read and use the Fahrenheit scale for measuring temperature

### Materials

*demonstration Fahrenheit thermometer
Fahrenheit thermometers
styrofoam cups, water and ice

### Mental Math

Have students substitute 1, then 2, then 3 for the letter **n** in each of the following:

1. n + 1 (2) (3) (4)
2. n + 2 (3) (4) (5)
3. n + n + 1 (3) (5) (7)
4. n + n + 2 (4) (6) (8)
5. n − 1 (0) (1) (2)

### Skill Review

Explain to students that reading a thermometer is like reading the linear scale of a ruler. Draw a demonstration 12-inch ruler on the board, marking inches and half-inches. Point to spots on the ruler at random and have the students identify each point to the closest half-inch.

---

## Understanding the Fahrenheit Scale

Juneau, Alaska has an average annual snowfall of about 106 inches. Read the Fahrenheit thermometer to find out what the temperature might be during a snowstorm.

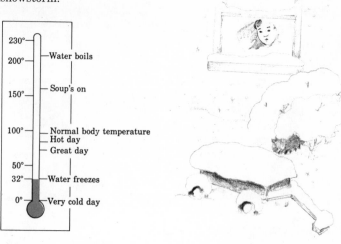

The temperature would be about __32__ degrees Fahrenheit.

We write __32__ °F.

### Getting Started

Write the temperature reading for each Fahrenheit thermometer.
Accept all reasonable answers.

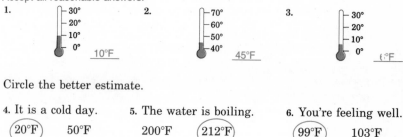

1. __10°F__
2. __45°F__
3. __(:°F__

Circle the better estimate.

4. It is a cold day.
   **(20°F)**    50°F

5. The water is boiling.
   200°F    **(212°F)**

6. You're feeling well.
   **(99°F)**    103°F

(one hundred one) **101**

---

## Teaching the Lesson

**Introducing the Problem**   Read the problem aloud and ask what information is asked for. Have students study the thermometer in their text. Explain that snow will fall when the air is the temperature of freezing water. Ask a student to tell you at what temperature, on the Fahrenheit scale, water freezes. (32°) Tell them we write the 32 with the superscript ° and capital F. Use the demonstration thermometer and have a student point to the place where water freezes. Explain that all thermometers are not marked minutely, and many times their readings will be an estimation. Ask students to complete the solution sentence. (32 degrees, 32°)

**Developing the Skill**   Explain that there are many different scales for measuring temperature, including one called the Fahrenheit scale. It is defined by water freezing and water boiling. Point out on the demonstration thermometer that water boils at 212 degrees. Ask if anyone knows what the air temperature is today. (Answers will vary.) Have them point to the temperature on the thermometer. Give each group of students a thermometer and a styrofoam cup filled with cold tap water. Have them measure the temperature. Let the water come to room temperature and measure again. Finally add ice to the water and measure the temperature after a few minutes.

## Practice

Write the temperature reading for each Fahrenheit thermometer.
Accept all reasonable answers.

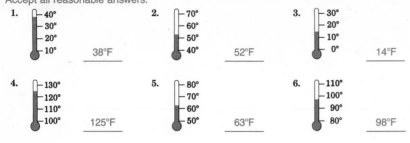

1. 38°F    2. 52°F    3. 14°F

4. 125°F    5. 63°F    6. 98°F

Circle the better estimate.

7. It's a warm day.    8. The tea water is hot.    9. You are going swimming.
   37°F  (87°F)          80°F  (180°F)               (84°F)  54°F

10. You need gloves.   11. You have a fever.       12. Build a snow fort.
    (27°F)  97°F           47°F  (101°F)               43°F  (21°F)

13. Make ice cubes.    14. Go on a picnic.         15. Tulip buds appear.
    (32°F)  65°F           30°F  (75°F)                 20°F  (50°F)

---

### EXCURSION

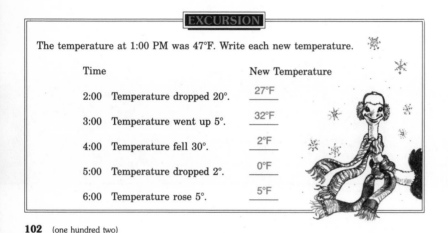

The temperature at 1:00 PM was 47°F. Write each new temperature.

| Time | | New Temperature |
|------|---|------|
| 2:00 | Temperature dropped 20°. | 27°F |
| 3:00 | Temperature went up 5°. | 32°F |
| 4:00 | Temperature fell 30°. | 2°F |
| 5:00 | Temperature dropped 2°. | 0°F |
| 6:00 | Temperature rose 5°. | 5°F |

---

## Correcting Common Errors

Some students may have difficulty relating temperature readings with events in life. Have them work with partners with a list similar to the one shown below where they circle the Fahrenheit temperature reading that they think is more appropriate.

| EVENT | TEMPERATURE | |
|-------|------|------|
| sledding | 30° | 70° |
| picnicking | 20° | 80° |
| wearing shorts | 50° | 90° |
| skiing | 20° | 70° |
| gardening | 30° | 60° |

Encourage them to identify an appropriate activity for the temperature reading not selected.

## Enrichment

Have students research the warmest and coldest temperatures recorded for a given day in your area. This information is commonly printed in daily newspapers and repeated on the television news. Have them compare these record extremes with the actual high and low temperature for the day.

---

## Practice

Have students complete the page. Remind students to read the thermometers according to their best estimate.

## Excursion

Write **35** on the board and ask students what the number would be if we added 16 to it. (51) Tell students to now add another 6, subtract 21 and add 2. Ask what the number would be. (38) Write on the board:

$$35 + 16 = 51$$
$$51 +  6 = 57$$
$$57 - 21 = 36$$
$$36 +  2 = 38$$

Likewise point out that the number decreased with each subtraction and increased with each addition. Tell students to add or subtract each change in temperature during the day to find the temperature at 6:00 PM.

## Extra Credit    *Geometry*

Tell students that a repeated pattern is said to demonstrate **translational symmetry.** Draw a row of X's on the board. Explain that this pattern has translational symmetry. Ask students to look around the classroom or school for examples of translational symmetry and sketch at least two examples that they find. Examples would include: a brick wall, a tiled floor, a row of identical windows, the pattern on a ventilating grill, or a string of beads. Encourage students to share the patterns they find with others in the class.

**102**

# Chapter Test

page 103

| Item | Objective |
|------|-----------|
| 1-4 | Read the time to one minute (See pages 87-88) |
| 5-6 | Choose the appropriate unit of length (See pages 93-94) |
| 7-8 | Add to find perimeter (See pages 95-96) |
| 9 | Choose the appropriate unit of capacity (See pages 97-98) |
| 10 | Choose the appropriate temperature reading (See pages 101-102) |

Write the time as you would see it on a digital clock.

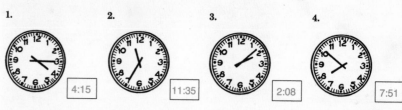

1.   `4:15`

2.   `11:35`

3.   `2:08`

4.   `7:51`

Circle the better estimate.

5. distance a car drives in one hour

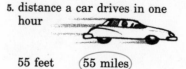

55 feet    (55 miles)

6. height of a puppy

(15 inches)    15 feet

Find the perimeter.

7.

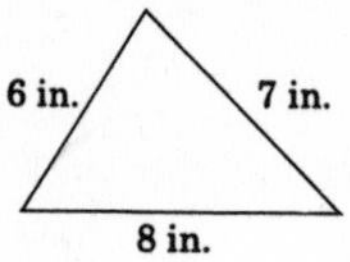

6 in.    7 in.

8 in.

21 in.

8.

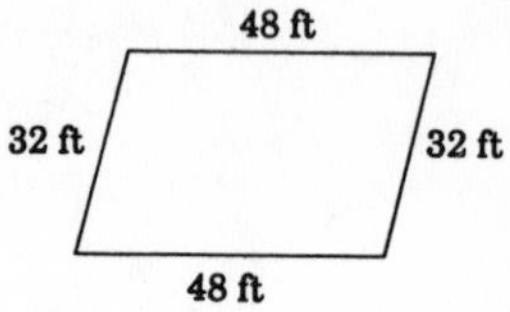

48 ft

32 ft    32 ft

48 ft

160 ft

Circle the better estimate.

9.

2 ounces    (2 quarts)

10.

(26°F)    66°F

(one hundred three) **103**

103

Circle the letter of the correct answer.

**1** 432 ◯ 562
    a >
    ⓑ <

**2** Round 741 to the nearest hundred.
    ⓐ 700
    b 800
    c NG

**3** What is the value of the 2 in 231,470?
    a tens
    b thousands
    c ten thousands
    ⓓ NG

**4**  249
  + 167
    a 316
    b 406
    ⓒ 416
    d NG

**5**  $38.27
  + 49.59
    a $77.86
    ⓑ $87.86
    c $88.86
    d NG

**6**  4,739
    2,156
  +  847
    a 7,642
    b 7,752
    c 7,842
    ⓓ NG

**7** Round each number to the nearest hundred and add.
  526
 + 295
    a 700
    ⓑ 800
    c 600
    d NG

**8**  634
  − 259
    a 425
    b 385
    c 325
    ⓓ NG

**9**  805
  − 328
    a 523
    b 427
    ⓒ 477
    d NG

**10**  $64.26
  − 12.87
    a $52.61
    ⓑ $51.39
    c $52.39
    d NG

**11** Round each number to the nearest ten and subtract.
  79
 − 24
    a 40
    b 50
    ⓒ 60
    d NG

**12** Round each number to the nearest hundred and subtract.
  725
 − 278
    ⓐ 400
    b 500
    c 300
    d NG

**13**
    a 8:15
    b 3:09
    ⓒ 3:42
    d NG

☐ score

**104** (one hundred four)

| Item | Objective |
| --- | --- |
| 1 | Compare numbers less than 1,000 (See pages 27-28) |
| 2 | Round to the nearest 100 (See pages 31-32) |
| 3 | Identify the value of a digit in a number less than 1,000,000 (See pages 35-36) |
| 4 | Add two 3-digit addends with two regroupings (See pages 45-46) |
| 5 | Add dollars and cents with regrouping (See pages 51-52) |
| 6 | Add three or four numbers (See pages 49-50) |
| 7 | Round addends to the nearest 100 and add (See pages 53-56) |
| 8-9 | Subtract two 3-digit numbers with two regroupings (See pages 67-68) |
| 10 | Subtract dollars and cents with regrouping (See pages 75-76) |
| 11 | Round addends to the nearest 10 and subtract (See pages 77-78) |
| 12 | Round numbers to the nearest 100 and subtract (See pages 77-78) |
| 13 | Read the time to one minute (See pages 87-88) |

### Alternate Cumulative Review

**Circle the letter of the correct answer.**

**1** 367 ◯ 376
  ⓐ <
  b >
  c =

**2** Round 337 to the nearest hundred
  ⓐ 300
  b 400
  c NG

**3** What is the value of the 6 in 763,891?
  a hundred thousands
  b thousands
  c tens
  ⓓ NG

**4**  326
 + 87
  a 513
  b 503
  ⓒ 413
  d NG

**5**  $64.37
 + 27.94
  a $82.31
  b $91.31
  ⓒ $92.31
  d NG

**6**  6,567
  1,436
 + 728
  a 8,711
  b 8,721
  c 8,821
  ⓓ NG

**7** Round each number to the nearest hundred and add.
  732
 + 377
  ⓐ 1,100
  b 1,000
  c 1,200
  d NG

**8**  726
 − 368
  ⓐ 358
  b 442
  c 354
  d NG

**9**  603
 − 257
  ⓐ 346
  b 456
  c 356
  d NG

**10**  $58.17
 − 32.69
  a $25.56
  ⓑ $25.48
  c $26.52
  d NG

**11** Round each number to the nearest ten and subtract.
  88
 − 31
  a 50
  b 40
  ⓒ 60
  d NG

**12** Round each number to the nearest hundred and subtract
  637
 − 281
  a 500
  b 400
  ⓒ 300
  d NG

**13** Write the time, 6 min. past 3 o'clock.
  a 1:15
  ⓑ 3:06
  c 3:10
  d NG

**104**

# Measuring to the Nearest Centimeter

## pages 105-106

### Objective

To use centimeters to measure length

### Materials

centimeter rulers with half-cm markings
tag board strips of various lengths

### Mental Math

Ask the following questions:

1. How many whole weeks are in 15 days? (2)
2. How many whole gallons are in 7 quarts? (1)
3. How many whole miles are in 12,000 feet? (2)
4. How many yards are in 9 feet? (3)
5. How many whole hours are in 90 minutes? (1)

### Skill Review

Besides inches and feet, ask what other customary units can be used to measure length. (yards, miles) Ask students what units they would use to measure: length of a hallway (feet or yards); height of a milk glass (inches); length of a baby (inches); height of a third grader (feet). Do not compare customary and metric units of measure.

---

### Measuring to the Nearest Centimeter

Jayne will begin the semester with a new box of crayons. About how long is each new crayon?

We want to measure a crayon length to the nearest centimeter.
We use a **centimeter** ruler.

✔ Remember, when the end of the object you are measuring falls halfway between centimeter lines, round to the next higher centimeter.

Jayne's crayon is about ___7___ centimeters long.

We write ___7___ cm.

### Getting Started

Measure each item to the nearest centimeter.

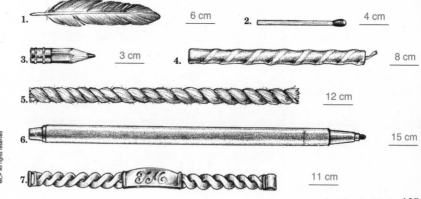

1. 6 cm      2. 4 cm

3. 3 cm      4. 8 cm

5. 12 cm

6. 15 cm

7. 11 cm

(one hundred five) **105**

---

## Teaching the Lesson

**Introducing the Problem**  Have a student read the problem aloud and identify what is being asked. Read the plan sentences and tell students that the centimeter is another unit used to measure length. Have them look at their centimeter rulers. Ask how many centimeters are on their ruler. (about 30 if it is also a 12 inch ruler) Tell students to look at the crayon and ruler illustrated in their texts and read the length of the crayon. (nearly 7 cm) Write on the board: **centimeters = cm.** Now have students fill in the length in their solution sentences. (7 centimeters, 7 cm)

**Developing the Skill**  Tell students that they are beginning to study a new system of measurement, the metric system. The system they studied in the last chapter is called the customary system. However, most of the world uses metric units and they will learn those units in this chapter. A centimeter is about the width of a child's thumbnail. The diameter of a nickel is about 2 cm. Give students an assortment of tag board strips and have them measure the length of each in centimeters.

## Practice

Measure each item to the nearest centimeter.

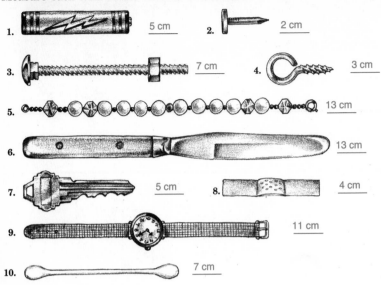

1. 5 cm
2. 2 cm
3. 7 cm
4. 3 cm
5. 13 cm
6. 13 cm
7. 5 cm
8. 4 cm
9. 11 cm
10. 7 cm

## Apply

Solve these problems.

11. Mario's mother had 63 centimeters of sausage. She used 47 centimeters of it for supper. How much was left?
16 cm

12. Julie's frog jumped 127 centimeters. Willie's frog jumped 88 centimeters. How much farther did Julie's frog jump?
39 cm

13. The sections of a mural painted by student artists were 65 centimeters, 82 centimeters and 56 centimeters wide. What was the total width of the mural?
203 cm

14. Larry and his dad compared their heights. Larry is 125 centimeters tall. His father is 172 centimeters. How much taller is Larry's dad?
47 cm

## Correcting Common Errors

Some students may measure incorrectly because they place their rulers so that the number 1 is at the end of the object. Have these students work in pairs measuring different objects. Have them check each other to be sure that they are placing the ruler properly and are measuring correctly.

## Enrichment

Tell students they will draw a family web. Tell them to write down the names of their brothers, sisters, mother, father, and as many aunts, uncles, grandparents, and cousins as they can remember. Tell them to scatter the names randomly on their papers then, have them form the web by drawing a red arrow connecting each parent to a daughter, and a blue arrow connecting each parent to a son. Ask them to describe any patterns they notice.

## Practice

Have students do the problems on the page. Before they begin, write the word **centimeter** and the abbreviation **cm** on the board. Tell them to use the abbreviation in expressing their answers. Remind them to round any length to the next higher centimeter if it falls *exactly* halfway between one centimeter mark and another.

## Extra Credit *Geometry*

Origami is a good way to reinforce concepts of symmetry. Obtain a package of origami paper or some other kind of thin paper, like tracing paper or onion skin. Demonstrate making a drinking cup. Start with a square piece of paper. Fold it diagonally. Now fold in the right and left corners as shown below. Take the two points at the top and fold them down in opposite directions. The cup is finished. Students can open it and fill it with water. Allow them to try the same example.

**106**

# Estimating Meters and Kilometers

pages 107-108

## Objective

To estimate lengths and distances using meters and kilometers

## Materials

meter stick marked in centimeters

## Mental Math

Have students round each number to the nearest ten and add:

1. $45 + 39 = (50 + 40 = 90)$
2. $13 + 85 = (10 + 90 = 100)$
3. $7 + 24 = (10 + 20 = 30)$
4. $50 + 37 = (50 + 40 = 90)$
5. $34 + 28 = (30 + 30 = 60)$
6. $62 + 45 = (60 + 50 = 110)$

## Skill Review

Ask a student to write the abbreviation for centimeter on the board. (cm) Draw an enlarged ruler on the board with centimeters and half-centimeters marked up to 10. Point to random spots on the ruler and have students read the lengths. Remind them to round any half-centimeter up to the next whole unit.

---

### Estimating Meters and Kilometers

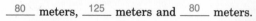

To keep animals away from the corn, Mrs. Lee is planning to put a fence around the whole cornfield. How much fencing will she need?

We want to find the perimeter, or total distance, around the field.

We know:
**1 meter = 100 centimeters**     **1 kilometer = 1,000 meters**

1 m = __100__ cm          1 km = __1,000__ m

The sides of the cornfield measure __125__ meters,

__80__ meters, __125__ meters and __80__ meters.

To find the perimeter, we add all the sides.

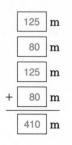

|       |     |
|-------|-----|
|       | 125 m |
|       | 80 m |
|       | 125 m |
| +     | 80 m |
|       | 410 m |

Mrs. Lee needs __410__ meters of fencing.

### Getting Started

Would you measure these in centimeters, meters or kilometers?

1. height of a house

   _____ m

2. length of a soccer field

   _____ m

Circle the better estimate.

3. width of a book

   (22 cm)     22 m

Find the perimeter.

4.  60 km / 64 km / 70 km     194 km

(one hundred seven) **107**

---

## Teaching the Lesson

**Introducing the Problem**  Tell students that this lesson introduces two new metric units for measuring length or distance, the meter and the kilometer. Read the problem aloud to the class and have them examine the illustration. Ask students to identify what is being asked. Then ask how the perimeter of the field could be calculated. (by adding the four sides) Tell students to read the equivalents. On the board, write: **meter = m, kilometer = km, 1 m = 100 cm, 1 km = 1,000 m.** Have students read the information sentence, filling in the lengths of the sides. Read the plan for the class and have a student write the problem on the board while the others complete it in their texts. (125m + 80m + 125m + 80m = 410m) Read the solution sentence aloud while students write the answer.

**Developing the Skill**  Let students examine a meter stick. Ask how many centimeters are in the meter. (100) Tell students that one meter is about the distance from the floor to a doorknob. Ask students to list lengths or distances that would be best measured in meters. Explain that the kilometer is made up of 1,000 meters. Give students a familiar distance to illustrate one kilometer. Ask what distances would be best measured in kilometers.

**Getting Started**  *Error Pattern Analysis*
mechanical errors 24, 26, 29; language errors 30, 31; measurement and geometry errors 75, 77

**107**

## Practice

Would you measure these in centimeters, meters or kilometers?

1. length of a car

    _____m_____

2. distance to the moon

    _____km_____

3. length of a paper clip

    _____cm_____

4. distance you can run in

    15 seconds _____m_____

5. height of a tall building

    _____m_____

6. length of your arm

    _____cm_____

7. width of your front door

    _____cm_____

8. length of your house

    _____m_____

Circle the better estimate.

9. your height

    (138 cm)    138 m

10. distance run in 30 minutes

    8 m    (8 km)

11. home run at Yankee Stadium

    98 cm    (98 m)

12. distance around the world at the equator

    40,000 m    (40,000 km)

Find the perimeter.

13.

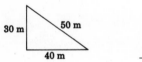

    _____120 m_____

14.

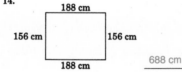

    _____688 cm_____

15.

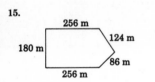

    _____902 m_____

16.

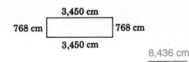

    _____8,436 cm_____

**108**   (one hundred eight)

**108**

# Estimating Milliliters and Liters

pages 109-110

## Objective

To estimate volume using milliliters and liters

## Materials

*transparent liter container
*4 eight-ounce milk glasses
*teaspoon and eye dropper

## Mental Math

Have students compute each sum:

1. 2 tens plus 3 fives. (35)
2. 3 hundreds plus 2 ones. (302)
3. 1 fifty plus 3 tens. (80)
4. 8 tens plus 14 tens. (220)
5. 10 fives plus 4 ones. (54)
6. 2 hundreds plus four tens minus 2 fives. (230)

## Skill Review

Remind students that volume is the amount of a substance that can be contained within a given space. Review these units that measure volume: cups, pints, quarts, and gallons. Ask for all the equivalents between these units. (2 c = 1 pt, 2 pts = 1 qt, 4 qts = 1 gal) Do not compare metric with customary measures.

---

### Estimating Milliliters and Liters

Jerry is making breakfast for his mother on Mother's Day. Will the bottle he is filling hold about 1 milliliter or 1 liter of orange juice?

We know:
**1 liter = 1,000 milliliters**

$$1 \text{ L} = \underline{\quad 1,000 \quad} \text{ mL}$$

Liters and milliliters are measures of **volume**.
**Volume** is the amount of space inside something.

It takes about 4 glasses to fill one liter bottle.

It takes an eyedropper to measure about one milliliter.

The volume of the juice bottle is about 1 ___liter___.

### Getting Started

Would you measure the volume of these in milliliters or liters?

1. milliliters

2. milliliters

3. liters

4. liters

(one hundred nine) **109**

---

## Teaching the Lesson

**Introducing the Problem**  Have students read the problem and identify what is being asked. Explain that the units they will learn in this lesson are called milliliters and liters. They can be used for measuring capacity; the amount of juice in the container pictured, for example. Explain that a liter is an amount defined by a cube that is 10 centimeters on each side. A milliliter is a thousandth of a liter. Read the equivalent measures and write the abbreviations on the board: **1 L = 1,000 mL.** Discuss the illustrations below the problem. It takes about 4 milk glasses to fill a liter container but about 20 drops from an eyedropper to make a milliliter. Ask the class to tell whether the volume of the juice bottle is more likely to be 1 L or 1 mL. (liter)

**Developing the Skill**  Tell students that one word used to describe volume is **capacity.** Point out that the capacity, or volume, of a container is the space within that container, or the space the container takes up. Use the milk glasses to fill a liter container. Students will notice that four glasses will not quite fill the liter. Let 20 drops fall from the eyedropper into the teaspoon to demonstrate the size of a milliliter.

## Practice

Would you measure the volume of these in milliliters or liters?

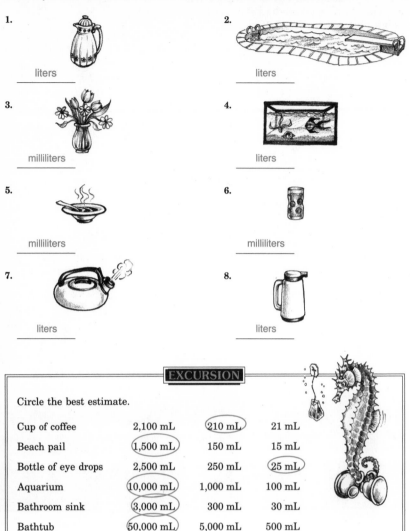

1. _____ liters

2. _____ liters

3. _____ milliliters

4. _____ liters

5. _____ milliliters

6. _____ milliliters

7. _____ liters

8. _____ liters

### EXCURSION

Circle the best estimate.

| | | | |
|---|---|---|---|
| Cup of coffee | 2,100 mL | (210 mL) | 21 mL |
| Beach pail | (1,500 mL) | 150 mL | 15 mL |
| Bottle of eye drops | 2,500 mL | 250 mL | (25 mL) |
| Aquarium | (10,000 mL) | 1,000 mL | 100 mL |
| Bathroom sink | (3,000 mL) | 300 mL | 30 mL |
| Bathtub | (50,000 mL) | 5,000 mL | 500 mL |

**110** (one hundred ten)

## Practice

Have students do the problems on the page. Explain that they are to choose the units of measurement most appropriate to the volume being measured.

## Excursion

Ask students how many milliliters are in a liter. (1,000) Remind students that 1 milliliter is measured with an eyedropper and 1 liter is about 4 glasses full.
Have students look at the 3 choices to estimate the volume of a cup of coffee. Ask if 2,100 mL is more or less than 1 liter. (more) Ask if this is a good estimate for a cup of coffee. (no) Ask students if 210 mL is more or less than 1 liter. (less) Ask students to estimate what part of a liter 210 mL is. (about 1/4) Repeat for 21 mL. Tell students they may want to think of each of the other containers in comparison to the size of 1 cup of coffee. Have students circle the best estimate for each container.

## Extra Credit    *Biography*

Karl Friedrich Gauss is considered one of the three giants in the history of math and science, along with Archimedes and Newton. Gauss was born in Germany in 1777, and his genius was discovered by a local duke who took charge of his education. Gauss received degrees from the university in Göttingen, and then became a professor and the director of the astronomical observatory there. Gauss' accomplishments included computing the orbit of a newly-discovered planetoid, Ceres, located between Mars and Jupiter; inventing the electric telegraph; and publishing his theories on prime and complex numbers. Complex numbers are used today in many areas of engineering and physics and are applied to solve problems that cannot be solved by real numbers.

# Estimating Grams and Kilograms

pages 111-112

## Objective

To estimate metric units for mass using grams and kilograms

## Materials

*items weighing between one and five grams
*items weighing between one and five kilograms
*pan balance
*5 gram and 5 kilogram weights

## Mental Math

Have students put these things in order from lightest to heaviest:

1. a banana
2. a bicycle tire
3. a car
4. a feather
5. an adult
6. a large watermelon
(4, 1, 2, 6, 5, 3)

## Skill Review

Have a student write the equivalence between pounds and ounces on the board. (1 lb = 16 oz) Have them name items best measured in pounds and those best measured in ounces. Do not compare metric with customary measures.

---

### Estimating Grams and Kilograms

Matthew and his brother are unpacking the groceries. Does the bag of flour weigh about 2 grams or 2 kilograms?

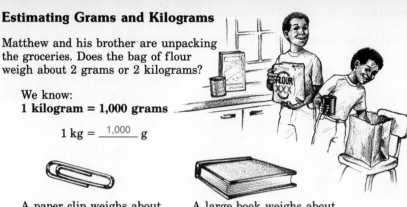

We know:
**1 kilogram = 1,000 grams**

1 kg = __1,000__ g

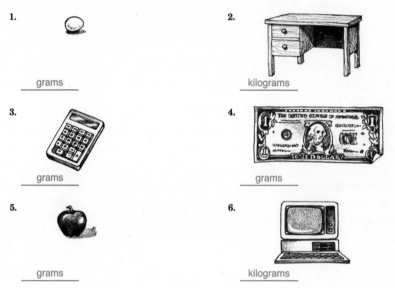

A paper clip weighs about 1 gram.

A large book weighs about 1 kilogram.

The bag of flour weighs about 2 __kilograms__.

### Getting Started

Would these items be weighed in grams or kilograms?

1.

_____grams_____

2.

_____kilograms_____

3.

_____grams_____

4.

_____grams_____

5.

_____grams_____

6.

_____kilograms_____

(one hundred eleven) **111**

---

## Teaching the Lesson

**Introducing the Problem**  Read the problem aloud. Ask students to identify the question. Explain that grams and kilograms are the metric units for weight. Write the equivalence between grams and kilograms on the board: **1 kg = 1,000 g.** Have them look at the pictures below the problem. Explain that the book, the large item, is weighed in kilograms while the paper clip, the small item, is weighed in grams. Ask a student to read the solution sentence while students write the answer in their texts. (about 2 kilograms)

**Developing the Skill**  Place a small object, 1 to 5 grams, on one pan of the balance. Have a student add gram weights to the other pan until the sides balance. Ask the class how many grams the item weighs. Have a different student weigh another item. Now place a heavier object, 1 to 5 kilograms, on one pan. Repeat the weighing process, adding kilogram weights until it is nearly in balance. You may want some 500 g weights to make it come out more even. After you have weighed two smaller and two larger objects, have students identify items they could measure in grams and those they could weigh in kilograms. Write **kilograms = kg** and **grams = g** as headings on the board and list these items.

**Practice**

Would these items be weighed in grams or kilograms?

1.

grams

2.

kilograms

3.

grams

4.

grams

5.

grams

6.

kilograms

**Apply**

Solve these problems.

7. Barbara weighs 48 kilograms. Amanda weighs 42 kilograms. Can they ride together in a canoe that has a 100 kilogram limit?

yes

8. When Robert was 10, he weighed 36 kilograms. Now he weighs 51 kilograms. How much weight has Robert gained?

15 kg

9. You are mailing a book. The postage due depends upon the weight of the package. The book weighs 428 grams, the packing 52 grams, and the box 129 grams. What is the total weight of the package?

609 g

10. Sandy weighed 3,895 grams when she was born. Her new baby brother weighed 4,188 grams. What is the difference in their birth weights?

293 g

## Correcting Common Errors

Some students will have difficulty choosing the appropriate unit. Have them work in cooperative groups with a raisin that weighs about 1 gram and a volume of an encyclopedia that weighs about 1 kilogram. They should pass around the items so that each student can hold each item. Explain that any weight can be expressed in grams or kilograms, but it is more convenient to express lighter weights in grams and heavier weights in kilograms. Have them make a list of five objects in the classroom they would weigh in grams and five they would weigh in kilograms. Be sure students actually lift these items to experience their relative weights.

## Enrichment

Ask students to bring in empty food containers that are marked in both metric and customary units for weight. Explain that both systems are used because in the United States we are gradually switching over from the customary system to the more universal metric system. Allow students to examine the containers to make them aware of how weights are labeled.

## Practice

Have students complete the problem on the page. Before the students begin write the words **gram** and **kilogram** on the board. Point out that in the last four problems they will have to do the actual calculations.

## Extra Credit   *Geometry*

Give each student a mimeographed paper with nine squares on it, each divided into 4 smaller squares. Instruct the students to use two different crayons to color each of the smaller squares, making sure each larger square ends up with a different color pattern. Be sure they use only one color inside each small square. There are 16 different possible ways to color the square with two colors. Display the colored designs on the bulletin board.

**112**

# Understanding the Celsius Scale

## pages 113-114

### Objective

To read and use the Celsius scale for measuring temperature

### Materials

*demonstration Celsius thermometer
Celsius thermometers
styrofoam cups, water, and ice

### Mental Math

Explain that on an average day the temperature may rise about 20° F from its nighttime low to its daytime high. Ask students to add 20° to each temperature.

1. 35° F (55° F)
2. 57° F (77° F)
3. 14° F (34° F)
4. 62° F (82° F)

### Skill Review

Ask students to tell the Fahrenheit temperature at which water freezes (32°) and that at which water boils (212°). Ask them for an average temperature for a day in winter, spring and summer. (Answers will vary with your climate.)

---

## Understanding the Celsius Scale

The first warm days of spring make the flowers bloom. Read the Celsius thermometer to see what the temperature might be on such a day.

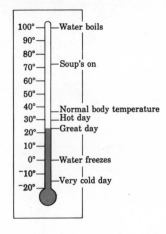

The temperature on a warm spring day would be about __22__ degrees

Celsius. We write __22__ °C.

### Getting Started

Write the temperature reading for each Celsius thermometer.
Accept all reasonable answers.

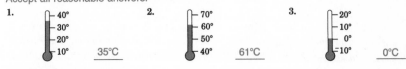

1. 35°C     2. 61°C     3. 0°C

Circle the better estimate.

4. Brrr, it's cold outside.
   (0°C)     20°C

5. I like my soup hot.
   30°C     (70°C)

6. It's time to plant seeds.
   (20°C)     35°C

(one hundred thirteen) **113**

---

## Teaching the Lesson

**Introducing the Problem**  Ask students to look at the thermometer illustrated in their texts while you read the problem. Have students identify what is being asked. Explain that on the Celsius scale, zero is the point at which water freezes, and 100 is the point at which water boils. Using the demonstration thermometer, have students identify these temperatures: water freezes (0°), normal body temperature (37°) and water boils (100°). Ask a student how the degrees are marked on the thermometer. (in 10° intervals) Explain that they have to estimate the readings between those marked. Have students identify different weather conditions and their temperatures. Read the solution sentence aloud. Have a student point to the temperature and read it from the demonstration thermometer. (22°) Have students complete the solution sentences in their texts. (22 degrees Celsius, 22° C)

**Developing the Skill**  Give each student a Celsius thermometer. Have them read the air temperature from the thermometer and have one student write this temperature on the board. Let students measure the temperature of tap water and of ice water and express their answers in Celsius degrees. If it is a cold day, let students measure the temperature of the outdoor air. Record the answers on the board.

## Practice

Write the temperature reading for each Celsius thermometer.
Accept all reasonable answers.

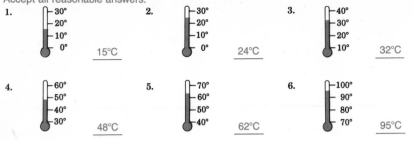

1. 15°C
2. 24°C
3. 32°C
4. 48°C
5. 62°C
6. 95°C

Circle the better estimate.

7. Wear a heavy coat.
   (5°C)    35°C

8. The cocoa is hot.
   35°C    (75°C)

9. Ice cubes are ready.
   (0°C)    50°C

10. Turn on the air conditioner.
   10°C    (38°C)

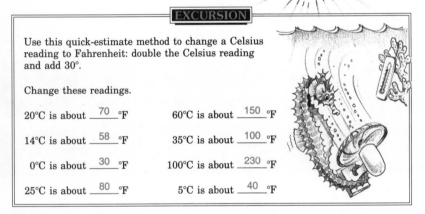

**EXCURSION**

Use this quick-estimate method to change a Celsius reading to Fahrenheit: double the Celsius reading and add 30°.

Change these readings.

20°C is about __70__ °F        60°C is about __150__ °F

14°C is about __58__ °F        35°C is about __100__ °F

0°C is about __30__ °F         100°C is about __230__ °F

25°C is about __80__ °F        5°C is about __40__ °F

**114**   (one hundred fourteen)

---

**114**

# Chapter Test

page 115

| Item | Objective |
|------|-----------|
| 1-3 | Measure objects to the nearest centimeter (See pages 105-106) |
| 4-5 | Choose the appropriate metric unit of length (See pages 107-108) |
| 6-7 | Find the perimeter in metric units (See pages 107-108) |
| 8-9 | Choose the appropriate metric unit of capacity (See pages 109-110) |
| 10 | Choose the appropriate metric unit of weight (See pages 111-112) |
| 11-13 | Write the temperature reading of a Celsius thermometer (See pages 113-114) |

Measure each item to the nearest centimeter.

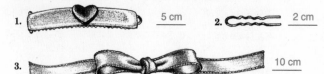

1. _5 cm_    2. _2 cm_

3. _10 cm_

Would you measure these in centimeters, meters, or kilometers?

4. length of a paper clip

_centimeters_

5. distance traveled by a car in one day

_kilometers_

Find the perimeter.

6. 28 m, 40 m, 36 m    _104 m_

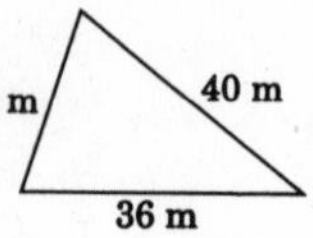

7. 468 km, 532 km, 532 km, 468 km    _2,000 km_

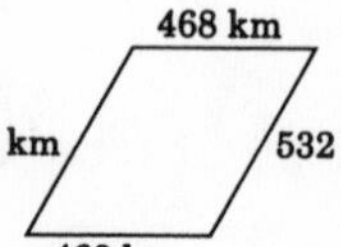

Circle the unit you would use to measure these items.

8.  (mL)  L

9.  mL  (L)

10.  g  (kg)

Write the temperature reading for each Celsius thermometer.
Accept all reasonable answers.

11. 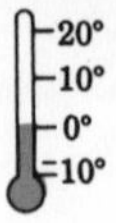 20° 10° 0° -10°    _0°C_

12. 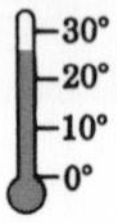 30° 20° 10° 0°    _25°C_

13. 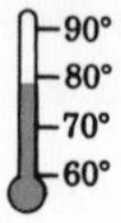 90° 80° 70° 60°    _78°C_

(one hundred fifteen) **115**

**115**

Circle the letter of the correct answer.

**1** 778 ◯ 709
- **ⓐ** >
- **b** <

**2** What is the value of the 5 in 390,516?
- **a** tens
- **b** thousands
- **c** hundred thousands
- **ⓓ** NG

**3** 684 + 926
- **a** 1,510
- **b** 1,600
- **ⓒ** 1,610
- **d** NG

**4** $28.36 + 51.47
- **a** $79.73
- **ⓑ** $79.83
- **c** $80.83
- **d** NG

**5** 6,254 / 1,862 / + 485
- **ⓐ** 8,601
- **b** 8,691
- **c** 8,701
- **d** NG

**6** Round each number to the nearest hundred and add. 624 + 256
- **a** 800
- **ⓑ** 900
- **c** 1,000
- **d** NG

**7** 836 − 259
- **a** 557
- **b** 623
- **c** 667
- **ⓓ** NG

**8** 605 − 296
- **a** 209
- **ⓑ** 309
- **c** 491
- **d** NG

**9** $82.46 − 27.38
- **a** $45.08
- **ⓑ** $55.08
- **c** $65.12
- **d** NG

**10** Round each number to the nearest hundred and subtract. 896 − 359
- **ⓐ** 500
- **b** 600
- **c** 700
- **d** NG

**11**
- **a** 6:08
- **ⓑ** 6:38
- **c** 7:30
- **d** NG

**12** Find the perimeter.
156 in. / 156 in. / 200 in.
- **a** 312 in.
- **b** 502 in.
- **ⓒ** 512 in.
- **d** NG

**13** Choose the best unit for measuring the height of a tall building.
- **a** centimeters
- **ⓑ** meters
- **c** kilometers
- **d** NG

☐ score

**116** (one hundred sixteen)

---

## Cumulative Review
page 116

| Item | Objective |
|---|---|
| 1 | Compare numbers less than 1,000 (See pages 27-28) |
| 2 | Identify the value of a digit in a number less than 1,000,000 (See pages 35-36) |
| 3 | Add two 3-digit numbers with two regroupings (See pages 45-46) |
| 4 | Add dollars and cents with regrouping (See pages 51-52) |
| 5 | Add three or four numbers (See pages 49-50) |
| 6 | Round addends to the nearest 100 and add (See pages 53-56) |
| 7-8 | Subtract two 3-digit numbers with two regroupings (See pages 67-68) |
| 9 | Subtract dollars and cents with regrouping (See pages 75-76) |
| 10 | Round numbers to the nearest 100 and subtract (See pages 77-78) |
| 11 | Read the time to one minute (See pages 87-88) |
| 12 | Add to find the perimeter (See pages 95-96) |
| 13 | Choose the appropriate unit of length (See pages 97-98) |

---

## Alternate Cumulative Review

Circle the letter of the correct answer.

**1** 621 ◯ 631
- **ⓐ** <
- **b** >
- **c** =

**2** What is the value of the 9 in 631,279?
- **a** tens
- **b** hundreds
- **c** thousands
- **ⓓ** NG

**3** 275 + 636
- **a** 811
- **ⓑ** 911
- **c** 801
- **d** NG

**4** $56.25 + 22.67
- **ⓐ** $78.92
- **b** $79.92
- **c** $78.82
- **d** NG

**5** 7,376 / 2,921 / + 437
- **a** 9,744
- **b** 10,634
- **ⓒ** 10,734
- **d** NG

**6** Round each number to the nearest hundred and add. 719 + 375
- **a** 1,200
- **ⓑ** 1,100
- **c** 1,000
- **d** NG

**7** 427 − 288
- **a** 261
- **b** 241
- **c** 239
- **ⓓ** NG

**8** 903 − 367
- **ⓐ** 536
- **b** 646
- **c** 666
- **d** NG

**9** $91.73 − 46.27
- **a** $55.54
- **b** $45.56
- **ⓒ** $45.46
- **d** NG

**10** Round each number to the nearest hundred and subtract 967 − 139
- **a** 1,000
- **b** 700
- **c** 800
- **ⓓ** NG

**11** What time is it? (Show a clock.)
- **ⓐ** 7:57
- **b** 11:40
- **c** 7:47
- **d** NG

**12** Find the perimeter of a rectangle 62 ft by 25 ft.
- **a** 87 ft.
- **b** 112 ft.
- **ⓒ** 174 ft.
- **d** NG

**13** What is the best unit for measuring a glass of juice?
- **a** quarts
- **ⓑ** ounces
- **c** gallons
- **d** NG

**116**

# Understanding Multiplication

## pages 117-118

### Objective

To review multiplication concepts

### Materials

paper cups and single counters

### Mental Math

Have volunteers make up word problems that incorporate each of these phrases. Have other students indicate the operation each phrase implies.

1. How many more would be needed?
2. How many do they have all together?
3. How much further do they have to go?
4. How far have they gone all together?
5. How much taller is she?
6. How much do they weigh all together?

### Skill Review

Have students copy and do the following column addition:

1. $5 + 5 + 5 = (15)$
2. $3 + 3 + 3 + 3 = (12)$
3. $10 + 10 + 10 = (30)$
4. $7 + 7 = (14)$
5. $2 + 2 + 2 + 2 + 2 = (10)$

---

## Understanding Multiplication

There is a Collector's Fair at the playground this Saturday. Silvia plans to show her penny collection. How many coins will she have in her display?

We want to find how many coins are in Silvia's display.

There are __5__ rows of pennies.

There are __4__ pennies in each row.

We can add the number of coins in each row.

$4 + 4 + 4 + 4 + 4 =$ __20__

We can multiply the number of rows by the number of coins in each.

**5 groups of 4 =** __20__

**5 fours =** __20__

$$\underset{\underset{\text{factor}}{\uparrow}}{5} \times \underset{\underset{\text{factor}}{\uparrow}}{4} = \underset{\underset{\text{product}}{\uparrow}}{20} \qquad \begin{array}{r} 4 \\ \times 5 \\ \hline 20 \end{array}$$

We can add the number of coins in each column.

$5 + 5 + 5 + 5 =$ __20__

We can multiply the number of columns by the number of coins in each.

**4 groups of 5 =** __20__

**4 fives =** __20__

$$\underset{\underset{\text{factor}}{\uparrow}}{4} \times \underset{\underset{\text{factor}}{\uparrow}}{5} = \underset{\underset{\text{product}}{\uparrow}}{20} \qquad \begin{array}{r} 5 \\ \times 4 \\ \hline 20 \end{array}$$

There are __20__ pennies in Silvia's display.

### Getting Started

Use both addition and multiplication to show how many are in each picture.

1. $\begin{array}{r} 3 \\ + 3 \\ \hline 6 \end{array}$  $2 \times 3 =$ __6__
   $3 \times 2 =$ __6__

2. $3 + 3 + 3 =$ __9__
   $3 \times 3 =$ __9__

(one hundred seventeen) **117**

---

## Teaching the Lesson

**Introducing the Problem**   Read the problem aloud while the class examines the illustration. Have a student explain what the problem asks. Have a student draw Silvia's collection on the board. Ask volunteers to complete the two information sentences. (5 rows across, 4 pennies in each row) Read the plan aloud. Have one student read the first method and demonstrate on the board by circling each row of five pennies. Have another student read the second approach and illustrate it on the board, circling five groups of four pennies each. Explain that the first shows that 4 groups of 5 equal 20, the second that 5 groups of 4 also equal 20. Have students complete these two sections and write the answer (20) in the solution sentence.

**Developing the Skill**   Have students work in pairs. Explain that one is to put four counters in each of three paper cups; the other, three counters in each of four cups. Illustrate the situation on the board by drawing two grids of circles, each 3 × 4. Circle three groups of four and four groups of three. Explain that the cups and your illustrations show the process of multiplication. Write **3 × 4 = 12** on the board and point out that we read this, **three times four equals twelve.** Show the class that multiplication is the same as column addition, by doing the problem on the board. $(4 + 4 + 4 = 12$ and $3 + 3 + 3 + 3 = 12)$

**117**

## Practice

Use both addition and multiplication to show how many are in each picture.

1.

$$\begin{array}{r} 4 \\ +4 \\ \hline 8 \end{array}$$

$2 \times 4 = \underline{8}$

$4 \times 2 = \underline{8}$

2.

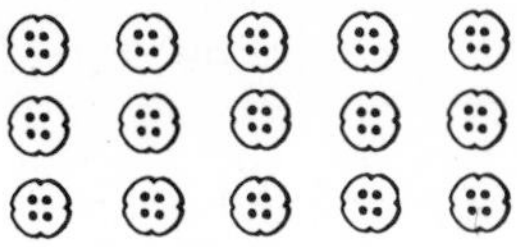

$3 + 3 + 3 + 3 + 3 = \underline{15}$

$5 \times 3 = \underline{15}$

$3 \times 5 = \underline{15}$

3.

$3 + 3 + 3 + 3 + 3 + 3 + 3 = \underline{21}$

$7 \times 3 = \underline{21}$

$3 \times 7 = \underline{21}$

4.

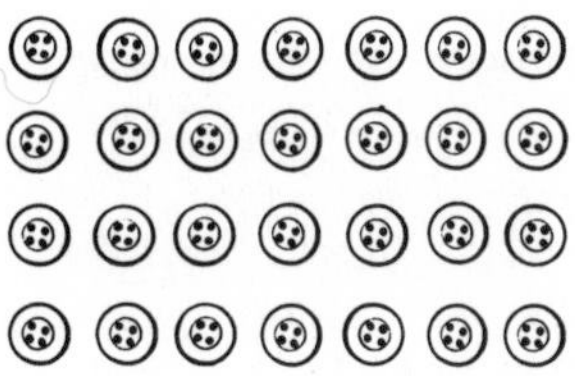

$$\begin{array}{r} 7 \\ 7 \\ 7 \\ +7 \\ \hline 28 \end{array}$$

$4 \times 7 = \underline{28}$

$7 \times 4 = \underline{28}$

5.

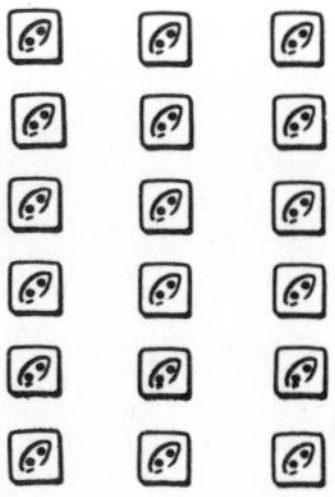

$$\begin{array}{r} 3 \\ 3 \\ 3 \\ 3 \\ 3 \\ +3 \\ \hline 18 \end{array}$$

$6 \times 3 = \underline{18}$

$3 \times 6 = \underline{18}$

6.

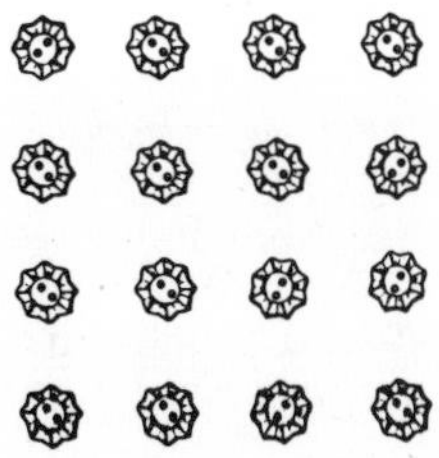

$$\begin{array}{r} 4 \\ 4 \\ 4 \\ +4 \\ \hline 16 \end{array}$$

$4 \times 4 = \underline{16}$

**118**   (one hundred eighteen)

**118**

# Multiplying, the Factor 2

## pages 119-120

### Objective

To review multiplication by the factor 2

### Materials

*a carton with a dozen eggs

### Mental Math

Ask students to think of eight different addition problems with a sum of 7. (0 + 7, 7 + 0, 1 + 6, 6 + 1, 2 + 5, 5 + 2, 3 + 4, 4 + 3) Repeat, asking for nine ways of making 8. (0 + 8, 8 + 0, 1 + 7, 7 + 1, 2 + 6, 6 + 2, 3 + 5, 5 + 3, 4 + 4)

### Skill Review

Remind the class that two threes is the same as three twos. (2 × 3 = 3 × 2) Illustrate on the board. Ask students to volunteer another multiplication problem that would give the same answer as:

1. 3 × 4 (4 × 3)   5. 4 × 6
2. 2 × 5 (5 × 2)   6. 3 × 9
3. 4 × 5           7. 2 × 3
4. 3 × 7           8. 5 × 7

---

## Multiplying, the Factor 2

Sun Li is helping her mother pack eggs in cartons. How many eggs does she pack into each carton?

The carton has 6 groups of ___2___ eggs each.

We can add. 2 + 2 + 2 + 2 + 2 + 2 = ___12___
We can also multiply.

$6 \times 2 = $ ___12___

$$\begin{array}{r} 2 \\ \times 6 \\ \hline 12 \end{array}$$

We can also think of it as 2 groups of ___6___ eggs each.

$2 \times 6 = $ ___12___

$$\begin{array}{r} 6 \\ \times 2 \\ \hline 12 \end{array}$$

Sun Li packs ___12___ eggs into each carton.

### Getting Started

Use both addition and multiplication to show how many are in each picture.

1.
$2 + 2 + 2 = $ ___6___
$3 \times 2 = $ ___6___
$2 \times 3 = $ ___6___

2.
$2 + 2 + 2 + 2 + 2 = $ ___10___
$5 \times 2 = $ ___10___
$2 \times 5 = $ ___10___

Multiply.

3. $7 \times 2 = $ ___14___

4. $2 \times 6 = $ ___12___

5.
$$\begin{array}{r} 4 \\ \times 2 \\ \hline 8 \end{array}$$

6.
$$\begin{array}{r} 2 \\ \times 2 \\ \hline 4 \end{array}$$

(one hundred nineteen) **119**

---

## Teaching the Lesson

**Introducing the Problem** Read the problem aloud emphasizing the question being asked. Have a student read the first version of the problem, volunteering the data required. (6 groups of 2 eggs each; 2 + 2 + 2 + 2 + 2 + 2 = 12) Have students circle six groups of 2 eggs on their pages. Write the problem both horizontally and vertically on the board and have a student complete them. (12, 12) Ask one student to explain how the second illustration differs from the first. (Two groups of 6 are shown.) Read the sentence describing the arrangement and have students complete it. (2 groups of 6 eggs each) Write the problem horizontally and vertically on the board and have another student work it while the others complete the problems and the solution sentences. (12, 12, 12)

**Developing the Skill** Show the class the egg carton. Have students name various ways the 12 eggs could be divided into groups. (2 sixes, 6 twos, 3 fours, 4 threes) Write these on the board. Label one of the problems showing that the first and second terms in the problem are called factors, and the answer is the product. One reason the terms have the same name is that they are interchangeable. Explain that like addition, multiplication is commutative.

**119**

## Practice

Use both addition and multiplication to show how many are in each picture.

1.

$2 + 2 + 2 + 2 + 2 + 2 + 2 + 2 + 2 = \underline{18}$

$9 \times 2 = \underline{18}$

$2 \times 9 = \underline{18}$

2.

$2 + 2 + 2 + 2 = \underline{8}$

$4 \times 2 = \underline{8}$

$2 \times 4 = \underline{8}$

3.

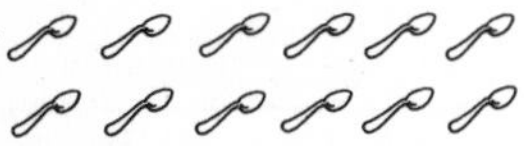

$2 + 2 + 2 + 2 + 2 + 2 = \underline{12}$

$6 \times 2 = \underline{12}$

$2 \times 6 = \underline{12}$

4.

$2 + 2 + 2 + 2 + 2 + 2 + 2 = \underline{14}$

$7 \times 2 = \underline{14}$

$2 \times 7 = \underline{14}$

Multiply.

5. $\begin{array}{r} 3 \\ \times 2 \\ \hline 6 \end{array}$
6. $\begin{array}{r} 2 \\ \times 2 \\ \hline 4 \end{array}$
7. $\begin{array}{r} 2 \\ \times 4 \\ \hline 8 \end{array}$
8. $\begin{array}{r} 5 \\ \times 2 \\ \hline 10 \end{array}$
9. $\begin{array}{r} 6 \\ \times 2 \\ \hline 12 \end{array}$
10. $\begin{array}{r} 2 \\ \times 7 \\ \hline 14 \end{array}$

11. $\begin{array}{r} 6 \\ \times 2 \\ \hline 12 \end{array}$
12. $\begin{array}{r} 2 \\ \times 8 \\ \hline 16 \end{array}$
13. $\begin{array}{r} 9 \\ \times 2 \\ \hline 18 \end{array}$
14. $\begin{array}{r} 2 \\ \times 6 \\ \hline 12 \end{array}$
15. $\begin{array}{r} 2 \\ \times 3 \\ \hline 6 \end{array}$
16. $\begin{array}{r} 4 \\ \times 2 \\ \hline 8 \end{array}$

17. $2 \times 9 = \underline{18}$

18. $3 \times 2 = \underline{6}$

19. $5 \times 2 = \underline{10}$

20. $2 \times 6 = \underline{12}$

21. $8 \times 2 = \underline{16}$

22. $2 \times 4 = \underline{8}$

## Apply

Solve these problems.

23. Kim has 2 trays of ice cubes. Each tray makes 8 cubes. How many cubes does Kim have? 16 cubes

24. Guido bought 6 sacks of fish hooks. Each sack held 2 fish hooks. How many fish hooks did Guido have? 12 fish hooks

**120** (one hundred twenty)

# Multiplying, the Factor 3

**pages 121-122**

## Objective

To multiply by the factor 3

## Materials

## Mental Math

Tell the students that the following is a cookie recipe. Ask them to double each ingredient so that twice as many cookies can be made.

1 stick of butter or 1/2 cup (2 sticks or 1 cup)
2 Tablespoons sugar (4 tbsp)
1 teaspoon vanilla (2 tsp)
1 cup ground nuts (2 c)
1 cup flour (2 c)

## Skill Review

Dictate the following problems to the class. Have them write each as column addition and as two different multiplication problems. Have them alternate between writing the multiplication horizontally and vertically.

1. $2 \times 3 = (6)$
2. $5 \times 2 = (10)$
3. $7 \times 2 = (14)$
4. $2 \times 1 = (2)$
5. $9 \times 2 = (18)$

---

## Multiplying, the Factor 3

Karen's grandmother puts a star on the chart every time Karen finishes a new book. How many books has she read?

We need to know how many stars are on Karen's chart.

There are ___3___ rows of stars.

There are ___4___ stars in each row.

We can add. $4 + 4 + 4 =$ ___12___
We can also multiply.

$$3 \times 4 = \underline{12} \qquad \begin{array}{r} 4 \\ \times 3 \\ \hline 12 \end{array}$$

We can also think of it as 4 groups of ___3___ stars each.

$$4 \times 3 = \underline{12} \qquad \begin{array}{r} 3 \\ \times 4 \\ \hline 12 \end{array}$$

Karen has read ___12___ new books.

### Getting Started

Use both addition and multiplication to show how many are in the picture.

1.
$3 + 3 + 3 + 3 + 3 =$ ___15___
$5 \times 3 =$ ___15___
$3 \times 5 =$ ___15___

Multiply.

2. $\begin{array}{r} 3 \\ \times 3 \\ \hline 9 \end{array}$     3. $\begin{array}{r} 3 \\ \times 8 \\ \hline 24 \end{array}$     4. $3 \times 6 =$ ___18___     5. $9 \times 3 =$ ___27___

(one hundred twenty-one) **121**

---

## Teaching the Lesson

**Introducing the Problem**  Have one student read the problem aloud and identify the question being asked. Read the information sentences and have students write the data. (3 rows, 4 stars in each row) Have a student read the first plan sentence. Explain the three ways of doing this problem; by column addition and two multiplication problems. Have students use these methods, filling in the data in their texts. Where this is illustrated in their texts, have them write the multiplication problem in horizontal and vertical forms. (3 × 4 = 12  4 × 3 = 12) Read the solution sentence aloud while students complete it in their texts. (12 new books)

**Developing the Skill**  Draw an array of x's having 3 rows with 11 x's in each row, on the board.
Tell students to count the array with you, starting with the first column and counting by threes to the right. (3, 6, 9, 12, 15, etc.) Point out that each of these numbers represents the product of 3 and some other digit. Write each number in the series on the board. (3, 6, 9, etc.) Have students come up and write a multiplication problem for each. (3 × 1 = 3, 3 × 2 = 6, 3 × 3 = 9, etc.)

**121**

Use both addition and multiplication to show how many are in each picture.

1.
(images of 3 rows of 9 crowns)

$3 + 3 + 3 + 3 + 3 + 3 + 3 + 3 + 3 =$ ___27___

$9 \times 3 =$ ___27___

$3 \times 9 =$ ___27___

2.
(images of 3 rows of 3 moons)

$3 + 3 + 3 =$ ___9___

$3 \times 3 =$ ___9___

Multiply.

| 3. | 4. | 5. | 6. | 7. | 8. |
|---|---|---|---|---|---|
| $\begin{array}{r} 3 \\ \times 4 \\ \hline 12 \end{array}$ | $\begin{array}{r} 5 \\ \times 3 \\ \hline 15 \end{array}$ | $\begin{array}{r} 3 \\ \times 2 \\ \hline 6 \end{array}$ | $\begin{array}{r} 3 \\ \times 6 \\ \hline 18 \end{array}$ | $\begin{array}{r} 2 \\ \times 5 \\ \hline 10 \end{array}$ | $\begin{array}{r} 4 \\ \times 3 \\ \hline 12 \end{array}$ |

| 9. | 10. | 11. | 12. | 13. | 14. |
|---|---|---|---|---|---|
| $\begin{array}{r} 2 \\ \times 3 \\ \hline 6 \end{array}$ | $\begin{array}{r} 2 \\ \times 8 \\ \hline 16 \end{array}$ | $\begin{array}{r} 6 \\ \times 3 \\ \hline 18 \end{array}$ | $\begin{array}{r} 7 \\ \times 2 \\ \hline 14 \end{array}$ | $\begin{array}{r} 3 \\ \times 8 \\ \hline 24 \end{array}$ | $\begin{array}{r} 4 \\ \times 2 \\ \hline 8 \end{array}$ |

| 15. | 16. | 17. | 18. | 19. | 20. |
|---|---|---|---|---|---|
| $\begin{array}{r} 9 \\ \times 2 \\ \hline 18 \end{array}$ | $\begin{array}{r} 3 \\ \times 5 \\ \hline 15 \end{array}$ | $\begin{array}{r} 8 \\ \times 2 \\ \hline 16 \end{array}$ | $\begin{array}{r} 8 \\ \times 3 \\ \hline 24 \end{array}$ | $\begin{array}{r} 3 \\ \times 7 \\ \hline 21 \end{array}$ | $\begin{array}{r} 3 \\ \times 5 \\ \hline 15 \end{array}$ |

21. $9 \times 3 =$ ___27___

22. $3 \times 7 =$ ___21___

23. $4 \times 3 =$ ___12___

24. $3 \times 8 =$ ___24___

25. $2 \times 6 =$ ___12___

26. $3 \times 9 =$ ___27___

27. $5 \times 2 =$ ___10___

28. $6 \times 3 =$ ___18___

29. $3 \times 5 =$ ___15___

**Apply**

Solve these problems.

30. Tennis cans hold 3 tennis balls each. How many tennis balls are in 6 cans?
18 balls

31. Pencils are sold in packages of 8. Dan bought 3 packages. How many pencils did Dan buy?
24 pencils

## Correcting Common Errors

Some students may have difficulty learning the facts of 3. Have them use grid paper to model these facts. In the first row, have them color 3 squares and write $1 \times 3 = 3$. In the next row, have them color 3 squares with one color and the adjacent 3 squares with another color and write $2 \times 3 = 6$. In the third row, have them show 3 sets of 3, alternating colors, and write $3 \times 3 = 9$. Have them continue in this manner to show all the facts of 3 through $9 \times 3$.

## Enrichment

Have students calculate the value of n in each problem. Explain that when they multiply anything other than a pure number, they must watch the labels; cents cannot be multiplied by cents, for example.

1. $3 \times n = 15$ (5)
2. $n \times 9 = 27$ (3)
3. $10 \times n¢ = 90¢$ (9¢)
4. $3 \times 3 = n$ (9)
5. $n° \times 8 = 24°$ (3°)
6. $20 \text{ min} \times n = 60 \text{ min}$ (3)

## Practice

Have students complete the page. Point out that the first two problems are to be done in each of the three ways shown.

## Extra Credit   *Geometry*

Give each student a geoboard, several rubber bands, a piece of paper and a pencil. Have them fold the paper in half and draw a triangle on one side, a rectangle on the other. Direct students to make at least five triangles and five rectangles on their geoboards. For each figure made, they are to count the number of nails touched by the rubber band and the number contained within the rubber band. Tell students to record their results on the appropriate triangle or rectangle side of their paper. When they are finished, have students describe any pattern they notice in the numbers. (The number of nails within will increase with the number of nails touched.)

# Multiplying, the Factor 4

**pages 123-124**

## Objective

To multiply by the factor 4

## Materials

## Mental Math

Ask students to subtract 10 from each sum:

1. $9 + 4 + 8$  $(21 - 10 = 11)$
2. $5 + 3 + 7$  $(15 - 10 = 5)$
3. $5 + 5 + 5 + 5$  $(20 - 10 = 10)$
4. $2 + 8 + 7$  $(17 - 10 = 7)$
5. $11 + 9 + 6$  $(26 - 10 = 16)$
6. $18 + 12$  $(30 - 10 = 20)$
7. $7 + 14 + 9$  $(30 - 10 = 20)$

## Skill Review

Ask students to provide quick answers to each of the multiplication problems you dictate.

1. $2 \times 3 = (6)$    2. $3 \times 5 = (15)$
3. $4 \times 2 = (8)$    4. $3 \times 9 = (27)$
5. $7 \times 3 = (21)$   6. $9 \times 2 = (18)$
7. $4 \times 3 = (12)$   8. $3 \times 3 = (9)$
9. $5 \times 2 = (10)$   10. $2 \times 2 = (4)$

---

**Multiplying, the Factor 4**

Mrs. Franklin put tomato plants in her garden so she can make tomato juice in the fall. How many plants is she growing?

We want to know the total number of tomato plants in the garden.

The garden has __8__ rows of plants.

There are __4__ plants across in each row.
We can add. $4 + 4 + 4 + 4 + 4 + 4 + 4 + 4 =$ __32__
We can also multiply.

$8 \times 4 =$ __32__   $\begin{array}{r} 4 \\ \times 8 \\ \hline 32 \end{array}$

We can also think of it as 4 groups of __8__ plants each.

$4 \times 8 =$ __32__   $\begin{array}{r} 8 \\ \times 4 \\ \hline 32 \end{array}$

Mrs. Franklin has __32__ tomato plants in her garden.

### Getting Started

Use both addition and multiplication to show how many are in the picture.

1.   $4 + 4 + 4 + 4 + 4 + 4 =$ __24__

$6 \times 4 =$ __24__

$4 \times 6 =$ __24__

Multiply.

2.  $\begin{array}{r} 5 \\ \times 4 \\ \hline 20 \end{array}$    3.  $\begin{array}{r} 3 \\ \times 4 \\ \hline 12 \end{array}$    4. $4 \times 4 =$ __16__    5. $4 \times 2 =$ __8__

---

## Teaching the Lesson

**Introducing the Problem**  Have a student read the problem aloud and identify the question being asked. Have another read the information sentences, supplying the number of rows (8) and the number of plants in each row. (4) Explain that there are at least two different ways to do this problem. They can add the number of plants in each row (4) eight times. Have students do this operation in the texts. Explain that they could also multiply to get the answer. Tell students to complete the two multiplication problems, writing answers for both the horizontal and vertical form. Ask if both multiplication problems will give the same answer. (yes) Read the solution sentence and have a student supply the answer as the others write the answer in the solution sentence.

**Developing the Skill**  Draw a number line from 0 through 40 on the board and have students mark points along the line that are multiples of 4. (4, 8, 12, etc.) While you point to the intervals have the class count aloud by fours from 0 through 40. Now have students identify the multiplication problems represented by each number. ($4 = 4 \times 1, 8 = 4 \times 2$, etc.)

**123**

**Practice**

Use both addition and multiplication to show how many are in each picture.

1.

4 + 4 + 4 + 4 + 4 + 4 = __24__

6 × 4 = __24__

4 × 6 = __24__

2.

4 + 4 + 4 + 4 + 4 = __20__

5 × 4 = __20__

4 × 5 = __20__

Multiply.

| 3. | 4. | 5. | 6. | 7. | 8. |
|---|---|---|---|---|---|
| 3 <br> × 4 <br> 12 | 5 <br> × 4 <br> 20 | 3 <br> × 2 <br> 6 | 2 <br> × 9 <br> 18 | 8 <br> × 3 <br> 24 | 2 <br> × 7 <br> 14 |

| 9. | 10. | 11. | 12. | 13. | 14. |
|---|---|---|---|---|---|
| 4 <br> × 6 <br> 24 | 7 <br> × 4 <br> 28 | 3 <br> × 7 <br> 21 | 4 <br> × 2 <br> 8 | 9 <br> × 4 <br> 36 | 9 <br> × 3 <br> 27 |

| 15. | 16. | 17. | 18. | 19. | 20. |
|---|---|---|---|---|---|
| 8 <br> × 2 <br> 16 | 6 <br> × 4 <br> 24 | 7 <br> × 2 <br> 14 | 2 <br> × 3 <br> 6 | 4 <br> × 4 <br> 16 | 6 <br> × 3 <br> 18 |

21. 6 × 4 = __24__          22. 3 × 4 = __12__          23. 9 × 4 = __36__

24. 4 × 8 = __32__          25. 3 × 9 = __27__          26. 2 × 8 = __16__

**Apply**

Solve these problems.

27. There are 4 tables in the room. There are 6 children at each table. How many children are there?
24 children

28. Mrs. Golic bought 4 toys for $8 apiece. How much did the toys cost Mrs. Golic?
$32

**124**   (one hundred twenty-four)

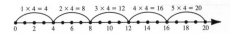

# Multiplying, the Factor 5

pages 125-126

## Objective

To multiply by the factor 5

## Materials

## Mental Math

Ask students to multiply 4 by:

1. the number of ears one person has. (4 × 2 = 8)
2. the number of feet two students have. (4 × 4 = 16)
3. the number of noses in a crowd of 7. (4 × 7 = 28)
4. the number of their toes. (4 × 10 = 40)

## Skill Review

Have students make up a multiplication chart. Tell them to write 2, 3, 4 along the top, 2 through 10 along the side. Tell them to fill in the chart by multiplying each top number by each side number.

---

**Multiplying, the Factor 5**

Each key on a calculator has a special job to do. How many keys are there on the calculator keyboard?

We need to find the total number of keys on the calculator.

We can see there are ___5___ rows of keys.

Each row has ___5___ keys.

We can add. **5 + 5 + 5 + 5 + 5 =** ___25___

We can also multiply.

$$5 \times 5 = \underline{\hspace{0.5cm}25} \qquad \begin{array}{r} 5 \\ \times 5 \\ \hline 25 \end{array}$$

There are ___25___ keys on the calculator keyboard.

### Getting Started

Use both addition and multiplication to show how many are in the picture.

1. (pencils pictured)

$5 + 5 + 5 + 5 =$ ___20___

$4 \times 5 =$ ___20___

$5 \times 4 =$ ___20___

Multiply.

2. $\begin{array}{r} 3 \\ \times 5 \\ \hline 15 \end{array}$   3. $\begin{array}{r} 8 \\ \times 5 \\ \hline 40 \end{array}$   4. $5 \times 6 =$ ___30___   5. $9 \times 5 =$ ___45___

(one hundred twenty-five) **125**

---

## Teaching the Lesson

**Introducing the Problem** Have students look at the calculator illustrated while you read the problem. Identify the question and explain that there are several ways they could answer it. Have students read the information sentences, filling in the information required. (5 rows, 5 keys) Read each sentence and tell students to do the indicated operation in their text while one student writes it on the board. Read the solution sentence aloud and have a student give the answer while the others complete that sentence in their texts. (30)

**Developing the Skill** Have students start at 5 and count aloud by five's through 50. Ask a volunteer to continue through 100. Explain that this may seem easy because they are used to counting out nickels. Because five is also half of ten, and when counting by fives, every other number will be a multiple of ten. Now write these addition problems on the board and have students work them: **5 + 5 = ,** **5 + 5 + 5 = , 5 + 5 + 5 + 5 = .** (10, 15, 20) Next to each of these problems write the multiplication problem that corresponds. (**5 × 2, 5 × 3, 5 × 4**) Have volunteers put the rest of the addition and multiplication problems for the factor five on the board, 5 × 5 through 5 × 10.

## Practice

Use both addition and multiplication to show how many are in each picture.

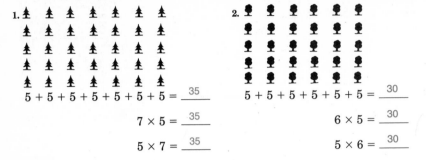

1. $5 + 5 + 5 + 5 + 5 + 5 + 5 = \underline{35}$

$7 \times 5 = \underline{35}$

$5 \times 7 = \underline{35}$

2. $5 + 5 + 5 + 5 + 5 + 5 = \underline{30}$

$6 \times 5 = \underline{30}$

$5 \times 6 = \underline{30}$

Multiply.

| 3. | 4. | 5. | 6. | 7. | 8. | 9. |
|---|---|---|---|---|---|---|
| 6 | 4 | 3 | 5 | 8 | 9 | 4 |
| ×5 | ×3 | ×5 | ×7 | ×5 | ×4 | ×8 |
| 30 | 12 | 15 | 35 | 40 | 36 | 32 |

| 10. | 11. | 12. | 13. | 14. | 15. | 16. |
|---|---|---|---|---|---|---|
| 7 | 4 | 5 | 5 | 2 | 6 | 5 |
| ×3 | ×5 | ×9 | ×5 | ×5 | ×4 | ×2 |
| 21 | 20 | 45 | 25 | 10 | 24 | 10 |

17. $5 \times 3 = \underline{15}$   18. $6 \times 5 = \underline{30}$   19. $5 \times 7 = \underline{35}$   20. $5 \times 9 = \underline{45}$

### EXCURSION

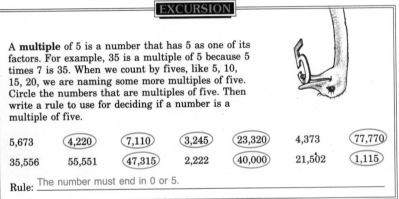

A **multiple** of 5 is a number that has 5 as one of its factors. For example, 35 is a multiple of 5 because 5 times 7 is 35. When we count by fives, like 5, 10, 15, 20, we are naming some more multiples of five. Circle the numbers that are multiples of five. Then write a rule to use for deciding if a number is a multiple of five.

| 5,673 | (4,220) | (7,110) | (3,245) | (23,320) | 4,373 | (77,770) |
|---|---|---|---|---|---|---|
| 35,556 | 55,551 | (47,315) | 2,222 | (40,000) | 21,502 | (1,115) |

Rule: The number must end in 0 or 5.

---

## Correcting Common Errors

If students have difficulty learning facts of 5, have them practice with partners. Have them draw a vertical number line from 0 through 50, marking it in intervals of 5. Have one partner write the addition problem to the left of each multiple of five on the number line while the other partner writes the corresponding multiplication problem.

```
              ┌0
         5   ┤5      (5 × 1)
     5 + 5   ┤10     (5 × 2)
 5 + 5 + 5   ┤15     (5 × 3)
5 + 5 + 5 + 5 ┤20    (5 × 4)
```

## Enrichment

Ask students how many fives are in 55 if, there are 10 fives in 50. (11) Tell them to complete a multiplication table for fives that goes up to the product 150. Have them use the table to figure the number of nickels in $4.00. (80)

## Practice

Have students do all the problems on the page. Remind the class that they can use addition to figure out any multiplication facts they are not sure of.

## Excursion

Have students write the multiples of 5 through 200. Help students to see that any number that ends in 0 or 5 is a multiple of 5. Have students write the rule. Now write several 4- and 5-digit numbers on the board and ask students to circle the numbers that are multiples of 5.

## Extra Credit   Logic

Write the following on the board:

| WOW | TOT | POP | BIB |
|---|---|---|---|
| 525 | 969 | 343 | 5445 |

Ask students what all of these have in common. Explain they are palindromes, or words or numbers which are the same whether they are read forward or backward. Also, explain 302 is not a palindrome, but if you reverse the numbers and add, it will make a palindrome:

```
 302
+203
 505
```

Using this method, ask students what palindrome they can make with these numbers: 36; (99) 342; (585) 4,205; (9,229) 3,406 (9,449). Have students list some other numbers which, when reversed and added, will form a palindrome.

# Multiplying, the Factors 1 and 0

pages 127-128

## Objective

To multiply by the factors 0 and 1

## Materials

single counters
paper cups

## Mental Math

1. In a school auditorium there are 10 rows of chairs with 5 chairs in each row. How many people can sit in the auditorium? (10 × 5 = 50)
2. In a package of cookies there are 8 cookies in a section and 3 sections in the box. How many cookies are in the box? (8 × 3 = 24)
3. There are 9 pencils in a pack and 3 packs. How many pencils are there all together? (9 × 3 = 27)

## Skill Review

Ask volunteers to count by two's from 2 to 20, by three's from 3 to 30, by four's from 4 to 40, and by fives from 5 to 50. Dictate, at random, some of these products and ask students to provide the multiplication problem that corresponds.

---

## Multiplying, the Factors 1 and 0

An elephant smells, drinks and feeds himself with his trunk. How many trunks do the elephants show? How many trunks do the tigers show?

We want to know how many trunks each group of animals has.

We see ___4___ elephants with ___1___ trunk each.

We see ___4___ tigers with ___0___ trunks each.

To find the total number of elephant

trunks, we multiply ___4___ by ___1___.

To find the total number of tiger trunks,

we multiply ___4___ by ___0___.

**4 elephants with 1 trunk each**       **4 tigers with 0 trunks each**

  4 × 1 = ___4___              4 × 0 = ___0___

  1 × 4 = ___4___              0 × 4 = ___0___

The elephants have ___4___ trunks showing.

The tigers have ___0___ trunks showing.

### Getting Started

Multiply.

| 1.  1<br>× 0<br>―――<br>0 | 2.  0<br>× 9<br>―――<br>0 | 3.  3<br>× 1<br>―――<br>3 | 4.  3<br>× 3<br>―――<br>9 | 5.  1<br>× 5<br>―――<br>5 | 6.  0<br>× 0<br>―――<br>0 |

7. 8 × 1 = ___8___     8. 0 × 3 = ___0___     9. 5 × 2 = ___10___     10. 1 × 6 = ___6___

(one hundred twenty-seven) **127**

---

## Teaching the Lesson

**Introducing the Problem**  Read the problem aloud and have a student identify the question being asked. Ask a student to read and complete the information sentences while the others complete the sentences in their texts. (4 elephants, 1 trunk each; 4 tigers, 0 trunks each) Read the first plan sentence as they write it in. (we multiply 4 by 1) Have one student read the second plan sentence while the others complete it in their texts. (multiply 4 by 0) Complete both sets of problems with the students. Read the solution sentences aloud while students complete them in their books. (elephants, 4 trunks; tigers, 0 trunks)

**Developing the Skill**  Have students put 3 paper cups on their desks with 1 counter in each cup. Write this on the board:
**3 × 1 = 3.** Now have them put 3 counters in one cup. Write this on the board: **1 × 3 = 3.** Explain that when they multiply by 1 they always get a product the same as the larger factor. Give students several problems to work: 6 × 1, 12 × 1, 483 × 1. Now have students put 3 empty cups on their desks. Write the equation on the board: **3 × 0 = 0.** Explain that no matter how many empty cups they put out, there would still be no counters in them. Anytime they multiply by zero, the product will be zero. Dictate these problems: 8 × 0, 84 × 0, 629 × 0.

**127**

## Practice

Multiply.

1.  6
   × 0
   ———
    0

2.  5
   × 9
   ———
   45

3.  3
   × 7
   ———
   21

4.  1
   × 7
   ———
    7

5.  8
   × 4
   ———
   32

6.  0
   × 7
   ———
    0

7.  1
   × 1
   ———
    1

8.  7
   × 4
   ———
   28

9.  0
   × 0
   ———
    0

10.  6
    × 5
    ———
    30

11.  4
    × 9
    ———
    36

12.  3
    × 2
    ———
     6

13.  1
    × 0
    ———
     0

14.  9
    × 1
    ———
     9

15. $4 \times 5 = \underline{20}$

16. $0 \times 8 = \underline{0}$

17. $3 \times 1 = \underline{3}$

18. $5 \times 0 = \underline{0}$

19. $6 \times 2 = \underline{12}$

20. $1 \times 8 = \underline{8}$

21. $9 \times 0 = \underline{0}$

22. $4 \times 3 = \underline{12}$

23. $5 \times 5 = \underline{25}$

24. $4 \times 1 = \underline{4}$

25. $8 \times 3 = \underline{24}$

26. $0 \times 6 = \underline{0}$

## Apply

Solve these problems.

27. If 8 students each had 1 pencil, how many pencils did they have all together?
8 pencils

28. A box of pencils costs $1. How much will 9 boxes cost?
$9

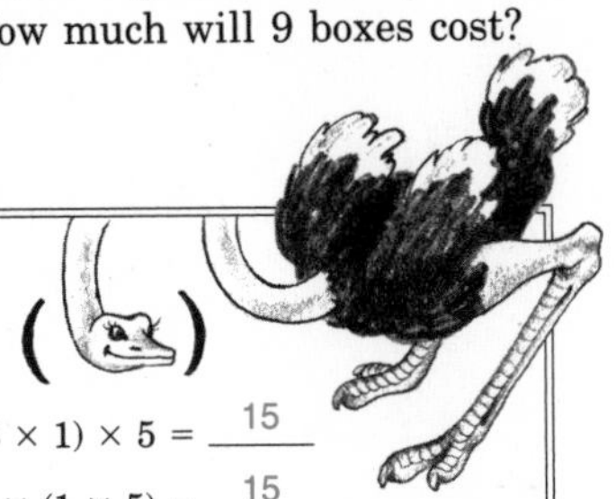

---

### EXCURSION

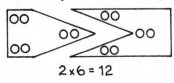

Do the work inside the parentheses first. Then circle yes or no to answer the question.

1. $5 + (4 \times 0) = \underline{5}$

   $(5 + 4) \times 0 = \underline{0}$

   Does $5 + (4 \times 0) = (5 + 4) \times 0$?

   yes or (no)

2. $(3 \times 1) \times 5 = \underline{15}$

   $3 \times (1 \times 5) = \underline{15}$

   Does $(3 \times 1) \times 5 = 3 \times (1 \times 5)$?

   (yes) or no

3. $4 \times (0 + 1) = \underline{4}$

   $4 \times (1 + 0) = \underline{4}$

   Does $4 \times (0 + 1) = 4 \times (1 + 0)$?

   (yes) or no

4. $2 \times (5 - 0) = \underline{10}$

   $(2 \times 5) - 0 = \underline{10}$

   Does $2 \times (5 - 0) = (2 \times 5) - 0$?

   (yes) or no

---

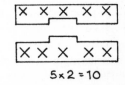
**128**

# Mixed Facts

pages 129-130

## Objectives

To review multiplication facts learned
To work mixed problems including
addition, subtraction, and multiplication

## Materials

*addition, subtraction and multiplica-
tion flash cards

## Mental Math

Explain that the letter n stands for a
number. Dictate these problems and
have students solve for n:

1. $2 \times n = 6$ (3)
2. $n - 10 = 21$ (31)
3. $5 \times 4 = n$ (20)
4. $n + 8 + 13 = 25$ (4)
5. $56 - n = 39$ (17)
6. $45 \times n = 0$ (0)

## Skill Review

Use the multiplication flash cards to
review multiplication facts $0 \times 1$
through $5 \times 10$. Look for a quick response time to be sure students know
the fact and are not stopping to calculate an answer by addition.

---

**Practicing Multiplication Facts**

Multiply.

| | | | | | | |
|---|---|---|---|---|---|---|
| 1. $\begin{array}{r} 3 \\ \times 9 \\ \hline 27 \end{array}$ | 2. $\begin{array}{r} 9 \\ \times 0 \\ \hline 0 \end{array}$ | 3. $\begin{array}{r} 3 \\ \times 7 \\ \hline 21 \end{array}$ | 4. $\begin{array}{r} 2 \\ \times 8 \\ \hline 16 \end{array}$ | 5. $\begin{array}{r} 2 \\ \times 9 \\ \hline 18 \end{array}$ | 6. $\begin{array}{r} 1 \\ \times 6 \\ \hline 6 \end{array}$ | 7. $\begin{array}{r} 5 \\ \times 6 \\ \hline 30 \end{array}$ |
| 8. $\begin{array}{r} 0 \\ \times 6 \\ \hline 0 \end{array}$ | 9. $\begin{array}{r} 2 \\ \times 2 \\ \hline 4 \end{array}$ | 10. $\begin{array}{r} 4 \\ \times 6 \\ \hline 24 \end{array}$ | 11. $\begin{array}{r} 9 \\ \times 2 \\ \hline 18 \end{array}$ | 12. $\begin{array}{r} 3 \\ \times 0 \\ \hline 0 \end{array}$ | 13. $\begin{array}{r} 4 \\ \times 8 \\ \hline 32 \end{array}$ | 14. $\begin{array}{r} 4 \\ \times 4 \\ \hline 16 \end{array}$ |
| 15. $\begin{array}{r} 9 \\ \times 3 \\ \hline 27 \end{array}$ | 16. $\begin{array}{r} 3 \\ \times 3 \\ \hline 9 \end{array}$ | 17. $\begin{array}{r} 6 \\ \times 1 \\ \hline 6 \end{array}$ | 18. $\begin{array}{r} 8 \\ \times 0 \\ \hline 0 \end{array}$ | 19. $\begin{array}{r} 7 \\ \times 4 \\ \hline 28 \end{array}$ | 20. $\begin{array}{r} 2 \\ \times 7 \\ \hline 14 \end{array}$ | 21. $\begin{array}{r} 4 \\ \times 2 \\ \hline 8 \end{array}$ |
| 22. $\begin{array}{r} 8 \\ \times 4 \\ \hline 32 \end{array}$ | 23. $\begin{array}{r} 0 \\ \times 8 \\ \hline 0 \end{array}$ | 24. $\begin{array}{r} 1 \\ \times 2 \\ \hline 2 \end{array}$ | 25. $\begin{array}{r} 4 \\ \times 7 \\ \hline 28 \end{array}$ | 26. $\begin{array}{r} 6 \\ \times 5 \\ \hline 30 \end{array}$ | 27. $\begin{array}{r} 5 \\ \times 8 \\ \hline 40 \end{array}$ | 28. $\begin{array}{r} 4 \\ \times 0 \\ \hline 0 \end{array}$ |
| 29. $\begin{array}{r} 4 \\ \times 5 \\ \hline 20 \end{array}$ | 30. $\begin{array}{r} 0 \\ \times 7 \\ \hline 0 \end{array}$ | 31. $\begin{array}{r} 9 \\ \times 5 \\ \hline 45 \end{array}$ | 32. $\begin{array}{r} 1 \\ \times 7 \\ \hline 7 \end{array}$ | 33. $\begin{array}{r} 5 \\ \times 3 \\ \hline 15 \end{array}$ | 34. $\begin{array}{r} 4 \\ \times 1 \\ \hline 4 \end{array}$ | 35. $\begin{array}{r} 6 \\ \times 0 \\ \hline 0 \end{array}$ |
| 36. $\begin{array}{r} 5 \\ \times 1 \\ \hline 5 \end{array}$ | 37. $\begin{array}{r} 6 \\ \times 4 \\ \hline 24 \end{array}$ | 38. $\begin{array}{r} 8 \\ \times 2 \\ \hline 16 \end{array}$ | 39. $\begin{array}{r} 3 \\ \times 7 \\ \hline 21 \end{array}$ | 40. $\begin{array}{r} 1 \\ \times 1 \\ \hline 1 \end{array}$ | 41. $\begin{array}{r} 0 \\ \times 5 \\ \hline 0 \end{array}$ | 42. $\begin{array}{r} 5 \\ \times 5 \\ \hline 25 \end{array}$ |

43. $9 \times 1 = \underline{9}$     44. $0 \times 5 = \underline{0}$     45. $1 \times 9 = \underline{9}$     46. $3 \times 7 = \underline{21}$

47. $8 \times 3 = \underline{24}$     48. $9 \times 5 = \underline{45}$     49. $6 \times 4 = \underline{24}$     50. $7 \times 5 = \underline{35}$

51. $0 \times 0 = \underline{0}$     52. $2 \times 6 = \underline{12}$     53. $4 \times 3 = \underline{12}$     54. $5 \times 0 = \underline{0}$

55. $5 \times 5 = \underline{25}$     56. $4 \times 6 = \underline{24}$     57. $2 \times 7 = \underline{14}$     58. $9 \times 4 = \underline{36}$

59. $3 \times 9 = \underline{27}$     60. $2 \times 8 = \underline{16}$     61. $4 \times 7 = \underline{28}$     62. $8 \times 0 = \underline{0}$

(one hundred twenty-nine) **129**

---

## Teaching the Lesson

**Introducing the Problem**   Explain that the next two
pages will give them practice with multiplication facts and
mixed multiplication, addition and subtraction practice. They
have already practiced multiplication fact recognition flash
cards, and the addition and subtraction fact flash cards. Do
an oral drill of the cards with students, emphasizing quick
response. Set aside any cards that students have trouble
with. Repeat troublesome cards.

**Developing the Skill**   As further activity, use the mixed
flash cards as the basis for a class competition. Have one
student start the competition standing next to the first person in the first row of the room. Show a card. Whomever
supplies the first correct answer moves on to the next student in the row, while the other student sits down. See
which student can go the farthest.

**129**

## Practicing Mixed Skills

Write the correct answer.

| 1. | 2. | 3. | 4. | 5. | 6. | 7. |
|---|---|---|---|---|---|---|
| 3 ×5 = 15 | 6 +7 = 13 | 1 ×8 = 8 | 4 ×7 = 28 | 8 +2 = 10 | 8 ×2 = 16 | 11 −4 = 7 |

| 8. | 9. | 10. | 11. | 12. | 13. | 14. |
|---|---|---|---|---|---|---|
| 9 +6 = 15 | 2 ×3 = 6 | 18 −9 = 9 | 2 ×0 = 0 | 4 +3 = 7 | 5 +8 = 13 | 5 ×9 = 45 |

| 15. | 16. | 17. | 18. | 19. | 20. | 21. |
|---|---|---|---|---|---|---|
| 2 ×1 = 2 | 1 ×4 = 4 | 7 ×0 = 0 | 17 −8 = 9 | 6 ×3 = 18 | 5 ×1 = 5 | 0 ×4 = 0 |

| 22. | 23. | 24. | 25. | 26. | 27. | 28. |
|---|---|---|---|---|---|---|
| 7 +5 = 12 | 2 ×5 = 10 | 9 +6 = 15 | 0 ×1 = 0 | 7 ×5 = 35 | 4 −0 = 4 | 8 +5 = 13 |

| 29. | 30. | 31. | 32. | 33. | 34. | 35. |
|---|---|---|---|---|---|---|
| 4 ×4 = 16 | 12 −6 = 6 | 8 ×5 = 40 | 9 ×4 = 36 | 0 +7 = 7 | 3 ×6 = 18 | 9 −1 = 8 |

| 36. | 37. | 38. | 39. | 40. | 41. | 42. |
|---|---|---|---|---|---|---|
| 8 +8 = 16 | 3 ×2 = 6 | 7 ×1 = 7 | 8 −8 = 0 | 2 ×6 = 12 | 7 +9 = 16 | 4 −3 = 1 |

| 43. | 44. | 45. | 46. | 47. | 48. | 49. |
|---|---|---|---|---|---|---|
| 7 ×3 = 21 | 6 +4 = 10 | 1 ×3 = 3 | 15 −8 = 7 | 1 ×5 = 5 | 5 ×9 = 45 | 14 −6 = 8 |

| 50. | 51. | 52. | 53. | 54. | 55. | 56. |
|---|---|---|---|---|---|---|
| 4 ×3 = 12 | 11 −5 = 6 | 9 +9 = 18 | 3 ×1 = 3 | 4 ×9 = 36 | 10 −7 = 3 | 8 ×1 = 8 |

| 57. | 58. | 59. | 60. | 61. | 62. | 63. |
|---|---|---|---|---|---|---|
| 15 −8 = 7 | 6 ×3 = 18 | 1 ×4 = 4 | 7 +6 = 13 | 8 +9 = 17 | 4 ×3 = 12 | 4 +3 = 7 |

| 64. | 65. | 66. | 67. | 68. | 69. | 70. |
|---|---|---|---|---|---|---|
| 6 +7 = 13 | 16 −9 = 7 | 5 ×4 = 20 | 2 ×3 = 6 | 6 ×5 = 30 | 9 −6 = 3 | 8 +7 = 15 |

**130** (one hundred thirty)

**130**

## Correcting Common Errors

Some students may answer incorrectly when working with a set of mixed problems because they do not carefully read the operation signs. Have them work with partners. One partner circles all the addition signs in the mixed set and they go through and practice all those facts. Then they proceed in the same manner for subtraction and then for multiplication.

## Enrichment

Make up one page each of one hundred mixed addition, subtraction, and multiplication facts. Give each student a copy of the 3 pages. Explain that they have three minutes to do the problems per page and that accuracy is very important. Have one student be the timer for each round. Have them check each other's work.

## Practice

Have students do all the problems on the page. Point out that for the mixed problems, they will have to be careful to read the sign before they do the problems.

## Mixed Practice

1. 8 × 5 (40)
2. $14.00 − 9.89 ($4.11)
3. 36 + 125 + 492 (653)
4. 6,365 + 2,291 (8,656)
5. 2 × 3 (6)
6. 1,800 − 942 (858)
7. 495 + 372 (867)
8. 9,000 − 6,533 (2,467)
9. 4 × 7 (28)
10. 6,758 − 3,226 (3,532)

## Extra Credit  *Applications*

Provide your students with practice in using a ruler in preparation for mapping. Students will need rulers and a sheet of 1/4-inch graph paper. Write a list of instructions similar to these on the board:

Using a ruler:

1. make a line 6 1/2 inches long.
2. make a line 2 1/4 inches long.
3. draw a square 4 1/4 inches by 4 1/4 inches.
4. make a rectangle 4 inches by 5 inches.
5. draw a house 7 1/2 inches tall and 4 1/2 inches wide.
6. draw a boat 5 3/4 inches long.

Instruct the students to follow each of the directions carefully and label each figure with the number of the direction. Tell them to use the lines on the graph paper and a ruler to help draw straight lines.

# Problem Solving Using a Plan

pages 131-132

## Objective

To use a four-step plan for problem solving

## Materials

## Mental Math

Explain that 2n stands for two times some number, n. Ask students to solve for n in the problems below and then figure out what 2n would be.

1. n + 10 = 25 (n = 15, 2n = 30)
2. 5 × n = 10 (n = 2, 2n = 4)
3. 4 + 4 + n = 12 (n = 4, 2n = 8)
4. 50 − 10 − n = 20 (n = 20, 2n = 40)
5. n = 4 × 4 (n = 16, 2n = 32)
6. 10 + 8 + 2 = n (n = 20, 2n = 40)
7. 40 − 35 = n (n = 5, 2n = 10)

### Using a Four-step Plan

Luis and Pedro decide to buy a planter and a card for their parents' anniversary. Luis has saved $8.45 and Pedro has saved $6.58. How much will they spend? How much money will they have left?

★ SEE

A planter costs $12.99. A card costs $1.50.

Luis has saved $8.45. Pedro has saved $6.58.

We need to find:
the total cost of a planter and card.
the combined savings of the two boys.
the difference between these two amounts.

★ PLAN

To find how much the planter and card cost together, we add $12.99 and $1.50.
To find how much money the boys had saved, we add $8.45 and $6.58.
To find the amount they have left, we subtract their costs from their total money.

★ DO

$$\begin{array}{ll} \$8.45 & \$12.99 \\ +\ 6.58 & +\ 1.50 \\ \hline \$15.03 & \$14.49 \end{array}$$

$$\begin{array}{r} \$15.03 \\ -\ 14.49 \\ \hline \$0.54 \end{array}$$

The boys will spend $14.49 and have $0.54 left over.

★ CHECK

$$\begin{array}{r} \$14.49 \\ +\ 0.54 \\ \hline \$15.03 \end{array}$$

(one hundred thirty-one) **131**

## Teaching the Lesson

Read the problem aloud. Explain that this problem cannot be solved in one step but must be broken down into parts. Have students look down the page. Ask someone to read the headings on the four parts of the problem. (SEE, PLAN, DO, CHECK) Ask another student to explain what these titles mean. (SEE: Read through the problem and the accompanying information to find the numbers needed to do the problem. PLAN: Think about the problem and how the numbers might be used in solving it. DO: Do the computations as they were imagined in the PLAN section. CHECK: Work the problem a different way to see if the answer is consistent.) Start with SEE section. Point out that the center section of the page has been left blank for computations. Have students find and fill in the price of the planter ($12.99) and of the card ($1.50); and Luiz' savings ($8.45) and Pedro's savings ($6.58). In the PLAN section, ask students to explain how they would calculate the total cost and the money saved. (add $8.45 and $6.58, = $15.03) In the

DO section, ask students to calculate the total cost of the items they want to buy and their total savings. ($14.49) Have them calculate the money left over. ($15.03 − 14.49 = $0.54) Explain that to check, they will add the total cost to the amount left over. Ask one student to explain what this sum should equal. (total savings, $15.03) Have students complete this section in their books.

**131**

Solve these problems. Remember to use the four-step plan.

1. Nathan's stamp album can hold 50 stamps. He had 18 stamps and a friend gave him 15 more. How many more stamps does he need to fill his album?
17 stamps

2. Sharon's pie recipe calls for 16 graham crackers. She has 2 packets of crackers with 6 crackers in each. How many more crackers does she need?
4 crackers

3. A 4-ounce box of nails costs $1.50, and a 2-ounce box costs $0.75. How much do 10 ounces of nails cost?
$3.75

4. Jason's new library book has 63 pages. He read 25 pages on Saturday and 28 on Sunday. How many pages does he have left to read?
10 pages

5. Cleve wants to buy a backpack that is marked $17.50. The sale sign says that $3 will be taken off the marked price. How much change will Cleve get back if he gives the clerk $20?
$5.50

6. A car dealer had 565 cars to sell. The first week in November he sold 18 used cars and 34 new ones. How many cars does he have left to sell?
513 cars

7. What if the sale sign in Exercise 5 said that $5 will be taken off the marked price? How much change would Cleve get back then?
$7.50

8. Read Exercise 4 again. Rewrite the exercise so that the number of pages Jason has left to read is 15.
Answers will vary.

9. In the United States, Thanksgiving Day is the fourth Thursday in November. What are the earliest and the latest dates on which this holiday can fall?
See Solution Notes.

10. In Canada, Thanksgiving Day is the second Monday in October. What are the earliest and the latest dates on which this holiday can fall?
See Solution Notes.

**132**   (one hundred thirty-two)

**Extra Credit**   *Applications*

Ask students to bring recent pictures of family members, friends and pets to class. If they are unable to do this the pictures could be taken from a magazine. Tell students to record the age of the person in each of the pictures. Tell them to estimate ages they don't know. Give students a piece of manilla paper and glue. Have them construct a picture graph which will show the ages of the people in the pictures.

# Solution Notes

1. Students may add to find the total number of Nathan's stamps and subtracting that from the number the book will hold. (18 + 15 = 33, 50 − 33 = 17) Some may see that, starting with the number of stamps the book holds, they can subtract the number Nathan has to begin with, then the number he receives.

2. Point out that to find the total number of crackers Sharon has, they can add (6 + 6) or multiply (6 × 2), before they subtract.

3. See that students first calculate the number of different-sized boxes they will need. (two 4 oz and one 2 oz or five 2 oz) Some students may be able to multiply $.75 × 5.

4. This problem resembles number 1. See if any students recognize the similarity in their PLAN.

5. Most students will do this problem by calculating the final cost of the jacket ($17.50 − $3 = $14.50) and then calculating the change from $20. Or start with $20 and subtract first the cost of the jacket and then the extra discount.

6. Some of the information in the problem is not needed. They can calculate the number of cars sold and subtract to find the number of cars (both new and used) left to sell.

## Higher-Order Thinking Skills

7. Analysis: $7.50; Students should recognize that $5 off is $2 more than $3 off, so Cleve will get $2 more change that he did in the original problem.

8. Synthesis: Sample answers would involve subtracting 5 pages from either Saturday or Sunday or adding 5 pages to the total number of pages in the book.

9. Synthesis: The earliest is November 22, when November 1 is the first Thursday of the month. The latest is November 28, when November 1 is the first Friday of the month.

10. Synthesis: The earliest is October 8, when October 1 is the first Monday of the month. The latest is October 14, when October 1 is the first Tuesday of the month.

# Using a Calculator, the Equals Key

pages 133-134

## Objective

To use the equals key on a simple calculator

## Materials

calculators

## Mental Math

Have students complete these series:

1. 2, 4, 6, (8, 10, 12, 14, . . . )
2. 3, 6, 9, (12, 15, 18, 21, . . . )
3. 4, 8, 12, (16, 20, 24, 28, . . . )
4. 5, 10, 15, (20, 25, 30, 35, . . . )
5. 10, 20, 30, (40, 50, 60, 70, . . . )

## Skill Review

Have students identify all the calculator operation keys. As they name them, draw each key on the board for the class. ( $+$, $-$, $\times$, $\div$, $=$ ) Dictate these problems to the class and have them solve the problems on their calculators.

1. 34 + 52 = (86)
2. 49 − 11 = (38)
3. 39 × 5 = (195)
4. 28 + 58 = (86)
5. 81 − 45 = (36)
6. 13 × 25 = (325)

---

### Using a Calculator, the Equal Key

Mr. Roberts deposits $150 in his savings account each month. How much money will Mr. Roberts have in his account in 4 more months?

We need to find his total savings after ____4____ more deposits.
The current balance in Mr. Roberts' account is ___$300___ .

He will deposit ___$150___ in his account each month. To find the total savings, we can use the calculator to add each deposit to the current balance.

300 $+$ 150 $+$ 150 $+$ 150 $+$ 150 $=$ ( 900 )

Mr. Roberts will have ___$900___ in his account in 4 months.

The equal key can be used to shorten the code for repeated addition or subtraction.

Every time we press the $=$ key, the number before it is added or subtracted. In this problem, we add the number 4 times, so we press the $=$ key 4 times.

300 $+$ 150 $=$ $=$ $=$ $=$ ( 900 )

In the problem 2 $+$ 3 $+$ 3 $+$ 3 $+$ 3 $+$ 3 $=$ ( 17 ), we add the number 5 times, so we press the $=$ key 5 times.

2 $+$ 3 $=$ $=$ $=$ $=$ $=$ ( 17 )

(one hundred thirty-three) **133**

---

## Teaching the Lesson

**Introducing the Problem** Have students read the problem and identify the question. Read the information sentences aloud. Have students volunteer the missing information and write that information in their texts. (current balance, $300; He will deposit $150 each month.) Ask a student to read the plan sentences. Work the calculator code with the students. Explain that the equals key has a special function in repeated operations. Each time the key is pressed it will do the last operation given, with the last number given. Have students read the next section of the model and survey the second calculator code. Explain that each time the $=$ is pressed after $+$ 150, the calculator will add 150 to the last sum. Pressing the equals key four times will add 150 four times. Have students try it with their calculators and write the answer in their texts. (900) Have them try the second example both ways and write the answer in their books. (17, 17)

**Developing the Skill** Point out that the advantage of using the equals key for repeated operations is that it saves time and it might keep them from making mistakes. Explain that the disadvantage is that they must be careful to enter the function to be repeated last since the equals key repeats only the last function. Explain that they must be careful to press the $=$ key the correct number of times.

## Practice

1. $4\boxed{+}3\boxed{+}3\boxed{+}3\boxed{=}\boxed{13}$

2. $4\boxed{+}3\boxed{=}\boxed{=}\boxed{=}\boxed{13}$

3. $25\boxed{-}5\boxed{-}5\boxed{-}5\boxed{-}5\boxed{=}\boxed{5}$

4. $25\boxed{-}5\boxed{=}\boxed{=}\boxed{=}\boxed{=}\boxed{5}$

5. $4\boxed{+}4\boxed{+}4\boxed{+}4\boxed{=}\boxed{16}$

6. $4\boxed{+}4\boxed{=}\boxed{=}\boxed{=}\boxed{16}$

7. $9\boxed{+}9\boxed{+}9\boxed{+}9\boxed{=}\boxed{36}$

8. $9\boxed{+}9\boxed{=}\boxed{=}\boxed{=}\boxed{36}$

9. $5\boxed{+}5\boxed{=}\boxed{=}\boxed{=}\boxed{20}$

10. $49\boxed{-}7\boxed{=}\boxed{=}\boxed{=}\boxed{=}\boxed{21}$

11. $16\boxed{-}2\boxed{=}\boxed{=}\boxed{=}\boxed{=}\boxed{=}\boxed{6}$

12. $720\boxed{-}240\boxed{=}\boxed{=}\boxed{=}\boxed{0}$

## Apply

Use your calculator to solve these problems.

13. Heather bought a bike that costs $215. She gave a down payment of $40. She will pay $35 a month until the bike is paid for. How much will she still owe after 3 months?
$70

14. Mrs. Gomez took a 7-day vacation. On the first day she drove 268 miles. On the second day she drove 196 miles. On each of the other days, Mrs. Gomez drove 225 miles. How far did she drive on her vacation?
1,589 miles

15. This is a record of Mary's savings account. Add each deposit and subtract each withdrawal to find the balance.

| Date | Deposit | Withdrawal | Balance |
|------|---------|------------|---------|
| Nov 1 | $36 | | $36 |
| Nov 8 | $68 | | $104 |
| Nov 13 | | $27 | $77 |
| Nov 15 | $49 | | $126 |
| Nov 20 | | $32 | $94 |
| Nov 23 | $75 | | $169 |
| Nov 28 | $63 | | $232 |
| Nov 30 | | $115 | $117 |

**134** (one hundred thirty-four)

# Chapter Test

page 135

| Item | Objective |
|------|-----------|
| 1-75 | Recall multiplication facts through 9 (See pages 119-129, 137-144, 147) |
| 76-78 | Understand the terms factor and product (See page 117) |

Multiply.

| | | | | | | | | | |
|---|---|---|---|---|---|---|---|---|---|
| 7<br>× 3<br>21 | 1<br>× 3<br>3 | 1<br>× 5<br>5 | 5<br>× 8<br>40 | 4<br>× 3<br>12 | 6<br>× 0<br>0 | 3<br>× 1<br>3 | 4<br>× 9<br>36 | 8<br>× 1<br>8 | 4<br>× 7<br>28 |
| 4<br>× 5<br>20 | 0<br>× 7<br>0 | 9<br>× 5<br>45 | 1<br>× 7<br>7 | 5<br>× 3<br>15 | 4<br>× 1<br>4 | 3<br>× 6<br>18 | 1<br>× 9<br>9 | 5<br>× 0<br>0 | 9<br>× 1<br>9 |
| 3<br>× 9<br>27 | 9<br>× 0<br>0 | 3<br>× 7<br>21 | 2<br>× 8<br>16 | 2<br>× 9<br>18 | 1<br>× 6<br>6 | 5<br>× 6<br>30 | 0<br>× 6<br>0 | 2<br>× 2<br>4 | 4<br>× 6<br>24 |
| 9<br>× 2<br>18 | 3<br>× 0<br>0 | 4<br>× 8<br>32 | 0<br>× 3<br>0 | 9<br>× 3<br>27 | 3<br>× 3<br>9 | 6<br>× 1<br>6 | 8<br>× 0<br>0 | 7<br>× 4<br>28 | 2<br>× 7<br>14 |
| 4<br>× 2<br>8 | 8<br>× 4<br>32 | 7<br>× 0<br>0 | 4<br>× 4<br>16 | 6<br>× 5<br>30 | 5<br>× 8<br>40 | 4<br>× 0<br>0 | 2<br>× 6<br>12 | 0<br>× 2<br>0 | 9<br>× 4<br>36 |
| 3<br>× 8<br>24 | 6<br>× 4<br>24 | 5<br>× 9<br>45 | 1<br>× 0<br>0 | 8<br>× 3<br>24 | 0<br>× 0<br>0 | 5<br>× 2<br>10 | 5<br>× 5<br>25 | 6<br>× 2<br>12 | 1<br>× 1<br>1 |

$7 \times 2 = \underline{14}$  $3 \times 4 = \underline{12}$  $5 \times 4 = \underline{20}$  $0 \times 5 = \underline{0}$  $3 \times 5 = \underline{15}$

$7 \times 0 = \underline{0}$  $8 \times 2 = \underline{16}$  $2 \times 3 = \underline{6}$  $2 \times 0 = \underline{0}$  $2 \times 1 = \underline{2}$

$1 \times 7 = \underline{7}$  $4 \times 1 = \underline{4}$  $5 \times 2 = \underline{10}$  $5 \times 7 = \underline{35}$  $2 \times 3 = \underline{6}$

In the problem $5 \times 3 = 15$,

the 5 is called a ___factor___,

the 3 is called a ___factor___,

and the 15 is called a ___product___.

**135**

Circle the letter of the correct answer.

1  527 ◯ 636
  a >
  ⓑ <

2  What is the value of the 9 in 439,206?
  a ones
  ⓑ thousands
  c ten thousands
  d NG

3  592
  + 837
  a 1,329
  ⓑ 1,429
  c 1,439
  d NG

4  $36.26
  +  7.97
  a $43.13
  b $44.13
  ⓒ $44.23
  d NG

5  979
  6,450
  +  926
  a 7,354
  b 8,255
  c 8,354
  ⓓ NG

6  Round each number to the nearest hundred and add.
  583
  + 268
  a 700
  b 800
  ⓒ 900
  d NG

7  802
  − 157
  a 545
  ⓑ 645
  c 755
  d NG

8  $78.56
  − 37.88
  a $30.68
  ⓑ $40.68
  c $41.32
  d NG

9  Round each number to the nearest hundred and subtract.
  723
  − 475
  ⓐ 200
  b 300
  c 400
  d NG

10
  a 6:00
  b 6:30
  ⓒ 12:30
  d NG

11  Find the perimeter.
  65 cm
  57 cm    57 cm
  65 cm
  a 114 cm
  b 112 cm
  c 130 cm
  ⓓ NG

12  Choose the best estimate for the height of an adult.
  a 2 cm
  ⓑ 2 m
  c 2 km

13  Choose the better estimate for the weight of a paper clip.
  ⓐ 1 g
  b 1 kg

☐ score

**136**  (one hundred thirty-six)

| Item | Objective |
|---|---|
| 1 | Compare numbers less than 1,000 (See pages 27-28) |
| 2 | Identify the value of a digit in a number less than 1,000,000 (See pages 35-36) |
| 3 | Add two 3-digit numbers with regrouping (See pages 43-44) |
| 4 | Add dollars and cents with re-grouping (See pages 51-52) |
| 5 | Add three or four numbers (See pages 49-50) |
| 6 | Round numbers to nearest 100 and add (See pages 53-56) |
| 7 | Subtract two 3-digit numbers with two regroupings (See pages 67-68) |
| 8 | Subtract dollars and cents with regrouping (See pages 75-76) |
| 9 | Round numbers to the nearest 100 and subtract (See pages 77-78) |
| 10 | Read the time to the minute (See pages 87-88) |
| 11 | Add to find the perimeter (See pages 95-96) |
| 12 | Choose appropriate metric unit of length (See pages 107-108) |
| 13 | Choose appropriate metric unit of weight (See pages 111-112) |

## Alternate Cumulative Review

Circle the letter of the correct answer.

1  384 ◯ 483
  a >
  ⓑ <
  c =

2  What is the value of the 8 in 821,653?
  a hundreds
  b thousands
  c ten thousands
  ⓓ NG

3  771
  + 578
  ⓐ 1,349
  b 1,249
  c 1,439
  d NG

4  $43.88
  +  8.43
  ⓐ $52.31
  b $51.31
  c $52.21
  d NG

5  287
  5,463
  +  747
  a 5,387
  b 6,387
  c 5,497
  ⓓ NG

6  Round each number to the nearest hundred and add.
  387
  + 578
  ⓐ 1,000
  b 900
  c 800
  d NG

7  707
  − 348
  a 441
  b 469
  ⓒ 359
  d NG

8  $95.23
  − 43.66
  ⓐ $51.57
  b $51.67
  c $52.57
  d NG

9  Round each number to the nearest hundred and subtract.
  812
  − 563
  ⓐ 200
  b 300
  c 400
  d NG

10  What time is it? (Show a clock.)
  a 8:37
  ⓑ 7:43
  c 6:42
  d NG

11  Find the perimeter of a triangle 22 m by 27 m by 17 m.
  a 49 m
  b 44 m
  ⓒ 66 m
  d NG

12  What metric unit would you use to find the height of a redwood tree?
  a centimeter
  ⓑ meter
  c kilometer
  d NG

**136**

# Reviewing Multiplication

**pages 137-138**

## Objective

To review multiplication facts through 5 × 9

## Materials

*multiplication flash cards

## Mental Math

Ask the students to tell what is meant by:

1. four threes (12)
2. five twos (10)
3. seven threes (21)
4. one eight (8)
5. three sevens (21)
6. eight twos (16)
7. five sixes (30)
8. four fives (20)

## Skill Review

Dictate these problems to the class and have students come to the board and work the problems as column addition:

1. 2 × 6 (12)       6. 5 × 6 (30)
2. 5 × 7 (35)       7. 2 × 9 (18)
3. 3 × 8 (24)       8. 1 × 9 (9)
4. 5 × 5 (25)       9. 5 × 9 (45)
5. 4 × 6 (24)      10. 0 × 6 (0)

---

## Reviewing Multiplication

Trudy helps her father take inventory in his hardware store every year. The first year she counted each object. Now she has learned a faster way to take inventory. Help Trudy count the number of boxes.

Trudy wants to know the total number of boxes.
She is counting __5__ rows of boxes of light bulbs.
There are __6__ boxes in each row.
Trudy can add the number of boxes.

$6 + 6 + 6 + 6 + 6 = $ __30__
But it would be faster to multiply.

$5 \times 6 = $ __30__

$$\begin{array}{r} 6 \\ \times\, 5 \\ \hline 30 \end{array}$$

Trudy can also think of it as 6 columns of __5__ boxes each.

$6 \times 5 = $ __30__

$$\begin{array}{r} 5 \\ \times\, 6 \\ \hline 30 \end{array}$$

Trudy counts __30__ boxes of light bulbs.

### Getting Started

Use both addition and multiplication to show how many are in the picture.

1.

$4 + 4 + 4 + 4 + 4 + 4 + 4 = $ __28__

$7 \times 4 = $ __28__

$4 \times 7 = $ __28__

(one hundred thirty-seven) **137**

---

## Teaching the Lesson

**Introducing the Problem**  Have students examine the problem and identify the question being asked. Read the information sentences and ask students to fill in the data required. (5 rows of boxes, 6 boxes in each row) Read aloud the first plan sentences and ask a student to do the addition. (30) Read the next section of the plan, and ask students to circle five groups of six. Tell the class to do the multiplication in their books while you do it on the board. (5 × 6 = 30) Read the next approach to the problem, explaining that she can think of the bulbs being in 6 columns of 5 boxes. Have students circle the X's to represent 6 groups of 5 X's, and do the multiplication in their texts. (6 × 5 = 30) Have students write the answer in the solution sentence (30) and then have the sentence read aloud.

**Developing the Skill**  Introduce the 100-facts multiplication chart. Tell students to make a chart of their own on graph paper to use until they have memorized all the multiplication facts. For this lesson they will complete the squares for facts through 5 × 9.

| x | 0 | 1 | 2 | 3 | 4 | 5 | 6 | 7 | 8 | 9 |
|---|---|---|---|---|---|---|---|---|---|---|
| 0 | 0 | 0 | 0 | 0 | 0 | 0 | 0 | 0 | 0 | 0 |
| 1 | 0 | 1 | 2 | 3 | 4 | 5 | 6 | 7 | 8 | 9 |
| 2 | 0 | 2 | 4 | 6 | 8 | 10 | 12 | 14 | 16 | 18 |
| 3 | 0 | 3 | 6 | 9 | 12 | 15 | 18 | 21 | 24 | 27 |
| 4 | 0 | 4 | 8 | 12 | 16 | 20 | 24 | 28 | 32 | 36 |
| 5 | 0 | 5 | 10 | 15 | 20 | 25 | 30 | 35 | 40 | 45 |

**137**

## Practice

Use both addition and multiplication to show how many are in each picture.

1.

$4 + 4 + 4 + 4 + 4 =$ ___20___

$5 \times 4 =$ ___20___

$4 \times 5 =$ ___20___

2.

$5 + 5 + 5 + 5 + 5 + 5 + 5 + 5 =$ ___40___

$8 \times 5 =$ ___40___

$5 \times 8 =$ ___40___

Multiply.

| 3. | 4. | 5. | 6. | 7. | 8. | 9. |
|---|---|---|---|---|---|---|
| $\begin{array}{r} 5 \\ \times 4 \\ \hline 20 \end{array}$ | $\begin{array}{r} 8 \\ \times 5 \\ \hline 40 \end{array}$ | $\begin{array}{r} 6 \\ \times 3 \\ \hline 18 \end{array}$ | $\begin{array}{r} 0 \\ \times 7 \\ \hline 0 \end{array}$ | $\begin{array}{r} 4 \\ \times 6 \\ \hline 24 \end{array}$ | $\begin{array}{r} 8 \\ \times 1 \\ \hline 8 \end{array}$ | $\begin{array}{r} 8 \\ \times 4 \\ \hline 32 \end{array}$ |

| 10. | 11. | 12. | 13. | 14. | 15. | 16. |
|---|---|---|---|---|---|---|
| $\begin{array}{r} 6 \\ \times 5 \\ \hline 30 \end{array}$ | $\begin{array}{r} 4 \\ \times 4 \\ \hline 16 \end{array}$ | $\begin{array}{r} 3 \\ \times 0 \\ \hline 0 \end{array}$ | $\begin{array}{r} 9 \\ \times 4 \\ \hline 36 \end{array}$ | $\begin{array}{r} 3 \\ \times 8 \\ \hline 24 \end{array}$ | $\begin{array}{r} 0 \\ \times 1 \\ \hline 0 \end{array}$ | $\begin{array}{r} 5 \\ \times 5 \\ \hline 25 \end{array}$ |

17. $7 \times 2 =$ ___14___   18. $3 \times 8 =$ ___24___   19. $5 \times 2 =$ ___10___   20. $1 \times 6 =$ ___6___

21. $6 \times 4 =$ ___24___   22. $3 \times 3 =$ ___9___   23. $8 \times 0 =$ ___0___   24. $7 \times 3 =$ ___21___

## Apply

Solve these problems.

25. Gina practices piano 2 hours a day, 3 days a week. How many hours does Gina practice each week?
6 hours

26. A field goal is worth 3 points. Raul kicked 4 of them in one game. How many points did Raul score for his team?
12 points

**138** (one hundred thirty-eight)

## Correcting Common Errors

If students are having difficulty with the facts, have them work with partners with fact cards where the fact less the answer is shown on one side and the fact with the answer on the reverse. They should take turns quizzing each other with the cards, practicing more often those facts that give them difficulty.

## Enrichment

Give students quarter or eighth inch graph paper. Tell them to draw arrays to demonstrate the following problems:
1. $5 \times 9$    2. $4 \times 12$
3. $6 \times 6$    4. $6 \times 3$
5. $8 \times 1$    6. $20 \times 0$
Let them decide how to use the paper. Some will circle the intersection of the lines, some will color in blocks. Then have them compare their arrays.

## Practice

Have students complete all the problems on the page. Remind them that in the first few they are expected to do the same problem three different ways, using addition and multiplication.

## Mixed Practice

1. $6 + 6 + 6 + 6$ (24)
2. $5 \times 0$ (0)
3. $302 - 171$ (131)
4. $\$375.27 + 252.98$ ($628.25)
5. $9 \times 1$ (9)
6. $6,090 - 4,368$ (1,722)
7. $493 + 2,176 + 658$ (3,327)
8. $597 - 328$ (269)
9. $3 \times 8$ (24)
10. $3,658 \times 4,075$ (7,733)

## Extra Credit   *Logic*

Remind students that a palindrome is a word or number which is the same read forward or backward. Explain that many numbers can be reversed and added that do not form palindromes, the first time. The process may have to be repeated several times, such as:

| 96 | 165 | 726 | 1,353 |
|---|---|---|---|
| +69 then | +561 then | +627 then | +3,531 |
| 165 | 726 | 1,353 | 4,884 |

Using this method, ask students what palindromes they can form from these numbers: 695 (5,335) 728 (45,254) 7,269 (687,786) 46,793 (683, 386)

**138**

# Multiplying, the Factor 6

pages 139-140

## Objective

To multiply by the factor 6

## Materials

*multiplication flash cards for the factor 6
*red and blue chalk

## Mental Math

Dictate these problems for quick recognition:

1. $13 - 5$ (8)    6. $7 + 5$ (12)
2. $14 + 6$ (20)    7. $6 - 0$ (6)
3. $19 + 8$ (27)    8. $5 + 6$ (11)
4. $4 - 1$ (3)    9. $9 - 9$ (0)
5. $16 - 8$ (8)    10. $9 + 4$ (13)

## Skill Review

Review multiplication facts with factors 4 and 5. Count from 4 through 40 by fours, from 5 through 50 by fives. Give the class these products and have them write a multiplication problem that corresponds:

1. 35 $(5 \times 7)$        6. 12 $(4 \times 3,$
                                              $2 \times 6)$
2. 24 $(4 \times 6, 8 \times 3)$    7. 15 $(5 \times 3)$
3. 50 $(5 \times 10)$        8. 10 $(5 \times 2)$
4. 4 $(4 \times 1, 2 \times 2)$    9. 28 $(4 \times 7)$
5. 40 $(5 \times 8)$        10. 30 $(5 \times 6)$

---

## Multiplying, the Factor 6

The Nature Club orders apples from the grocer for their spring hike. How many apples does the club order?

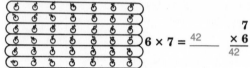

We want to know the total number of apples in the order.
The grocer wraps __6__ apples in each package.

He prepares __7__ packages for the Nature Club.

We can add. $6 + 6 + 6 + 6 + 6 + 6 + 6 = $ __42__
We can also multiply.

$$7 \times 6 = \underline{42} \qquad \begin{array}{r} 6 \\ \times 7 \\ \hline 42 \end{array}$$

We can also think of it as 6 groups of __7__ apples each.

$$6 \times 7 = \underline{42} \qquad \begin{array}{r} 7 \\ \times 6 \\ \hline 42 \end{array}$$

The Nature Club orders __42__ apples.

### Getting Started

Use addition and multiplication to show how many are in the picture.

1.

$6 + 6 + 6 + 6 + 6 + 6 = $ __36__

$6 \times 6 = $ __36__

---

## Teaching the Lesson

**Introducing the Problem**  Have students study the problem and tell what is being asked. Read the information sentences aloud and have students supply the data required. (6 apples in each package, 7 packages) Have students read the plan sentences and explain that, as before, there are three ways to approach this problem. Work through the three methods with the students. Have individual students show each method on the board. Read the solution sentence aloud and have a student supply the answer while others write it in their texts. (42 apples)

**Developing the Skill**  One way students can visualize multiplying by the factor 6 is to see it as the sum of facts with a factor of 4 and facts with a factor of 2. Use red and blue chalk to draw this array on the board:

```
XXXX  XX
XXXX  XX
XXXX  XX
XXXX  XX
XXXX  XX
```

Point out that there are two arrays here, one $4 \times 5$, the other $2 \times 5$. Ask a student to do each of these problems on the board. $(4 \times 5 = 20, 2 \times 5 = 10)$ Ask someone to give the dimensions of the array as a whole. $(5 \times 6)$ Ask another to explain how many **X**'s are in the whole array. $(20 + 10 = 30)$. Repeat this process for the problem $6 \times 9$, breaking it up into $4 \times 9$ and $2 \times 9$.

**139**

**Practice**

Use addition and multiplication to show how many are in the picture.

1.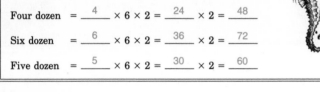

$6 + 6 + 6 + 6 + 6 + 6 + 6 + 6 + 6 =$ __54__

$9 \times 6 =$ __54__

$6 \times 9 =$ __54__

Multiply.

| 2. | 3. | 4. | 5. | 6. | 7. | 8. |
|---|---|---|---|---|---|---|
| 2 | 2 | 5 | 3 | 7 | 4 | 6 |
| $\times 1$ | $\times 3$ | $\times 6$ | $\times 5$ | $\times 2$ | $\times 7$ | $\times 9$ |
| 2 | 6 | 30 | 15 | 14 | 28 | 54 |

| 9. | 10. | 11. | 12. | 13. | 14. | 15. |
|---|---|---|---|---|---|---|
| 7 | 5 | 2 | 4 | 7 | 1 | 6 |
| $\times 0$ | $\times 8$ | $\times 6$ | $\times 4$ | $\times 6$ | $\times 3$ | $\times 0$ |
| 0 | 40 | 12 | 16 | 42 | 3 | 0 |

16. $8 \times 6 =$ __48__       17. $9 \times 5 =$ __45__       18. $7 \times 4 =$ __28__       19. $4 \times 6 =$ __24__

20. $6 \times 7 =$ __42__       21. $8 \times 4 =$ __32__       22. $3 \times 1 =$ __3__       23. $2 \times 7 =$ __14__

24. $3 \times 3 =$ __9__       25. $9 \times 6 =$ __54__       26. $5 \times 7 =$ __35__       27. $0 \times 5 =$ __0__

---

**EXCURSION**

One dozen is 12 or $6 \times 2$, so three dozen is $3 \times 6 \times 2$ or $18 \times 2$ or 36. Notice that when you multiply a number by 2, it is the same as doubling the number. You can think of $18 \times 2$ as $18 + 18$ or 36. Use this idea to find the missing numbers.

Seven dozen = __7__ $\times 6 \times 2 =$ __42__ $\times 2 =$ __84__

Four dozen = __4__ $\times 6 \times 2 =$ __24__ $\times 2 =$ __48__

Six dozen = __6__ $\times 6 \times 2 =$ __36__ $\times 2 =$ __72__

Five dozen = __5__ $\times 6 \times 2 =$ __30__ $\times 2 =$ __60__

---

## Correcting Common Errors

If students have difficulty learning some of the facts of 6, help them practice by using the doubling strategy. If $2 \times 6 = 12$, then $4 \times 6$ is twice as much, or 24.

If $2 \times 6 = 12$ then $4 \times 6 = 24$
If $3 \times 6 = 18$ then $6 \times 6 = 36$
If $4 \times 6 = 24$ then $8 \times 6 = 48$

They also can learn facts by counting on. If $4 \times 6 = 24$, then $5 \times 6 = 24 + 6$, or 30.

If $4 \times 6 = 24$ then $5 \times 6 = 24 + 6$, or 30
If $6 \times 6 = 36$ then $7 \times 6 = 36 + 6$, or 42
If $8 \times 6 = 48$ then $9 \times 6 = 48 + 6$, or 54

## Enrichment

Have students survey two classes for students' birthdays, stopping as soon as they find two students with the same birthday. They should only ask for the day of the month, not the month. Explain that the probability of finding two the same in a group of 23 people is about one chance in 2, in a group of 32 about 3 chances in 4 and in a group of 50, nearly certain. Tell them to record how many students they had surveyed when they came to two with the same birthday.

---

## Practice

Have students do all the problems on the page. Remind students to use addition to help with any multiplication facts they are unsure of.

## Excursion

Have students double several numbers. Ask students what number is used as a factor to double a number. (2) Have students read the paragraph and work the problems.

## Extra Credit   *Geometry*

Give each student a geoboard, several rubber bands and graph paper. Remind them that they can draw geoboard figures on graph paper by using the intersection of the lines as the position of the nails.

Tell them to make as many different triangles as possible in which the rubber band touches 4, 5, 6, 7 and 8 nails. Ask them to illustrate on graph paper each triangle they make on the geoboard. Have them label the triangles with a 4, 5, 6, 7 or 8 depending on the number of nails touched.

# Multiplying, the Factor 7

pages 141-142

## Objective

To multiply by the factor 7

## Materials

*multiplication flash cards for the factors 6 and 7
*blue and red chalk

## Mental Math

Dictate these problems to the class:

1. $2 \times (3 + 4)$ (14)
2. $2 \times (10 - 1)$ (18)
3. $3 \times (5 + 3)$ (24)
4. $5 \times (10 - 7)$ (15)
5. $(5 + 2) \times 4$ (28)
6. $(9 + 1) \times 4$ (40)
7. $(15 - 7) \times 5$ (40)

## Skill Review

Have one student count by six's from 0 through 60. Have another write the corresponding multiplication facts on the board. ($6 \times 0 = 0$, $6 \times 1 = 6$, etc.) Erase the board work and go around the room with the flash cards, checking for quick recognition of the factor 6 multiplication facts.

---

## Multiplying, the Factor 7

Bananas grow best in a hot, damp climate. They grow in bunches, at the end of long, tall stalks. How many bananas are there on this stalk?

We are looking for the total number of bananas on the stalk.

There are ___8___ bunches of bananas.

Each bunch has ___7___ bananas on it.
We can add. $7 + 7 + 7 + 7 + 7 + 7 + 7 + 7 = $ ___56___
We can also multiply.

$8 \times 7 = $ ___56___ $\quad \begin{array}{r} 7 \\ \times 8 \\ \hline 56 \end{array}$

We can also think of it as 7 groups of ___8___ bananas each.

$7 \times 8 = $ ___56___ $\quad \begin{array}{r} 8 \\ \times 7 \\ \hline 56 \end{array}$

There are ___56___ bananas on the stalk.

### Getting Started

Use addition and multiplication to show how many are in the picture.

1.

$7 + 7 + 7 + 7 + 7 + 7 + 7 = $ ___49___

$7 \times 7 = $ ___49___

---

## Teaching the Lesson

**Introducing the Problem**  Read the problem aloud to the class and have students tell what is being asked. Have students complete the two information sentences in their texts as you read them. (8 bunches; Each has 7 bananas.) Explain that there are three ways of doing this problem. Work through the three methods with the students. Have them complete each problem in their texts while an individual works the problem at the board. Have a student read the solution sentence while the others write the answer in their texts.

**Developing the Skill**  As in the last lesson, present the factor 7 as the sum of the multiplication of two smaller factors. Draw this array on the board in red and blue:

```
XXXXXX  X
XXXXXX  X
XXXXXX  X
XXXXXX  X
XXXXXX  X
XXXXXX  X
XXXXXX  X
```

Explain that there are two arrays here, one $6 \times 7$, the other $1 \times 7$. Ask a student to do each of these problems on the board. ($6 \times 7 = 42$, $1 \times 7 = 7$). Ask another student to give the dimensions of the array as a whole. ($7 \times 7$) Ask how many **X**'s are in the whole array. ($42 + 7 = 49$) Write **7 × 7 = 49** on the board. Repeat this process with a divided array for the problem $7 \times 8$ and $7 \times 9$.

## Practice

Use addition and multiplication to show how many are in each picture.

1.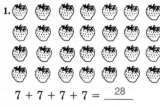

$7 + 7 + 7 + 7 =$ __28__

$4 \times 7 =$ __28__

$7 \times 4 =$ __28__

2. ○○○○○○○ (rows of ovals)

$7 + 7 + 7 + 7 + 7 =$ __35__

$5 \times 7 =$ __35__

$7 \times 5 =$ __35__

Multiply.

3. $\begin{array}{r} 6 \\ \times\, 6 \\ \hline 36 \end{array}$
4. $\begin{array}{r} 7 \\ \times\, 5 \\ \hline 35 \end{array}$
5. $\begin{array}{r} 8 \\ \times\, 3 \\ \hline 24 \end{array}$
6. $\begin{array}{r} 0 \\ \times\, 7 \\ \hline 0 \end{array}$
7. $\begin{array}{r} 9 \\ \times\, 6 \\ \hline 54 \end{array}$
8. $\begin{array}{r} 3 \\ \times\, 4 \\ \hline 12 \end{array}$
9. $\begin{array}{r} 5 \\ \times\, 9 \\ \hline 45 \end{array}$

10. $\begin{array}{r} 4 \\ \times\, 4 \\ \hline 16 \end{array}$
11. $\begin{array}{r} 3 \\ \times\, 2 \\ \hline 6 \end{array}$
12. $\begin{array}{r} 9 \\ \times\, 7 \\ \hline 63 \end{array}$
13. $\begin{array}{r} 8 \\ \times\, 7 \\ \hline 56 \end{array}$
14. $\begin{array}{r} 5 \\ \times\, 5 \\ \hline 25 \end{array}$
15. $\begin{array}{r} 7 \\ \times\, 7 \\ \hline 49 \end{array}$
16. $\begin{array}{r} 6 \\ \times\, 1 \\ \hline 6 \end{array}$

17. $\begin{array}{r} 7 \\ \times\, 6 \\ \hline 42 \end{array}$
18. $\begin{array}{r} 4 \\ \times\, 8 \\ \hline 32 \end{array}$
19. $\begin{array}{r} 7 \\ \times\, 9 \\ \hline 63 \end{array}$
20. $\begin{array}{r} 6 \\ \times\, 3 \\ \hline 18 \end{array}$
21. $\begin{array}{r} 6 \\ \times\, 9 \\ \hline 54 \end{array}$
22. $\begin{array}{r} 1 \\ \times\, 7 \\ \hline 7 \end{array}$
23. $\begin{array}{r} 3 \\ \times\, 3 \\ \hline 9 \end{array}$

24. $7 \times 8 =$ __56__
25. $1 \times 8 =$ __8__
26. $6 \times 8 =$ __48__
27. $9 \times 4 =$ __36__
28. $0 \times 0 =$ __0__
29. $8 \times 6 =$ __48__
30. $4 \times 6 =$ __24__
31. $7 \times 3 =$ __21__

## Apply

Solve these problems.

32. Rita bought 8 packages of cereal. Each package contained 7 ounces. How many ounces of cereal did Rita buy? 56 ounces

33. David ate 3 apricots with his lunch. He ate 4 more apricots for supper. How many apricots did David eat?
7 apricots

**142** (one hundred forty-two)

## Correcting Common Errors

Some students may have difficulty with facts of seven because they think they must learn 10 new facts. Use the order property to show that students already know many of these facts. For example, $2 \times 7 = 7 \times 2 = 14$. So, the only new facts that they need to learn are $8 \times 7 = 56$ and $9 \times 7 = 63$.

## Enrichment

Have students make a $5 \times 5$ array of dots. Starting in one corner, ask them to mark the array off in this way:

Have them write down the number of dots contained in each new corner. (1, 3, 5, etc.) Ask what pattern the numbers make (the series of odd numbers) and the sum of all the numbers. (25) Let them try a larger square array.

## Practice

Have students work all the problems on the page. Tell them to read the last two problems carefully before they solve them.

## Mixed Practice

1. $525 + 396 + 58$ (979)
2. $0 \times 0$ (0)
3. $\$6.95 + 0.38 + 2.46$ ($9.79)
4. $1,000 - 437$ (563)
5. $5 \times 9$ (45)
6. $8,560 - 258$ (8,302)
7. $4,256 + 3,992$ (8,248)
8. $6 \times 3$ (18)
9. $459 - 327$ (132)
10. $\$95.00 - 49,38$ ($45.62)

## Extra Credit   *Measurement*

Tell students that there are many different non-standard units of measure. Have students list something in the classroom with the same measure as:
the length of their thumb
the length of one of their hairs
the length of their foot
the length of their stride
the length of their arm, from the tip of their middle finger to their elbow
the width of their little finger
the area of their hand
Have students find something on their body that has the same measure as: 1 centimeter, 1 meter, 1 inch, 1 foot, 1 yard.

**142**

# Multiplying, the Factors 8 and 9

**pages 143-144**

## Objective

To multiply by factors 8 and 9

## Materials

*multiplication flash cards

## Mental Math

Ask students to identify the larger amount for each of the following:

1. $3 \times 5$   (<)   $2 \times 8$
2. $7 \times 4$   (>)   $3 \times 9$
3. $2 \times 9$   (<)   $3 \times 7$
4. $5 \times 5$   (>)   $3 \times 8$
5. $4 \times 6$   (=)   $3 \times 8$
6. $8 \times 7$   (>)   $9 \times 6$
7. $5 \times 9$   (>)   $6 \times 7$

## Skill Review

Review multiplication facts with flash cards, leaving out only the three which will be new to this lesson: $8 \times 8$, $8 \times 9$ and $9 \times 9$. Show the first card and ask students in the first row or group to answer together. Move across the room, having students answer group by group. Hold back any cards students seem to have trouble with and go through those again at the end.

---

### Multiplying, the Factors 8 and 9

The boys and girls in the third grade like to play the game of streets and alleys. How many students are playing if there are 9 rows with 8 students in each row?

We want to know how many students are playing the game.

There are __9__ rows of students.

There are __8__ people in each row.
We can add. $8 + 8 + 8 + 8 + 8 + 8 + 8 + 8 + 8 =$ __72__
We can multiply.

$9 \times 8 =$ __72__    $\begin{array}{r} 8 \\ \times 9 \\ \hline 72 \end{array}$

We can also think of this as 8 groups of __9__ students each.

$8 \times 9 =$ __72__    $\begin{array}{r} 9 \\ \times 8 \\ \hline 72 \end{array}$

There are __72__ students playing the game.

### Getting Started

Use addition and multiplication to show how many are in the picture.

1.

$9 + 9 + 9 + 9 + 9 + 9 + 9 + 9 + 9 =$ __81__

$9 \times 9 =$ __81__

(one hundred forty-three) **143**

---

## Teaching the Lesson

**Introducing the Problem**   Read the problem aloud. Have students identify what is being asked. Have students complete the information sentences, filling in the data from the illustration (9 rows, 8 persons in each row.) Work through the three methods with the class, asking students to show each method on the board while the class completes the problems in their texts. In the final method, point out the commutative property of multiplication; the factors can appear in any order. Read the solution sentence aloud and have a student supply the answer while the others write it in their texts.

**Developing the Skill**   There are only three new multiplication facts in this lesson: $8 \times 8 = 64$, $8 \times 9 = 72$, $9 \times 9 = 81$. Have students refer to the chart of 100 multiplication facts that they made in the first lesson in this chapter and add all the facts they have learned since. Present the three new facts using arrays as you did in the last two lessons. Explain that breaking an $8 \times 8$ array into smaller arrays ($5 \times 8$ and $3 \times 8$), multiplying, and then adding the results is an example of the distributive property: $8 \times 8 = (5 + 3) \times 8 = (5 \times 8) + (3 \times 8)$.

## Practice

Use addition and multiplication to show how many are in the picture.

1.

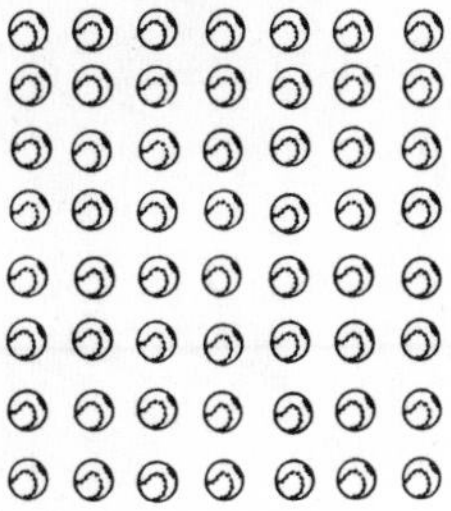

(8 rows of circles, 7 per row)

$8 + 8 + 8 + 8 + 8 + 8 + 8 =$ ___56___

$7 \times 8 =$ ___56___

$8 \times 7 =$ ___56___

Multiply.

| | | | | | | | |
|---|---|---|---|---|---|---|---|
| 2. $\begin{array}{r} 6 \\ \times 6 \\ \hline 36 \end{array}$ | 3. $\begin{array}{r} 6 \\ \times 9 \\ \hline 54 \end{array}$ | 4. $\begin{array}{r} 7 \\ \times 8 \\ \hline 56 \end{array}$ | 5. $\begin{array}{r} 6 \\ \times 8 \\ \hline 48 \end{array}$ | 6. $\begin{array}{r} 9 \\ \times 8 \\ \hline 72 \end{array}$ | 7. $\begin{array}{r} 2 \\ \times 8 \\ \hline 16 \end{array}$ | 8. $\begin{array}{r} 7 \\ \times 6 \\ \hline 42 \end{array}$ |
| 9. $\begin{array}{r} 8 \\ \times 7 \\ \hline 56 \end{array}$ | 10. $\begin{array}{r} 6 \\ \times 7 \\ \hline 42 \end{array}$ | 11. $\begin{array}{r} 9 \\ \times 7 \\ \hline 63 \end{array}$ | 12. $\begin{array}{r} 8 \\ \times 8 \\ \hline 64 \end{array}$ | 13. $\begin{array}{r} 8 \\ \times 9 \\ \hline 72 \end{array}$ | 14. $\begin{array}{r} 9 \\ \times 5 \\ \hline 45 \end{array}$ | 15. $\begin{array}{r} 7 \\ \times 9 \\ \hline 63 \end{array}$ |

16. $7 \times 7 =$ ___49___      17. $9 \times 6 =$ ___54___      18. $5 \times 5 =$ ___25___      19. $1 \times 9 =$ ___9___

20. $7 \times 9 =$ ___63___      21. $5 \times 7 =$ ___35___      22. $8 \times 7 =$ ___56___      23. $7 \times 6 =$ ___42___

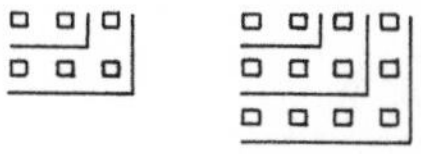

24. $3 \times 9 =$ ___27___      25. $8 \times 9 =$ ___72___      26. $6 \times 6 =$ ___36___      27. $4 \times 8 =$ ___32___

28. $7 \times 8 =$ ___56___      29. $0 \times 9 =$ ___0___      30. $9 \times 9 =$ ___81___      31. $7 \times 0 =$ ___0___

## Apply

Solve these problems.

32. Candles are sold 9 to a package. Tracy bought 6 packages. How many candles did she buy?

54 candles

33. It takes 5 hours to bake a turkey. Mrs. Frank put the turkey in the oven at 9:30 in the morning. At what time would the turkey be baked?

2:30

**144** (one hundred forty-four)

# Basic Properties

**pages 145-146**

## Objective

To understand some basic properties of multiplication

## Materials

## Mental Math

Dictate the following word problems:

1. Jenny's mother puts four rows of three cookies on each sheet. How many cookies are there on each sheet? (12)
2. Then she puts two sheets in the oven at once. How many does she bake at one time? (24)
3. Jenny's favorite recipe makes 48 cookies. If they bake two sheets at a time, how many times will they have to fill the oven to make them all? (twice)
4. Baking at 350° F, the cookies take 10 minutes. If they put a batch in the oven at 3:45, when will they be done? (3:55)

## Skill Review

Ask students if the order in which numbers are added matters. (no) Remind students that this is the commutative property of addition. Explain that addition is also associative. This means that the terms can be grouped in any way: $(3 + 6) + 2 = 3 + (6 + 2)$

---

## Basic Properties

There are some ideas that are important when we multiply.

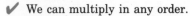

✔ We can multiply in any order.

$$\begin{array}{c} 5 \\ \times\, 3 \\ \hline 15 \end{array} \qquad \begin{array}{c} 3 \\ \times\, 5 \\ \hline 15 \end{array}$$

$3 \times 5 = \underline{15}$

$5 \times 3 = \underline{15}$

✔ We can group any two factors.

$(4 \times 2) \times 3 = ?$      $4 \times (2 \times 3) = ?$

$\underline{8} \times 3 = \underline{24}$      $4 \times \underline{6} = \underline{24}$

✔ Multiplying by 1 does not affect the answer.

$3 \times 1 = \underline{3}$      $1 \times 3 = \underline{3}$

✔ Multiplying by 0 always results in 0.

$7 \times 0 = \underline{0}$      $0 \times 7 = \underline{0}$

### Getting Started

Multiply.

1.
$$\begin{array}{c} 0 \\ \times\, 0 \\ \hline 0 \end{array}$$
2.
$$\begin{array}{c} 6 \\ \times\, 4 \\ \hline 24 \end{array}$$
3.
$$\begin{array}{c} 4 \\ \times\, 6 \\ \hline 24 \end{array}$$
4.
$$\begin{array}{c} 3 \\ \times\, 1 \\ \hline 3 \end{array}$$

5. $5 \times 1 = \underline{5}$   6. $7 \times 6 = \underline{42}$   7. $6 \times 7 = \underline{42}$   8. $0 \times 4 = \underline{0}$

9. $(5 \times 1) \times 3 = ?$      10. $5 \times (1 \times 3) = ?$

$\underline{5} \times 3 = \underline{15}$      $5 \times \underline{3} = \underline{15}$

---

## Teaching the Lesson

**Introducing the Problem** This lesson formalizes some of the basic properties of multiplication. Write these problems on the board for students to do: **5 × 3, 3 × 5.** (15, 15) This illustrates the commutative property of multiplication. Addition has the same property. Now write the second set of problems on the board and have students complete them. **(4 × 2) × 3 = 8 × 3 =** (24) and **4 × (2 × 3) = 4 × 6 =** (24) Explain that if all the factors are to be multiplied, it doesn't matter which ones are multiplied first. The answer will be the same. This is the associative property of multiplication. Addition has the same property. Write the next two problems on the board for students to work: **3 × 1, 1 × 3.** Explain that any number multiplied by one has itself as a product. This is called the identity element of multiplication. The final property is illustrated by the last problems. Write **7 × 0 and 0 × 7** on the board. Have a student do these on the board. Remind them that no matter how many zeros you have, you still have zero.

**Developing the Skill** Write several examples of each of these properties on the board and have students come up and work them while the others do them at their desks.

## Practice

Multiply.

| | | | | | | |
|---|---|---|---|---|---|---|
| 1. $\begin{array}{r} 6 \\ \times 0 \\ \hline 0 \end{array}$ | 2. $\begin{array}{r} 1 \\ \times 9 \\ \hline 9 \end{array}$ | 3. $\begin{array}{r} 8 \\ \times 7 \\ \hline 56 \end{array}$ | 4. $\begin{array}{r} 4 \\ \times 1 \\ \hline 4 \end{array}$ | 5. $\begin{array}{r} 3 \\ \times 9 \\ \hline 27 \end{array}$ | 6. $\begin{array}{r} 9 \\ \times 3 \\ \hline 27 \end{array}$ | 7. $\begin{array}{r} 0 \\ \times 4 \\ \hline 0 \end{array}$ |
| 8. $\begin{array}{r} 8 \\ \times 8 \\ \hline 64 \end{array}$ | 9. $\begin{array}{r} 5 \\ \times 1 \\ \hline 5 \end{array}$ | 10. $\begin{array}{r} 1 \\ \times 8 \\ \hline 8 \end{array}$ | 11. $\begin{array}{r} 8 \\ \times 1 \\ \hline 8 \end{array}$ | 12. $\begin{array}{r} 9 \\ \times 6 \\ \hline 54 \end{array}$ | 13. $\begin{array}{r} 5 \\ \times 7 \\ \hline 35 \end{array}$ | 14. $\begin{array}{r} 7 \\ \times 5 \\ \hline 35 \end{array}$ |

15. $4 \times 2 = \underline{\phantom{0}8\phantom{0}}$    16. $0 \times 6 = \underline{\phantom{0}0\phantom{0}}$    17. $8 \times 9 = \underline{\phantom{0}72\phantom{0}}$    18. $3 \times 2 = \underline{\phantom{0}6\phantom{0}}$

19. $0 \times 0 = \underline{\phantom{0}0\phantom{0}}$    20. $4 \times 7 = \underline{\phantom{0}28\phantom{0}}$    21. $6 \times 8 = \underline{\phantom{0}48\phantom{0}}$    22. $7 \times 9 = \underline{\phantom{0}63\phantom{0}}$

23. $(0 \times 3) \times 2 = ?$        24. $4 \times (1 \times 5) = ?$        25. $(2 \times 2) \times 3 = ?$

$\underline{\phantom{0}0\phantom{0}} \times 2 = \underline{\phantom{0}0\phantom{0}}$        $4 \times \underline{\phantom{0}5\phantom{0}} = \underline{\phantom{0}20\phantom{0}}$        $\underline{\phantom{0}4\phantom{0}} \times 3 = \underline{\phantom{0}12\phantom{0}}$

26. $(5 \times 1) \times 6 = ?$        27. $8 \times (3 \times 0) = ?$        28. $9 \times (1 \times 7) = ?$

$\underline{\phantom{0}5\phantom{0}} \times 6 = \underline{\phantom{0}30\phantom{0}}$        $8 \times \underline{\phantom{0}0\phantom{0}} = \underline{\phantom{0}0\phantom{0}}$        $9 \times \underline{\phantom{0}7\phantom{0}} = \underline{\phantom{0}63\phantom{0}}$

---

### EXCURSION

Circle the word or words which describe how the left side in each number sentence is different from the right side. Compute each side of the sentence, and circle the side which was easier to compute.

1. $2 \times (1 \times 6) = (2 \times 1) \times 6$        order    (grouping)

$\underline{\phantom{0}12\phantom{0}} = \underline{\phantom{0}12\phantom{0}}$

2. $3 \times (2 \times 0) = 0 \times (3 \times 2)$        (order)    grouping

$\underline{\phantom{0}0\phantom{0}} = \underline{\phantom{0}0\phantom{0}}$

3. $(1 \times 4) \times (2 \times 3) = (3 \times 1) \times (2 \times 4)$    (order)    (grouping)

$\underline{\phantom{0}24\phantom{0}} = \underline{\phantom{0}24\phantom{0}}$

---

# Practicing Multiplication Facts

**pages 147-148**

## Objective

To review multiplication facts

## Materials

*multiplication flash cards
100-fact multiplication charts

## Mental Math

Dictate these problems:

1. 8 + 2 (10)      8. 4 + 3 (7)
2. 9 − 4 (5)       9. 6 × 4 (24)
3. 8 × 3 (24)    10. 8 − 3 (5)
4. 8 × 9 (72)    11. 5 − 5 (0)
5. 9 − 8 (1)      12. 5 × 5 (25)
6. 5 + 4 (9)      13. 6 − 1 (5)
7. 4 × 0 (0)      14. 6 + 0 (6)

## Skill Review

Have students count aloud with you:

1. from 0 through 60 by six's.
2. from 0 through 70 by seven's.
3. from 0 through 80 by eight's.
4. from 0 through 90 by nine's.
5. from 0 through 100 by ten's.

**147**

---

### Practicing Multiplication Facts

Multiply.

| | | | | | | | | | |
|---|---|---|---|---|---|---|---|---|---|
| 1 ×3 = 3 | 2 ×2 = 4 | 6 ×3 = 18 | 7 ×8 = 56 | 3 ×5 = 15 | 3 ×1 = 3 | 2 ×0 = 0 | 4 ×5 = 20 | 5 ×3 = 15 | 2 ×1 = 2 |
| 9 ×8 = 72 | 4 ×2 = 8 | 6 ×8 = 48 | 8 ×5 = 40 | 3 ×9 = 27 | 2 ×6 = 12 | 9 ×0 = 0 | 6 ×0 = 0 | 3 ×8 = 24 | 2 ×7 = 14 |
| 2 ×5 = 10 | 0 ×9 = 0 | 7 ×5 = 35 | 8 ×2 = 16 | 8 ×8 = 64 | 7 ×6 = 42 | 9 ×5 = 45 | 6 ×1 = 6 | 0 ×2 = 0 | 9 ×4 = 36 |
| 1 ×1 = 1 | 5 ×5 = 25 | 4 ×1 = 4 | 2 ×8 = 16 | 4 ×4 = 16 | 0 ×0 = 0 | 7 ×2 = 14 | 2 ×4 = 8 | 3 ×6 = 18 | 5 ×0 = 0 |
| 5 ×9 = 45 | 0 ×4 = 0 | 4 ×7 = 28 | 1 ×2 = 2 | 7 ×3 = 21 | 1 ×0 = 0 | 3 ×3 = 9 | 6 ×6 = 36 | 1 ×6 = 6 | 5 ×7 = 35 |
| 7 ×0 = 0 | 6 ×9 = 54 | 0 ×1 = 0 | 5 ×8 = 40 | 7 ×7 = 49 | 5 ×6 = 30 | 9 ×1 = 9 | 5 ×1 = 5 | 4 ×8 = 32 | 7 ×9 = 63 |
| 2 ×9 = 18 | 0 ×7 = 0 | 9 ×3 = 27 | 5 ×4 = 20 | 6 ×2 = 12 | 9 ×6 = 54 | 2 ×3 = 6 | 7 ×4 = 28 | 8 ×4 = 32 | 1 ×5 = 5 |
| 6 ×4 = 24 | 1 ×4 = 4 | 8 ×0 = 0 | 0 ×8 = 0 | 4 ×0 = 0 | 8 ×3 = 24 | 9 ×9 = 81 | 8 ×1 = 8 | 3 ×2 = 6 | 0 ×6 = 0 |
| 6 ×5 = 30 | 5 ×2 = 10 | 9 ×7 = 63 | 4 ×6 = 24 | 3 ×0 = 0 | 9 ×1 = 9 | 3 ×7 = 21 | 3 ×4 = 12 | 0 ×5 = 0 | 4 ×9 = 36 |
| 8 ×7 = 56 | 7 ×1 = 7 | 4 ×3 = 12 | 8 ×9 = 72 | 0 ×3 = 0 | 1 ×8 = 8 | 8 ×6 = 48 | 9 ×2 = 18 | 1 ×7 = 7 | 6 ×7 = 42 |

---

## Teaching the Lesson

**Introducing the Problem**   Have students use their 100-fact multiplication charts completed in the last lesson. Have students start with the column for zeros and read aloud through the column for nines. Starting with the row for zero, tell them to read again, row by row until they have read the nines. Ask a student to explain the pattern. (The rows and columns are identical.) Explain that the chart reveals the commutative property of multiplication. Ask students to read the chart as though the first number of a multiplication problem is found along the side of the chart, the second number along the top. Direct them to find the answer to the problem 5 × 8. Now ask them to find 8 × 5. Ask if they are in the same place on the chart (no) and if the answer is the same. (yes) Many of the products on the chart can be found in pairs like this. Now have students circle each of the products that is not part of a pair. (1, 4, 9, 16, 25, 36, 49, 64, 81) Ask what they notice about these numbers. (They form a diagonal, and they are the products of identical factors.)

**Developing the Skill**   Hand out fresh 100-fact multiplication charts and have students fill them in as quickly and accurately as possible. Let them check their own work using their old chart for the answers.

## Practice

Complete the circles.

1.
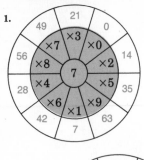

2.
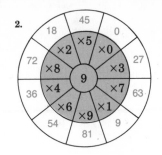

3.
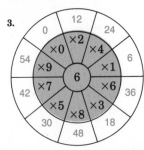

4.
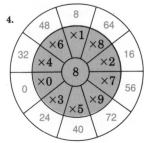

EXCURSION

These machines are programmed to multiply. Write the missing factors and products on the In and Out cards.

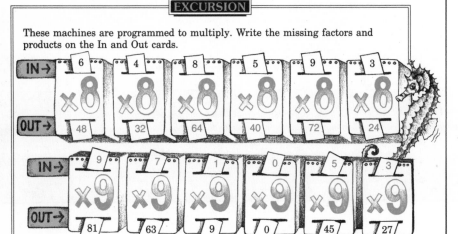

**148** (one hundred forty-eight)

# Problem Solving, Drawing Pictures

## pages 149-150

### Objective

To solve problems by illustrating them

### Materials

55 pennies
paper equilateral triangles, 8 inches on a side
paper squares, 6 inches on a side

### Mental Math

Have students tell whether they would need to trade in order to do these problems. Then have them do the subtraction.

1. 34 − 11 (no trade, 23)
2. 58 − 9 (trade required, 49)
3. 45 − 43 (no trade, 2)
4. 24 − 17 (trade required, 7)
5. 170 − 30 (no trade, 40)
6. 144 − 24 (no trade, 120)

## Drawing a Picture

We are making a triangle by arranging pennies in rows on a table. The first row has 1 penny, the second row has 2 and so on. How many pennies will we need if the triangle is to have 10 rows?

### ★ SEE

We want to know how many pennies there will be in the whole triangle. Each row will have one more penny than the row above.

There are __10__ rows in the triangle.

### ★ PLAN

We can draw a picture of the triangle.

Then we could add the number of pennies in each row.

### ★ DO

$1 + 2 + 3 + 4 + 5 + 6 + 7 + 8 + 9 + 10 =$ __55__

We will need __55__ pennies to make the triangle.

### ★ CHECK

We can check by counting the pennies in the drawing.

We count __55__ pennies.

(one hundred forty-nine) **149**

## Teaching the Lesson

Read the problem aloud. Remind students that it can be solved using the four-step method. Ask one student to read the name of each step aloud. (SEE, PLAN, DO, CHECK) Begin with the SEE section and work through the four steps of the method with the class. Ask students to explain how the drawing illustrates the problem and helps to solve it. Explain that many problems can be clarified by drawings. Ask students if they can think of a problem that can be solved with a drawing. Brain teasers can often be solved only with diagrams.

**Apply**

Draw a picture to help you solve the problem. Remember to use the four-step plan.

1. What 6 coins together make 50¢?
   4 dimes, 2 nickels

2. How many different ways can you cut a rectangular cake into 8 equal pieces?
   See Solution Notes.

3. Draw 5 straight lines through these points so that there are exactly 3 points on each line.

   .
   . . .
   . . .

4. How many sides does a figure have that is formed by folding in the corners of a triangle, so they meet in the center? The sides of the triangle are all the same length.
   6 sides

5. What figure is formed when you fold each corner of a square into the center?
   a square

6. Hang the clothes in the closet so that a shirt always hangs between a dress and a coat. What is the fourteenth garment?
   a shirt

7. Draw 2 rows of 9 dots, one row directly under the other. Explain how you can use your drawing to prove that $2 \times 9 = 9 \times 2$.
   Answers may vary.

8. Small cans of fruit juice come in packs of 6. Describe two different ways to find the number of cans in 5 such packs.
   See Solution Notes.

9. Multiply some numbers by 9. Each time, add the digits in the product until you have a one-digit sum. Describe what happens. Do you think this will happen for any whole number you multiply by 9?
   See Solution Notes.

10. Merlin put a factor in a box and made a magic multiplying machine. The box multiplies any number you put in by this factor. If the answer is always 0, what factor did Merlin put in the box?
    0

**150** (one hundred fifty)

## Extra Credit  *Numeration*

Have students make a crossword puzzle using numbers instead of words. The clues should be given as multiplication facts. Tell students to exchange papers and complete the puzzles.

Ex.

| Down | Across |
|------|--------|
| 1. $4 \times 4 =$ | 1. $2 \times 6 =$ |
| 2. $3 \times 8 =$ | 3. $5 \times 5 =$ |
| 4. $9 \times 6 =$ | 5. $8 \times 8 =$ |
| 9. $9 \times 9 =$ | 7. $1 \times 4 =$ |

# Solution Notes

1. Encourage students to try several combinations of coins in order to find one that is correct. There is one other solution: one quarter and 5 nickels.

2. Illustrate possible arrangements on the board after students have had time to try them on paper. Some possible arrangements are given.

   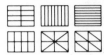

3. Have students copy the arrangement of dots so that they can try several solutions in order to arrive at one that works.

4. To help students solve this problem, give them equilateral triangles with sides of about 8 inches. Have them do the folding and illustrate the solution in their text.

5. Give each student a paper square and let them fold it, then draw the solution in their text.

6. Add to the problem that a coat is the first item in the closet. Help students see that they need not draw each item of clothing, but can abbreviate it: C for coat, S for shirt, D for dress. The solution might look like this: CSDCSDCSDCSDCS.

## Higher-Order Thinking Skills

7. Synthesis: A sample answer is that held one way the drawing shows 2 groups of 9, or 18; held another way, the drawing shows 9 groups of 2, or 18.

8. Analysis: Students can describe a 5 by 6 array as $6 + 6 + 6 + 6 + 6$ or as $5 \times 6$.

9. Analysis: The sum of the digits in the product of 9 and any whole number is 9 if you keep adding until you get a single digit sum.
   $9 \times 5 = 45$     $4 + 5 = 9$
   $9 \times 56 = 504$    $5 + 0 + 4 = 9$
   $9 \times 86 = 774$    $7 + 7 + 4 = 18$
                            $1 + 8 = 9$

   Encourage students to make 3 more problems that prove this to be true.

10. Analysis: The product of 0 and any number is 0, therefore the number hidden in the box has to be 0.

# Using a Calculator, the Multiplication Key

pages 151-152

## Objective

To multiply using a calculator

## Materials

calculators

## Mental Math

Ask students to tell what operation has been used in the following problems:

1. 4 ☐ 8 = 32 (×)
2. 7 ☐ 2 = 5 (−)
3. 13 ☐ 1 = 13 (×)
4. 9 ☐ 3 = 6 (−)
5. 8 ☐ 0 = 0 (×)
6. 8 ☐ 0 = 8 (+ or − )
7. 5 ☐ 5 = 10 (+)
8. 5 ☐ 2 = 10 (×)

## Skill Review

Review the way in which addition and subtraction can be done on a calculator. Ask a student to come to the board and write how 5 + 6, would be done on a calculator. (5 ⊞ 6 ⊟ 11) Have another student demonstrate how 9 − 3 would be done. (9 ⊟ 3 ⊟ 6) Dictate a number of short addition and subtraction problems for the students to work using calculators.

---

### Using a Calculator, the Multiplication Key

Craig is taking orders that are called into the High Street Hardware warehouse. Help Craig complete this order.

We need to find the total cost of each item and the total cost of the order.
We know the cost of each item and the number of items ordered.
To find the cost of each item, we multiply the cost of one, by the number of that kind ordered.

The quantity that is entered into the calculator before the multiplication sign, will be multiplied by the number entered after the ⊠ sign.

| | | | |
|---|---|---|---|
| Light bulbs | 2 ⊠ 7 ⊟ | 14 | |
| Electric cords | 6 ⊠ 9 ⊟ | 54 | |
| Switch boxes | 7 ⊠ 8 ⊟ | 56 | |
| Electric tape | 5 ⊠ 8 ⊟ | 40 | |

To find the total cost of the order, we add the costs of all the items.

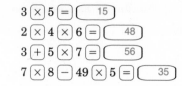

14 ⊞ 54 ⊞ 56 ⊞ 40 ⊟ 164

The total cost of the order is $164.

Complete these codes:

3 ⊠ 5 ⊟ 15
2 ⊠ 4 ⊠ 6 ⊟ 48
3 ⊞ 5 ⊠ 7 ⊟ 56
7 ⊠ 8 ⊟ 49 ⊠ 5 ⊟ 35

(one hundred fifty-one) **151**

---

## Teaching the Lesson

**Introducing the Problem**   Read the problem aloud while students examine the picture. Tell them that they are going to use a calculator to help Craig. Have a student read the plan sentences. Explain that the list of items and their prices are written in a form ready for entry in the calculator. The boxed operations indicate operation keys. The numbers are entered using the number keys. Using the calculator, have students complete each of the multiplication problems indicated. (14, 54, 56, 40) Work through the next section with the students having them write the products from the first section in the spaces indicated. (14, 54, 56, 40) Then have them work the addition on the calculator. (164) Ask for the total cost of the order. ($164) Read the solution sentence while students fill in the answer. Have students complete the problems indicated at the bottom of the page, carefully following the operations indicated.

**Developing the Skill**   Dictate multiplication problems to groups of two students. Explain that you want to see who can accurately complete the problem first using a calculator. If the two arrive at different answers, have a third student work the problem to verify the answer. Move around the room in this way, emphasizing speed and accuracy.

## Practice

Complete these codes.

1. $6 \times 9 = \boxed{54}$
2. $7 \times 5 = \boxed{35}$
3. $4 \times 2 \times 6 = \boxed{48}$
4. $3 \times 2 \times 8 = \boxed{48}$
5. $7 - 3 \times 7 = \boxed{28}$
6. $6 \times 8 - 25 = \boxed{23}$
7. $4 \times 9 + 73 = \boxed{109}$
8. $56 - 49 \times 5 = \boxed{35}$
9. $87 - 84 \times 9 - 25 = \boxed{2}$
10. $8 \times 5 - 29 + 37 = \boxed{48}$

## Apply

Find the total cost of each item.

11.

| Item | Cost Per Item | Number of Items | Cost |
|------|------|------|------|
| Wrench | $8 | 6 | $48 |
| Screwdriver | $3 | 9 | $27 |
| Pliers | $5 | 4 | $20 |
| Hammer | $9 | 3 | $27 |
| | | Total Cost | $122 |

12.

| Item | Cost Per Item | Number of Items | Cost |
|------|------|------|------|
| Skillet | $7 | 7 | $49 |
| Saucepan | $4 | 8 | $32 |
| Cookie jar | $6 | 5 | $30 |
| Breadboard | $9 | 6 | $54 |
| | | Total Cost | $165 |

### EXCURSION

Enter each of these codes to find the value of the letter. Write the letter over its value to find the secret message.

1. $9 \times 6 = \boxed{T}$
2. $29 + 58 = \boxed{U}$
3. $(125 - 119) \times 6 = \boxed{S}$
4. $36 + 18 + 43 = \boxed{M}$
5. $2 \times 4 \times 7 = \boxed{P}$
6. $(9 \times 8) - 43 = \boxed{H}$
7. $87 - 59 + 38 = \boxed{D}$
8. $37 + 48 - 51 = \boxed{A}$

$$\frac{M}{97} \quad \frac{A}{34} \quad \frac{T}{54} \quad \frac{H}{29}$$

$$\frac{A}{34} \quad \frac{D}{66} \quad \frac{D}{66} \quad \frac{S}{36}$$

$$\frac{U}{87} \quad \frac{P}{56}$$

**152** (one hundred fifty-two)

---

## Practice

Have students complete the problems on the page. Caution them to watch the signs indicated and to check each number they enter. Remind them that $\boxed{CE}$ allows them to correct the last entry in case of a mistake.

## Excursion

Have students enter each code on their calculators to find the value of each letter. They should then write that letter above its value to discover the secret message. Have students work in groups to write more secret messages.

## Extra Credit *Applications*

Baseball runs are scored by a player moving from home plate, around the three bases and back to home. If this is done all in one turn, it's called a home run. If other players are on each of the bases four runs would score, which is called a grand slam home run.

Tell students Roger Maris holds the season record for home runs, totalling 61! If all of his home runs were grand slams, how many runs would he have helped score? ($61 \times 4 = 244$) If 30 home runs were grand slams and the rest only 1-run homers, what would be the total runs scored? ($30 \times 4 = 120 + (61 - 30) = 151$)

# Chapter Test

| Item | Objective |
|---|---|
| 1-33 | Recall multiplication facts through 9 (See pages 119-129, 137-144, 147) |
| 34-36 | Solve word problems involving multiplication facts (See pages 119-129, 137-144, 147) |

Multiply.

| | | | | | | |
|---|---|---|---|---|---|---|
| **1.** 9 ×9 = 81 | **2.** 8 ×7 = 56 | **3.** 5 ×5 = 25 | **4.** 7 ×9 = 63 | **5.** 7 ×6 = 42 | **6.** 6 ×9 = 54 | **7.** 9 ×5 = 45 |
| **8.** 8 ×5 = 40 | **9.** 5 ×7 = 35 | **10.** 7 ×8 = 56 | **11.** 7 ×7 = 49 | **12.** 7 ×9 = 63 | **13.** 9 ×6 = 54 | **14.** 8 ×9 = 72 |
| **15.** 9 ×8 = 72 | **16.** 6 ×8 = 48 | **17.** 8 ×6 = 48 | **18.** 8 ×8 = 64 | **19.** 6 ×6 = 36 | **20.** 8 ×9 = 72 | **21.** 6 ×5 = 30 |

**22.** 7 × 9 = _63_   **23.** 7 × 8 = _56_   **24.** 6 × 9 = _54_   **25.** 6 × 7 = _42_

**26.** 9 × 8 = _72_   **27.** 6 × 9 = _54_   **28.** 6 × 7 = _42_   **29.** 7 × 6 = _42_

**30.** 7 × 7 = _49_   **31.** 8 × 6 = _48_   **32.** 8 × 7 = _56_   **33.** 9 × 9 = _81_

Solve these problems.

**34.** There are 6 rows of trees. Each row has 9 trees in it. How many trees are there?
54 trees

**35.** Balloons are sold in packages of 8. Rhonda bought 7 packages. How many balloons did Rhonda buy?
56 balloons

**36.** Use your calculator to find the total cost of this order.

| Number | Item | Cost | Total |
|---|---|---|---|
| 5 | Hammers | $9 | $45 |
| 4 | Wrenches | $3 | $12 |
| 9 | Pliers | $7 | $63 |
| | Total Cost | | $120 |

| SALE | |
|---|---|
| Washers | $1 |
| Hammers | $9 |
| Screwdrivers | $4 |
| Wrenches | $3 |
| Pliers | $7 |

Circle the letter of the correct answer.

**1** 627 ◯ 623
  **(a)** >
  **b** <

**2** What is the value of the 0 in 328,650?
  **a** tens
  **b** hundreds
  **c** thousands
  **(d)** NG

**3** $28.37
 + 9.26
  **a** $37.53
  **(b)** $37.63
  **c** $38.63
  **d** NG

**4**  325
   87
 + 5,682
  **a** 5,104
  **b** 6,004
  **c** 6,104
  **(d)** NG

**5** Round each number to the nearest hundred and add.
  575
 + 385
  **a** 900
  **b** 800
  **c** 700
  **(d)** NG

**6** 703
 − 259
  **a** 344
  **(b)** 444
  **c** 556
  **d** NG

**7** $39.26
 − 8.75
  **a** $20.51
  **(b)** $30.51
  **c** $31.51
  **d** NG

**8** Round each number to the nearest hundred and subtract.
  712
 − 379
  **(a)** 300
  **b** 400
  **c** 500
  **d** NG

**9**
  **a** 7:15
  **b** 8:15
  **(c)** 3:40
  **d** NG

**10** Find the perimeter.
87 m  87 m
  125 m
  **a** 174 m
  **b** 212 m
  **(c)** 299 m
  **d** NG

**11** Choose the better estimate of length.
  **(a)** 35 ft
  **b** 35 yd

**12** Choose the better estimate of weight.
  **(a)** 8 oz
  **b** 8 lb

**13**
  **(a)** 4 × 5 = 20
  **b** 5 × 5 = 25
  **c** 6 × 5 = 30
  **d** NG

☐ score

**154** (one hundred fifty-four)

---

# Cumulative Review

| Item | Objective |
|---|---|
| 1 | Compare numbers less than 1,000 (See pages 27-28) |
| 2 | Identify the value of a digit in a number less than 1,000,000 (See pages 35–36) |
| 3 | Add dollars and cents with regrouping (See pages 51-52) |
| 4 | Add three or four numbers (See pages 49-50) |
| 5 | Round numbers to the nearest 100 and add (See pages 53-56) |
| 6 | Subtract two 3-digit numbers with two regroupings (See pages 67-68) |
| 7 | Subtract dollars and cents with regrouping (See pages 75-76) |
| 8 | Round numbers to the nearest 100 and subtract (See pages 77-78) |
| 9 | Read the time to the minute (See pages 87-88) |
| 10 | Add to find the perimeter (See pages 95-96) |
| 11 | Choose the appropriate metric unit of length (See pages 107-108) |
| 12 | Choose the appropriate unit of weight (See pages 99-100) |
| 13 | Write an equation to represent an array (See pages 137-144) |

---

## Alternate Cumulative Review

Circle the letter of the correct answer.

**1** 635 ◯ 653
 **a** >
 **(b)** <
 **c** =

**2** What is the value of the 3 in 638,520?
 **(a)** ten thousands
 **b** thousands
 **c** hundred thousands
 **d** NG

**3** $63.59
 + 8.26
 **a** $72.85
 **b** $55.33
 **c** $71.75
 **(d)** NG

**4**  621
   96
 + 3,374
 **a** 3,991
 **(b)** 4,091
 **c** 4,981
 **d** NG

**5** Round each number to the nearest hundred and add.
  673
 + 579
 **a** 1,100
 **(b)** 1,300
 **c** 1,200
 **d** NG

**6** 807
 − 549
 **a** 342
 **b** 1356
 **(c)** 258
 **d** NG

**7** $47.15
 − 6.84
 **(a)** $40.31
 **b** $40.21
 **c** $41.71
 **d** NG

**8** Round each number to the nearest hundred and subtract.
  523
 − 287
 **a** 300
 **b** 400
 **(c)** 200
 **d** NG

**9** What time is it? (Show a clock.)
 **a** 11:30
 **(b)** 6:55
 **c** 7:55
 **d** NG

**10** Find the perimeter of a pentagon that is 29 cm on each side.
 **a** 106 cm
 **(b)** 145 cm
 **c** 135 cm
 **d** NG

**11** What unit would you use to measure the distance traveled on a vacation?
 **a** kilogram
 **b** meter
 **(c)** kilometer
 **d** NG

**12** What unit would you use to measure the weight of potatoes?
 **a** tons
 **b** ounces
 **(c)** pounds
 **d** NG

**154**

# Multiplying by 10 and 100

pages 155-156

## Objective

To multiply when 10 or 100 is a factor

## Materials

pennies

## Mental Math

Ask what number n stands for:

1. $n \times 5 = 45$ (9)
2. $n \times 9 = 0$ (0)
3. $7 \times 8 = n$ (56)
4. $4 \times n = 36$ (9)
5. $7 \times n = 42$ (6)
6. $n \times n = 25$ (5)

## Skill Review

Draw a place value chart on the board and have a student label place values from ones through thousands. Have volunteers enter these numbers: 365, 820, 1, 499, 54. Write random numbers on the board and ask the class to identify the number of tens, hundreds, and thousands in each number. Write the number 3,522 this way: three thousands, five hundreds, two tens, and two ones. Have a student write 4,129 in words.

**Multiplying by 10 and 100**

Ted is getting ready for the neighborhood carnival's Penny Toss game. How many pennies does he have stacked? How many pennies does he have in jars?

PENNY TOSS

We are looking for the total number of pennies stacked, and the total number in the jars.

There are ___5___ stacks of 10 pennies each.

There are ___5___ jars with 100 pennies in each jar. To find the total number of pennies in the stacks,

we multiply ___5___ by 10. ___5___ $\times$ **10** = ___50___ To find the total number of pennies in the jars,

we multiply ___5___ by 100. ___5___ $\times$ **100** = ___500___

There are ___50___ pennies in stacks

and ___500___ pennies in jars. Look for the pattern in these multiplications.

$$5 \times 1 = 5 \qquad 5 \times 10 = 50 \qquad 5 \times 100 = 500$$

### Getting Started

Complete the pattern.

1. $8 \times 1 =$ ___8___
   $8 \times 10 =$ ___80___
   $8 \times 100 =$ ___800___

2. $4 \times 1 =$ ___4___
   $4 \times 10 =$ ___40___
   $4 \times 100 =$ ___400___

3. $1 \times \$5 =$ ___$5___
   $10 \times \$5 =$ ___$50___
   $100 \times \$5 =$ ___$500___

Multiply.

4. $6 \times 10 =$ ___60___

5. $4 \times 10 =$ ___40___

6. $100 \times \$2 =$ ___$200___

(one hundred fifty-five) **155**

## Teaching the Lesson

**Introducing the Problem**   Read the problem aloud and have students identify the question being asked. Help students fill in the information sentences in their texts. (5 of 10, 5 of 100) Have students read and complete the plan sentences. ($5 \times 10 = 50$, $5 \times 100 = 500$) Have a student look at the pattern sentence and describe it for the class. (The first problem, $5 \times 1$, illustrates the identity principle of multiplication discussed in the last chapter. When ten is multiplied by 5, the product is 5 followed by one zero. In the problem $5 \times 100$, the answer is 5 with two zeros annexed.)

**Developing the Skill**   Explain that when they multiply by 10 or 100, they can do simple multiplication and then add zeros. Write these patterns on the board:

| | | |
|---|---|---|
| $3 \times 1 = 3$ | $3 \times 10 = 30$ | $3 \times 100 = 300$ |
| $7 \times 1 = 7$ | $7 \times 10 = 70$ | $7 \times 100 = 700$ |

Ask students to come to the board and add examples of their own. Show students that when they multiply by ten, they can take the digit they multiply by and add one zero to get the answer. Similarly when multiplying by 100, they can multiply and add two zeros.

Complete the pattern.

1. $7 \times 1 = \underline{7}$

   $7 \times 10 = \underline{70}$

   $7 \times 100 = \underline{700}$

2. $1 \times 3 = \underline{3}$

   $10 \times 3 = \underline{30}$

   $100 \times 3 = \underline{300}$

3. $1 \times 1 = \underline{1}$

   $1 \times 10 = \underline{10}$

   $1 \times 100 = \underline{100}$

4. $9 \times 1 = \underline{9}$

   $9 \times 10 = \underline{90}$

   $9 \times 100 = \underline{900}$

5. $1 \times \$6 = \underline{\$6}$

   $10 \times \$6 = \underline{\$60}$

   $100 \times \$6 = \underline{\$600}$

6. $\$2 \times 1 = \underline{\$2}$

   $\$2 \times 10 = \underline{\$20}$

   $\$2 \times 100 = \underline{\$200}$

Multiply.

7. $4 \times 10 = \underline{40}$

8. $100 \times 9 = \underline{900}$

9. $3 \times 1 = \underline{3}$

10. $5 \times 100 = \underline{500}$

11. $7 \times 100 = \underline{700}$

12. $10 \times 8 = \underline{80}$

13. $2 \times \$100 = \underline{\$200}$

14. $100 \times 7 = \underline{700}$

15. $100 \times 8 = \underline{800}$

16. $1 \times 10 = \underline{10}$

17. $5 \times 10 = \underline{50}$

18. $5 \times 100 = \underline{500}$

19. $4 \times \$10 = \underline{\$40}$

20. $10 \times 3 = \underline{30}$

21. $100 \times \$3 = \underline{\$300}$

---

**EXCURSION**

Think about these statements. They all express the same idea.

   4 oranges + 6 oranges = 10 oranges

   4 sixes + 6 sixes = 10 sixes

   $(4 \times 6) + (6 \times 6) = 10 \times 6 = 60$

Now use this idea to solve these problems.

$(2 \times 6) + (8 \times 6) = \underline{10} \times 6 = \underline{60}$    $(3 \times 8) + (7 \times 8) = \underline{10} \times 8 = \underline{80}$

$(5 \times 7) + (5 \times 7) = \underline{10} \times 7 = \underline{70}$    $(6 \times 3) + (4 \times 3) = \underline{10} \times 3 = \underline{30}$

$(1 \times 9) + (9 \times 9) = \underline{10} \times 9 = \underline{90}$    $(4 \times 5) + (6 \times 5) = \underline{10} \times 5 = \underline{50}$

**156** (one hundred fifty-six)

---

## Correcting Common Errors

Some students may have difficulty when 10 and 100 are factors. Make 3 stacks of 10 pennies. Ask, "How many groups of 10 pennies are there?" (3) "How many pennies in all?" (30) Have a student write 3 × 10 = 30 on the chalkboard. Ask, "How many zeros in 10?" (1) "How many zeros in the product?" (1) Draw 3 jars, indicating that each jar contains 100 pennies. Ask, "How many groups of 100 pennies?" (3) "How many pennies in all?" (300) Have a student write 3 × 100 = 300 on the chalk- board. Ask, "How many zeros in 100?" (2) "How many zeros in the product?" (2)

## Enrichment

Some students may not be familiar with the properties of the multiples of 9. Have students make a chart listing the first 10 multiples of nine, and the sum of each number's digits.

| Product | Sum of the digits: |
|---|---|
| 9 | 9 |
| 18 | $1 + 8 = 9$ |
| 27 | $2 + 7 = 9$, and so on |

## Practice

Have students do all the problems on the page. Tell them to remember dollar signs and to watch whether they are multi- plying by 1, 10, or 100.

## Excursion

Write on the board:
**$(4 \times 6) + (6 \times 6) = 24 + 36 = (60)$**
**$(4 \times 6) + (6 \times 6) = 10 \times 6 = (60)$**
Discuss the statements with the students. Ask students to work the problems mentally and tell which was easier. (sec- ond one) Tell students they found the second problem eas- ier to work because they counted the total number of sixes first and then only needed to multiply by 10. Have students solve the problems.

## Extra Credit    *Measurement*

Have students estimate how many times they can do the listed activity within the given time limit. Then have them actually time each activity, using a stop watch. Subtract a point for each number away from the student's estimate their actual time is. The student with the overall lowest score is the best estimator of time.

Ask how many times they can do the following activities in 15 seconds:
  Snap your fingers.
  Blink your eyes.
  Touch your toes from a standing position.
  Clap your hands.

Now, have them guess how many of the following they can do in 30 seconds:
  Hop on one foot.
  Jump rope.
  Say your full name.
  Walk the length of your classroom.

# Multiplying by Multiples of 10 and 100

pages 157-158

## Objective

To multiply by multiples of 10 and 100

## Materials

24 dimes and 100 pennies

## Mental Math

Have students change these amounts to cents:

1. 4 dimes, 3 pennies (43¢)
2. 2 dimes, 2 nickels (30¢)
3. 9 dimes, 1 nickel, 2 pennies (97¢)
4. 1 quarter, 2 nickels, 3 pennies (38¢)
5. 2 quarters, 1 dime, 1 nickel, 4 pennies (69¢)
6. 3 quarters, 2 pennies (77¢)

## Skill Review

Write these multiplication problems on the board for students to solve on paper.

1. **4 × 10** (40)
2. **2 × 100** (200)
3. **5 × 10** (50)
4. **8 × 10** (80)
5. **10 × 10** (100)
6. **0 × 100** (0)

---

## Multiplying by Multiples of 10 and 100

Mr. Wang cleaned out his garage and found some money hidden on a back shelf. How many pennies are in the rolls? How many pennies are in the bags?

We want to find how many pennies are in the rolls, and in the bags.

There are ___4___ rolls of ___50___ pennies each.

Each of the ___4___ bags contains ___500___ pennies.

To find the number of pennies in the rolls,

we multiply ___4___ by 50. ___4___ × 50 = ___200___

To find the number of pennies in the bags,

we multiply ___4___ by 500. ___4___ × 500 = ___2,000___

There are ___200___ pennies in the rolls.

There are ___2,000___ pennies in the bags.

Look for the pattern in these multiplications.

$$4 \times 5 = 20 \qquad 4 \times 50 = 200 \qquad 4 \times 500 = 2,000$$

### Getting Started

Complete the pattern.

1. 3 × 2 = ___6___

   3 × 20 = ___60___

   3 × 200 = ___600___

2. 7 × $6 = ___$42___

   7 × $60 = ___$420___

   7 × $600 = ___$4,200___

3. 5 × 3 = ___15___

   50 × 3 = ___150___

   500 × 3 = ___1,500___

Multiply.

4. 4 × 300 = ___1,200___

5. $20 × 9 = ___$180___

6. 400 × 2 = ___800___

(one hundred fifty-seven) **157**

---

## Teaching the Lesson

**Introducing the Problem**    Have students read the problem and tell what is being asked. Ask a student to complete the information sentences. (4 rolls of 50 pennies each; Each of 4 bags contains 500 pennies.) Help students complete the plan sentences. (4 × 50 = 200, 4 × 500 = 2000) Remind them of the pattern for multiplying tens and hundreds while students work the problems in their books. Have one student read the solution sentences aloud. (200 pennies in the rolls, 2,000 pennies in the bags) Ask students to examine the three problems at the bottom of the model and describe the pattern. (number of zeros in factor equals number in the product)

**Developing the Skill**    Put a stack of 6 dimes on the desk and ask students how many dimes are in the stack. (6) Ask how many cents are in the same stack. (60) Have a student write the multiplication on the board: **6 × 10 = 60** Now make three more stacks of dimes and ask how many cents are represented by the four stacks. (240) Write the multiplication on the board: **4 × 60 = 240**. Explain that there is another way of thinking of this process: 4 × 60 = (4 × 6) × 10 = 24 × 10 = 240. Use this pattern to do several more problems for the class.

**157**

Complete the pattern.

1. $9 \times 8 =$ ___72___
   $90 \times 8 =$ ___720___
   $900 \times 8 =$ ___7,200___

2. $2 \times \$5 =$ ___$10___
   $2 \times \$50 =$ ___$100___
   $2 \times \$500 =$ ___$1,000___

3. $6 \times 8 =$ ___48___
   $6 \times 80 =$ ___480___
   $6 \times 800 =$ ___4,800___

4. $4 \times 6 =$ ___24___
   $40 \times 6 =$ ___240___
   $400 \times 6 =$ ___2,400___

5. $5 \times 7 =$ ___35___
   $5 \times 70 =$ ___350___
   $5 \times 700 =$ ___3,500___

6. $7 \times \$8 =$ ___$56___
   $70 \times \$8 =$ ___$560___
   $700 \times \$8 =$ ___$5,600___

Multiply.

7. $5 \times 50 =$ ___250___

8. $800 \times 2 =$ ___1,600___

9. $40 \times 7 =$ ___280___

10. $600 \times 3 =$ ___1,800___

11. $50 \times 9 =$ ___450___

12. $500 \times 0 =$ ___0___

13. $600 \times 6 =$ ___3,600___

14. $\$3 \times 300 =$ ___$900___

15. $4 \times 800 =$ ___3,200___

16. $900 \times \$3 =$ ___$2,700___

17. $60 \times 9 =$ ___540___

18. $20 \times 3 =$ ___60___

19. $700 \times \$4 =$ ___$2,800___

20. $90 \times 9 =$ ___810___

21. $100 \times 5 =$ ___500___

**Apply**

Solve these problems.

22. Pencils are sold in packages of 20 each. The school store orders 9 packages. How many pencils does the store order?
180 pencils

23. A jet aircraft can travel 500 miles in an hour. How far can the jet travel in 3 hours?
1,500 miles

24. Captain Barker flew 2,500 miles on Monday. She flew another 1,600 miles on Tuesday. How far did she fly both days?
4,100 miles

25. A television set can be purchased for $200. How much do 7 sets cost?
$1,400

## Correcting Common Errors

Some students will write an incorrect number of zeros when multiplying by powers of ten. Have them complete the table shown below. For each answer, have them compare the number of zeros in the multiples of ten, hundred, and thousand with the number of zeros in the product.

| ×   | 2       | 4       | 7       | 8       |
|-----|---------|---------|---------|---------|
| 30  | (60)    | (120)   | (210)   | (240)   |
| 40  | (80)    | (160)   | (280)   | (320)   |
| 60  | (120)   | (240)   | (420)   | (480)   |
| 200 | (400)   | (800)   | (1,400) | (1,600) |
| 600 | (1,200) | (2,400) | (4,200) | (4,800) |
| 900 | (1,800) | (3,600) | (6,300) | (7,200) |

## Enrichment

Give students a shoe box lid, ten counters and two pencils. The pencils are used to divide the space in the lid into 3 sections. Explain that you want them to arrange the counters in as many ways as they can to create different sums. Each different way should be recorded as an equation, such as, $2 + 4 + 4 = 10$.

## Practice

Have students complete the page. Explain that they should break the problem down ($5 \times 50 = (5 \times 5) \times 10$) if they have any trouble. Remind them to read the final problems very carefully.

## Mixed Practice

1. $6,258 + 1,256 + 1,727$ (9,241)
2. $3,000 - 38$ (2,962)
3. $7 \times 9$ (63)
4. $\$25.96 + 2.75 + 3.71$ ($32.42)
5. $708 - 453$ (255)
6. $8 \times 8$ (64)
7. $\$40.02 - 25.38$ ($14.64)
8. $9 \times 6$ (54)
9. $156 + 2,326 + 5,400$ (7,882)
10. $6,376 - 4,137$ (2,239)

## Extra Credit *Applications*

Have the students bring in a road map of their state. Make sure the maps have a legend that tells the population of most cities. Ask the students to find the five largest cities, the five smallest towns and the average population of each. Give them a list of towns and cities to locate on their maps. They could also practice locating distances between cities or towns, as well as the highways to take to reach certain destinations. A conclusion to the activity could be to have students plan a day of sightseeing, plot their course and record the mileage.

# Multiplying 1-digit Factors, No Trades

## pages 159-160

## Objective

To multiply by 1-digit factors with no trade

## Materials

ten-strips and single counters
3-digit place value charts

## Mental Math

Have students identify the missing coins:

1. 94¢ = 3 quarters, ___ dimes, and 9 pennies. (1)
2. 28¢ = 1 dime, ___ nickels, and 3 pennies (3)
3. 56¢ = ___ quarters, 1 nickel, and 1 penny (2)
4. 84¢ = 2 quarters, 3 dimes, and ___ pennies (4)

## Skill Review

Give each student ten-strips and single counters. Have them make the following numbers with the counters: 43, 72, 31, 58, 18 and 27. Ask a volunteer to illustrate each number in an equation as the sum of ten-strips and single counters by drawing them on the board.

---

### Multiplying by 1-digit Factors, No Trade

Ilene's dog eats one bag of dog food each week. How many ounces of dog food does her pet eat in 3 weeks?

We want the number of ounces of

dog food eaten in ___3___ weeks.

Ilene's dog eats ___132___ ounces of dog food in 1 week.

To find the total number of ounces,

we multiply ___132___ by ___3___.

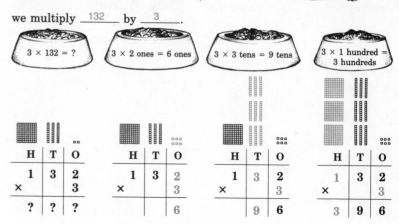

Ilene's dog eats ___396___ ounces of dog food in 3 weeks.

### Getting Started

Multiply.

1.  43
  × 2
  ‾‾‾
  86

2.  143
  ×  2
  ‾‾‾‾
  286

3.  11
  × 8
  ‾‾‾
  88

4.  120
  ×  4
  ‾‾‾‾
  480

Copy and multiply.

5. 3 × 21
63

6. 3 × 213
639

7. 1 × 48
48

8. 2 × 423
846

(one hundred fifty-nine) **159**

---

## Teaching the Lesson

**Introducing the Problem** Have the class read the problem and identify the question. Read the information sentences aloud and ask a student to provide the data required. (dog food eaten in 3 weeks, 132 ounces in 1 week) Now have a student read the plan sentence (multiply 132 by 3) as students write this in their books. Explain that in order to multiply they are going to separate 132 into hundreds, tens, and ones. Direct their attention to the problem as shown in their text. Work through the steps of the problem with the class, showing each step on the board. Have the class complete the problem and transfer the answer to the solution sentence. (396 ounces of dog food)

**Developing the Skill** Write the number 322 on the board in this way: **322 = 3 hundreds + 2 tens + 2 ones**. Explain that to multiply by a number as large as 322, they will be breaking the number down into its components, like those illustrated on the board, and multiplying each component separately. Now write: **2 × 322 = 2 × 3 hundreds +2 × 2 tens + 2 × 2 ones**. Have a student come to the board and do the multiplication. (644) Point out that when they multiply multi-digit numbers, they must start with ones, move to tens, and then hundreds. Have them work several problems on their 3-digit place value charts.

## Practice

Multiply.

1. 32 × 3 = 96
2. 124 × 2 = 248
3. 242 × 2 = 484
4. 41 × 2 = 82
5. 112 × 3 = 336
6. 310 × 3 = 930
7. 121 × 4 = 484
8. 33 × 2 = 66
9. 131 × 2 = 262
10. 313 × 3 = 939
11. 142 × 2 = 284
12. 212 × 4 = 848
13. 121 × 3 = 363
14. 333 × 3 = 999
15. 414 × 2 = 828
16. 31 × 3 = 93
17. 444 × 2 = 888
18. 536 × 1 = 536
19. 344 × 2 = 688
20. 212 × 4 = 848

## Copy and Do

21. 5 × 111 (555)
22. 1 × 987 (987)
23. 4 × 21 (84)
24. 3 × 223 (669)
25. 2 × 341 (682)
26. 3 × 33 (99)
27. 2 × 431 (862)
28. 1 × 892 (892)
29. 2 × 44 (88)
30. 3 × 232 (696)
31. 1 × 793 (793)
32. 2 × 143 (286)

## Apply

Solve these problems.

33. Martha has 3 sacks of marbles. Each sack contains 120 marbles. How many marbles does Martha have? 360 marbles
34. Lucia bought a clock for $29.36. She gave the clerk $30. How much change should Lucia get? $0.64
35. On Sunday, 2,456 people visited the Art Museum. We know 956 of the visitors were children. How many of the visitors were adults? 1,500 visitors
36. Sean ran 5 kilometers each day. How far did Sean run in 21 days? 105 kilometers

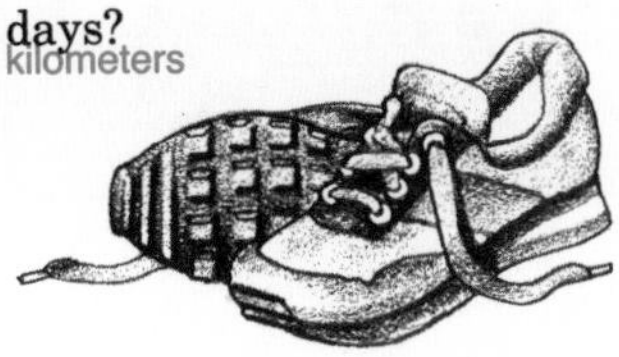



## Correcting Common Errors

Some students may begin multiplying with hundreds rather than with ones. Remind them to start in the same place as they do in addition and subtraction. One or more students may point out that it does not make any difference in the exercises in this lesson, which involve no renaming. Tell them that in the very next lesson, it will make a difference, and they will get incorrect answers if they do not multiply from right to left.

## Enrichment

Ask students how many hours are in a day (24) and how many hours are shown on the face of a clock (12). Tell them to imagine other clocks; one showing 8 hours and another showing 6. Have them draw the clock faces. Tell them to illustrate these times on their new clocks: 2 PM, 12 noon, and 7 AM.

## Practice

Have students complete all the problems. Point out that although we write numbers from left to right, we multiply from right to left, always starting with ones.

## Mixed Practice

1. 8 × 100 (800)
2. 7 × 7 (49)
3. $75.00 − 39.72 ($35.28)
4. 4,656 + 29 + 353 (5,038)
5. 10 × 6 (60)
6. 9 × 9 (81)
7. 4,060 − 2,553 (1,507)
8. $25.38 + 1.98 + 0.75 ($28.11)
9. 5 + 8 + 7 + 3 + 4 (27)
10. 8,376 + 1,468 (9,844)

## Extra Credit *Applications*

Have your students find out what birds are commonly found in your area. A bird watching guide book is a good source. Ask them to make a tally chart listing the names of ten birds. Have the students make simple pine cone feeders to attract the birds. Spread pinecones with peanut butter and roll them in birdseed. Attach the feeders to a bush or tree near a window at school. Appoint one or two students to watch for birds at different times of the day, and remind them to be patient. Have the students keep a tally of the different kinds of birds they see. Keep the tally for two weeks. At the end of that time ask the students to make a bar graph showing the results of their bird count.

# Multiplying by 1-digit Factors, One Trade

## pages 161-162

### Objective

To multiply by 1-digit factors with one trade

### Materials

ten-strips and single counters

### Mental Math

Have students name these numbers:

1. three forties (120)
2. five sixties (300)
3. two ninties (180)
4. seven fifties (350)
5. thrity twos (60)
6. forty nines (360)

### Skill Review

Remind students that when multiplying a multi-digit number by a 1-digit number, they start with ones. Write these problems on the board and have students do them on paper.

1. **121 × 4** = (484)
2. **332 × 3** = (996)
3. **312 × 2** = (624)
4. **634 × 1** = (634)
5. **114 × 2** = (228)

Jason collects stamps from foreign countries. He has filled 4 scrapbook pages with the same number of stamps. How many stamps has he collected?

We want to find the number of stamps Jason has saved so far.

Each page contains ___16___ stamps.

Jason has filled ___4___ pages with stamps.

To find the total number of stamps,

we multiply ___16___ by ___4___.

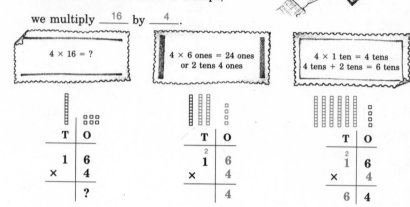

| $4 \times 16 = ?$ | $4 \times 6$ ones $= 24$ ones or 2 tens 4 ones | $4 \times 1$ ten $= 4$ tens $4$ tens $+ 2$ tens $= 6$ tens |

| T | O |
|---|---|
| 1 | 6 |
| × | 4 |
|   | ? |

| T | O |
|---|---|
| ²1 | 6 |
| × | 4 |
|   | 4 |

| T | O |
|---|---|
| ²1 | 6 |
| × | 4 |
| 6 | 4 |

Jason has collected ___64___ stamps.

### Getting Started

Multiply.

1.  25
   × 3
   ——
    75

2.  18
   × 4
   ——
    72

3.  32
   × 3
   ——
    96

4.  22
   × 5
   ——
   110

Copy and multiply.

5. 19 × 4
   76

6. 23 × 4
   92

7. 14 × 6
   84

8. 48 × 2
   96

(one hundred sixty-one) **161**

## Teaching the Lesson

**Introducing the Problem**  Have students read and identify the problem. Ask students to read the information sentences, (contains 16 stamps, has filled 4 pages) and the plan sentences, (Multiply 16 by 4.) and fill them in. Have students examine the first step of the model and move on to the second. Ask a student to multiply 4 by 6. (24) Explain that they write the ones in this product (4) in the ones column, and write the 2 over the tens column. Now have them look at third step and ask a student to tell the class the product of 4 and 1. (4) Point out that the 2 tens left from the one's multiplication will be added in now. (4 + 2 = 6) Have students complete the solution sentence. (64 stamps)

**Developing the Skill**  Demonstrate another problem on the board: **24 × 3**. Ask someone to explain where the multiplication should start. (in the ones column) Ask another to multiply ones. (3 × 4 = 12) Ask what number will be written in the ones column of the answer (2) and what number will be carried over to the tens column to be added later. (1) Have students use the counters to clarify the trade; 3 × 4 = 12 ones = 1 ten and 2 ones. Let another student multiply tens and add to complete the problem. (72) Dictate several similar problems.

**161**

## Practice

Multiply.

| | | | | | | | | | |
|---|---|---|---|---|---|---|---|---|---|
| 1. | $\begin{array}{r} 35 \\ \times\ 2 \\ \hline 70 \end{array}$ | 2. | $\begin{array}{r} 24 \\ \times\ 3 \\ \hline 72 \end{array}$ | 3. | $\begin{array}{r} 16 \\ \times\ 5 \\ \hline 80 \end{array}$ | 4. | $\begin{array}{r} 47 \\ \times\ 2 \\ \hline 94 \end{array}$ | 5. | $\begin{array}{r} 33 \\ \times\ 3 \\ \hline 99 \end{array}$ |
| 6. | $\begin{array}{r} 27 \\ \times\ 3 \\ \hline 81 \end{array}$ | 7. | $\begin{array}{r} 19 \\ \times\ 4 \\ \hline 76 \end{array}$ | 8. | $\begin{array}{r} 12 \\ \times\ 5 \\ \hline 60 \end{array}$ | 9. | $\begin{array}{r} 26 \\ \times\ 3 \\ \hline 78 \end{array}$ | 10. | $\begin{array}{r} 18 \\ \times\ 4 \\ \hline 72 \end{array}$ |
| 11. | $\begin{array}{r} 49 \\ \times\ 1 \\ \hline 49 \end{array}$ | 12. | $\begin{array}{r} 19 \\ \times\ 3 \\ \hline 57 \end{array}$ | 13. | $\begin{array}{r} 13 \\ \times\ 4 \\ \hline 52 \end{array}$ | 14. | $\begin{array}{r} 24 \\ \times\ 4 \\ \hline 96 \end{array}$ | 15. | $\begin{array}{r} 37 \\ \times\ 2 \\ \hline 74 \end{array}$ |
| 16. | $\begin{array}{r} 14 \\ \times\ 6 \\ \hline 84 \end{array}$ | 17. | $\begin{array}{r} 24 \\ \times\ 2 \\ \hline 48 \end{array}$ | 18. | $\begin{array}{r} 12 \\ \times\ 7 \\ \hline 84 \end{array}$ | 19. | $\begin{array}{r} 38 \\ \times\ 2 \\ \hline 76 \end{array}$ | 20. | $\begin{array}{r} 12 \\ \times\ 8 \\ \hline 96 \end{array}$ |

## Copy and Do

21. $47 \times 2$
94

22. $36 \times 2$
72

23. $14 \times 7$
98

24. $16 \times 3$
48

25. $23 \times 4$
92

26. $17 \times 4$
68

27. $31 \times 1$
31

28. $11 \times 5$
55

29. $18 \times 3$
54

30. $12 \times 6$
72

31. $14 \times 5$
70

32. $42 \times 2$
84

---

**EXCURSION**

Study this pattern.

$47 \times 2 = 40$ two's + 7 two's = 80 + 14 = 94

Use it to help you complete the rest of the multiplications.

1. $24 \times 3 = \underline{20}$ three's + $\underline{4}$ three's = $\underline{60}$ + $\underline{12}$ = $\underline{72}$

2. $37 \times 2 = \underline{30}$ two's + $\underline{7}$ two's = $\underline{60}$ + $\underline{14}$ = $\underline{74}$

3. $17 \times 4 = \underline{10}$ four's + $\underline{7}$ four's = $\underline{40}$ + $\underline{28}$ = $\underline{68}$

4. $12 \times 7 = \underline{10}$ seven's + $\underline{2}$ seven's = $\underline{70}$ + $\underline{14}$ = $\underline{84}$

## Correcting Common Errors

When students multiply the ones, they may not trade but write both digits in the answer.

| INCORRECT | CORRECT |
|---|---|
| | 1 |
| $\begin{array}{r} 38 \\ \times\ 2 \\ \hline 616 \end{array}$ | $\begin{array}{r} 38 \\ \times\ 2 \\ \hline 76 \end{array}$ |

Have them work with partners and place-value materials to model the problem.

## Enrichment

Have students think about the 8- and 6-hour clocks they devised in the last lesson. Ask them to explain the problem with these clocks. (The clock is in the same configuration 3 or 4 times a day.) Ask each student to devise a different way of distinguishing one part of the day from another, as our AM and PM does.

## Practice

Have students do all the problems on the page. Remind them to start multiplying in the ones column, writing any tens over the tens column to be added in last.

## Excursion

Discuss with the students how multiplying by decades helps us to work problems mentally. Have students complete the problems.

## Extra Credit *Applications*

Have the students make a simple rain gauge. Ask them to mark off a glass or plastic jar in quarter inches. Set the jar out in a safe but open place at home or school. Ask the students to take measurements each time it rains or snows and record the results. Have students make a bar graph to show the amount of rainfall for two-week period. Have the class compare their results with the official measurements given by the TV weather report or the newspaper.

# Multiplying by 1-digit Factors, One Trade

## pages 163-164

### Objective

To multiply by 1-digit factors with one trade and products up to 3 digits

### Materials

### Mental Math

Have students tell how many tens are in each product:

1. $7 \times 6$ (4)  
2. $8 \times 5$ (4)  
3. $9 \times 2$ (1)  
4. $9 \times 8$ (7)  
5. $6 \times 4$ (2)  
6. $3 \times 3$ (0)  
7. $5 \times 2$ (1)  
8. $8 \times 8$ (6)  
9. $4 \times 7$ (2)  
10. $3 \times 2$ (0)

### Skill Review

Put this model on the board and tell students to follow it as they do these problems:

```
  1
 25
× 3
 75
```

1. $17 \times 5$ (85)  
2. $25 \times 3$ (75)  
3. $47 \times 2$ (94)  
4. $22 \times 6$ (132)  
5. $29 \times 3$ (87)

---

**Multiplying by 1-digit Factors, One Trade**

The A & R Railroad hired a crew of men to repair its tracks. How many miles of track has the crew repaired so far?

**TRACK REPAIRS**

| Week | Miles |
|------|-------|
| 1 | 25 |
| 2 | 25 |
| 3 | 25 |
| 4 | 25 |
| 5 | 25 |

We want to find the total number of miles repaired.

The crew repaired __25__ miles of track each week.

The men have worked for __5__ weeks.

To find the total number of miles repaired,

we multiply __25__ by __5__.

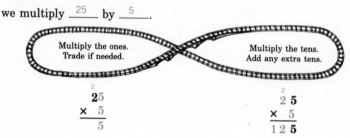

Multiply the ones. Trade if needed.

Multiply the tens. Add any extra tens.

```
  2
 25
× 5
  5
```

```
 2
 25
× 5
125
```

The crew has repaired __125__ miles of track.

### Getting Started

Multiply.

1.  $\begin{array}{r} 37 \\ \times\ 3 \\ \hline 111 \end{array}$

2.  $\begin{array}{r} 48 \\ \times\ 4 \\ \hline 192 \end{array}$

3.  $\begin{array}{r} 29 \\ \times\ 6 \\ \hline 174 \end{array}$

4.  $\begin{array}{r} 82 \\ \times\ 7 \\ \hline 574 \end{array}$

Copy and multiply.

5. $67 \times 9$ — 603  
6. $73 \times 3$ — 219  
7. $52 \times 8$ — 416  
8. $9 \times 81$ — 729

(one hundred sixty-three) **163**

---

## Teaching the Lesson

**Introducing the Problem**  Have students read and identify the problem. Ask a volunteer to read and complete the information sentences. (repaired 25 miles, worked for 5 weeks) Read the plan sentences aloud, asking a student to supply the information required. (Multiply 25 by 5.) Work the two stages of the problem on the board with the students. Remind them that 12 tens is the same as 1 hundred and 2 tens. Have them transfer the answer to the solution sentence. (125 miles)

**Developing the Skill**  Put a 3-digit place value chart on the board and write this problem in it:

| hundreds | tens | ones |
|----------|------|------|
|          | 2    | 4    |
| ×        |      | 6    |
| (1       | 4    | 4)   |

Ask the class to tell you where to start the multiplication. (ones column) Have a student multiply ones, write down the 4, and explain what to do with the 2 tens that result. (Write them over the tens column to be added later.) Have another student multiply tens ($6 \times 2 = 12$) and add in 2 tens. ($12 + 2 = 14$) Ask the class where the 14 will be written in the answer. (1 in the hundreds, 4 in the tens) Do at least one more problem with the class.

## Practice

Multiply.

| | | | | |
|---|---|---|---|---|
| 1. $67 \times 4$ <br> 268 | 2. $39 \times 6$ <br> 234 | 3. $55 \times 7$ <br> 385 | 4. $79 \times 2$ <br> 158 | 5. $80 \times 8$ <br> 640 |
| 6. $45 \times 7$ <br> 315 | 7. $71 \times 8$ <br> 568 | 8. $96 \times 7$ <br> 672 | 9. $93 \times 2$ <br> 186 | 10. $47 \times 3$ <br> 141 |
| 11. $64 \times 9$ <br> 576 | 12. $56 \times 4$ <br> 224 | 13. $87 \times 8$ <br> 696 | 14. $60 \times 6$ <br> 360 | 15. $39 \times 7$ <br> 273 |
| 16. $72 \times 3$ <br> 216 | 17. $94 \times 9$ <br> 846 | 18. $28 \times 6$ <br> 168 | 19. $46 \times 8$ <br> 368 | 20. $76 \times 5$ <br> 380 |
| 21. $53 \times 7$ <br> 371 | 22. $49 \times 8$ <br> 392 | 23. $76 \times 2$ <br> 152 | 24. $43 \times 4$ <br> 172 | 25. $86 \times 5$ <br> 430 |

### Copy and Do

26. $52 \times 6$
312
27. $9 \times 68$
612
28. $43 \times 6$
258
29. $8 \times 26$
208
30. $75 \times 3$
225
31. $40 \times 9$
360
32. $9 \times 17$
153
33. $7 \times 88$
616
34. $5 \times 34$
170
35. $7 \times 48$
336
36. $57 \times 6$
342
37. $84 \times 8$
672

### Apply

Solve these problems.

38. The Apollo 16 orbited the moon 64 times. Each orbit took 4 hours. How many hours did the Apollo 16 orbit the moon?

256 hours

39. The Soyuz 19 orbited the earth 96 times. The Apollo 18 orbited the earth 136 times. How many more orbits did the Apollo 18 make?

40 orbits

## Correcting Common Errors

Some students may trade correctly but forget to add the renamed number.

| INCORRECT | CORRECT |
|---|---|
| 3 | 3 |
| 45 | 45 |
| $\times 7$ | $\times 7$ |
| 285 | 315 |

Have students use a place-value form like the following to chart the steps.

| | 100s | 10s | 1s |
|---|---|---|---|
| $7 \times 5$ ones | | 3 | 5 |
| $7 \times 4$ tens | 2 | 8 | 0 |
| | 3 | 1 | 5 |

## Enrichment

Have students draw a 12-hour clock face with 24 hours on it. See how many different ways they can find to arrange the two sets of numbers. Ask if 2 in the afternoon will look any different than 2 in the morning. (no) Have them illustrate various times on their clocks.

## Practice

Have students do all the problems on the page. Remind them to add the tens traded in the ones multiplication. Remind them to label their answers in the final two problems.

## Mixed Practice

1. $173 + 468$ (641)
2. $300 - 256$ (44)
3. $10 \times \$6$ ($60)
4. $4 \times 300$ (1,200)
5. $\$1.76 + 2.78 + .28$ ($4.82)
6. $2,758 - 639$ (2,119)
7. $4,376 + 2,120$ (6,496)
8. $7 \times 8$ (56)
9. $30 \times 7$ (210)
10. $4,020 - 1,216$ (2,804)

## Extra Credit   *Biography*

Pythagoras was born in Samos, Greece, about 569 B.C. He travelled extensively before settling in Italy where he formed a brotherhood called the Pythagoreans. This society, made up of aristocrats of the day, kept Pythagoras' chief discoveries secret. Because of this secrecy, the society was hated and mistrusted by other groups. Because of this many of Pythagoras' followers, and perhaps Pythagoras himself, were murdered. Pythagoras is best remembered for his work in geometry, especially for his theorem about right triangles. The theorem states that the square of the hypotenuse of a right triangle equals the sum of the squares of the other two sides. This theorem came from the practice of ancient Egyptian farmers who wanted to lay out square corners for their fields. Although Pythagoras never wrote any books, his theories were published by Euclid about 200 years later.

# Multiplying by 1-digit Factors, Two Trades

**pages 165-166**

## Objective

To multiply by 1-digit factors with 2 trades

## Materials

## Mental Math

Dictate these problems:

1. $4 + 3 - 2 + 9 = (14)$
2. $(4 + 5) \times 4 = (36)$
3. $8 - 5 + 12 - 4 = (11)$
4. $11 + 15 - 3 + (4 \times 5) = (43)$
5. $6 + 15 + 10 - (3 \times 1) = (28)$
6. $10 + 10 - 5 + 25 = (40)$
7. $(7 \times 5) + 10 - 2 = (43)$

## Skill Review

Have students do these problems, being careful to show the trade:

| | | | | | | | |
|---|---|---|---|---|---|---|---|
| 1. $\begin{array}{r} \overset{1}{45} \\ \times\ 3 \\ \hline (135) \end{array}$ | 2. $\begin{array}{r} \overset{5}{29} \\ \times\ 6 \\ \hline (174) \end{array}$ | 3. $\begin{array}{r} \overset{2}{48} \\ \times\ 5 \\ \hline (240) \end{array}$ | 4. $\begin{array}{r} \overset{2}{63} \\ \times\ 7 \\ \hline (441) \end{array}$ |
| 5. $\begin{array}{r} \overset{3}{46} \\ \times\ 5 \\ \hline (230) \end{array}$ | 6. $\begin{array}{r} \overset{4}{85} \\ \times\ 8 \\ \hline (680) \end{array}$ | 7. $\begin{array}{r} \overset{5}{77} \\ \times\ 8 \\ \hline (616) \end{array}$ | 8. $\begin{array}{r} \overset{6}{39} \\ \times\ 7 \\ \hline (273) \end{array}$ |

---

## Multiplying by 1-digit Factors, Two Trades

Mr. Harris made 4 round trips on business, from Ellis to Washington. How many travel miles should Mr. Harris record on his expense report?

Mr. Harris wants to know how many miles he drove, so he can fill out his expense report.

The distance between Ellis and Washington is ___138___ miles.

A round trip between the cities is 2 times the distance between them, or ___276___ miles.

Mr. Harris made ___4___ round trips.

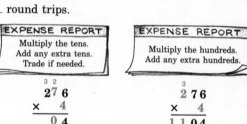

EXPENSE REPORT
Multiply the ones. Trade if needed.

$\begin{array}{r} \overset{2}{27}\overset{}{6} \\ \times\ \ 4 \\ \hline 4 \end{array}$

EXPENSE REPORT
Multiply the tens. Add any extra tens. Trade if needed.

$\begin{array}{r} \overset{3\,2}{27}6 \\ \times\ \ 4 \\ \hline 0\,4 \end{array}$

EXPENSE REPORT
Multiply the hundreds. Add any extra hundreds.

$\begin{array}{r} \overset{3}{2}76 \\ \times\ \ 4 \\ \hline 1{,}1\,04 \end{array}$

Mr. Harris should record ___1,104___ miles on his expense report.

### Getting Started

Multiply.

1. $\begin{array}{r} 246 \\ \times\ \ 3 \\ \hline 738 \end{array}$    2. $\begin{array}{r} 508 \\ \times\ \ 7 \\ \hline 3{,}556 \end{array}$    3. $\begin{array}{r} 621 \\ \times\ \ 5 \\ \hline 3{,}105 \end{array}$

Copy and multiply.

4. $623 \times 6$
3,738

5. $290 \times 4$
1,160

6. $257 \times 8$
2,056

---

## Teaching the Lesson

**Introducing the Problem** Read the problem aloud while students examine the picture. Have a student explain what a round trip is. (twice the distance to travel between two places) Have a student read the information sentences. Read the plan sentence aloud and point out the problem worked in three steps below. Put the three stages of the problem on the board and have students work them with you. Have students complete the solution sentence. (1, 104)

## Developing the Skill

Explain that each time students multiply and get a 2-digit product, one digit will go in the column being multiplied and the other over the next column, ready to be added into the next multiplication. Do this problem in three steps on the board with the students:

$\begin{array}{r} \overset{1}{253} \\ \times\ \ 6 \\ \hline 8 \end{array}$    $\begin{array}{r} \overset{3\,1}{253} \\ \times\ \ 6 \\ \hline 18 \end{array}$    $\begin{array}{r} \overset{3\,1}{253} \\ \times\ \ 6 \\ \hline 1518 \end{array}$

Dictate several more problems for students to do on paper showing the 3 steps.

**165**

Multiply.

| | | | |
|---|---|---|---|
| 1. $\begin{array}{r} 326 \\ \times\ \ 4 \\ \hline 1,304 \end{array}$ | 2. $\begin{array}{r} 845 \\ \times\ \ 7 \\ \hline 5,915 \end{array}$ | 3. $\begin{array}{r} 329 \\ \times\ \ 9 \\ \hline 2,961 \end{array}$ | 4. $\begin{array}{r} 334 \\ \times\ \ 6 \\ \hline 2,004 \end{array}$ |
| 5. $\begin{array}{r} 212 \\ \times\ \ 3 \\ \hline 636 \end{array}$ | 6. $\begin{array}{r} 296 \\ \times\ \ 8 \\ \hline 2,368 \end{array}$ | 7. $\begin{array}{r} 427 \\ \times\ \ 2 \\ \hline 854 \end{array}$ | 8. $\begin{array}{r} 725 \\ \times\ \ 5 \\ \hline 3,625 \end{array}$ |
| 9. $\begin{array}{r} 487 \\ \times\ \ 7 \\ \hline 3,409 \end{array}$ | 10. $\begin{array}{r} 183 \\ \times\ \ 2 \\ \hline 366 \end{array}$ | 11. $\begin{array}{r} 675 \\ \times\ \ 9 \\ \hline 6,075 \end{array}$ | 12. $\begin{array}{r} 526 \\ \times\ \ 3 \\ \hline 1,578 \end{array}$ |
| 13. $\begin{array}{r} 416 \\ \times\ \ 6 \\ \hline 2,496 \end{array}$ | 14. $\begin{array}{r} 807 \\ \times\ \ 6 \\ \hline 4,842 \end{array}$ | 15. $\begin{array}{r} 219 \\ \times\ \ 5 \\ \hline 1,095 \end{array}$ | 16. $\begin{array}{r} 438 \\ \times\ \ 7 \\ \hline 3,066 \end{array}$ |

**Copy and Do**

17. $157 \times 8$
1,256

18. $4 \times 538$
2,152

19. $175 \times 9$
1,575

20. $416 \times 3$
1,248

21. $239 \times 7$
1,673

22. $757 \times 2$
1,514

23. $5 \times 919$
4,595

24. $9 \times 630$
5,670

25. $4 \times 212$
848

26. $8 \times 326$
2,608

27. $808 \times 3$
2,424

28. $5 \times 394$
1,970

**Apply**

Solve these problems.

29. Juanita started with $24.50. She spent $19.38. How much did she have left?
$5.12

30. The school cafeteria served 146 lunches each day for one week. How many lunches were served?
730 lunches

31. Bill bought a sweater for $29.50 and a shirt for $16.37. How much did he spend?
$45.87

32. The custodian set up 8 rows of chairs, with 125 chairs in each row. How many chairs were used?
1,000 chairs

## Correcting Common Errors

Some students may add the renamed number before they multiply.

| INCORRECT | CORRECT |
|---|---|
| $\begin{array}{r} 1\,2 \\ 247 \\ \times\ \ \ 3 \\ \hline 981 \end{array}$ | $\begin{array}{r} 1\,2 \\ 247 \\ \times\ \ \ 3 \\ \hline 741 \end{array}$ |

Remind students that the traded value has already been multiplied by the second factor. Have students use a place-value form like the following to chart the steps.

| | 100s | 10s | 1s |
|---|---|---|---|
| $3 \times 7$ ones | | 2 | 1 |
| $3 \times 4$ tens | 1 | 2 | 0 |
| $3 \times 2$ hundreds | 6 | 0 | 0 |
| | 7 | 4 | 1 |

## Enrichment

Students are ready to extend their 100-fact multiplication charts to include 10, 11 and 12. Give them half-inch graph paper and tell them to draw a new multiplication chart, with sides numbered from 1 through 12. They can copy facts through 9, but have them work out the tables for 10, 11 and 12. Remind them to use addition to work out any facts they are not sure of.

## Practice

Have students complete the page. Remind them to show each trade. Point out that the last two problems require answers with labels.

## Mixed Practice

1. $8 + 19 + 7 + 10$ (44)
2. $232 \times 3$ (696)
3. $6,538 - 4,295$ (2,243)
4. $50.10 - 25.92$ ($24.18)
5. $100 \times 8$ (800)
6. $376 + 257$ (633)
7. $4 \times 120$ (480)
8. $50 \times 6$ (300)
9. $800 - 27$ (773)
10. $8,276 + 598 + 176$ (9,050)

## Extra Credit  *Geometry*

Each student will need 25 identical triangles. Make one triangle out of heavy paper or card stock, trace it 10 times on a piece of paper, and reproduce it. Give each student 2½ sheets and ask them to cut out their 25 triangles. The activity is more interesting if different colored paper is used. When students have finished making the triangles, ask them to arrange them on their desks so that each triangle is touching another and there are no spaces in between. Tell them that this kind of a pattern is possible no matter what kind of triangle is used, and is called a tessellation. After they have made one arrangement, have them try another. Ask students to explain why this is called "tiling".

# Multiplying Money

**pages 167-168**

## Objective

To multiply money by 1-digit factors with up to two trades

## Materials

## Mental Math

Have students round each of these numbers:

1. 245 to the nearest 10 (250)
2. 92 to the nearest 10 (90)
3. 420 to the nearest 100 (400)
4. 569 to the nearest 100 (600)
5. 128 to the nearest 10 (130)
6. 128 to the nearest 100 (100)

## Skill Review

Ask students to tell the number of pennies in a dime (10) and the number of dimes in a dollar. (10) Write **$4.25** on the board and have students label the positions for pennies, dimes, and dollars:

```
dollars  dimes  pennies
$   4  .  2      5
```

Ask a student to read this amount aloud. Dictate several dollar amounts and have students enter them on this place value chart.

---

## Multiplying Money

Erica is starting a lawn mowing service. On one Saturday, she mows lawns for 7 hours. How much money does she earn?

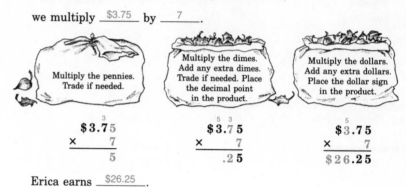

We want to know how much money Erica earns for 7 hours of work.

Erica earns __$3.75__ per hour for mowing lawns.

She works for __7__ hours on Saturday.

To find the total amount of money Erica earns,

we multiply __$3.75__ by __7__.

**Multiply the pennies. Trade if needed.**

$$\begin{array}{r} \overset{3}{\$3.7}5 \\ \times\ \ \ \ 7 \\ \hline 5 \end{array}$$

**Multiply the dimes. Add any extra dimes. Trade if needed. Place the decimal point in the product.**

$$\begin{array}{r} \overset{5}{\ }\overset{3}{\$3.7}5 \\ \times\ \ \ \ 7 \\ \hline .25 \end{array}$$

**Multiply the dollars. Add any extra dollars. Place the dollar sign in the product.**

$$\begin{array}{r} \overset{5}{\$}3.75 \\ \times\ \ \ \ 7 \\ \hline \$26.25 \end{array}$$

Erica earns __$26.25__.

### Getting Started

Multiply.

1.  $\begin{array}{r} \$2.36 \\ \times\ \ \ 4 \\ \hline \$9.44 \end{array}$

2.  $\begin{array}{r} \$1.81 \\ \times\ \ \ 6 \\ \hline \$10.86 \end{array}$

3.  $\begin{array}{r} \$4.87 \\ \times\ \ \ 3 \\ \hline \$14.61 \end{array}$

4.  $\begin{array}{r} \$6.50 \\ \times\ \ \ 7 \\ \hline \$45.50 \end{array}$

Copy and multiply.

5. $6.07 × 9
$54.63

6. $5.43 × 8
$43.44

7. $9.16 × 2
$18.32

8. $7.68 × 5
$38.40

(one hundred sixty-seven) **167**

---

## Teaching the Lesson

**Introducing the Problem**   Read the problem aloud and have a student read the information sentences. ($3.75 per hour, 7 hours) Now read the plan sentences aloud while the class completes them in their texts. (We multiply $3.75 by 7.) Explain that they will start multiplying in the pennies column. Put the problem on the board and work through the three steps of the problem with students, making sure they understand that multiplying money is like multiplying other numbers. Complete the problem and have students transfer the answer to the solution sentence, putting in the dollar sign and decimal point.

**Developing the Skill**   Explain that multiplying money is like multiplying other 3- and 4-digit numbers. Point out, however, that they will have to keep their numbers in straight columns, expressing their answers with dollar signs and decimal points. Ask students what the comma is for in this number: 3,458. (It separates thousands and hundreds.) Ask what the decimal point is for in this number: $3.27. (It separates dollars and dimes.) Neither of these markers changes the way they will multiply. Help the class do another sample problem, following the pattern in the model.

**167**

## Practice

Multiply.

| | | | |
|---|---|---|---|
| 1. $6.45<br>× 3<br>$19.35 | 2. $4.57<br>× 9<br>$41.13 | 3. $3.87<br>× 6<br>$23.22 | 4. $4.81<br>× 4<br>$19.24 |
| 5. $8.32<br>× 8<br>$66.56 | 6. $2.79<br>× 5<br>$13.95 | 7. $7.23<br>× 7<br>$50.61 | 8. $9.10<br>× 2<br>$18.20 |
| 9. $1.71<br>× 8<br>$13.68 | 10. $5.39<br>× 4<br>$21.56 | 11. $7.05<br>× 5<br>$35.25 | 12. $6.21<br>× 8<br>$49.68 |

### Copy and Do

13. $2.76 × 2
$5.52

14. $7.31 × 9
$65.79

15. $1.89 × 7
$13.23

16. $4.66 × 3
$13.98

17. $8.96 × 6
$53.76

18. $5.83 × 4
$23.32

19. $3.29 × 5
$16.45

20. $6.83 × 8
$54.64

---

### EXCURSION

A **prime number** is one having only two factors, itself and 1. For example, 5 is prime because its only factors are 5 and 1.

$$5 \times 1 = 5$$

Numbers that are not prime are called **composites**. For example, 6 is composite because its factors include 1, 2, 3 and 6.

$$1 \times 6 = 6 \qquad 2 \times 3 = 6$$

List all the factors of the numbers below. Then tell whether each number is prime or composite.

| Number | Factors | Prime or Composite |
|---|---|---|
| 7 | 1, 7 | Prime |
| 2 | 1, 2 | Prime |
| 9 | 1, 3, 9 | Composite |
| 21 | 1, 3, 7, 21 | Composite |
| 17 | 1, 17 | Prime |
| 28 | 1, 2, 4, 7, 14, 28 | Composite |

**168** (one hundred sixty-eight)

---

### Practice

Have students complete the page. Remind them to express each answer with a dollar sign and decimal point.

### Excursion

Read the explanation of prime and composite numbers with the students. Remind students that a number which has factors other than itself and 1, is not prime. Ask students if 8 is prime. (no) Ask what 8 is called. (composite number) Give students more practice identifying prime and composite numbers. Tell students they need only find one factor other than the number itself and 1, to name the number a composite. Tell students that 1 is not considered to be prime or composite. Have students complete the exercise. Remind students to list all the factors of each number.

### Extra Credit   *Careers*

Arrange for an adding machine or cash register to be brought into the classroom. Invite a cashier, salesperson, or company representative to demonstrate the use of the machine. If possible, have students try to use the machine. Have students list some of the jobs where they would be expected to know how to use one of these machines. Also, discuss why a person using an adding machine still must have math skills.

**168**

# Practicing Multiplication and Mixed Skills

## pages 169-170

### Objective

To practice multiplication, addition and subtraction

### Materials

*flash cards for addition, subtraction, and multiplication

### Mental Math

Have students round each number to the nearest 10 and add:

1. 75 + 21 (80 + 20 = 100)
2. 34 + 12 (30 + 10 = 40)
3. 77 + 42 (80 + 40 = 120)
4. 91 + 5 (90 + 10 = 100)
5. 53 + 121 (50 + 120 = 170)

### Skill Review

Ask a student to demonstrate this multiplication with two trades on the board:

$$
\begin{array}{r}
2\,3 \\
135 \\
\times\ \ 7 \\
\hline
945
\end{array}
$$

Write these problems on the board for students to do on paper.

1. **374 × 8** (2,992)  2. **34 × 5** (170)
3. **172 × 5** (860)  4. **12 × 6** (72)

---

## Practicing Multiplication

Multiply.

| | | | | |
|---|---|---|---|---|
| 1. 23 ×5 = 115 | 2. 36 ×8 = 288 | 3. 54 ×4 = 216 | 4. 58 ×8 = 464 | 5. 19 ×9 = 171 |
| 6. 75 ×3 = 225 | 7. 81 ×9 = 729 | 8. 47 ×7 = 329 | 9. 63 ×2 = 126 | 10. 96 ×6 = 576 |
| 11. 46 ×5 = 230 | 12. 58 ×6 = 348 | 13. 39 ×8 = 312 | 14. 56 ×2 = 112 | 15. 85 ×4 = 340 |

| | | | |
|---|---|---|---|
| 16. 135 ×7 = 945 | 17. 356 ×2 = 712 | 18. 575 ×6 = 3,450 | 19. 812 ×8 = 6,496 |
| 20. 286 ×4 = 1,144 | 21. 576 ×3 = 1,728 | 22. 637 ×9 = 5,733 | 23. 750 ×5 = 3,750 |
| 24. 414 ×4 = 1,656 | 25. 387 ×2 = 774 | 26. 409 ×6 = 2,454 | 27. 710 ×7 = 4,970 |
| 28. $1.56 ×3 = $4.68 | 29. $6.36 ×7 = $44.52 | 30. $4.05 ×4 = $16.20 | 31. $3.85 ×8 = $30.80 |

### Copy and Do

| | | | |
|---|---|---|---|
| 32. $9.81 × 6 $58.86 | 33. $5.95 × 2 $11.90 | 34. $7.50 × 9 $67.50 | 35. $2.83 × 5 $14.15 |
| 36. 6 × 225 1,350 | 37. 935 × 3 2,805 | 38. 6 × $2.57 $15.42 | 39. $6.80 × 8 $54.40 |
| 40. 7 × $0.98 $6.86 | 41. 4 × 408 1,632 | 42. 5 × 193 965 | 43. 6 × 343 2,058 |

---

## Teaching the Lesson

**Introducing the Problem**  This lesson is a review of multiplication skills learned so far including quick recognition of facts and the ability to multiply by a 1-digit factor with up to two trades. Ask 4 students to come to the board to work the following problems which progress from problems with no trades, to one with two trades.

| | | | |
|---|---|---|---|
| 21 ×4 (84) | 123 ×3 (369) | 4 26 ×7 (182) | 5 3 364 ×8 (2912) |

**Developing the Skill**  The second page of this lesson is a series of problems mixing addition, subtraction, and multiplication skills. Remind students how they trade to do addition and subtraction. Have students come to the board to do these problems:

| | | | |
|---|---|---|---|
| 54 +33 87 | 1 59 +35 94 | 1 1 358 + 93 451 | 98 −24 74 |
| 2 15 3̸5̸ −27 8 | 2 13 14 3̸ 4̸ 4̸ − 85 259 | | |

**Practicing Mixed Skills**

Write the correct answer.

1. 327
+285
___
612

2. 612
× 3
___
1,836

3. 875
−236
___
639

4. 45
× 6
___
270

5. 394
− 8
___
386

6. 576
× 7
___
4,032

7. 428
+157
___
585

8. 916
−287
___
629

9. 3,240
− 86
___
3,154

10. 2,471
+1,796
___
4,267

11. 326
× 8
___
2,608

12. 57
× 9
___
513

13. $24.50
− 9.67
___
$14.83

14. $3.75
× 6
___
$22.50

15. 809
−275
___
534

16. $14.76
+ 8.37
___
$23.13

17. 284
× 5
___
1,420

18. $67.45
− 28.72
___
$38.73

19. 257
+398
___
655

20. 751
× 2
___
1,502

21. 2,408
−1,969
___
439

22. 126
× 9
___
1,134

23. $2.57
× 7
___
$17.99

24. 3,975
+2,861
___
6,836

**Copy and Do**

25. 403 − 286
117

26. $8.75 − 2.38
$6.37

27. 3,476 + 2,658
6,134

28. 396 × 4
1,584

29. 826 + 97
923

30. 483 − 291
192

31. 85 × 7
595

32. 9 × $2.38
$21.42

33. 4 × 750
3,000

34. $73.45 + 30.20
$103.65

35. 4,276 − 88
4,188

36. 2 × 703
1,406

**170** (one hundred seventy)

**170**

# Estimating

**pages 171-172**

## Objective

To solve word problems using estimating

## Materials

## Mental Math

Dictate these problems:

1. Valentine's Day is February 14. If today is February 2, how many days is it until the holiday? (12 days)
2. How many weeks and days are there between February 2 and 14? (1 week, 5 days)
3. You are going to start your valentines two weeks ahead. When will you begin? (January 31)

## Skill Review

Write these amounts on the board and have students round each one to the nearest 10¢, and to the nearest dollar:

1. **$4.59** ($4.60, $5)
2. **$9.32** ($9.30, $9)
3. **$12.49** ($12.50, $12)

Have them round these to the nearest ten dollars:

1. **$42** ($40)     3. **$89** ($90)
2. **$5** ($10)      4. **$108** ($110)

---

### Estimating

The track team needs new uniforms for the season. About how much will it cost for 5 pairs of athletic socks?

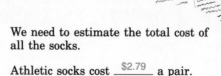

We need to estimate the total cost of all the socks.

Athletic socks cost __$2.79__ a pair.

The team will buy __5__ pairs.

To estimate, we round the cost of one pair to the nearest dollar. Then we multiply by the number of pairs bought.

$$\$2.79 \rightarrow \begin{array}{r} \boxed{\$3} \\ \times\ 5 \\ \hline \$15 \end{array}$$

The 5 pairs of athletic socks will cost about __$15__.

### Getting Started

Estimate the total cost by rounding each amount to the nearest dollar and multiplying.

1. the cost of 5 jackets

   $250

2. the cost of 6 leotards

   $42

3. the cost of 2 sweatsuits

   $40

4. the cost of 3 shorts and tops

   $42

Solve these problems. Use estimation to check the answers.

5. How much is a jacket and a sweatsuit?
   $69.70

6. How much more is a sweatsuit than a shorts and top?
   $5.46

(one hundred seventy-one)  **171**

---

## Teaching the Lesson

**Introducing the Problem**   Read the problem aloud while the students look at the illustration. Have a student identify the question being asked. Ask a student to read and complete the information sentences. ($2.79 a pair, will buy 5 pairs) Read the plan aloud and explain that the word, about, in the problem implies that estimation will be used. Ask a volunteer to round $2.79 to the nearest dollar ($3) and do the multiplication on the board. ($15) Ask a student to read the completed solution sentence.

**Developing the Skill**   Explain that the rounding skills they have learned will be used to solve problems that require an approximate answer. Ask students to give examples of times when it is convenient to estimate. Point out that it is useful to round off the price of items in order to get an idea of the cost. Write this amount on the board: **$4.23**. Ask a student to round it to the nearest dollar and explain how they did it. ($4) Now write on the board: **$6.55**. Have a student round that to the nearest dollar. ($7) Now ask someone to explain how a number like $3.50 is rounded. (up to $4) Explain that although 50¢ is half-way between one dollar and the next, it is always rounded up. Dictate several amounts for students to round to the nearest dollar.

| | | | |
|---|---|---|---|
| Darts | $ 1.15 | Racquetball Racket | $28.15 |
| Dart Board | $12.50 | Can of Racquetballs | $ 3.27 |
| Tennis Racket | $29.15 | Table Tennis Paddles | $ 4.39 |
| Can of Tennis Balls | $ 2.97 | Can of Table Tennis Balls | $ 2.79 |
| Golf Balls | $ 1.38 | Basketballs | $ 6.89 |

Estimate the total cost by rounding each amount
to the nearest dollar and multiplying.

1. the cost of 6 golf balls

$6

2. the cost of 8 basketballs

$56

3. the cost of 3 dart boards

$39

4. the cost of 7 cans of table
tennis balls

$21

5. the cost of 6 cans of tennis
balls

$18

6. the cost of 4 table tennis
paddles

$16

7. the cost of 9 cans of
racquetballs

$27

8. the cost of 5 darts

$5

**Apply**

Solve these problems. Use estimation to check the answers.

9. What is the cost of a tennis
racket and a can of tennis
balls?
$32.12

10. How much less than the dart
board is the basketball?
$5.61

11. What is the cost of 8 golf
balls?
$11.04

12. How much more is the tennis
racket than the racquetball
racket?
$1.00

**172** (one hundred seventy-two)

## Correcting Common Errors

Some students may estimate incorrectly because they have difficulty rounding money. Have them work with partners with a number line extending from $1.00 through $2.00, marked off and labeled in 5-cent intervals. Dictate the following amounts and have students mark points for them on the number line and tell whether the amount is closer to $1 or to $2.
$1.23 ($1)   $1.75 ($2)   $1.49 ($1)
$1.89 ($2)   $1.51 ($2)   $1.60 ($2)
Be sure that students understand that money rounded to the nearest dollar should not show a cents point or any digits in cents places because all parts of a dollar are dropped.

## Enrichment

Give students a catalog. Explain that they have $100 to spend. They must pick at least 3 different items but the total cost is not to exceed $100. Without using pencil and paper, have them see how close they can come to $100.

## Practice

Have students complete the page. Remind them to write amounts with dollar signs.

## Mixed Practice

1. 501 − 376 (125)
2. 2,743 + 6,607 (9,350)
3. 8 + 12 + 25 (45)
4. 38 × 8 (304)
5. 263 × 4 (1,052)
6. $80.01 − 27.65 ($52.36)
7. 742 − 534 (208)
8. 8 × 125 (1,000)
9. $98.76 + 101.27 ($200.03)
10. $6 × 60 ($360)

## Extra Credit   *Careers*

Collect enough mail-order catalogs for each student to have one. On slips of paper, describe different situations when someone might want to place a catalog order, such as: its time to buy school clothes; its spring, and time to clean up the yard. Have students study them, noting how they are organized and the procedure used to order from them. Give students a budget limit of $100 that must include tax, shipping and other charges. Tell each student to select a slip of paper, and write a catalog order of things that a person in the situation described might buy. Remind them not to exceed their budget.

# Problem Solving, Drawing Pictures

## pages 173-174

## Objective

To use drawing pictures in problem solving

## Materials

graph paper,
large squares

## Mental Math

Read each of the following digits individually to students and ask them to read the numbers back to you:

1. 1 9 2 comma 0 0 0 (one hundred ninety two thousand)
2. 1 comma 4 2 8 (one thousand four hundred twenty eight)
3. 7 8 (seventy eight)
4. 6 3 9 0 (six thousand three hundred ninety)
5. 1 3 comma 0 5 4 (thirteen thousand fifty four)
6. 9 comma 7 0 2 (nine thousand seven hundred two)
7. 2 6 6 (two hundred sixty six)

---

### Drawing a Picture

A parking lot has 9 rows of 8 parking spaces each. The fourth and fifth spaces in every third row have trees in them. The outside spaces in every row are reserved for the handicapped or for emergency vehicles. How many regular parking spaces are there in the lot?

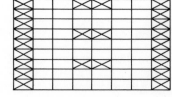

★ SEE

We want to know how many spaces are left for regular parking.

There are ___9___ rows of parking spaces.

There are ___8___ spaces in each row.

In every third row, ___2___ spaces are lost to trees.

In every row ___2___ spaces are used for special vehicles.

★ PLAN

We can draw a picture of the parking lot, crossing out the closed parking spaces. Then we can count the regular spaces left.

★ DO

We count ___48___ spaces left for regular parking.

★ CHECK

We can check by adding the spaces open in each row.

$$4 + 6 + 6 + 4 + 6 + 6 + 4 + 6 + 6 = \underline{\quad 48 \quad}$$

(one hundred seventy-three) **173**

---

## Teaching the Lesson

Read the problem aloud and ask students to survey the illustration. Remind them of the SEE-PLAN-DO-CHECK method they have used for problem solving. Work through the four steps of the problem with the students. Have them complete the SEE sentences, (9 rows of spaces, 8 spaces in each row, every third row 2 spaces lost, every row 2 spaces for special vehicles) Explain that the parking plan is not a drawing of the parking lot since it does not allow access to the spaces. It is a diagram useful for solving the problem. In order to check the problem, diagram the parking lot on the board and have volunteers come up and count the spaces left in each row. List the number by each row and have a student add. (48)

Explain that it is possible to diagram many problems and arrive at a solution without having to draw a realistic picture. Remind students of the coat/shirt/dress problem on page 150 in Chapter 7. Ask students if they had to actually draw each piece of clothing in order to solve the problem. (no)

## Apply

Draw a picture to help you solve each problem. Remember to use the four-step plan.

1. Abby, Donna, Ellie and Fran have just finished a 400-meter race. Abby finishes 30 meters ahead of Ellie, but 2 meters behind Donna. Fran finishes 10 meters behind Donna. What is the order of the four girls as they cross the finish line?
Donna, Abby, Fran, Ellie

2. A Super-Duper ball bounces twice its height when it is dropped. Carl dropped a Super-Duper ball from the roof of a 12-foot garage. How high will the ball bounce after 5 bounces?
384 feet

3. You win at Bingo if you are the first to cover 5 numbers in a straight line on the Bingo card. A bingo card has 5 rows of 5 squares each. How many different ways can you win at Bingo?
12 ways

4. The distance around a rectangle is 10 centimeters. The length of each of the two longer sides is 3 centimeters. What is the length of each of the two shorter sides?
2 centimeters

5. Mary buys 4 cards that cost 50¢ each. Mark buys cards that cost $1.00 each. How many can he buy without spending more than Mary?
2 cards

6. Suppose a minivan can hold 8 people, and a car can hold 6. How many minivans and cars will hold exactly 50 people?
See Solution Notes.

7. Andy has $5. He says that he can buy 8 fruit bars for 90¢ each and have some money left over. Tell whether Andy is correct and prove your answer.
See Solution Notes.

174 (one hundred seventy-four)

## Extra Credit *Numeration*

Have students bring an egg carton to school, and number the cups randomly, using numbers 0 through 9. Give each student 3 marbles or other small objects. Have students place the objects in the carton, close the lid and shake it. Then tell them to open the lid and add or multiply the three numbers in the cups where the objects landed, and write the equation and sum on their papers. Have students repeat several times, and exchange papers to correct each other. The student receives a point every time addition or multiplication facts are completed correctly.

# Solution Notes

1. The easiest way for students to visualize this problem is to start with the first girl named (Abby) and fill in the others before and after her. If students are confused, draw a finish line on the board with Abby written across it. Have them fill in the names.

2. Although this problem is thermodynamically impossible, have students treat it like science fiction.

3. To help students solve this problem give each a square of graph paper, five squares on a side. Demonstrate for students that the total of 12 comes from the sum of one for every row (5), one for every column (5), and two diagonals.

4. Remind students that a rectangle has two long sides that are the same length and two short sides, also the same length.

## Higher-Order Thinking Skills

5. Analysis: Mary spent a total of 4 × 50¢, or $2.00. At $1.00 per card, if Mark buys 2 cards, he will spend the same amount as Mary. Students can draw the correct number of cards for each and label each with its cost.

6. Synthesis: There are two possible answers: 1 minivan and 7 cars or 4 minivans and 3 cars. Students should recognize that they are dealing with the sum of two products and should draw symbolic pictures of each kind of vehicle until the requirements of the problem are satisfied.

7. Evaluation: He is not correct. Proofs will vary. A sample could say that 8 × 9 dimes is 72 dimes, much more than 50 dimes, or $5.00. Another sample could say that 90¢ is almost 1 dollar. So, 8 fruit bars would cost almost 8 dollars, or actually 8 dollars less 8 dimes or $7.20. Students might represent the bars and the money symbolically to show how their costs exceeds $5.00.

# Money and the Calculator

## pages 175-176

### Objective

To use the calculator to solve problems with money

### Materials

simple calculators

### Mental Math

Have students identify the amount indicated by n:

1. $4 + 9 = n$ ($13$)
2. $n - 8 = $4$ ($12$)
3. $n \times 5 = $20$ ($4$)
4. $50 - n = $25$ ($25$)
5. $10 + 23 = n$ ($33$)
6. $12 \times n = $36$ (3, not $3$)

### Skill Review

Ask students to identify the operation keys on their calculators.
$\boxed{+}$, $\boxed{-}$, $\boxed{\times}$, $\boxed{\div}$, $\boxed{=}$ Have another explain the functions performed by the $\boxed{C}$ and $\boxed{CE}$ keys. (clear the entire problem, clear the last entry) Ask what is meant by the phrase, enter a number into the calculator. (Touch the appropriate number keys, from left to right, to tell the calculator the number to use.)

---

## Money and the Calculator

Mr. Ryan is buying 6 dress shirts, 3 sport shirts and 4 ties. What is the cost of his purchases?

We want to know the total cost of Mr. Ryan's purchases. We are given the cost of each item.

Mr. Ryan bought __6__ dress shirts, __3__ sport

shirts and __4__ ties.

To find the cost of each clothing item, we multiply the cost of one by the number of that kind purchased. We must use the $\boxed{\cdot}$ key to enter the money, so $16.45 is entered as 16 $\boxed{\cdot}$ 45. It is not necessary to enter a $\boxed{\cdot}$ sign when there are no dimes or pennies in the amount.

| | | |
|---|---|---|
| Dress shirts | 16 $\boxed{\cdot}$ 45 $\boxed{\times}$ 6 $\boxed{=}$ | ( 98.7 ) |
| Sport shirts | 11 $\boxed{\cdot}$ 98 $\boxed{\times}$ 3 $\boxed{=}$ | ( 35.94 ) |
| Ties | 7 $\boxed{\cdot}$ 25 $\boxed{\times}$ 4 $\boxed{=}$ | ( 29 ) |

✔ The calculator does not print zeros to the far right of decimal point and does not print a dollar sign. The cost of the shirts appears as 98.7. We have to write in the dollar sign and zeros for the answer to read $98.70.

To find the total cost of Mr. Ryan's purchases, we add the cost of each kind of clothing.

✔ When entering a number into the calculator, we too can drop the zeros to the far right of a decimal point.

$98.70 = 98 \boxed{\cdot} 7$

__98__ $\boxed{\cdot}$ __7__ $\boxed{+}$ __35__ $\boxed{\cdot}$ __94__ $\boxed{+}$ __29__ $\boxed{=}$ ( 163.64 )

The total cost of Mr. Ryan's purchases is __$163.64__.

---

## Teaching the Lesson

**Introducing the Problem** Have students read the problem and identify the question being asked. Have a volunteer read the information in the ad, and then complete the information sentences. (bought 6 dress and 3 sport shirts, 4 ties) Read the plan sentences aloud. Now have them look at their calculators and find the $\boxed{\cdot}$ key. Write the amount **$16.45** on the board and ask a student to explain what the decimal point is for. (separates dollars from cents) Ask a student to explain how they can use the calculator to find each amount that Mr. Ryan spent. (multiply) Have them multiply the amounts indicated in their texts. Ask a student to write the results of each multiplication on the board and see that the class agrees. (98.7, 35.94, 29) Explain that the calculator does not use dollar signs so they will have to write that symbol. Point out that the calculator will also drop any zeros on the far right of the decimal point. Because we express dollars and cents with two decimal places to the right, they should add zeros. Read the section of the model which

deals with adding the cost of each kind of clothing, and have students do the addition on their calculators. Ask them to write each amount in the blanks, and the answer in the final space. (98.7 + 35.94 + 29 = 163.64) Have them complete the solution sentence.

**Developing the Skill** Have students use the ad to practice this skill further. Ask them to total the price of 2 belts and 3 sweaters. ($19.98 + 83.37 = $103.35)

# Chapter Test

page 177

Multiply.

1. $\begin{array}{r} 32 \\ \times\ 3 \\ \hline 96 \end{array}$ 　2. $\begin{array}{r} 24 \\ \times\ 4 \\ \hline 96 \end{array}$ 　3. $\begin{array}{r} 13 \\ \times\ 3 \\ \hline 39 \end{array}$ 　4. $\begin{array}{r} 34 \\ \times\ 2 \\ \hline 68 \end{array}$

5. $\begin{array}{r} 122 \\ \times\ 4 \\ \hline 488 \end{array}$ 　6. $\begin{array}{r} 333 \\ \times\ 3 \\ \hline 999 \end{array}$ 　7. $\begin{array}{r} 214 \\ \times\ 2 \\ \hline 428 \end{array}$ 　8. $\begin{array}{r} 221 \\ \times\ 4 \\ \hline 884 \end{array}$

9. $\begin{array}{r} 48 \\ \times\ 6 \\ \hline 288 \end{array}$ 　10. $\begin{array}{r} 37 \\ \times\ 8 \\ \hline 296 \end{array}$ 　11. $\begin{array}{r} 59 \\ \times\ 4 \\ \hline 236 \end{array}$ 　12. $\begin{array}{r} 86 \\ \times\ 7 \\ \hline 602 \end{array}$

13. $\begin{array}{r} 138 \\ \times\ 5 \\ \hline 690 \end{array}$ 　14. $\begin{array}{r} 376 \\ \times\ 9 \\ \hline 3,384 \end{array}$ 　15. $\begin{array}{r} 529 \\ \times\ 6 \\ \hline 3,174 \end{array}$ 　16. $\begin{array}{r} 862 \\ \times\ 3 \\ \hline 2,586 \end{array}$

17. $\begin{array}{r} \$1.86 \\ \times\ 7 \\ \hline \$13.02 \end{array}$ 　18. $\begin{array}{r} \$7.83 \\ \times\ 4 \\ \hline \$31.32 \end{array}$ 　19. $\begin{array}{r} \$6.39 \\ \times\ 8 \\ \hline \$51.12 \end{array}$ 　20. $\begin{array}{r} \$4.08 \\ \times\ 9 \\ \hline \$36.72 \end{array}$

Solve these problems.

21. Penny worked out in the gym for 56 minutes every day. How many minutes did Penny work out each week?
392 minutes

22. Jack fills 138 crates of apples each day. He works 8 days. How many crates of apples does Jack fill?
1,104 crates

23. Ted works 8 hours on Saturday. He earns $5.26 each hour. How much does Ted make?
$42.08

24. $5.62 × 3 = $16.86

$5.62 is a __factor__ and

$16.86 is a __product__.

**177**

Circle the letter of the correct answer.

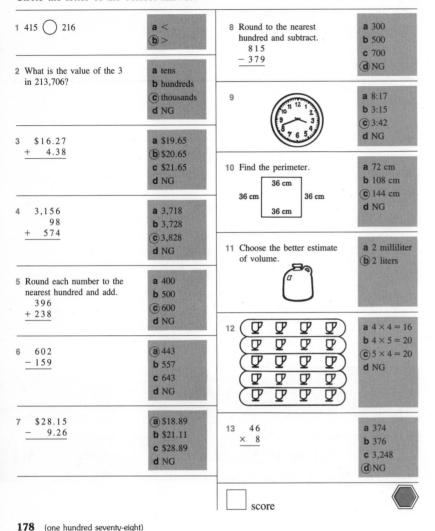

1  415 ◯ 216
   a <
   **b** >

2  What is the value of the 3 in 213,706?
   a tens
   b hundreds
   **c** thousands
   d NG

3  $16.27
   +  4.38
   a $19.65
   **b** $20.65
   c $21.65
   d NG

4  3,156
     98
   +  574
   a 3,718
   b 3,728
   **c** 3,828
   d NG

5  Round each number to the nearest hundred and add.
   396
   + 238
   a 400
   b 500
   **c** 600
   d NG

6  602
   − 159
   **a** 443
   b 557
   c 643
   d NG

7  $28.15
   −  9.26
   **a** $18.89
   b $21.11
   c $28.89
   d NG

8  Round to the nearest hundred and subtract.
   815
   − 379
   a 300
   b 500
   c 700
   **d** NG

9
   a 8:17
   b 3:15
   **c** 3:42
   d NG

10  Find the perimeter.
   36 cm
   36 cm   36 cm
   36 cm
   a 72 cm
   b 108 cm
   **c** 144 cm
   d NG

11  Choose the better estimate of volume.
   a 2 milliliter
   **b** 2 liters

12
   a 4 × 4 = 16
   b 4 × 5 = 20
   **c** 5 × 4 = 20
   d NG

13  46
   ×  8
   a 374
   b 376
   c 3,248
   **d** NG

☐ score

**178**  (one hundred seventy-eight)

---

## Cumulative Review

| Item | Objective |
|---|---|
| 1 | Compare numbers less than 1,000 (See pages 27-28) |
| 2 | Identify the value of a digit in a number less than 1,000,000 (See pages 35-36) |
| 3 | Add dollars and cents with regrouping (See pages 51-52) |
| 4 | Add three or four numbers (See pages 49-50) |
| 5 | Round numbers to nearest 100 and add (See pages 53-56) |
| 6 | Subtract two 3-digit numbers with two regroupings (See pages 67-68) |
| 7 | Subtract dollars and cents with regrouping (See pages 75-76) |
| 8 | Round numbers to the nearest 100 and subtract (See pages 77-78) |
| 9 | Read time to the minute (See pages 87-88) |
| 10 | Add to find perimeter (See pages 95-96) |
| 11 | Choose appropriate metric unit of volume (See pages 111-112) |
| 12 | Match an array with the appropriate equation (See pages 139-140) |
| 13 | Multiply 2-digit by 1-digit number (See pages 157-158) |

---

## Alternate Cumulative Review

Circle the letter of the correct answer.

1  477 ◯ 476
   **a** >
   b <
   c =

2  What is the value of the 9 in 376,491?
   **a** tens
   b hundreds
   c thousands
   d NG

3  $27.62
   +  4.19
   a $21.71
   b $31.71
   c $21.81
   **d** NG

4  2,657
     46
   +  392
   **a** 3,095
   b 2,985
   c 2,095
   d NG

5  Round each number to the nearest hundred and add.
   681   a 600
   + 127  **b** 800
         c 900
         d NG

6  507
   − 249
   **a** 258
   b 366
   c 342
   d NG

7  $56.21
   −  7.68
   a $51.47
   b $63.89
   **d** $48.53
   d NG

8  Round to the nearest hundred and subtract.
   327   a 200
   − 191  b 300
         **c** 100
         d NG

9  What time is it? (Show a clock.)
   a 7:50
   b 11:34
   **c** 6:58
   d NG

10  Find the perimeter of a rectangle 27 m by 16 m.
   a 54 m
   **b** 86 m
   c 43 m
   d NG

11  What unit would you use to measure mass?
   a liters
   b meters
   **c** grams
   d NG

12  Write the multiplication problem.
   a 4 × 5 = 20   XXXXXX
   **b** 6 × 4 = 24   XXXXXX
   c 5 + 4 = 20   XXXXXX
   d NG          XXXXXX

**178**

# Recognizing Plane Figures

**pages 179-180**

## Objective

To recognize plane figures including the circle, triangle, rectangle, square, pentagon and hexagon

## Materials

*pictures and paper cutouts of circles, triangles, squares, rectangles, pentagons, and hexagons

## Mental Math

Introduce an addition short-cut. Have students add: 13 + 8 (21), 23 + 8 (31) and 33 + 8. (41) Tell them to use this pattern and add:

1. 18 + 4, 28 + 4, 38 + 4 (22, 32, 42)
2. 15 + 6, 45 + 6, 85 + 6 (21, 51, 91)
3. 16 + 8, 36 + 8, 76 + 8 (24, 44, 84)

## Skill Review

Explain that everything has a shape, either irregular, like a fried egg, or regular, like a window. Ask students to give examples of objects with regular and irregular shapes.

### Recognizing Plane Figures

**Plane figures** are those that appear on flat surfaces. Some plane figures, like squares and triangles, have straight sides and corners. Others, like circles, have curved sides and no corners.

Study these plane figures.

side    corner

Circle    Triangle    Rectangle    Square    Pentagon    Hexagon

### Getting Started

Write the name of the plane figure you see in each of these.

1.  circle

2. rectangle

3. square

4. triangle

Complete the table.

5.

| Figure | Name | Number of Straight Sides | Number of Corners |
|--------|------|--------------------------|-------------------|
| □ | square | 4 | 4 |
| ○ | circle | 0 | 0 |
| ▭ | rectangle | 4 | 4 |

(one hundred seventy-nine) **179**

## Teaching the Lesson

**Introducing the Problem** Read the definition of plane figures aloud. Ask volunteers to identify the shapes represented by the objects in the picture. Have students examine the six plane figures illustrated below the definition. Ask how the circle differs from the other figures. (It has curved sides.) Explain that the names for some of the figures reflect the figures themselves: "tri" means three, "rect" means at right angles, "pent" means five, and "hex", six. Ask volunteers to tell the number of sides in a triangle (3), rectangle (4), square (4), pentagon (5) and hexagon. (6) Now ask them to tell the number of corners in each figure: triangle (3), rectangle (4), square (4), pentagon (5) and hexagon. (6) Ask what they notice about these two sets of numbers. (The number of sides equals the number of corners.) Ask someone to describe the difference between a square and a rectangle. (Sides are equal in a square and rectangles have sides of 2 different lengths.) Remind students while the fig-

ures illustrated seem to have equal sides, only the square must have sides of equal length. Draw several triangles on the board with obviously unequal sides.

**Developing the Skill** Write the words **circle, triangle, square, rectangle, pentagon** and **hexagon** across the board. Ask students to give as many real examples of each figure as they can and list the examples beneath the word.

## Practice

Write the name of the plane figure you see in each of these.

1.
square

2.
triangle

3.
triangle

4.
rectangle

5.
circle

6.
rectangle

7.
circle

8.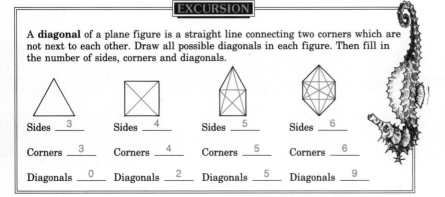
square

Complete the table.

9.

| Figure | Name | Number of Straight Sides | Number of Corners |
|--------|------|--------------------------|-------------------|
| ⬡ | hexagon | 6 | 6 |
| ▭ | rectangle | 4 | 4 |
| ◺ | triangle | 3 | 3 |
| ⬠ | pentagon | 5 | 5 |

---

**EXCURSION**

A **diagonal** of a plane figure is a straight line connecting two corners which are not next to each other. Draw all possible diagonals in each figure. Then fill in the number of sides, corners and diagonals.

Sides 3    Sides 4    Sides 5    Sides 6

Corners 3    Corners 4    Corners 5    Corners 6

Diagonals 0    Diagonals 2    Diagonals 5    Diagonals 9

---

## Correcting Common Errors

Some students may have difficulty identifying plane figures since their everyday-life experiences are not two-dimensional. Use paper cutouts of the six figures in this lesson as flash cards. Have students identify the figure and give the number of sides and corners. Then have them identify an object in the classroom that has the same shape.

## Enrichment

Provide students with a good picture of a bicycle, or let them go outside to examine a real one. They must all use the same model, however. Ask them to find as many plane figures on the bike as possible. Encourage them to look from many angles. Have them make a drawing of the bike, outlining or pointing to the figures they found. See who found the most figures.

## Practice

Have students complete the page. Leave the figure names on the board to remind students of their spellings.

## Excursion

Draw a rectangle on the board. Start at one corner and tell students if you draw a straight line from this corner to the next corner you would be tracing over one of the rectangle's sides. Return to the starting corner and tell students that if you skipped a corner and drew a line from this corner to the next corner around the figure, you would be drawing a diagonal. Draw the diagonal and then ask a student to draw another diagonal in the rectangle. Ask if more diagonals can be drawn. (no) Remind students that they skip a corner when drawing a diagonal. Have students read the excursion directions and complete the activity.

## Extra Credit  *Measurement*

Prepare activities listed below and team score sheets, for a Measurement Meet. Divide students into groups of four. Divide the score sheet into four columns with the headings: Player, Estimate, Measure, Points. The team with the least number of points wins.

Broad Jump: Students take turns jumping. The group estimates the length of each student's jump, beforehand, and records it on the scoresheet. Then they measure and record the actual jump. Subtract to find the difference, and record this number as the point total.

Bean Bag Toss: Students estimate the length of the toss. Then students toss bean bags, measure the actual toss and record the difference as points. Continue for other activities such as blowing a cotton ball with a straw and ring toss.

Direct students to note whether or not their estimating skills improved by the end of the meet.

# Finding the Area of Plane Figures

## pages 181-182

### Objective

To find the area of plane figures

### Materials

*a large ceramic tile
centimeter graph paper

### Mental Math

Explain this subtraction shortcut to the class. To subtract 9 from 21, they could start by subtracting 10: 21 − 10 = 11. Because they have subtracted one more than necessary, and 9 is one less than 10, they will add 1 to get the answer: 11 + 1 = 12. Have them do these problems:

1. 46 − 9 (46 − 10 = 36, 36 + 1 = 37)
2. 78 − 9 (78 − 10 = 68, 68 + 1 = 69)
3. 62 − 9 (62 − 10 = 52, 52 + 1 = 53)
4. 33 − 9 (33 − 10 = 23, 23 + 1 = 24)

### Skill Review

Have volunteers go to the board and draw and label the six plane figures they have learned: circle, triangle, square, rectangle, pentagon and hexagon. Have other students write the number of sides and corners in each.

---

## Finding the Area of Plane Figures

Alan is tiling the top of a table for his bedroom. How many tiles will it take to cover the entire top?

**Area** is the number of square units it takes to cover the surface of a plane figure.

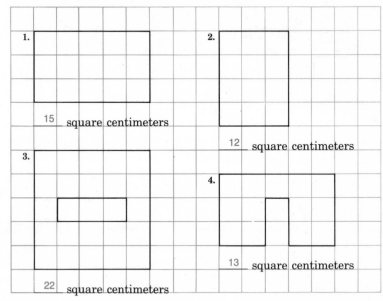

It will take ___8___ tiles to cover Alan's table.

We say the area of the table is ___8___ square units.

### Getting Started

In the grids that follow, each square covers 1 square centimeter. Write the number of square centimeters in each plane figure.

1. 15 square centimeters
2. 12 square centimeters
3. 22 square centimeters
4. 13 square centimeters

(one hundred eighty-one) **181**

---

## Teaching the Lesson

**Introducing the Problem** Have a student read the problem and identify the question being asked. Read the definition of area aloud. Have a student tell the number of tiles that will be needed to cover the table (8) and have students write it in the information sentence. Explain that the square units being used in this problem are the tiles. Read the solution sentence aloud and have a volunteer give the area of the table top. (8 square units)

**Developing the Skill** Explain that square units are used to measure area because they fit together in a regular pattern. Now hold up the tile and a piece of centimeter graph paper. Explain that you want to find out the area of the tiled surface in units of square centimeters. Have a student explain how to find the area of the tile. (Lay it down on the graph paper, trace around it and count the number of squares covered.) Demonstrate and find the area of the tile. (Answers depend on tile used.) Help them see that when the outline of the tile cuts centimeter squares in half, they will have to count two halves to make one whole square centimeter. Some students will see that multiplication is a shortcut to finding the area of rectangles and squares, but encourage the use of counting in this lesson.

## Practice

Write the number of square centimeters in each plane figure.

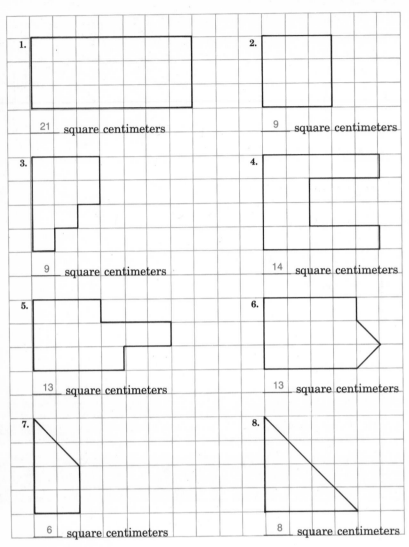

1. 21 square centimeters

2. 9 square centimeters

3. 9 square centimeters

4. 14 square centimeters

5. 13 square centimeters

6. 13 square centimeters

7. 6 square centimeters

8. 8 square centimeters

**182** (one hundred eighty-two)

## Practice

Have students do all the problems on the page. Remind them to count the half squares as well as the whole ones.

## Mixed Practice

1. 805 − 728 (77)
2. 3,278 + 6,409 (9,687)
3. 63 × 7 (441)
4. $3.42 × 5 ($17.10)
5. 8,276 − 5,754 (2,522)
6. 208 + 215 + 493 (916)
7. 1,276 + 3,840 (5,116)
8. $59.02 − 17.36 ($41.66)
9. 7 × 350 (2,450)
10. 656 − 9 (647)

## Extra Credit *Applications*

Divide the class into groups of five students each. Give each group the name of a race car such as Corvette, Porsche, etc. Designate one child in each group to be the race car driver. Number the other children as members of the pit crew-1, 2, 3, 4. Give each team 20 points and assign them a section of the chalkboard. Tell students each team must make 4 pit stops during their race. At pit stop 1, player 1 writes the table of sixes. Each driver will evaluate the team's answers, and record points earned on the board. If all is correct, team earns 10 points. Mistakes cost 1 point each. At pit stop 2, player 2 writes the table of sevens. If all is correct, team earns 10 points. Mistakes cost 2 points each. At pit stop 3, player 3 writes the table of eights. Mistakes cost 3 points each. At pit stop 4, player 4 writes the table of nines. Mistakes cost 4 points each. For the last lap, the driver tallies the team's points. The first team to finish receives 10 bonus points. The team with the highest score wins the race.

# Recognizing Solid Figures

### pages 183-184

### Objective

To recognize solid geometric figures

### Materials

*models of cylinders, spheres, cubes and rectangular prisms
*household objects with these shapes

### Mental Math

Present another subtraction short-cut. Have students subtract: 14 − 7 (7), 24 − 7 (17) and 34 − 7. (27) Tell them to use this pattern to do these problems:

1. 15 − 8, 25 − 8, 35 − 8 (7, 17, 27)
2. 18 − 9, 48 − 9, 68 − 9 (9, 39, 59)
3. 12 − 7, 42 − 7, 82 − 7 (5, 35, 75)

### Skill Review

Tell students that when a magazine cover is traced onto graph paper, it covers 280 whole square centimeters and 20 half cm. Ask what the area of the magazine cover is. (280 + 10 = 290 square centimeters) If the magazine is opened up and both front and back covers are traced onto graph paper, what will be the total area? (580 sq cm)

---

## Recognizing Solid Figures

Ann is the pitcher for the Madison softball team. What solid figure will she use during each game?

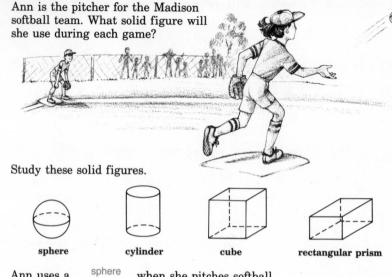

Study these solid figures.

| sphere | cylinder | cube | rectangular prism |

Ann uses a ___sphere___ when she pitches softball.

### Getting Started

Write the name of the solid figure you see in each of these.

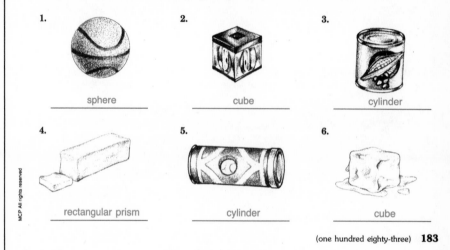

| 1. sphere | 2. cube | 3. cylinder |
| 4. rectangular prism | 5. cylinder | 6. cube |

---

## Teaching the Lesson

**Introducing the Problem**   Read the problem aloud. Explain that every object having three dimensions has a shape, sometimes regular, like Ann's softball. Have students look at the solid figures illustrated in the problem. Read the names of the figures as students study them. Ask someone to explain what a softball's shape is called. (sphere) Have one student read the solution sentence while the others complete it. (sphere) Some students may confuse the circle and the sphere. Hold up the circle cutout you used previously and a model of a sphere. Ask a volunteer to explain how these figures differ. (One is flat. The other is not.)

**Developing the Skill**   Write the words **sphere, cylinder, cube** and **rectangular prism** on the board. Have students copy these names on paper. Now ask students to volunteer the names of as many common objects as they can that have these shapes. Use household objects as examples in order to get them started. Put their examples on the board while they list them on paper. Ask students if they think one shape is more common than others. They may find that rectangular prisims are easier to think of than spheres, for example. Ask if they know why this is so. (Because it is difficult to stack spheres, to make them stay put and to fit them together closely.)

## Practice

Write the name of the solid figure you see in each of these.

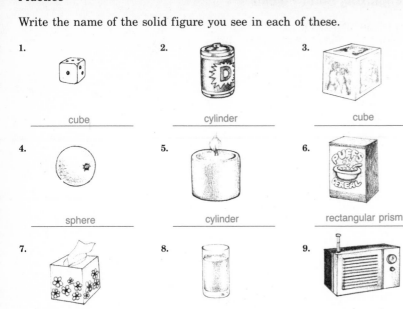

1. cube

2. cylinder

3. cube

4. sphere

5. cylinder

6. rectangular prism

7. cube

8. cylinder

9. rectangular prism

---

**EXCURSION**

A **line of symmetry** divides one figure into two figures that are exactly the same shape. Can you imagine a line of symmetry through each of these figures? Write **yes** or **no**.

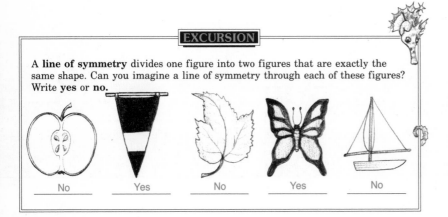

No    Yes    No    Yes    No

---

**184**

# Finding the Volume of Solid Figures

**pages 185-186**

## Objective

To find the volume of solid geometric figures

## Materials

*a box with 12 unit cubes

## Mental Math

Encourage students to use shortcuts to do these problems:

1. 56 − 9 (47)
2. 84 + 8 (92)
3. 76 − 8 (68)
4. 64 + 7 (71)
5. 35 − 6 (29)
6. 55 + 7 (62)
7. 76 + 5 (81)
8. 99 − 9 (90)
9. 71 − 7 (64)
10. 73 − 9 (64)

## Skill Review

Ask a student what is meant by the area of a plane figure. (the number of square units that can be contained within the figure) Draw a grid of square units on the board and a triangular shape on the grid. Ask a student to demonstrate how the squares can be counted to calculate the area of the figure. Have students volunteer units that can be used to measure area. (square centimeters or square inches)

### Finding the Volume of Solid Figures

Grant is packing gift boxes in a large carton. How many boxes will it take to fill the carton?

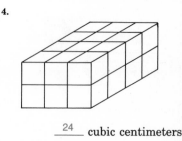

**Volume** is the number of cubic units it takes to fill a solid figure.

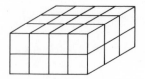

The carton will hold __24__ boxes.

The volume of the carton is

__24__ cubic units.

### Getting Started

In the figures that follow, the volume of each cube is measured in cubic centimeters. Write the number of cubic centimeters in each solid figure.

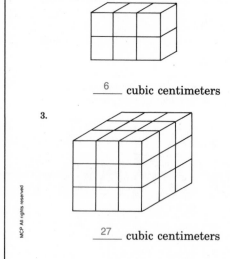

1.

__6__ cubic centimeters

2.

__4__ cubic centimeters

3.

__27__ cubic centimeters

4.

__24__ cubic centimeters

(one hundred eighty-five) **185**

## Teaching the Lesson

**Introducing the Problem** Read the problem aloud as students examine the illustration. Ask a student to read the definition of volume. Explain that volume is like area, but in three dimensions. The units for measuring volume are cubes instead of squares. Read the information sentence aloud and have a student volunteer the number of blocks. (24) Explain that they can simply count the number of blocks in the illustration in their texts. Point out, however, that some cubes are hidden behind others. While there are 19 cubes visible, it is understood that there are 24 all together. Now ask someone to read the solution sentence, explaining the volume of the box. (24 cubic units)

**Developing the Skill** Show the class the empty box and twelve cubes. Have a volunteer come up and pack the cubes in the box. Show the packed box to the class and ask someone to explain how they could describe the volume. (Because 12 cubes fill the box, its volume is 12 cubic units.) Ask students if the volume would be any different if the cubic units were bigger or smaller. (Yes, with smaller units more could fit; with larger units, fewer could fit.) Explain that there are many possible units for measuring volume including cubic centimeters and cubic inches. Ask a student to explain a cubic centimeter and cubic inch. (cubes; 1 cm and 1 inch on each side)

**185**

**Practice**

Write the number of cubic centimeters in each solid figure.

1.
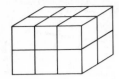
_12_ cubic centimeters

2.
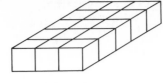
_15_ cubic centimeters

3.
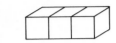
_3_ cubic centimeters

4.
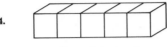
_5_ cubic centimeters

5.
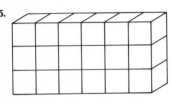
_18_ cubic centimeters

6.
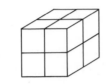
_8_ cubic centimeters

7.
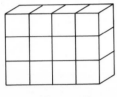
_12_ cubic centimeters

8.
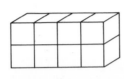
_8_ cubic centimeters

9.
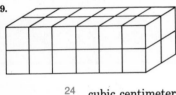
_24_ cubic centimeters

10.
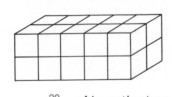
_20_ cubic centimeters

**186** (one hundred eighty-six)

# Recognizing Right Angles

## Objective

To recognize a 90° angle

## Materials

scissors
*cardboard rectangle
*set of plane cardboard figures

## Mental Math

Have students round the numbers in these problems to check the given answers:

1. 9 + 8 + 3 = 42 (10 + 10 + 0 = 20, The answer is wrong.)
2. 6 + 8 + 4 + 9 = 27 (10 + 10 + 0 + 10 = 30, The answer could be right.)
3. 8 + 5 + 5 + 3 = 41 (10 + 10 + 10 + 0 = 30, wrong)
4. 7 + 3 + 9 + 2 + 7 = 24 (10 + 0 + 10 + 0 + 10 = 30, wrong)

## Skill Review

Draw the six plane figures on the board. Have individual students label each figure. Now draw each of the solid figures, showing perspective as best you can. Ask students to label each of these.

---

**Recognizing Right Angles**

The corner of a plane figure makes an **angle**. Angles that make square corners are called **right angles**. How many right angles are there in the plane figure at the right?

Study these right angles.

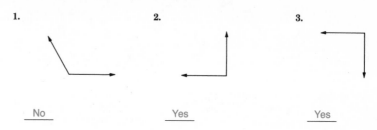

There are ___4___ right angles in plane figure A.

**Getting Started**

Is the angle a right angle? Write **yes** or **no**.

1.          2.          3.

No          Yes          Yes

Write the number of right angles in each plane figure.

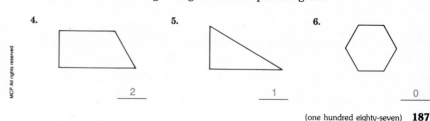

4.          5.          6.

2          1          0

(one hundred eighty-seven) **187**

---

## Teaching the Lesson

**Introducing the Problem**  Read the definitions of angle and right angle aloud. Ask students to study the plane figure and four right angles illustrated in their text. Read the solution sentence aloud and ask a student to count the number of right angles in the plane figure. (4) Have the class complete the sentence in their books.

**Developing the Skill**  Draw on the board an angle that is not a right angle. Ask the class how many sides an angle has. (2) Ask if an angle can be a plane figure. (No, there are no two-sided plane figures.) Now hold up your scissors and explain that the space between the blades forms an angle. Point out that when you hold the scissors up to the corner of a rectangle such as a piece of paper, the blades form a right angle. Ask students how many right angles the rectangle has. (4) Demonstrate each angle with the scissors. Now ask the class to look around the room and give examples of other right angles as you list them on the board. There are many possible answers: doors, windows, books, desks and even the room itself.

**187**

**Practice**

Is the angle a right angle? Write **yes** or **no**.

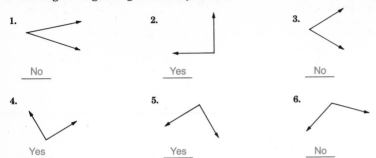

1. No

2. Yes

3. No

4. Yes

5. Yes

6. No

Write the number of right angles in each plane figure.

7. 1

8. 1

9. 4

10. 2

11. 0

12. 1

**EXCURSION**

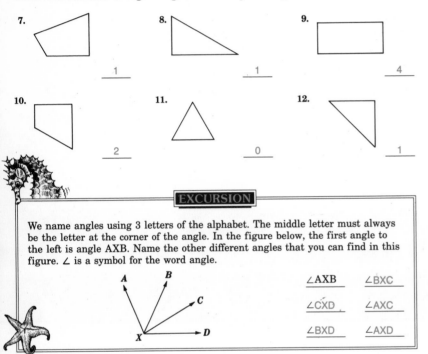

We name angles using 3 letters of the alphabet. The middle letter must always be the letter at the corner of the angle. In the figure below, the first angle to the left is angle AXB. Name the other different angles that you can find in this figure. ∠ is a symbol for the word angle.

∠AXB          ∠BXC

∠CXD          ∠AXC

∠BXD          ∠AXD

**188**  (one hundred eighty-eight)

# Recognizing Congruent Figures

## pages 189-190

### Objective

To recognize congruent figures

### Materials

\*pairs of congruent triangles and rectangles
tracing paper
scissors

### Mental Math

Have students round each of these numbers to the nearest ten to check addition:

1. 39 + 44 + 13 = 74 (40 + 40 + 10 = 90, Answer is wrong.)
2. 56 + 33 + 21 = 110 (60 + 30 + 20 = 110, right)
3. 87 + 61 + 35 = 183 (90 + 60 + 40 = 190, probably right)

### Skill Review

Ask students to draw the six plane figures on the board and label each one. (circle, triangle, rectangle, square, pentagon, hexagon) Ask students to tell the number of angles in each figure. (none, 3, 4, 4, 5, 6) Have individuals come to the board and identify any right angles.

---

## Recognizing Congruent Figures

Plane figures that are the same size and shape are called **congruent figures.** Which of the triangles at the right are congruent?

Congruent figures have the same __size__ and __shape__.

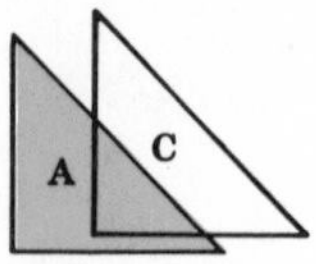

Triangle __A__ and triangle __C__ are congruent.

### Getting Started

Circle the letters of the two congruent figures in each row.

1.

 A     B    C     D

2.

 E    F     G     H

3.

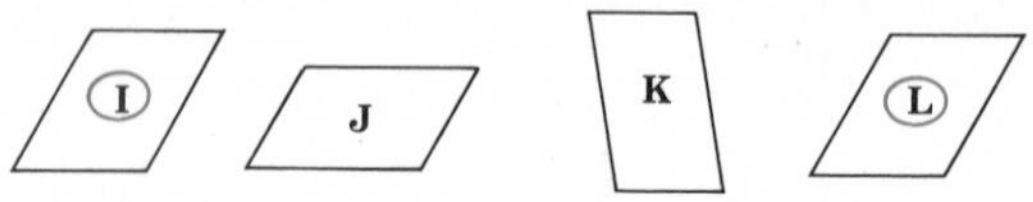

I    J    K    L

---

## Teaching the Lesson

**Introducing the Problem**   Read the introduction aloud, explaining that two of the triangles pictured are congruent. Have a student read and complete the information sentence. (same size and shape) Ask them to imagine that the triangles pictured can be flipped over. Ask which of the triangles is not the same size. (B) Have them examine the next illustration. Explain that it shows one of the triangles being flipped over. Ask which two triangles are the same size and shape. (A and C) Have students complete the solution sentence in their books.

**Developing the Skill**   Reinforce the fact that triangles A and C in the model are the same. Have students trace and label the triangles in their text. Then ask them to cut the two out and put one on top of the other. Ask if they match. (yes) Now place your collection of triangles and rectangles on a desk and have students come up and identify the congruent pairs. When a pair has been identified, hold them up. Have a student trace them on the board. Explain that the figures do not have to be oriented in the same direction in order to be congruent. Trace a congruent pair on the board at obviously different angles. Explain that the figures are still congruent. Have a student repeat what makes two figures congruent. (same size and shape)

**189**

**Practice**

Circle the letters of the two congruent figures in each row.

1.

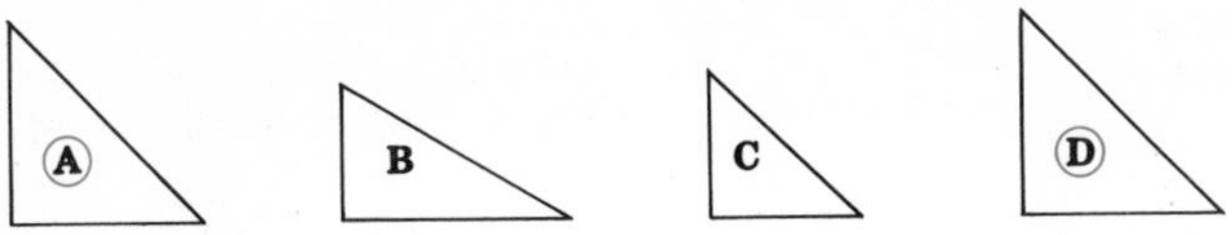

2.

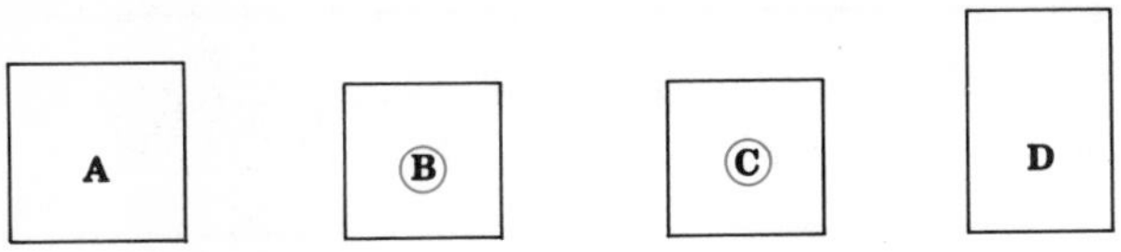

3.

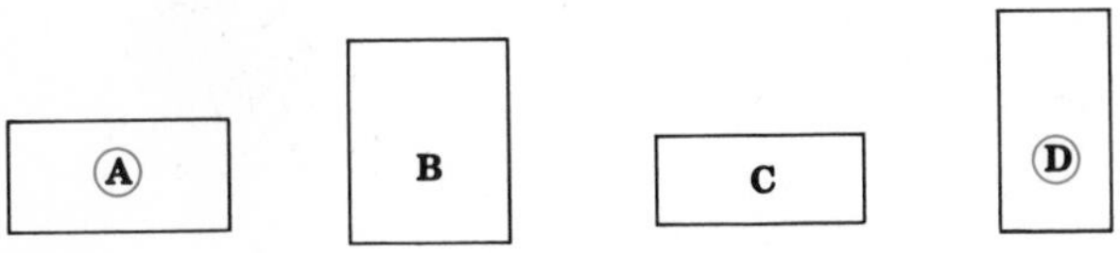

4.

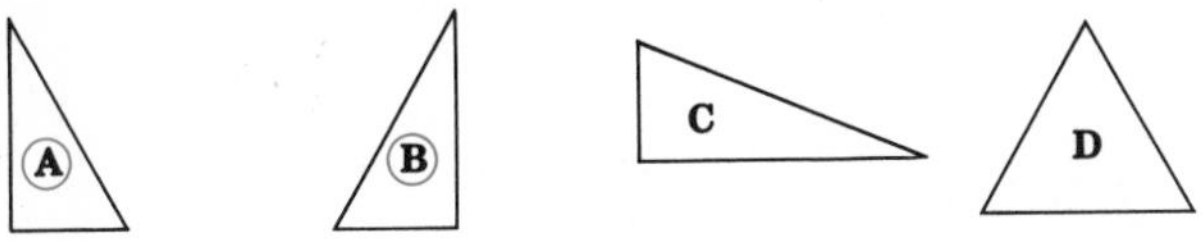

5.

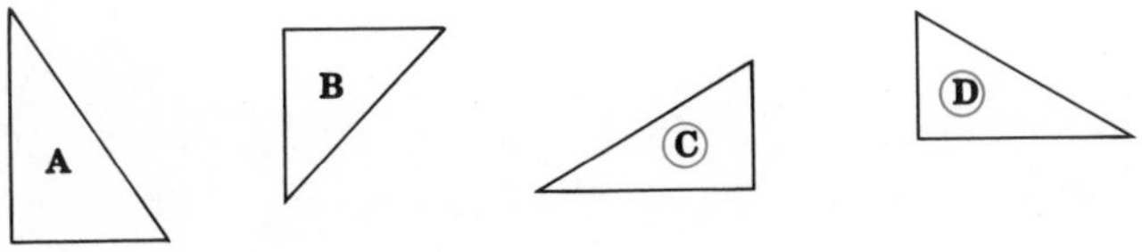

6.

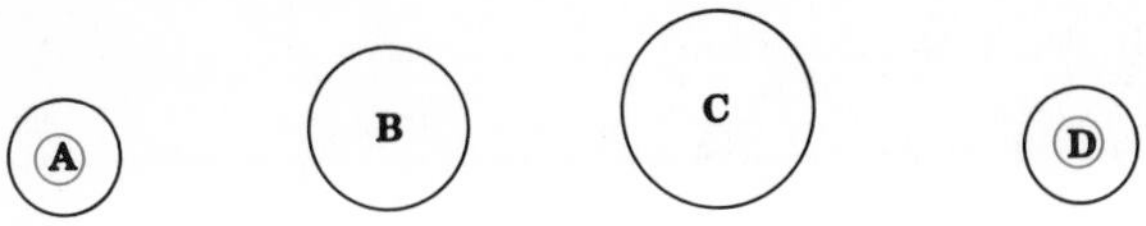

**190**  (one hundred ninety)

**190**

# Understanding Bar Graphs

## pages 191-192

### Objective

To interpret bar graphs

### Materials

graph paper with centimeter squares
*overhead projector

### Mental Math

Ask students to tell you the date:

1. one week from February 3 (Feb. 10)
2. two weeks from August 10 (Aug. 24)
3. two months from September 1 (Nov. 1)
4. one year after March 3, 1934 (March 3, 1935)
5. one year, one month after January 15, 1855 (February 15, 1856)

### Skill Review

Ask students what a survey is. (You ask a number of people the same question and record their answer.) Ask students how many take the bus to school and how many do not take the bus. Write **take the bus** and **do not take the bus** on the board with the student totals beneath. Explain that this is a brief survey.

---

## Understanding Bar Graphs

Each of the students in Mr. Del Sonno's class voted on his favorite color. These are the results of the vote:

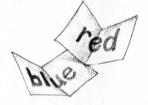

| Mr. Del Sonno's Class | | | |
|---|---|---|---|
| Ben | yellow | Liza | yellow |
| Sam | green | Kurt | red |
| Trudy | red | Nate | green |
| Sonja | blue | Flo | blue |
| Dorothy | red | Rex | blue |
| Martin | green | Tabatha | red |
| Juan | blue | Terry | blue |
| Rhea | blue | Andy | green |

Tally the number of student votes for each color.

| Favorite Colors | | Totals |
|---|---|---|
| Red | IIII | 4 |
| Blue | IIII I | 6 |
| Green | IIII | 4 |
| Yellow | II | 2 |

Make a bar graph showing vote totals for each color.

**Favorite Colors**

| | | | | | | | | | | | |
|---|---|---|---|---|---|---|---|---|---|---|---|
| Red | | | | | | | | | | | |
| Blue | | | | | | | | | | | |
| Green | | | | | | | | | | | |
| Yellow | | | | | | | | | | | |
| | 0 | 1 | 2 | 3 | 4 | 5 | 6 | 7 | 8 | 9 | 10 |

### Getting Started

Use the bar graph to answer these questions.

1. How many children voted for blue? _____6_____

2. How many children voted for green? _____4_____

3. Which color won the vote? _____blue_____

4. Which color is the least favorite? _____yellow_____

---

## Teaching the Lesson

**Introducing the Problem**   Have a student read the problem aloud while the class looks at the results of the vote. Direct their attention to the tally sheet and ask a student to explain what the lines on the sheet mean. (Each vote is represented by a slash mark. Groups of five are marked with a horizontal mark to make them easier to count.) Ask students to look at the tally sheets and see if they can tell which color received the most votes without reading the numerical totals at the far right. (Yes, by looking to see which has the most marks.) Now have them look at the grid. Explain that this graph is ready to be made into a picture of the survey. By filling in one block for each vote, it will be easy to tell at a glance which color received the most votes. Have students fill in the bar graph. Use the overhead projector to demonstrate the graph and have students compare theirs to yours.

**Developing the Skill**   Put a tally chart on the board listing math, reading, science, and social studies. Ask students to vote for their favorite subject and mark the votes on the chart, demonstrating the way to mark off fives as you tally. Now give students graph paper and have them transfer the information from the tally sheet onto a bar graph. Outline the bar graph on the board before they begin.

**191**

## Practice

During their nature study, the students in Mr. Del Sonno's class voted on their favorite birds. Here are the results of that vote:

| Mr. Del Sonno's Class | | | |
|---|---|---|---|
| Ben | Bluebird | Liza | Robin |
| Sam | Robin | Kurt | Cardinal |
| Trudy | Robin | Nate | Robin |
| Sonja | Blackbird | Flo | Bluebird |
| Dorothy | Robin | Rex | Cardinal |
| Martin | Cardinal | Tabatha | Bluebird |
| Juan | Cardinal | Terry | Robin |
| Rhea | Blackbird | Andy | Cardinal |

Tally the number of student votes for each bird.

| Favorite Birds | | Totals |
|---|---|---|
| Robin | ⅢⅠ | 6 |
| Bluebird | ‖‖ | 3 |
| Cardinal | ⅢⅠ | 5 |
| Blackbird | ‖ | 2 |

Make a bar graph showing vote totals for each bird.

| Favorite Birds | | | | | | | | | | | | | | |
|---|---|---|---|---|---|---|---|---|---|---|---|---|---|---|
| Robin | | | | | | | | | | | | | | |
| Bluebird | | | | | | | | | | | | | | |
| Cardinal | | | | | | | | | | | | | | |
| Blackbird | | | | | | | | | | | | | | |

0  1  2  3  4  5  6  7  8  9  10  11  12  13  14

Use the bar graph to answer these questions.

1. How many children voted for the robin? ___6___

2. How many children voted for the cardinal? ___5___

3. How many votes did the blackbird get? ___2___

4. How many more votes did the cardinal get than the blackbird? ___3___

5. Which bird is the favorite? ___robin___

**192**  (one hundred ninety-two)

## Correcting Common Errors

Some students may have difficulty reading amounts on a bar graph. Discuss how they can either use a straightedge, such as a ruler, to align the end of the bar with the number on the horizontal scale, or count the number of squares in the bar.

## Enrichment

Draw these patterns on the board:

```
XX      XXX     XXXX
XX      XXX     XXXX
        XXX     XXXX
                XXXX
```

Ask students to tell how many marks are in each. (4, 9, 16) Explain that these are called **square numbers.** Have them figure out the triangular numbers. (Ex. 3, 6, 10)

```
X       X       X
XX      XX      XX
        XXX     XXX
                XXXX
```

## Practice

Have students complete the page. Explain that the problem is similar to the one they have just completed.

## Mixed Practice

1. $9 \times 600$ (5,400)
2. $657 + 308$ (965)
3. $83.21 - 7.58$ ($75.63)
4. $2,050 - 1,963$ (87)
5. $276 \times 3$ (828)
6. $4,093 + 2,727$ (6,820)
7. $7 \times 195$ (1,365)
8. $600 - 437$ (163)
9. $24.56 + 7.03$ ($31.59)
10. $21.80 - 4.93$ ($16.87)

## Extra Credit  *Applications*

Tell students in professional football, teams score points in the following ways:

Touchdown = 6 points
Extra Point = 1 point (only with touchdown)
Field Goal = 3 points
Safety = 2 points

If a team scores nine points, they could do so by several methods: touchdown and field goal; 3 field goals; touchdown, extra point and safety.
The Crashers beat the Mashers 8 to 5. Try to list all the ways each team might have scored their totals. (8 = 1 touchdown, 1 safety; 2 field goals, 1 safety; 4 safeties. 5 = 1 field goal, 1 safety)

# Understanding Picture Graphs

**pages 193-194**

## Objective

To understand picture graphs

## Materials

## Mental Math

Describe an addition shortcut, using the problem 43 + 35. Point out that 43 = 40 + 3 and that the problem can be rearranged, 40 + 3 + 35. Ask them to add 3 and 35. (38) Now have them add 40. (78) Have them use this mental shortcut to do the following problems:

1. 31 + 58 (30 + 1 + 58 = 89)
2. 15 + 82 (10 + 5 + 82 = 97)
3. 42 + 17 (40 + 2 + 17 = 59)
4. 22 + 64 (20 + 2 + 64 = 86)

## Skill Review

Draw a simple bar graph on the board showing the number of students wearing blue and the number not wearing blue. Ask the class whether they can tell at a glance which is the larger group. (yes) Have a student identify this kind of graph. (bar graph)

## Understanding Picture Graphs

Roberto collects stamps from Europe. He made a picture graph to show the number of stamps he had collected each month. How many stamps did Roberto collect in July?

**STAMP COLLECTION**

| June | 🖼 🖼 🖼 🖼 |
| July | 🖼 🖼 |
| August | 🖼 🖼 🖼 |
| September | 🖼 🖼 🖼 |

Each 🖼 stands for 5 stamps.

We want to find the number of stamps Roberto collected in July.

The graph shows ___2___ stamps for July.

Each picture stands for ___5___ actual stamps. To find the number of stamps collected in

July, we multiply ___5___ by ___2___.

July

$$\underline{5} \times \underline{2} = \underline{10}$$

Roberto collected ___10___ stamps in July.

### Getting Started

Use the picture graph to answer these questions.

1. How many stamps did Roberto collect in September? ___15___

2. How many stamps did Roberto collect in June? ___20___

3. How many stamps did Roberto collect from June through September? ___60___

4. How many more stamps did Roberto collect in June than in July? ___10___

5. In which months did Roberto collect the same number of stamps? ___August, September___

6. In which month did Roberto collect the most stamps? ___June___

(one hundred ninety-three) **193**

## Teaching the Lesson

**Introducing the Problem** Have students look at the picture while you read the problem aloud. Explain that under the picture there is a **legend**, the part of the graph that explains the meaning of each picture. Have a student read the first information sentence and explain how many stamp pictures are shown for the month of July. (2) Have another read the second information sentence, about the legend. (Each stands for 5 actual stamps.) Read the plan sentences aloud, having a student volunteer the required numbers. (Multiply 5 by 2.) Have students do the multiplication in the spaces provided (5 × 2 = 10), and complete the conclusion sentence.

**Developing the Skill** Ask the class why Roberto used a picture of one stamp to stand for each five he actually collected. (It is easier to draw and to read.) Point out that picture graphs do not require graph paper. Give each student a piece of paper. Ask the class how many made their beds this morning and how many did not. Put these totals on the board in labeled columns: **made bed, did not make bed.** Have students devise a symbol of their own to stand for each two students in the survey, and make a picture graph depicting the results. See if any students figure out how to show a single student. (perhaps cutting their symbol in half.)

**193**

**Practice**

Use the picture graph to answer these questions.

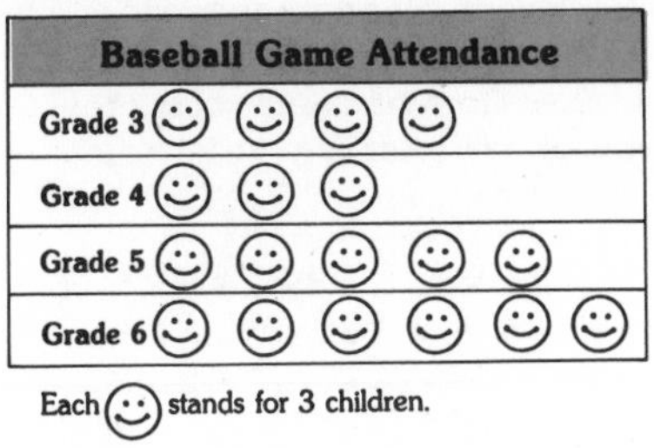


1. How many children from Grade 3 attended the ball game? 12
2. How many children from Grade 4 attended the ball game? 9
3. Which class had the smallest attendance? Grade 4
4. Which class had the largest attendance? Grade 6
5. How many children from Grade 5 and Grade 6 attended the ball game? 33

Use the picture graph to answer these questions.

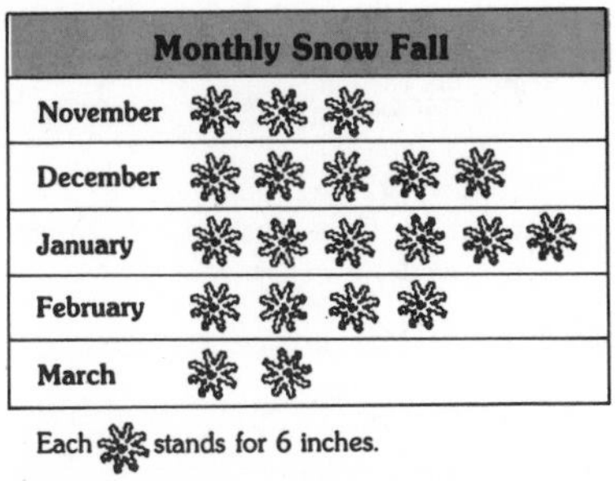


How many inches of snow fell:

6. in December? 30
7. in March? 12
8. in January? 36
9. in December and January? 66
10. How much more snow fell in November than in March? 6 in.
11. How much less snow fell in February than in January? 12 in.
12. How much snow fell in all 5 months? 120 in.



## Correcting Common Errors

When interpreting picture graphs, some students may ignore the key and read each picture as 1 unit. To help them attend to the key, have them write the value of the picture as given in the key on, at least, one of the pictures in the graph. For some students, you may want to have them write the value on each and every picture.

## Enrichment

Have students make a bar graph or picture graph showing distances between Chicago and other large cities. You can write the distances on the board or let students use an atlas. All numbers should be rounded to the nearest hundred. Let each square or picture on the graph represent 100 miles.

## Practice

Have students answer all the questions on the page. Remind them to multiply the number of symbols by the worth of each symbol to get each total.

## Extra Credit *Logic*

Tell students you will read a mystery, and they must use logic to solve the crime.

Senator Curry left a $1,000 bill on his desk. Later, when he came back for it, the money had disappeared. Only two other people were in the house at the time; the butler and the maid, whom he questioned.

The maid said, "For safe-keeping, I folded the bill and placed it under the red book on your desk." The Senator looked there, but didn't find the money.

The butler said, "Yes, sir. I found the bill under the red book. Thinking it might get lost, I placed it inside the book, between pages 133 and 134." Senator Curry opened the book, but again no money.

Ask students who stole the $1,000 bill, and what evidence they used to solve the mystery.

(The butler was guilty. The pages of a book are even on the left and odd on the right. Pages 133 and 134 were, therefore, on either side of the same leaf.)

# Understanding Number Pairs

## Objective

To understand how number pairs locate a point on a graph

## Materials

graph paper with large squares
*overhead projector

## Mental Math

Tell students to add 4 to the following numbers and multiply by 2:

1. 6 (+4 = 10, × 2 = 20)
2. 3 (+4 = 7, × 2 = 14)
3. 9 (+4 = 13, × 2 = 26)
4. 11 (+4 = 15, × 2 = 30)
5. 0 (+4 = 4, × 2 = 8)
6. 96 (+4 = 100, × 2 = 200)

## Skill Review

Put the school's attendance figures for the previous day on the board: students present, students absent. Ask students to come to the board and make a picture graph using this information. Have one outline the graph with row headings and space for the symbols. Tell them a circle stands for 10 students. Have one student draw the symbols for those present, another for those absent.

---

### Understanding Number Pairs

**Number pairs** can be used to show locations on a graph or map. The pair (4, 3) shows the location of letter $G$. What pair shows the location of letter $B$?

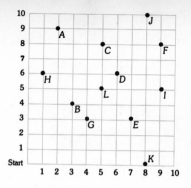

In a number pair, the first number is read across the bottom. The second number is read up the graph.

Count 3 units across the bottom.  (3, 4)  Count 4 units up the graph.

The letter $B$ is named by the pair ___(3, 4)___.

### Getting Started

Write the letter for each number pair. Use the graph.

1. (2, 9) ___A___
2. (6, 6) ___D___
3. (9, 5) ___I___
4. (3, 4) ___B___
5. (5, 8) ___C___
6. (8, 10) ___J___

Write the number pair for each letter. Use the graph.

7. $H$ ___(1, 6)___
8. $E$ ___(7, 3)___
9. $F$ ___(9, 8)___
10. $G$ ___(4, 3)___
11. $K$ ___(8, 0)___
12. $L$ ___(5, 5)___

(one hundred ninety-five) **195**

---

## Teaching the Lesson

**Introducing the Problem** Read the description of number pairs aloud while students study the graph. Explain that the order in which the numbers are listed is very important; (3, 4) is not the same as (4, 3). Point out the rule that states the first number is located by numbers written across the bottom of the graph, the second by numbers up the side. Use the overhead projector to demonstrate how to count over 3 and up 4 to find the point (3, 4), to locate point B. Have a student complete the solution sentence while the others write the coordinates in their books. (3, 4)

**Developing the Skill** Draw this grid on the board:

5
4
3
2
1
start    1 2 3 4 5

Explain that there is a house at point (5, 2). Have a student come to the board and draw a small house at that point. Have another draw a tree at (1, 4). Explain that a driveway runs between (2, 2) and (4, 4). Have a student draw it in. Have another put a car at the end of the driveway at (5, 5). As they are working on this, remind students of the importance of the order of the numbers in each pair.

**195**

## Practice

Write the letter for each number pair.

1. (1, 2) __H__   2. (9, 6) __J__

3. (3, 9) __K__   4. (6, 7) __L__

5. (5, 4) __O__   6. (7, 5) __B__

7. (4, 5) __Q__   8. (8, 1) __N__

9. (2, 5) __I__   10. (1, 8) __C__

Write the number pair for each letter.

11. S __(9, 9)__   12. Q __(4, 5)__

13. F __(8, 3)__   14. M __(9, 3)__

15. J __(9, 6)__   16. A __(4, 6)__

17. B __(7, 5)__   18. O __(5, 4)__

19. P __(7, 9)__   20. H __(1, 2)__

Use the graph to find the letters to spell each word.

21. $\dfrac{M}{(9,3)}$ $\dfrac{A}{(4,6)}$ $\dfrac{T}{(6,3)}$ $\dfrac{H}{(1,2)}$,
22. $\dfrac{P}{(7,9)}$ $\dfrac{E}{(8,8)}$ $\dfrac{N}{(8,1)}$ $\dfrac{C}{(1,8)}$ $\dfrac{I}{(2,5)}$ $\dfrac{L}{(6,7)}$,

23. $\dfrac{G}{(5,1)}$ $\dfrac{R}{(3,2)}$ $\dfrac{A}{(4,6)}$ $\dfrac{P}{(7,9)}$ $\dfrac{H}{(1,2)}$
24. $\dfrac{P}{(7,9)}$ $\dfrac{A}{(4,6)}$ $\dfrac{P}{(7,9)}$ $\dfrac{E}{(8,8)}$ $\dfrac{R}{(3,2)}$,

25. $\dfrac{I}{(2,5)}$ $\dfrac{A}{(4,6)}$ $\dfrac{M}{(9,3)}$ $\dfrac{D}{(6,8)}$ $\dfrac{O}{(5,4)}$ $\dfrac{N}{(8,1)}$ $\dfrac{E}{(8,8)}$.

## Correcting Common Errors

Some students may interpret number pairs incorrectly and think of (3, 4) as 3 up and 4 across. Correct by having students read a number pair with the words "across" and "up." For example, they would read (3, 4) not as "three, four," but as "3 across, 4 up." Another hint that might help is to say, "It is right to go right first." However, when graphing negative numbers students will have to decide whether to go right or left first.

## Enrichment

Have students graph the arrangement of desks in your room. They can make a map, numbering desks along each coordinate to match the rows. Tell them to write the number pairs that describe each seated student, as they appear on the grid.

## Practice

Have students complete the page. Remind them once more that the first number is read along the bottom, the second up the side.

## Mixed Practice

1. 974 + 383 (1,357)
2. 4,000 − 2,506 (1,494)
3. $65.92 + 17.58 ($83.50)
4. 482 × 8 (3,856)
5. 93 × 3 (279)
6. 6,372 + 2,459 (8,831)
7. 17 + 29 + 36 + 18 (100)
8. 7 × 103 (721)
9. 943 − 621 (322)
10. $6.72 − 3.84 ($2.88)

## Extra Credit   *Measurement*

Ask students to bring in three tin cans of the same size. Have them cover the outside of one can with black construction paper. Label the cans A, B, C. Pour equal amounts of water into the black can and one of the others. Leave the third can empty. Make sure the cans remain in the sun all day. Tell students to make a chart with three columns and label them A, B and C. Have the students measure the water temperature in each can with a Fahrenheit thermometer and record the results on the chart. After several hours have the students take measurements in all three cans again. Record the findings on the chart. Ask the students to discuss the results. Which temperature was the highest at the start? Which temperature was the highest at the end of the experiment? Where do they think the heat came from? Which of the cans did the best job of collecting heat? Why?

# Problem Solving, Acting It Out

## pages 197-198

### Objective

To solve problems by acting out the solution

### Materials

play money: half-dollars, quarters, dimes, nickels, pennies
containers: 2 cups, 1 pint, 2 quarts
single counters and 15-inch strings
demonstration clock
step ladder

### Mental Math

Ask students to tell which is more:

1. 2 quarters or 10 dimes (10 dimes)
2. 1 dime or 9 pennies (1 dime)
3. 3 dimes or 1 quarter (3 dimes)
4. 1 half-dollar or 8 nickels (1 half-dollar)
5. 20 nickels or 10 dimes (same)
6. 8 dimes or 3 quarters (8 dimes)
7. 35 pennies or 6 nickels (35 pennies)

## Acting It Out

Name 5 different ways to make change for 50¢.

★ SEE

We have 50¢. We are looking for 5 different ways to make change for this amount.

★ PLAN

We can exchange 2 quarters for the 50¢ piece. We can continue to exchange coins until we have found 5 different ways to equal 50¢.

★ DO

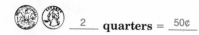

___2___ **quarters** = _50¢_

___1___ **quarter,** ___2___ **dimes,** ___1___ **nickel** = _50¢_

___4___ **dimes,** ___2___ **nickels** = _50¢_

___5___ **dimes** = _50¢_

___3___ **dimes,** ___4___ **nickels** = _50¢_

★ CHECK

| 25¢ | 25¢ | 10¢ | 10¢ | 10¢ |
|-----|-----|-----|-----|-----|
| + 25¢ | 10¢ | 10¢ | 10¢ | 10¢ |
| 50¢ | 10¢ | 10¢ | 10¢ | 10¢ |
| | + 5¢ | 10¢ | 10¢ | 5¢ |
| | 50¢ | 5¢ | 10¢ | 5¢ |
| | | + 5¢ | + 10¢ | 5¢ |
| | | 50¢ | 50¢ | + 5¢ |
| | | | | 50¢ |

(one hundred ninety-seven) **197**

## Teaching the Lesson

Have a student read the problem aloud. Remind the class of the SEE-PLAN-DO-CHECK method of solving problems and have a student read the SEE section. Explain that they want to find five different combinations of coins that will equal 50¢. Have another student read the PLAN section. Point out that the model suggests that they start with the largest coins first; two quarters. Work through the DO and CHECK steps of the problem, illustrating solutions on the board, as students fill in the necessary information. Explain that actually working this problem out with coins may be the fastest way of solving it. Point out that other problems may be best worked by acting them out. Ask the class to imagine that it is 3:15. Ask what time it will be in half-an-hour. (3:45) Now ask how many figured the time by imagining a clock face. Explain that making the clock move in their minds was the simplest way of solving the problem.

**197**

Act out the problems to help you solve them.

1. There are 3 rows of desks with 5 desks in each row. How many desks are there in all?
15 desks

2. How many different ways can you make change for a dollar? Don't use any coin smaller than a nickel. Don't use any coin more than 4 times in any group.
11 ways

3. How many cups are there all together in 2 quarts, 1 pint and 1 cup?
11 cups

4. Carlos put 65 record albums into boxes. Each box held 9 albums. How many albums were left over?
2 albums

5. What 6 coins equal $1.30?
1-50¢ 2-25¢ 3-10¢ or 5-25¢ 1-5¢

6. What 6 coins equal $1.51?
1-50¢ 4-25¢ 1-1¢

7. Four people meet on the street. Each one shakes the hand of the other. How many handshakes are there in all?
6 handshakes

8. It takes 2 hours and 30 minutes to bake a roast. If the meat was started at 3:45, what time will it be done?
6:15

9. There are quarters, dimes, nickels, and pennies in a bag. Tony reaches in and takes out 4 coins. Two of them are pennies, and the other 2 coins are different from each other. What is the greatest amount that Tony could have?
37¢

10. There are quarters, dimes, nickels, and pennies in a bag. Terry reaches in and takes out 4 coins. Two of them are alike, and the other 2 coins are different from each other. What is the least amount that Terry could have?
17¢

11. Kenny has a can without a top or a bottom lid. He makes a straight cut down the side from the top edge to the bottom edge. Then he unfolds the can and lays it flat. What shape does he have now?
A rectangle

12. Karen uses square-shaped tiles to make a model of a rectangle. She used 36 tiles to make the model. If the model is 9 tiles long, then how many tiles wide is it? Prove that your answer is correct.
4 tiles wide

**198** (one hundred ninety-eight)

## Extra Credit   *Numeration*

Make or provide a 10-bead abacus for each pair of students. A simple abacus could be made using cardboard, heavy string, tape, and wooden beads or macaroni rings. Give each student two index cards. Have them write any number, up to four digits on one card, and the words for that number on the other. Collect the cards, shuffle, and give some to each pair of students. Each student takes a card, shows the number on his abacus and reads it aloud. He scores 1 point for a two-digit numeral, 2 points for a three-digit numeral, etc., for each number he shows correctly. Have pairs exchange cards several times. The player with the most points at the end, is the winner.

# Solution Notes

1. Suggest that students make a small model of such an arrangement.

2. Have students make as many arrangements as they can. Have them make change in turn and record the coins used on the board.

3. Have students demonstrate the problem, filling each container cup by cup. Have one student tally the number of cups on the board.

4. Give each group of students 65 counters and 9 or 10 boxes. Have them distribute the counters until they can no longer fill a box.

5. Have students arrange play money in different ways until they have made $1.30.

6. Have students act this problem out as they did Problem 5.

7. Have students break into groups of four and begin to shake hands. See if the answers of all the groups agree.

8. Have one student use the demonstration clock to move forward two and a half hours from the starting time.

## Higher-Order Thinking Skills

9. Analysis: Students should recognize that they should choose the coin in the bag with the greatest value, the quarter. Since the 2 coins must be different, the coin with the next greatest value should be a dime. Encourage students to act out the situation.

10. Analysis: Students should recognize that they should start with the coins that have the least value and follow the description in the problem: 2 pennies, 1 nickel, and 1 dime.

11. Synthesis: Students can act it out. If no cylinder is available, such as a paper towel core, suggest that they make one with tape and a piece of paper. At this point, some will recognize that they start with a rectangle to get a cylinder.

12. Evaluation: Proofs may vary, but most students will use markers to show the 9 by 4 array.

# Chapter Test

page 199

| Item | Objective |
|------|-----------|
| 1-3 | Find the area of a plane figure in square units (See pages 181-182) |
| 4-6 | Identify solid figures (See pages 183-184) |
| 7-9 | Find the volume of space figures in cubic units (See pages 185-186) |
| 10 | Tell when two plane figures are congruent (See pages 189-190) |
| 11 | Make a bar graph (See pages 191-192) |
| 12 | Identify a number pair for a point on a graph (See pages 195-196) |

**199**

Write the number of square units in each figure.

1.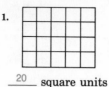

_20_ square units

2.

_8_ square units

3.

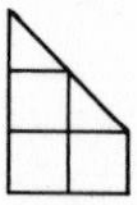

_4_ square units

Write the name of each solid figure.

4.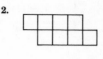

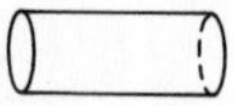

cylinder

5.

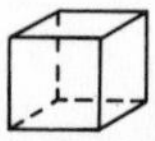

cube

6.

sphere

Write the number of cubic units in each figure.

7.

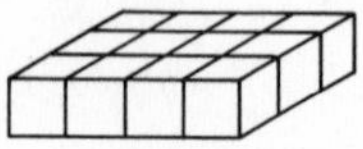

_12_ cubic units

8.

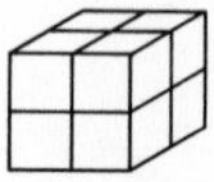

_8_ cubic units

9.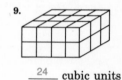

_24_ cubic units

10. Circle the letters of the congruent figures.

A    (B)    (C)    D

11. Make a bar graph to show the number of haircuts each child has had.

| Haircuts | |
|------|------|
| Mary | ⅢⅡ Ⅱ |
| Art | ⅢⅡ Ⅲ |
| Pat | ⅢⅡ |

**Haircuts**

| | | | | | | | | | |
|---|---|---|---|---|---|---|---|---|---|
| Mary | | | | | | | | | |
| Art | | | | | | | | | |
| Pat | | | | | | | | | |

0 1 2 3 4 5 6 7 8 9

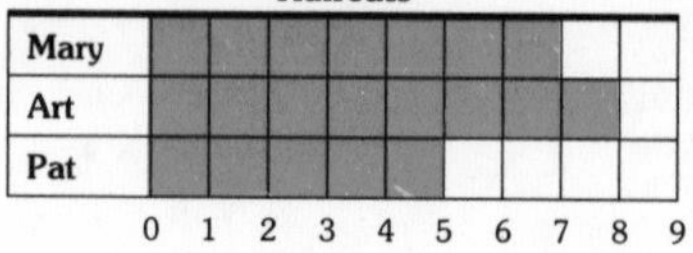

12. Write the number pair for A. _(4, 3)_

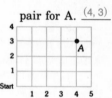

(one hundred ninety-nine) **199**

Circle the letter of the correct answer.

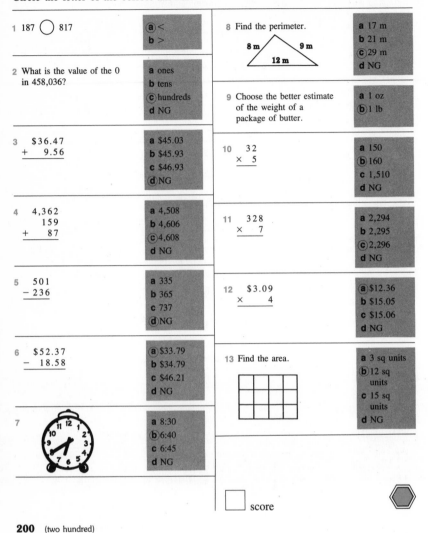

1  187 ◯ 817
    (a) <
    b >

2  What is the value of the 0 in 458,036?
    a ones
    b tens
    (c) hundreds
    d NG

3  $36.47
    +   9.56
    a $45.03
    b $45.93
    c $46.93
    (d) NG

4  4,362
    159
    +   87
    a 4,508
    b 4,606
    (c) 4,608
    d NG

5  501
    − 236
    a 335
    b 365
    c 737
    (d) NG

6  $52.37
    − 18.58
    (a) $33.79
    b $34.79
    c $46.21
    d NG

7
    a 8:30
    (b) 6:40
    c 6:45
    d NG

8  Find the perimeter.
    8 m     9 m
      12 m
    a 17 m
    b 21 m
    (c) 29 m
    d NG

9  Choose the better estimate of the weight of a package of butter.
    a 1 oz
    (b) 1 lb

10  32
    × 5
    a 150
    (b) 160
    c 1,510
    d NG

11  328
    × 7
    a 2,294
    b 2,295
    (c) 2,296
    d NG

12  $3.09
    × 4
    (a) $12.36
    b $15.05
    c $15.06
    d NG

13  Find the area.
    a 3 sq units
    (b) 12 sq units
    c 15 sq units
    d NG

◻ score

**200**   (two hundred)

---

# Cumulative Review
**page 200**

| Item | Objective |
| --- | --- |
| 1 | Compare numbers less than 1,000 (See pages 27-28) |
| 2 | Identify the value of a digit in a number less than 1,000,000 (See pages 35-36) |
| 3 | Add dollars, cents with regrouping (See pages 51-52) |
| 4 | Add three or four numbers (See pages 49-50) |
| 5 | Subtract two 3-digit numbers with two regroupings (See pages 67-68) |
| 6 | Subtract dollars, cents with regrouping (See pages 75-76) |
| 7 | Read the time to the minute (See pages 87-88) |
| 8 | Add to find perimeter (See pages 95-96) |
| 9 | Choose appropriate metric unit of weight (See pages 111-112) |
| 10 | Multiply 2-digit number by 1-digit number with regrouping (See pages 163-164) |
| 11 | Multiply 3-digit number by 1-digit number with two regroupings (See pages 165-166) |
| 12 | Multiply dollars and cents by 1-digit number with regrouping (See pages 167-168) |
| 13 | Find area of plane figure in square units (See pages 181-182) |

---

## Alternate Cumulative Review

**Circle the letter of the correct answer.**

1  765 ◯ 567
    (a) >
    b <
    c =

2  What is the value of the 6 in 736,821?
    a hundreds
    (b) thousands
    c ten thousands
    d NG

3  $47.39
    +   8.35
    a $55.64
    b $56.74
    (c) $55.74
    d NG

4  6,722
    243
    +   96
    (a) 7,061
    b 6,951
    c 7,051
    d NG

5  907
    − 429
    a 522
    (b) 478
    c 586
    d NG

6  $71.64
    − 57.89
    a $26.25
    b $24.85
    c $23.75
    (d) NG

7  What time is it? (Show a clock.)
    (a) 7:49
    b 10:38
    c 8:49
    d NG

8  Find the perimeter of a rectangle 4 cm by 6 cm.
    a 10 cm
    b 24 cm
    (c) 20 cm
    d NG

9  What unit would you use to measure the mass of a pencil?
    a meters
    b liters
    (c) grams
    d NG

10  63
    × 4
    (a) 252
    b 2,412
    c 242
    d NG

11  427
    × 6
    (a) 2,562
    b 2,522
    c 24,162
    d NG

12  $6.08
    × 3
    a $180.24
    b $18.54
    (c) $18.24
    d NG

13  Find the area of a rectangle 6 in. by 8 in.
    a 28 sq in.
    b 14 sq in.
    (c) 48 sq in.
    d NG

# Understanding Division

pages 201-202

## Objective

To divide by making sets

## Materials

paper cups
counters

## Mental Math

Dictate these problems to review zeros and ones:

1. $3 + 0 = (3)$
2. $0 \times 5 = (0)$
3. $6 - 1 = (5)$
4. $8 \times 1 = (8)$
5. $25 \times 0 = (0)$
6. $18 \times 1 = (18)$
7. $10 + 1 = (11)$

## Skill Review

Draw a $4 \times 3$ array of dots on the board. Explain that the multiplication problem illustrated is $4 \times 3$ or $3 \times 4$. Have students make arrays, marked off in sets, for these problems:

1. $5 \times 4$     4. $9 \times 2$
2. $3 \times 6$     5. $7 \times 3$
3. $4 \times 1$     6. $21 \times 0$

---

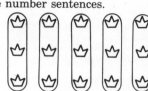

### Understanding Division

Mary Lou's mother is giving her a surprise party. She has enough prizes to give each person an equal number. How many prizes will each person receive?

We want to know how many prizes each person will receive.
There are ___4___ people at the party.

Mary Lou's mother has ___12___ prizes to give away. To find the number of prizes for each person,

we divide ___12___ into ___4___ equal groups.

We write: **$12 \div 4 =$ ___3___**.
We say: **twelve divided by 4 equals 3.**

Each person will receive ___3___ prizes.

| We can use division to find |
| the number in each group, |
| or the number of groups. |

$$12 \div 4 \qquad = 3$$
$$\uparrow \qquad \uparrow \qquad \uparrow$$
**dividend    divisor    quotient**
$$\downarrow \qquad \downarrow \qquad \downarrow$$
$$12 \div 3 \qquad = 4$$

### Getting Started

Answer the questions and complete the number sentences.

1. 15 in all
   5 groups
   How many in each group? ___3___

   $15 \div 5 =$ ___3___

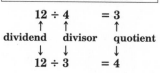

(two hundred one) **201**

---

## Teaching the Lesson

**Introducing the Problem**   Read the problem aloud and have students identify the question being asked. Have a student read and complete the information sentences. (4 people, 12 prizes) Read the plan sentences having students supply the numbers. (We divide 12 into 4 groups.) Direct their attention to the array below and have them circle four groups of three. Write the problem on the board and ask them to complete it in their books. ($12 \div 4 = 3$) Read the next sentence aloud. Then have a student read the solution sentence while the others complete it in their texts. (3 prizes) Read the final section aloud. Explain that division is not commutative like multiplication. Introduce the terms dividend, divisor, and quotient and show how the order of the numbers matters in division: $12 \div 3 = 4$, but $12 \div 3 = 4$.

**Developing the Skill**   Give each student 6 paper cups and 18 counters. Tell them to evenly divide the 18 counters among 3 paper cups. When they are finished, ask a student to tell how many counters are in each cup. (6) Write on the board: **$18 \div 3 = 6$.** Now have them divide 18 counters among 6 cups. Write **$18 \div 6 = 3$** on the board.

**201**

## Practice

Answer the questions and complete the number sentences.

1. 6 in all
   2 in each group
   How many groups? ___3___

   $6 \div 2 = $ ___3___

2. 15 in all
   5 groups
   How many in each group? ___3___

   $15 \div 5 = $ ___3___

3. 16 in all
   8 in each group
   How many groups? ___2___

   $16 \div 8 = $ ___2___

4. 9 in all
   3 in each group
   How many groups? ___3___

   $9 \div 3 = $ ___3___

5. 24 in all
   6 in each group
   How many groups? ___4___

   $24 \div 6 = $ ___4___

6. 24 in all
   4 in each group
   How many groups? ___6___

   $24 \div 4 = $ ___6___

Answer the questions and complete the number sentences.

7. How many blue ribbons? ___24___

8. How many groups of 4? ___6___

9. $24 \div 4 = $ ___6___

10. How many groups of 6? ___4___

11. $24 \div 6 = $ ___4___

12. How many groups of 3? ___8___

13. $24 \div 3 = $ ___8___

**202**  (two hundred two)

---

## Correcting Common Errors

Some students may add or multiply the numbers in a division fact instead of dividing. Have them work with partners with 24 counters. Have them arrange the counters to make 4 groups with the same number of counters in each. Ask, "How many counters?" (24) "How many groups?" (4) "How many in each group?" (6) Write 24 ÷ 4 = 6 on the chalkboard. Follow the same procedure for other division facts.

## Enrichment

Remind students that in multiplication, the two numbers multiplied are factors. The answer is the product. Explain that some products are called prime numbers, because they have as factors only themselves and 1. The first prime number is 2. Its only factors are 2 and 1. The next is 3 because its factors are 3 and 1. Have students find the first 5 prime numbers. (2, 3, 5, 7, 11)

---

## Practice

Have students complete the problems on the page. Explain that they are to circle the groups indicated in each problem and then count the number of groups.

## Mixed Practice

1. $7.52 × 5 ($37.60)
2. $10.00 − 6.38 ($3.62)
3. 427 + 674 (1,101)
4. 23 + 45 + 19 + 31 (118)
5. 5,020 − 1,738 (3,282)
6. 7 × 47 (329)
7. 2,793 + 5,476 (8,269)
8. 50 × 8 (400)
9. 764 − 580 (184)
10. 253 × 9 (2,277)

## Extra Credit   *Applications*

Illustrate the face of a gas pump on the board. Ask a volunteer to explain how gasoline in sold. (by the gallon) Point out that most states put a tax on gas and that, as a result, the price usually ends with nine tenths. Have a student come to the board and point to the different parts of the pump as you explain them: price per gallon, total number of gallons pumped, and total amount owed. If you have a set of calculators, show students how to multiply the price per gallon times the number of gallons to calculate the total amount due. Ask students to record these figures when their car is being filled at the gas station the next time. Help students use the calculator to multiply and show that the amount paid was correct.

# Dividing by 2

**pages 203-204**

## Objective

To divide with 2 as the divisor

## Materials

paper cups
counters

## Mental Math

Dictate the following word problems:

1. Ralph has a candy bar with 9 squares that he wants to share with 2 friends. How many squares will each of the 3 get? (3)
2. Mary Ellen and her two friends each have 25¢. They want to put their money together to buy a chocolate bar costing 65¢. Will they have enough? (yes, 75¢)
3. A pack of gum costs 35¢. What will two packs cost? (70¢)

## Skill Review

Dictate the following problems that have factors of 2:

1. 8 × 2 = (16)
2. 2 × 7 = (14)
3. 12 × 2 = (24)
4. 10 × 2 = (20)
5. 2 × 10 = (20)
6. 1 × 2 = (2)
7. 2 × 25 = (50)
8. 2 × 0 = (0)

---

## Dividing by 2

After recess, Miss Crandle asked the students with wet gloves to hang them on hooks to dry. How many children had wet gloves?

We want to know how many children had wet gloves.

There are __12__ gloves hanging on hooks.

Each child wore a pair, or __2__ gloves.

To find the number of children, we divide

__12__ by __2__ .

12 ÷ 2 = __6__

There were __6__ children with wet gloves.

### Getting Started

Answer the questions and complete the number sentences.

1. How many in all? __8__

   How many in each group? __4__

   How many groups? __2__

   8 ÷ 4 = __2__

2. How many in all? __10__

   How many groups? __2__

   How many in each group? __5__

   10 ÷ 2 = __5__

Complete the number sentences.

3. 6 ÷ 2 = __3__     4. 12 ÷ 2 = __6__     5. 4 ÷ 2 = __2__     6. 14 ÷ 2 = __7__

(two hundred three) **203**

---

## Teaching the Lesson

**Introducing the Problem**   Read the problem aloud while students look at the illustration. Have students identify the question being asked. Tell students to read the information sentences, and supply the data from the picture. (12 gloves hanging, Each child wore 2.) Read the plan sentences aloud and ask for the numbers required. (We divide 12 by 2.) Ask students to circle pairs of gloves in the picture. Now write the division problem on the board, **12 ÷ 2 = ,** and ask a student to provide the answer. (6) Tell students to complete the solution sentence. (6 children)

**Developing the Skill**   Begin by having students count by twos from 2 through 20. Now give each student several cups and 20 counters. Draw this chart on the board:

| total counters | number of cups | counters per cup |
| --- | --- | --- |
| 18 | 2 | |
| 8 | 4 | |
| 10 | 5 | |
| 20 | 2 | |

Add as many more lines as you like. Have students use their cups and counters to figure out the number of counters per cup. Ask a student to come to the board and complete the chart as the class does each problem. After each line is complete, write the division problem on the board. To the right of the first line, for example, write **18 ÷ 2 = 9.**

**203**

## Practice

Answer the questions and complete the number sentences.

1.

How many in all? ___18___

How many groups? ___2___

How many in each group? ___9___

$18 \div 2 =$ ___9___

2.

How many in all? ___14___

How many in each group? ___7___

How many groups? ___2___

$14 \div 7 =$ ___2___

3.

How many in all? ___6___

How many groups? ___3___

How many in each group? ___2___

$6 \div 3 =$ ___2___

4.

How many in all? ___16___

How many groups? ___2___

How many in each group? ___8___

$16 \div 2 =$ ___8___

Complete the number sentences.

5. $6 \div 2 =$ ___3___   6. $12 \div 2 =$ ___6___   7. $10 \div 2 =$ ___5___   8. $14 \div 2 =$ ___7___

9. $18 \div 2 =$ ___9___   10. $4 \div 2 =$ ___2___   11. $8 \div 2 =$ ___4___   12. $16 \div 2 =$ ___8___

### EXCURSION

Find two figures in the second column that, when put together, will match one of the numbered figures in the first column. Write their letters on the blanks.

1. ○   ___b___   ___f___

2. ▢   ___c___   ___g___

3. ▭   ___a___   ___e___

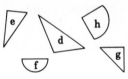

---

---

## Practice

Have students do the problems on the page. Remind them of the way in which multiplication and division are related: if $2 \times 7 = 14$, then $14 \div 2 = 7$, for example. This may help them figure out division facts they are unsure of.

## Excursion

Have students read the directions. Tell students they may want to draw a line of symmetry or a diagonal on the figure to help them see each figure's parts. Note: the use of manipulative geometric shapes and their parts can be helpful for students to see halves of figures. Have students complete the activity.

## Extra Credit   *Careers*

Have students make a list of some common math skills such as counting, measuring, adding, subtracting, telling time, reading graphs and charts and others. Tell students to make a questionnaire listing these skills, to be filled out by parents, school, and community workers. Have them ask these people to tell which of the skills are used regularly in their jobs. Ask students to tabulate questionnaires and make a bar graph showing how many different jobs require each skill. Discuss the importance of developing our individual math skills for use now and in the future.

# Dividing by 3

**pages 205-206**

## Objective

To divide with 3 as the divisor

## Materials

paper cups
counters

## Mental Math

Have students count together:

1. from 4 to 12 by twos (4, 6, 8, 10, 12)
2. from 6 to 12 by threes (6, 9, 12)
3. from 18 to 10 by twos (18, 16, 14, 12, 10)
4. from 18 to 9 by threes (18, 15, 12, 9)

## Skill Review

Have students make a division table for 2:

| ÷ | 2 |
|---|---|
| 4 | 2 |
| 6 | 3 and so on. |

Demonstrate the format on the board. Finish filling in the left-hand column with **8, 10, 12, 14, 16** and **18**. Explain that the number in the left-hand column is to be divided by 2 and the answer written in the right-hand column. Have students complete the chart.

---

## Dividing by 3

Alan is cleaning out his closet. He finds 15 loose tennis balls. How many cans will he need to pack them all?

We want to know the number of cans needed to hold all the tennis balls.

Alan finds __15__ balls.

A can holds __3__ balls.

To find the number of cans, we divide

__15__ by __3__.

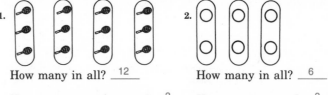

$$15 \div 3 = \underline{5}$$

Alan will need __5__ cans.

### Getting Started

Answer the questions and complete the number sentences.

1. How many in all? __12__

   How many in each group? __3__

   How many groups? __4__

   $12 \div 3 = \underline{4}$

2. How many in all? __6__

   How many groups? __3__

   How many in each group? __2__

   $6 \div 3 = \underline{2}$

Complete the number sentences.

3. $18 \div 3 = \underline{6}$  4. $15 \div 3 = \underline{5}$  5. $21 \div 3 = \underline{7}$  6. $27 \div 3 = \underline{9}$

(two hundred five) **205**

---

## Teaching the Lesson

**Introducing the Problem**  Have a student read the problem aloud and identify the question being asked. Read the information sentences aloud and ask students to supply the numbers needed. (finds 15 balls, can holds 3) Draw 15 circles on the board and read the plan sentence to the class, asking students to provide answers. (We divide 15 by 3.) Have a student come to the board and circle groups of three, each representing the contents of one of the cans. Ask students to circle groups of three in the picture. Write the problem on the board, **15 ÷ 3 = ,** and have a student write the quotient. (5) Direct the class to complete the problem and the solution sentence in their texts. (5, 5)

**Developing the Skill**  Ask students to lay out 6 counters and three cups. Ask how many counters would go in each cup. (2) Have them put out 9 counters and three cups. Ask how many counters are in each. (3) Let them continue to 18 counters. Now have students look at the division chart for twos they just made. Ask them to draw a division chart for threes. Put the chart on the board in the same format:

| ÷ | 3 |
|---|---|
| 6 | |
| 9 | |

Have them complete the first four lines based on their work with counters and rest of the chart with or without relying on the counters.

**205**

Answer the questions and complete the number sentences.

1.

How many in all? __24__

How many groups? __3__

How many in each group? __8__

$24 \div 3 =$ __8__

2.

How many in all? __21__

How many in each group? __7__

How many groups? __3__

$21 \div 7 =$ __3__

Complete the number sentences.

3. $15 \div 3 =$ __5__     4. $16 \div 2 =$ __8__     5. $12 \div 3 =$ __4__     6. $8 \div 2 =$ __4__

7. $10 \div 2 =$ __5__     8. $18 \div 3 =$ __6__     9. $6 \div 3 =$ __2__     10. $14 \div 2 =$ __7__

11. $27 \div 3 =$ __9__     12. $9 \div 3 =$ __3__     13. $18 \div 2 =$ __9__     14. $4 \div 2 =$ __2__

15. $8 \div 2 =$ __4__     16. $24 \div 3 =$ __8__     17. $16 \div 2 =$ __8__     18. $21 \div 3 =$ __7__

19. $10 \div 2 =$ __5__     20. $12 \div 3 =$ __4__     21. $6 \div 2 =$ __3__     22. $15 \div 3 =$ __5__

23. $14 \div 2 =$ __7__     24. $6 \div 3 =$ __2__     25. $24 \div 3 =$ __8__     26. $18 \div 2 =$ __9__

**Apply**

Solve these problems.

27. Mickey wanted to invite his 24 classmates to his home for dinner. His father said they could only come 3 at a time. How many dinners will it take to invite the whole class?
8 dinners

28. The teacher divided 18 old magazines among 3 of her students for work on a project. How many magazines did each student have to work with?
6 magazines

**206**   (two hundred six)

## Correcting Common Errors

Some students may have difficulty understanding division by 3. Have them work with partners and counters. Have them arrange 21 counters so that there are 3 groups with the same number of counters in each group. Ask, "How many counters?" (21) "How many groups?" (3) "How many in each group?" (7) Write $21 \div 3 = 7$ on the chalkboard. Follow the same procedure for other division facts where the divisors are three.

## Enrichment

Another way to think about prime numbers is to draw an array for each number. Any number that makes an even rectangular array with the same number in each row is *not* a prime number. If no even array can be found, the number *is* prime. Put the following examples on the board:

```
                            00000
00000      000000           00000
00000      00000            00000
  10         11               15
```

Have students illustrate 10 through 20 with arrays and circle the prime numbers. (11, 13, 17, 19)

## Practice

Have students complete the problems on the page. Remind them of the relationship between the multiplication tables they have already learned and these division problems.

## Mixed Practice

1. $817 - 432$ (385)
2. $2{,}051 + 4{,}792$ (6,843)
3. $\$58.19 - 29.19$ ($29.00)
4. $43 \times 8$ (344)
5. $165 + 294 + 217$ (676)
6. $\$2.83 \times 4$ ($11.32)
7. $3{,}020 - 1{,}718$ (1,302)
8. $673 + 427$ (1,100)
9. $200 \times 8$ (1,600)
10. $507 - 88$ (419)

## Extra Credit   *Geometry*

Tell students to construct the following grid on graph paper:

```
1 •
2 •
3 •
4 •
5 •
6 •
7 •
8 •
  • • • • • • • • •
  0 1 2 3 4 5 6 7 8
```

Using a straightedge, have them connect 1 to 1, 2 to 2, and so on. Ask if they made any curved lines. (no) Ask why the combination of straight lines looks curved. (The short, straight segments arranged in successive angles appear to form a curved line.)

# Dividing by 4

pages 207-208

## Objective

To divide with 4 as the divisor

## Materials

*division flash cards for twos and threes
counters

## Mental Math

Have students find the value for n in each problem:

1. $n \times 5 = 45$    (9)
2. $n \div 6 = 2$    (12)
3. $7 \times 6 = n$    (42)
4. $16 \div n = 8$    (2)
5. $8 \times n = 40$    (5)
6. $8 \div n = 4$    (2)
7. $n \times n = 16$    (4)

## Skill Review

Have students count aloud by twos from 2 through 20 and by threes from 3 through 30. Use division flash cards for the tables of 2 and 3 to quiz the class on quick recognition of division facts. Hold aside any cards they seem to have trouble with and go over those facts again at the end.

---

## Dividing by 4

Therese is using baskets of flowers to decorate the tables for a banquet. How many flowers will she put into each basket?

We want to know the number of flowers that Therese will put into each basket.

Therese has __4__ baskets to make up.

She has __24__ flowers to fill the baskets.

To find the number of flowers, we divide

__24__ by __4__.

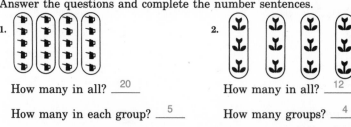

$24 \div 4 = $ __6__

Therese will put __6__ flowers into each basket.

### Getting Started

Answer the questions and complete the number sentences.

1. How many in all? __20__

How many in each group? __5__

How many groups? __4__

$20 \div 5 = $ __4__

2. How many in all? __12__

How many groups? __4__

How many in each group? __3__

$12 \div 4 = $ __3__

Complete the number sentences.

3. $24 \div 4 = $ __6__    4. $16 \div 4 = $ __4__    5. $8 \div 4 = $ __2__    6. $32 \div 4 = $ __8__

(two hundred seven) **207**

---

## Teaching the Lesson

**Introducing the Problem** Read the problem aloud and ask students to look at the picture for the information required to solve the problem. Have students complete the information sentences. (4 baskets, 24 flowers) Read the plan aloud, asking a student to supply the numbers. (We divide 24 by 4.) Write the problem on the board, **24 ÷ 4 = ,** and have a volunteer work it. (6) Ask students to complete the plan sentence, circle each flower basket, and complete the division in their texts. (6) Have a student read the solution sentence and supply the answer, while the others complete the sentence in their books. (6 flowers in each basket)

**Developing the Skill** Have students make 2 groups of 4 counters on their desks. Ask how many counters there were in all. (8) Write **8 ÷ 4 = 2** on the board. Now have them make 3 groups of 4 counters and write **12 ÷ 4 = 3** on the board. Continue, having students make 4 and 5 groups of 4 counters, writing **16 ÷ 4 = 4** and **20 ÷ 4 = 5** on the board. Ask students to make a division table for fours in the same way they made tables for twos and threes:

| ÷ | 4 |
|---|---|
| 8 | 2 |
| 12 | 3 |
| 16 | 4 |
| 20 | 5 and so on through 40 ÷ 4 = 10. |

**207**

## Practice

Answer the questions and complete the number sentences.

1.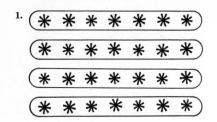

How many in all? __28__

How many groups? __4__

How many in each group? __7__

$28 \div 4 =$ __7__

2.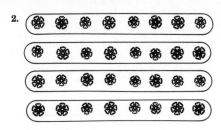

How many in all? __32__

How many in each group? __8__

How many groups? __4__

$32 \div 8 =$ __4__

Complete the number sentences.

3. $20 \div 4 =$ __5__    4. $21 \div 3 =$ __7__    5. $36 \div 4 =$ __9__    6. $12 \div 4 =$ __3__

7. $24 \div 3 =$ __8__    8. $24 \div 4 =$ __6__    9. $16 \div 2 =$ __8__    10. $28 \div 4 =$ __7__

11. $9 \div 3 =$ __3__    12. $20 \div 4 =$ __5__    13. $16 \div 4 =$ __4__    14. $18 \div 3 =$ __6__

15. $32 \div 4 =$ __8__    16. $10 \div 2 =$ __5__    17. $27 \div 3 =$ __9__    18. $28 \div 4 =$ __7__

19. $18 \div 2 =$ __9__    20. $12 \div 4 =$ __3__    21. $6 \div 3 =$ __2__    22. $8 \div 4 =$ __2__

23. $15 \div 3 =$ __5__    24. $16 \div 4 =$ __4__    25. $32 \div 4 =$ __8__    26. $14 \div 2 =$ __7__

### Apply

Solve these problems.

27. Chan brought 36 fortune cookies to school. He shared them among his 4 friends. How many cookies did each friend receive?

9 cookies

28. Sal has 16 pages to study for a test on Friday. He has 4 days to prepare for the test. How many pages should he study each day?

4 pages

**208**   (two hundred eight)

---

**208**

# Dividing by 5

## pages 209-210

### Objective

To divide with 5 as the divisor

### Materials

nickels
counters
*division flash cards, divisors from 2
    through 5

### Mental Math

Dictate these problems:

1. 15¢ + 5¢ + 10¢ = (30¢)
2. 25¢ + 25¢ − 5¢ = (45¢)
3. 5¢ + 5¢ + 5¢ + 75¢ = (90¢)
4. $1.00 − 25¢ − 5¢ = (70¢)
5. $1.00 − 20¢ − 15¢ − 5¢ = (60¢)

### Skill Review

Have students make three number
lines: one from 0 through 18 marked
by twos, one from 0 through 27
marked by threes, and one from 0
through 36 marked by fours. They
should then write the corresponding
multiplication fact above each number.
Put this sample on the board.

$$1 \times 2 \quad 2 \times 2 \quad 3 \times 2 \quad 4 \times 2 \quad 5 \times 2$$
$$0 \quad 2 \quad 4 \quad 6 \quad 8 \quad 10 \ldots$$

Explain that as $1 \times 2 = 2$ and
$2 \times 2 = 4$, likewise $2 \div 1 = 2$ and
$4 \div 2 = 2$, and so on.

---

## Dividing by 5

The school district chess league
has 20 players in all. How many
chess players are on each team?

We want to know the number of players on
each team.

There are ___20___ chess players.

The players are divided into ___5___ teams.

To find the number of players, we divide

___20___ by ___5___.

| Blue Hills | Lincoln | Washington | Green | Oak |
| IIII | IIII | IIII | IIII | IIII |

$20 \div 5 =$ ___4___

There are ___4___ players on each team.

### Getting Started

Answer the questions and complete the number sentences.

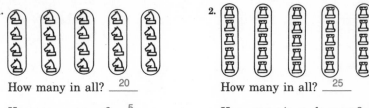

1.

How many in all? ___20___

How many groups? ___5___

How many in each group? ___4___

$20 \div 5 =$ ___4___

2.

How many in all? ___25___

How many in each group? ___5___

How many groups? ___5___

$25 \div 5 =$ ___5___

Complete the number sentences.

3. $15 \div 5 =$ ___3___   4. $10 \div 5 =$ ___2___   5. $30 \div 5 =$ ___6___   6. $25 \div 5 =$ ___5___

(two hundred nine) **209**

---

## Teaching the Lesson

**Introducing the Problem**  Have a student read the
problem aloud and identify the question being asked. Ask
how many teams are shown in the picture. (5) Have a student complete the information sentences. (20 chess players,
divided into 5 teams) Read the plan sentences aloud, having
a student supply the numbers required. (We divide 20 by
5.) Ask students to circle each team and its players. Write
the problem on the board, **20 ÷ 5 =** , and have a student
solve it. (4) Ask students to read the solution sentence and
complete the answer. (4 players on each team)

**Developing the Skill**  Ask students to count aloud with
you from 5 through 45. Ask them to count by nickels from
5¢ through 45¢. Pass out counters and have them make
two groups of 5 on their desk. Ask how many counters
there are altogether. (10) On the board write **10 ÷ 5 = 2**.
Put the partial division table on the board and fill in the first
fact:

| ÷ | 5 |
|---|---|
| 10 | 2 |
| 15 | |
| 20 | and so on. |

Ask students to complete the chart, using the counters and
increasing the number of groups of five by one each time.

**Practice**

Answer the questions and complete the number sentences.

1.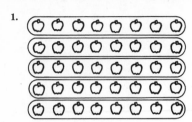

How many in all? __40__

How many groups? __5__

How many in each group? __8__

40 ÷ 5 = __8__

2. 

How many in all? __45__

How many in each group? __9__

How many groups? __5__

45 ÷ 9 = __5__

Complete the number sentences.

3. 40 ÷ 5 = __8__     4. 20 ÷ 4 = __5__     5. 20 ÷ 5 = __4__     6. 24 ÷ 3 = __8__

7. 9 ÷ 3 = __3__     8. 45 ÷ 5 = __9__     9. 10 ÷ 5 = __2__     10. 32 ÷ 4 = __8__

11. 30 ÷ 5 = __6__     12. 10 ÷ 2 = __5__     13. 45 ÷ 5 = __9__     14. 25 ÷ 5 = __5__

15. 35 ÷ 5 = __7__     16. 15 ÷ 5 = __3__     17. 24 ÷ 4 = __6__     18. 21 ÷ 3 = __7__

19. 36 ÷ 4 = __9__     20. 10 ÷ 5 = __2__     21. 16 ÷ 2 = __8__     22. 20 ÷ 5 = __4__

23. 16 ÷ 4 = __4__     24. 27 ÷ 3 = __9__     25. 30 ÷ 5 = __6__     26. 35 ÷ 5 = __7__

**Apply**

Solve these problems.

27. Amanda is paring 45 apples to make tarts. She puts 5 apples into each tart. How many tarts will she make?
9 tarts

28. Morris arranges 40 dried seeds on a page of his science notebook. He puts 5 seeds in each row. How many rows of seeds does he have?
8 rows

**210**   (two hundred ten)

# Writing Division Another Way

**pages 211-212**

## Objective

To write division problems with the bracket

## Materials

30 pennies, 6 nickels
*division flash cards

## Mental Math

Ask students to estimate the following:

1. Does a sack of flour weigh 5 oz or 5 lb? (5 lb)
2. Does a bicycle weigh 5 lb or 25 lb? (25 lb)
3. Is it 300 mi or 3000 mi from New York to Los Angeles? (3000 mi)
4. Does a feather weigh 1 gram or 1 kilogram? (1 gram)

## Skill Review

Use division flash cards with divisors from 2 through 5 to quiz students on quick recognition of division facts. Ask each to answer the division problem shown on the card and then make up a multiplication problem using the same numbers.

---

### Writing Division Another Way

Lonnie needs quarters to play the computer game. How many times can Lonnie play the game with the money he has?

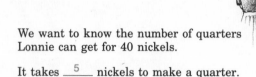

We want to know the number of quarters Lonnie can get for 40 nickels.

It takes __5__ nickels to make a quarter.

Lonnie has __40__ nickels.

To find the number Lonnie will have,

we divide __40__ by __5__.

$$40 \div 5 = \underline{\quad 8 \quad}$$

Lonnie will have __8__ quarters.

This division can be written another way.

$$\overset{\text{divisor}}{\underset{\underset{\text{dividend} \quad \text{quotient}}{\uparrow \qquad \uparrow}}{40 \div 5 = 8}} \quad \text{or} \quad \overset{\text{divisor} \ \text{quotient}}{\underset{\underset{\text{dividend}}{\uparrow}}{\overset{8}{5\overline{)40}}}}$$

### Getting Started

Divide.

1. $2\overline{)8}$    (4)
2. $4\overline{)36}$    (9)
3. $5\overline{)25}$    (5)
4. $3\overline{)18}$    (6)
5. $4\overline{)24}$    (6)

6. $3\overline{)27}$    (9)
7. $2\overline{)16}$    (8)
8. $4\overline{)16}$    (4)
9. $5\overline{)40}$    (8)
10. $4\overline{)32}$    (8)

11. $5\overline{)10}$    (2)
12. $2\overline{)18}$    (9)
13. $4\overline{)12}$    (3)
14. $4\overline{)28}$    (7)
15. $3\overline{)15}$    (5)

(two hundred eleven) **211**

---

## Teaching the Lesson

**Introducing the Problem**  Read the problem aloud and ask the class to look at the picture. Have students identify the problem and then read and complete the information sentences. (5 nickels to a quarter, has 40 nickels) Read the plan sentences and have a student supply the numbers. (We divide 40 by 5.) Write the problem on the board in the form they have seen already, **40 ÷ 5 =** , and ask a student to do the division. (8) Have students read and complete the solution sentence. (will have 8 quarters) Remind them that each part of a division problem has a name. The number being divided is called the dividend, the number it is divided by is the divisor, and the answer is the quotient. Label the parts of the problem on the board. Explain that division problems can be written another way, and illustrate the same problem on the board with the standard bracket:

$$\overset{8}{5\overline{)40}}$$

Label dividend, divisor, and quotient.

**211**

**Developing the Skill**  Show the class 30 pennies and explain you want to exchange them for nickels. Have a student come up and arrange the pennies in groups of five. Ask the student to explain how many nickels you would get for 30 pennies. (6) Now write the division on the board in both forms:

$$30 \div 5 = 6, \qquad \overset{6}{5\overline{)30}}$$

Divide.

1. $2\overline{)18}$ → 9  2. $4\overline{)20}$ → 5  3. $4\overline{)32}$ → 8  4. $2\overline{)6}$ → 3  5. $5\overline{)25}$ → 5

6. $4\overline{)8}$ → 2  7. $2\overline{)12}$ → 6  8. $3\overline{)12}$ → 4  9. $5\overline{)45}$ → 9  10. $4\overline{)12}$ → 3

11. $3\overline{)27}$ → 9  12. $2\overline{)16}$ → 8  13. $5\overline{)20}$ → 4  14. $3\overline{)24}$ → 8  15. $3\overline{)18}$ → 6

16. $5\overline{)40}$ → 8  17. $5\overline{)10}$ → 2  18. $2\overline{)14}$ → 7  19. $4\overline{)16}$ → 4  20. $4\overline{)32}$ → 8

21. $5\overline{)35}$ → 7  22. $4\overline{)36}$ → 9  23. $3\overline{)21}$ → 7  24. $5\overline{)45}$ → 9  25. $5\overline{)15}$ → 3

26. $3\overline{)24}$ → 8  27. $2\overline{)10}$ → 5  28. $4\overline{)24}$ → 6  29. $2\overline{)8}$ → 4  30. $2\overline{)18}$ → 9

31. $3\overline{)21}$ → 7  32. $3\overline{)6}$ → 2  33. $5\overline{)10}$ → 2  34. $3\overline{)15}$ → 5  35. $5\overline{)30}$ → 6

36. $4\overline{)24}$ → 6  37. $5\overline{)35}$ → 7  38. $4\overline{)36}$ → 9  39. $4\overline{)28}$ → 7  40. $5\overline{)40}$ → 8

---

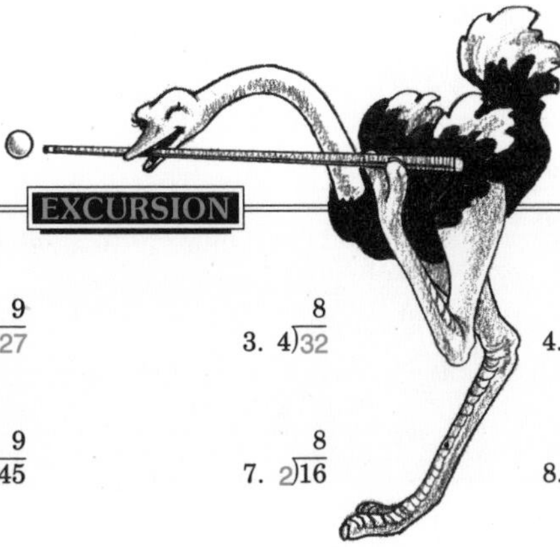

**EXCURSION**

Write the missing numbers.

1. $5\overline{)35}$ → 7  2. $3\overline{)27}$ → 9  3. $4\overline{)32}$ → 8  4. $2\overline{)18}$ → 9

5. $4\overline{)20}$ → 5  6. $5\overline{)45}$ → 9  7. $2\overline{)16}$ → 8  8. $3\overline{)18}$ → 6

## Correcting Common Errors

Some students may confuse the numbers when writing division problems using the division box. Have them work with partners to complete pairs of problems like those shown below.

$$40 \div 5 = \square \qquad 5\overline{)40}^{\square}$$

$$24 \div 3 = \square \qquad 3\overline{)24}^{\square}$$

Encourage students to read both forms of the problem in the same way, namely, "40 divided by 5." Discourage use of the phrase "goes into."

## Enrichment

Have students draw a factor table on graph paper with half inch squares. Ask them to put the factors 1 through 9 along the bottom and the numbers 1 through 15 along the side. Opposite each number have them color in the squares that represent that number's factors.

```
        4 X X   X
        3 X   X   and so on.
numbers ↑ 2 X X
        1 X
     factors → 1 2 3 4 . . .
```

Have each student describe the pattern. (Accept all reasonable answers.)

## Practice

Have students do the problems on the page. Tell them to write each answer over the ones column in the dividend. This habit will be useful when the problems become longer and more complicated.

## Excursion

Write on the board:   $3 \times 8 = \underline{\quad}$

$$3\overline{)\phantom{8}}^{8} \qquad 8\overline{)\phantom{3}}^{3}$$

Tell students to find the missing number in each of these problems. Ask students the product of $3 \times 8$. (24) Remind students that 3 and 8 are factors of 24 so $24 \div 3 = 8$ and $24 \div 8 = 3$. Repeat for more multiplication facts and their products. Remind students that multiplication and division are opposite operations.

Have students write the missing numbers in the problems.

## Extra Credit   *Geometry*

Hold up a piece of paper and point to each corner. Explain that each is called a right angle. Draw a right angle on the board, labeling it with a small square. Point out that this is the way right angles are labeled. Now give each student a piece of paper. Have them fold it in half one way and then the other. Let them cut off the extra paper in an arc. Have them label the right angle. Tell them that this piece of folded paper is a good angle checker. Bring a collection of boxes to class. Tell students to check the corners of the boxes to see that they are all right angles. After students have checked the boxes, let them look around the room for other examples of right angles.

# Multiplying and Dividing

pages 213-214

## Objective

To understand the relationship between multiplication and division

## Materials

3 × 5 unruled index cards

## Mental Math

Dictate the following word problems:

1. Anna purchased 3 rolls of ribbon, each with 25 yards. How many yards does she have altogether? (75 yd)
2. Skip earned $1.00 raking leaves and decided to share it with three friends. How much will each have? ($.25)
3. Ms. Mason bought 45 books for her class. They came boxed in sets of 5. How many sets did she buy? (9)

## Skill Review

Have students provide the missing numbers:

1. ___×5 = 20 (4)
2. 8 × 4 = ___ (32)
3. 5 × ___=25 (5)
4. ___×6 = 30 (5)
5. ___×0 = 0 (could be any number)
6. 7 × 3 = ___ (21)
7. 9 × ___=9 (1)

---

## Multiplying and Dividing

If we divide 24 by 6, we get 4. If we multiply 4 by 6, we get 24 again. Let's think more about this relationship.

✔ We can find quotients by thinking of missing factors.

$32 ÷ 8 =$ ___4___    ( $4 × 8 = 32$ )

✔ We can find missing factors by dividing.

( $35 ÷ 7 = 5$ )    ___5___ $× 7 = 35$

✔ We can multiply to check division and divide to check multiplication.

$15 ÷ 3 = 5$ ( $5 × 3 = 15$ )    $2 × 8 = 16$ ( $16 ÷ 8 = 2$ )

### Getting Started

Write the missing numbers. Check your answers with multiplication or division.

1. $12 ÷ 3 =$ ___4___
2. $8 × 5 =$ ___40___
3. $5\overline{)20}$ (4)
4. $2 ×$ ___4___ $= 8$
5. $3\overline{)18}$ (6)
6. ___3___ $× 4 = 12$
7. $40 ÷ 5 =$ ___8___
8. $3 × 7 =$ ___21___
9. ___5___ $× 7 = 35$
10. $24 ÷ 4 =$ ___6___
11. $3\overline{)15}$ (5)
12. $4 × 9 =$ ___36___

(two hundred thirteen) **213**

---

## Teaching the Lesson

**Introducing the Problem**   Read the text of the problem aloud while students examine the picture. Read the first of the missing factor sentences aloud. Ask a student to complete the division (4) and then read the multiplication problem in the thought cloud. Have a student read the next sentence, providing the factor for the multiplication problem (5), and then read the division problem. Ask students to read the final sentences and related problems.

**Developing the Skill**   Write these problems on the board:

$$4 × 5 = 20$$
$$20 ÷ 5 = 4$$

Draw an array of 5 rows of 4 objects. Circling each row, explain that they can think of 5 groups of 4 in an array of 20 as $4 × 5 = 20$ or 20 objects divided into 5 groups of 4 as $20 ÷ 5 = 4$. Point out that knowing the multiplication tables will help them figure out division facts they are unsure of, and that the division tables can help them in multiplication. Tell the class that some number, n, multiplied by 4 equals 36. Ask how they can find the missing factor. ($36 ÷ 4 = 9$, n = 9) Repeat this missing factor drill several times.

## Practice

Write the missing numbers. Check your answers with multiplication or division.

1. $15 \div 3 = \underline{5}$     2. $4 \times 4 = \underline{16}$     3. $5)\overline{40}$ (quotient $\underline{8}$)     4. $3 \times 8 = \underline{24}$

5. $2 \times \underline{4} = 8$     6. $9 \div 3 = \underline{3}$     7. $2)\overline{14}$ (quotient $\underline{7}$)     8. $\underline{6} \times 5 = 30$

9. $4)\overline{24}$ (quotient $\underline{6}$)     10. $6 \times 3 = \underline{18}$     11. $5 \times \underline{4} = 20$     12. $10 \div 2 = \underline{5}$

13. $4)\overline{12}$ (quotient $\underline{3}$)     14. $2 \times \underline{8} = 16$     15. $12 \div 2 = \underline{6}$     16. $\underline{8} \times 4 = 32$

17. $5 \times \underline{7} = 35$     18. $5)\overline{25}$ (quotient $\underline{5}$)     19. $4 \times 3 = \underline{12}$     20. $3)\overline{6}$ (quotient $\underline{2}$)

21. $6 \div 2 = \underline{3}$     22. $3 \times \underline{5} = 15$     23. $4)\overline{36}$ (quotient $\underline{9}$)     24. $7 \times 3 = \underline{21}$

25. $2)\overline{16}$ (quotient $\underline{8}$)     26. $10 \div 5 = \underline{2}$     27. $9)\overline{27}$ (quotient $\underline{3}$)     28. $9 \times 5 = \underline{45}$

29. $2 \times \underline{4} = 8$     30. $\underline{4} \times 7 = 28$     31. $9)\overline{18}$ (quotient $\underline{2}$)     32. $35 \div 5 = \underline{7}$

## Apply

Solve these problems.

33. There are 24 books divided evenly on 3 shelves. How many books are on each shelf?
8 books

34. There are 5 apples in each of 6 baskets. How many apples are there altogether?
30 apples

35. Each package of cocoa contains 2 servings. How many servings are there in 7 packages?
14 servings

36. A milk crate will hold 4 gallon jugs of milk. How many crates are needed to hold 28 jugs?
7 crates

## Correcting Common Errors

For all students, not just those who are having difficulty with division, it is important to make the connection between division and multiplication. Have students practice this relationship by making index cards with a multiplication fact on one side and the related division fact on the reverse side. Have students work in pairs where they take turns quizzing each other, first by showing the division fact and asking for the related multiplication fact and then by doing the reverse.

## Enrichment

Draw a simple, different shape for each of these weights: 1 lb, 8 oz, 4 oz, 2 oz and 1 oz on the board.
Using each weight only one time per problem, tell students to combine the weights to show the following amounts:

1. 9 oz (one 8 oz, one 1 oz)
2. 17 oz (one 1 lb, one 1 oz)
3. 7 oz (one 4 oz, one 2 oz, one 1 oz)
4. 21 oz (one 1 lb, one 4 oz, one 1 oz)
5. 28 oz (one 1 lb, one 8 oz, one 4 oz)

## Practice

Have students complete the problems on the page. Explain that the problems are mixed multiplication and division so they will have to watch signs carefully.

## Mixed Practice

1. $321 \times 8$ (2,568)
2. $\$30.10 - 15.17$ ($14.93)
3. $703 - 452$ (251)
4. $6,959 + 86$ (7,045)
5. $4 \times 562$ (2,248)
6. $107 + 4,356$ (4,463)
7. $\$27.03 - 19.57$ ($7.46)
8. $\$5.62 \times 5$ ($28.10)
9. $763 + 78$ (841)
10. $80 \times 7$ (560)

## Extra Credit   *Applications*

Make up a sample catalog order form including the headings: description, item number, quantity, price and total price. Go through each section with the class, explaining what is being asked for by each term. Bring several catalogs to class. Tell students to look at one and pick out several things they would like to order. Ask them to fill in all the information required on the order blank. Have individual students explain each of the following: addressing the envelope, sales tax and the shipping charges.

# Problem Solving, Making a List

## pages 215-216

### Objective

To solve problems using a list as an aid

### Materials

### Mental Math

Ask students to tell you which time is most likely to be correct:

1. eating breakfast, 7:30 AM or 7:30 PM? (7:30 AM)
2. lunchtime recess, 12:30 AM or 12:30 PM? (12:30 PM)
3. grocery shopping, 4:30 PM or 4:30 AM? (4:30 PM)
4. Saturday afternoon movie, 2:00 AM or 2:00 PM? (2:00 PM)
5. bedtime, 8:30 PM or 7:00 AM? (8:30 PM)
6. television evening news, 6:30 PM or 11:00 AM? (6:30 PM)
7. time for homework, 5:00 AM or 7:00 PM? (7:00 PM)

### Making a List

Willie counted 31 wheels on the bicycles and tricycles going by his window. How many of each kind passed by?

#### ★ SEE

Willie counted 31 bicycle and tricycle wheels. Bikes have 2 wheels and tricycles have 3. We need to find how many of each kind Willie saw.

#### ★ PLAN

Make a list starting with 16 bicycles and 0 tricycles. This combination of 32 wheels is not a solution. List other possible combinations, with one less bike each time. Write the number of tricycles that will keep the number of wheels at or near 31. Any combination totalling 31 is a solution to the problem.

#### ★ DO

| BICYCLES | 16 | 15 | 14 | 13 | 12 | 11 | 10 | 9 | 8 | 7 | 6 | 5 | 4 | 3 | 2 | 1 | 0 |
|---|---|---|---|---|---|---|---|---|---|---|---|---|---|---|---|---|---|
| TRICYCLES | 0 | 0 | 1 | 2 | 3 | 3 | 4 | 5 | 5 | 6 | 7 | 7 | 8 | 9 | 9 | 10 | 11 |
| TOTAL WHEELS | 32 | 30 | 31 | 32 | 33 | 31 | 32 | 33 | 31 | 32 | 33 | 31 | 32 | 33 | 31 | 32 | 33 |
| YES OR NO | NO | NO | YES | NO | NO | YES | NO | NO | YES | NO | NO | YES | NO | NO | YES | NO | NO |

There are 5 possible solutions:

| Bikes | 14 | 11 | 8 | 5 | 2 |
|---|---|---|---|---|---|
| Tricycles | 1 | 3 | 5 | 7 | 9 |

#### ★ CHECK

$(14 \times 2) + (1 \times 3) = \underline{31}$     $(11 \times 2) + (3 \times 3) = \underline{31}$

$(8 \times 2) + (5 \times 3) = \underline{31}$     $(5 \times 2) + (7 \times 3) = \underline{31}$

$(2 \times 2) + (9 \times 3) = \underline{31}$

## Teaching the Lesson

Read the problem aloud. Ask students if they think there is one solution or many possibilities. (several solutions possible) Remind them of the SEE-PLAN-DO-CHECK problem solving method. Have one student read the SEE section, another the PLAN section. Reproduce the DO section list on the board. Explain that the list contains all the possible combinations of bicycles and tricycles. This has been insured by starting with 16 bicycles, 0 tricycles and decreasing the number of bikes while increasing the number of trikes. Have a student pick out the possible answers from the list write them in the solution table in their texts. (14 bikes and 1 tricycle; 11 bikes and 3 tricycles; 8 bikes and 5 tricycles; 5 bikes and 7 tricycles; 2 bikes and 9 tricycles) Show students that the CHECK consists of taking each combination, multiplying by 2 or 3 and then adding to see if the total number of wheels is in fact 31. Have students complete this section in their books. Explain that many problems are best worked by listing all the possibilities in a logical order, rather than making random guesses. The order is very important, as it helps work through the possibilities without repetition.

**Apply**

Make lists to help you solve these problems.

1. How many different 3-digit numbers can you make using the digits 1, 2 and 3?
   6 numbers

2. There were 9 people at the party and each shook hands with the other. How many handshakes were there?
   36 handshakes

3. List all the addition number sentences in which the sum of two numbers is 10. You may use a number more than once.

   | | |
   |---|---|
   | 0 + 10 = 10 | 1 + 9 = 10 |
   | 2 + 8 = 10 | 3 + 7 = 10 |
   | 4 + 6 = 10 | 5 + 5 = 10 |
   | 6 + 4 = 10 | 7 + 3 = 10 |
   | 8 + 2 = 10 | 9 + 1 = 10 |
   | 10 + 0 = 10 | |

4. The planet Logo has 2-legged and 3-legged creatures. If in one day you count 25 legs passing by, how many of each creature did you see?
   Possible answers include:

   | 3-legged | 2-legged |
   |---|---|
   | 7 | 2 |
   | 5 | 5 |
   | 3 | 8 |
   | 1 | 11 |

5. How many different 4-digit numbers can you write using the digits 4, 5, 6 and 7?
   24 numbers

6. Jeans come in blue, black or brown. The 3 sizes of jeans are small, medium and large. How many different jeans all together, can shoppers buy?
   9 jeans

7. What if the digits in Exercise 5 were changed to 2, 4, 6, and 8. Then how many different 4-digit numbers could you write?
   24

8. Write a division problem about a pizza cut into slices for 4 friends where the answer is, "Each friend had 3 slices."
   Answers will vary.

9. Find the quotient for 4 ÷ 2 and then for 8 ÷ 2. Make a list of other division problems like this. Tell how doubling the dividend affects the quotient.
   See Solution Notes.

10. Two ducks watch the wheels of the cars that pass. The first duck said she counted 24 wheels. The second duck said he counted only 22. Which was correct and why?
    See Solution Notes.

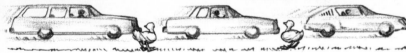

**216** (two hundred sixteen)

**Extra Credit** *Careers*

Invite a student who has a paper route to come to your classroom to discuss the job. Ask the student to demonstrate and discuss the math skills needed to run a successful route. Some of these might include: counting, record keeping, scheduling, and making change. Set up a role playing situation involving the speaker making a subscription collection from one of the students in the class. Plan that the carrier will make a mistake in making change, and see if anyone in the class will notice and correct it.

# Solution Notes

1. Encourage students to arrange numbers in some order to help avoid duplication: 123, 132, 213, 231, 312, 321, for example.

2. Encourage students to give each person a name or a label. Have them see how many different combinations of the letters they can make. In this case the order makes no difference. AB will be the same as BA.

3. Some students may not see that 4 + 6 is different from 6 + 4. You can use red and white dice to show that a red 4 plus a white 6 is different from a red 6 plus a white 4.

4. There is similarity between this problem and the bicycle and tricycle wheels. Have them list all the possibilities and circle those that meet all conditions.

5. It is important that students try these numbers in some order. Suggest that they do numbers that begin with 4 first, then 5, and so on.

6. Suggest that they start by finding all the different possibilities with blue jeans.

## Higher-Order Thinking Skills

7. Analysis: Changing the digits but not the number of digits has no effect on the result as long as all the digits still are different, one from the other.

8. Synthesis: All problems will involve one of the sentences from the number-sentence family shown below.

   | | |
   |---|---|
   | 4 × 3 = 12 | 12 ÷ 3 = 4 |
   | 3 × 4 = 12 | 12 ÷ 4 = 3 |

   Some problems may require a list of total number of pieces and the number that goes to each friend until the requirements of the problem are met.

9. Analysis: Doubling the dividend without changing the divisor will double the quotient. Students should list enough exercises to convince themselves of this.

10. Synthesis: The first duck probably was correct since cars usually have 4 wheels and 24 is a multiple of 4 while 22 is not. A list of the first six multiples of 4 will clearly show this.

# Using a Calculator, the Division Key

pages 217-218

## Objective

To use the division key on a simple calculator

## Materials

simple calculators

## Mental Math

Have students count backwards:

1. from 36 by fours (36, 32, 28, 24, 20, 16, 12, 8, 4)
2. from 45 by fives (45, 40, 35, 30, 25, 20, 15, 10, 5)
3. from 81 by nines to 36 (81, 72, 63, 54, 45, 36)
4. from 18 by twos to 4 ( 18, 16, 14, 12, 10, 8, 6, 4)

## Skill Review

Write these problems on the board. Ask students to fill in the correct calculator keys:

1. ☐ $\times$ 6 = 24 (4)
2. 25 ☐ 5 ☐ 5 ($\div$, =)
3. 8 $\times$ ☐ = 40 (5)
4. 81 = ☐ $\times$ 9 (9)
5. 6 ☐ ☐ = 30 (x, 5)
6. 14 ☐ 2 = 7 ($\div$)
7. ☐ $\times$ ☐ = 9 (3, 3 or 1, 9)

---

## Using a Calculator, the Division Key

Division is a shortcut for repeated subtraction. Division tells us how many times a number can be subtracted from another number.

Notice that 12 $\div$ 4 = 3 is a short cut way of writing that 4 can be subtracted from 12 three times before we get 0.

Complete these codes that show that division is a shortcut to repeated subtraction.

1. 12 $-$ 4 $-$ 4 $-$ 4 = ( 0 )
2. 12 $\div$ 4 = ( 3 )
3. 25 $-$ 5 $-$ 5 $-$ 5 $-$ 5 $-$ 5 = ( 0 )
4. 25 $\div$ 5 = ( 5 )
5. 12 $-$ 12 = ( 0 )
6. 12 $\div$ 12 = ( 1 )
7. 21 $-$ 3 $-$ 3 $-$ 3 $-$ 3 $-$ 3 $-$ 3 $-$ 3 = ( 0 )
8. 21 $\div$ 3 = ( 7 )
9. 30 $-$ 5 $-$ 5 $-$ 5 $-$ 5 $-$ 5 $-$ 5 = ( 0 )
10. 30 $\div$ 5 = ( 6 )

Complete these shortcut codes. Write the answers in the screens.

11. 9 $\div$ 3 = ( 3 )
12. 14 $\div$ 2 = ( 7 )
13. 8 $\div$ 4 = ( 2 )
14. 5 $\div$ 5 = ( 1 )
15. 18 $\div$ 3 = ( 6 )
16. 20 $\div$ 4 = ( 5 )
17. 16 $\div$ 2 = ( 8 )
18. 5 $\div$ 1 = ( 5 )
19. 35 $\div$ 5 = ( 7 )
20. 24 $\div$ 3 = ( 8 )

(two hundred seventeen) **217**

---

## Teaching the Lesson

**Introducing the Problem** Read the first paragraph aloud as students examine the illustration. Give each student a calculator and ask them to find the division key. $\div$ Read the next sentence describing division as repeated subtraction. Write this problem on the board: **12 ÷ 4 = 3** and have students enter the figures in their texts. Draw a 3 × 4 array on the board. Show students that they could subtract rows of three, four times or they could divide the total, 12, by 4 and get 3 as the quotient. Have students complete the first ten problems. Explain that some will be repeated subtraction, and others will be division. After students have had time to understand the relationship between subtraction and division, have them complete the problems at the bottom.

**Developing the Skill** Draw an array of dots, 4 × 6. Show students repeated addition of fours on the array, counting with the class by fours to 24. (4, 8, 12, 16, 20, 24) Show how the array indicates multiplication: $4 \times 6 = 24$. Have them count backwards with you along the array from 24 by fours to see repeated subtraction. (24, 20, 16, 12, 8, 4) Now circle 4 groups of 6 on the array and write **24 ÷ 4 = 6.** Have students find the division key on their calculators. Explain that it is used like the other operation keys, entered between the dividend and the divisor. Dictate several division problems for students to do on their calculators.

## Practice

Use your calculator to complete the cross-number puzzle.

**Across**
1. $9 \times 7$
2. $35 + 18$
3. $427 + 486$
5. $1{,}276 - 639$
7. $91 - 38$
8. $6 \div 3$
9. $968 - 509$
11. $3{,}426 - 3{,}385$
15. $20 \div 4 \times 5$
17. $28 \div 7$
18. $7 \times 7$
19. $96 + 85 - 138$
20. $168 - 79 - 46$
24. $4 \times 3 \div 6 \times 35$
25. $196 + 77 - 28$
26. $6 \div 3 \times 18$

**Down**
1. $953 - 285$
2. $7 \times 8$
4. $5 \times 5 \times 5$
6. $2{,}988 + 4{,}563$
10. $18 \div 9 \times 486$
12. $36 \times 4$
13. $4 \div 1$
14. $486 + 278$
16. $6 \times 9$
21. $(43 + 65) \times 3$
22. $(75 \times 6) + 216$
23. $45 \div 5$
24. $38 + 47 + 89 - 98$

**218** (two hundred eighteen)

**218**

# Chapter Test

page 219

| Item | Objective |
|------|-----------|
| 1-24 | Recall division facts (See pages 203-212) |
| 25-44 | Find missing numbers in multiplication and division facts by using inverse operations (See pages 213-214) |

Divide.

1. $15 \div 3 = \underline{5}$     2. $4\overline{)12}$ with $3$     3. $2\overline{)10}$ with $5$     4. $30 \div 5 = \underline{6}$

5. $5\overline{)40}$ with $8$     6. $21 \div 3 = \underline{7}$     7. $14 \div 2 = \underline{7}$     8. $2\overline{)6}$ with $3$

9. $4\overline{)16}$ with $4$     10. $45 \div 9 = \underline{5}$     11. $6 \div 3 = \underline{2}$     12. $18 \div 2 = \underline{9}$

13. $3\overline{)24}$ with $8$     14. $28 \div 4 = \underline{7}$     15. $5\overline{)15}$ with $3$     16. $3\overline{)27}$ with $9$

17. $9 \div 3 = \underline{3}$     18. $25 \div 5 = \underline{5}$     19. $4 \div 2 = \underline{2}$     20. $3\overline{)18}$ with $6$

21. $2\overline{)16}$ with $8$     22. $20 \div 4 = \underline{5}$     23. $24 \div 4 = \underline{6}$     24. $5\overline{)10}$ with $2$

Write the missing numbers. Check your answers with multiplication or division.

25. $15 \div 5 = \underline{3}$     26. $9 \times 4 = \underline{36}$     27. $6\overline{)36}$ with $6$     28. $3 \times \underline{8} = 24$

29. $4\overline{)28}$ with $7$     30. $\underline{5} \times 8 = 40$     31. $32 \div 4 = \underline{8}$     32. $9 \times 3 = \underline{27}$

33. $\underline{2} \times 9 = 18$     34. $4 \times 4 = \underline{16}$     35. $3 \times 6 = \underline{18}$     36. $25 \div 5 = \underline{5}$

37. $12 \div 3 = \underline{4}$     38. $2\overline{)8}$ with $4$     39. $4\overline{)36}$ with $9$     40. $35 \div 5 = \underline{7}$

41. $4\overline{)8}$ with $2$     42. $12 \div 2 = \underline{6}$     43. $4\overline{)32}$ with $8$     44. $5\overline{)20}$ with $4$

(two hundred nineteen) **219**

**219**

Circle the letter of the correct answer.

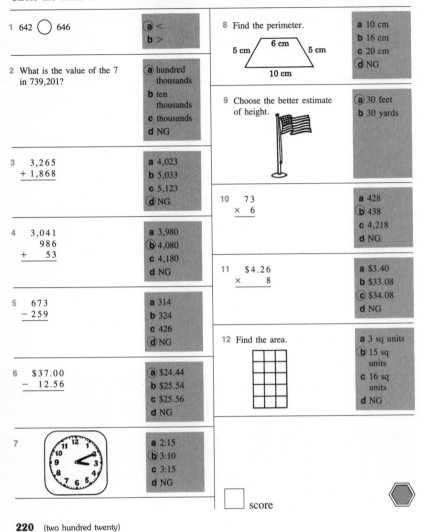

1  642 ◯ 646
  ⓐ <
  b >

2  What is the value of the 7 in 739,201?
  ⓐ hundred thousands
  b ten thousands
  c thousands
  d NG

3  3,265
 + 1,868
  a 4,023
  b 5,033
  c 5,123
  ⓓ NG

4  3,041
   986
 +  53
  a 3,980
  ⓑ 4,080
  c 4,180
  d NG

5  673
 − 259
  a 314
  b 324
  c 426
  ⓓ NG

6  $37.00
 − 12.56
  ⓐ $24.44
  b $25.54
  c $25.56
  d NG

7  (clock)
  a 2:15
  ⓑ 3:10
  c 3:15
  d NG

8  Find the perimeter.
  6 cm
  5 cm   5 cm
  10 cm
  a 10 cm
  b 16 cm
  c 20 cm
  ⓓ NG

9  Choose the better estimate of height.
  ⓐ 30 feet
  b 30 yards

10  73
  × 6
  a 428
  ⓑ 438
  c 4,218
  d NG

11  $4.26
  ×   8
  a $3.40
  b $33.08
  ⓒ $34.08
  d NG

12  Find the area.
  a 3 sq units
  ⓑ 15 sq units
  c 16 sq units
  d NG

◻ score

# Cumulative Review
page 220

| Item | Objective |
|------|-----------|
| 1 | Compare numbers less than 1,000 (See pages 27-28) |
| 2 | Identify the value of a digit in a number less than 1,000,000 (See pages 35-36) |
| 3 | Add two 4-digit numbers (See pages 47-48) |
| 4 | Add three or four numbers (See pages 49-50) |
| 5 | Subtract two 3-digit numbers with one regrouping (See pages 65-66, 170) |
| 6 | Subtract dollars and cents with regrouping (See pages 75-76, 170) |
| 7 | Read the time to the minute (See pages 87-88) |
| 8 | Add to find perimeter (See pages 95-96) |
| 9 | Choose appropriate metric unit of length (See pages 107-108) |
| 10 | Multiply 2-digit number by 1-digit number with regrouping (See pages 163-164) |
| 11 | Multiply dollars and cents by 1-digit number with regrouping (See pages 167-168) |
| 12 | Find the area of a plane figure in square units (See pages 181-182) |

## Alternate Cumulative Review

Circle the letter of the correct answer.

1  886 ◯ 884
  ⓐ >
  b <
  c =

2  What is the value of the 0 in 764,021?
  a tens
  ⓑ hundreds
  c thousands
  d NG

3  4,692
 + 2,738
  a 6,320
  b 6,330
  c 7,320
  ⓓ NG

4  6,407
   364
 +  52
  ⓐ 6,823
  b 6,833
  c NG

5  492
 − 157
  a 245
  ⓑ 335
  c 345
  d NG

6  $52.00
 − 21.37
  a $30.62
  b $30.73
  c $31.63
  ⓓ NG

7  What time is it? (Show a clock.)
  a 11:10
  b 1:55
  ⓒ 2:55
  d NG

8  Find the perimeter of a triangle 18 m by 37 m by 25 m.
  ⓐ 80 m
  b 55 m
  c 62 m
  d NG

9  What unit would you use to measure a trip in a car?
  a meters
  ⓑ kilometers
  c centimeters
  d NG

10  85
  ×4
  ⓐ 340
  b 3,220
  c 322
  d NG

11  $6.25
  ×7
  ⓐ $43.75
  b $43.93
  c $42.75
  d NG

12  Find the area of a 7 cm square.
  a 42 cm
  b 13 square cm
  ⓒ 49 square cm
  d NG

# Dividing by 6

pages 221-222

## Objective

To divide with 6 as the divisor

## Materials

## Mental Math

Have students identify the place value of the 4 in the following:

1. 14 (ones)
2. 946 (tens)
3. 4,692 (thousands)
4. 9,564 (ones)
5. 14,332 (thousands)
6. 82,450 (hundreds)
7. 44,116 (ten thousands and thousands)

## Skill Review

Have the class recite the multiplication table for sixes: $1 \times 6 = 6$, $2 \times 6 = 12$, $3 \times 6 = 18$, etc. Now have students count by sixes, each student volunteering one number in the series. (6, 12, 18, etc.) When they reach 54, have the next student in line start the series over again until everyone has had a turn.

### Dividing by 6

Ronnie sees a sale on fishing bobbers at his favorite sporting goods store. How much will he pay for 1 bobber?

We want to find the cost of 1 bobber.

The bobbers are on sale at 6 for __48¢__.

To find the cost of 1, we divide __48¢__ by __6__.

$48¢ \div 6 =$ __8¢__ ( $8¢ \times 6 = 48¢$ )

Ronnie will pay __8¢__ for 1 bobber.

### Getting Started

Complete the number sentences.

1. $36 \div 6 =$ __6__
2. $12 \div 6 =$ __2__
3. $40 \div 5 =$ __8__
4. $18 \div 6 =$ __3__
5. $12 \div 3 =$ __4__
6. $24 \div 6 =$ __4__
7. $32 \div 4 =$ __8__
8. $30 \div 6 =$ __5__

Divide.

9. $6\overline{)42}$ → 7
10. $5\overline{)25}$ → 5
11. $6\overline{)48}$ → 8
12. $6\overline{)12}$ → 2

13. $3\overline{)18}$ → 6
14. $6\overline{)30}$ → 5
15. $6\overline{)54}$ → 9
16. $4\overline{)28}$ → 7

(two hundred twenty-one) **221**

## Teaching the Lesson

**Introducing the Problem**  Have students read the problem and look over the illustration. Have students identify the question being asked. Ask a student to find the data and read the information sentence aloud. (6 for 48¢) Instruct students to complete the plan sentence. (We divide 48¢ by 6.) Write the problem on the board **48¢ ÷ 6 =** Ask a student to suggest a multiplication problem using the same numbers (8¢ × 6 = 48¢) and complete the problem on the board. (48¢ ÷ 6 = 8¢) Ask a student to write the solution on the board showing the cent sign in the answer. (will pay 8¢ for 1 bobber)

**Developing the Skill**  Write this missing factor problem on the board: **5 × ___ = 20.** Ask a student to write a division sentence that means the same thing. (20 ÷ 5 = ___) Have a student solve the division problem and fill in the missing factor in the multiplication problem. Write **6 × ___ = 12** and have a student write and solve the problem as division. (12 ÷ 2 = 6) Continue doing all the problems for division by six through 6 × ___ = 54 and 54 ÷ 6 = 9. Have students make up a chart for division by sixes like those they made for twos, threes, fours, and fives.

**221**

## Practice

Complete the number sentences.

1. $18 \div 6 = \underline{3}$    2. $36 \div 6 = \underline{6}$    3. $32 \div 4 = \underline{8}$    4. $20 \div 5 = \underline{4}$

5. $24 \div 3 = \underline{8}$    6. $48 \div 6 = \underline{8}$    7. $15 \div 3 = \underline{5}$    8. $54 \div 6 = \underline{9}$

9. $36 \div 6 = \underline{6}$    10. $14 \div 2 = \underline{7}$    11. $24 \div 6 = \underline{4}$    12. $18 \div 6 = \underline{3}$

Divide.

13. $6\overline{)30}$ = 5    14. $4\overline{)28}$ = 7    15. $6\overline{)48}$ = 8    16. $6\overline{)54}$ = 9    17. $3\overline{)9}$ = 3

18. $3\overline{)27}$ = 9    19. $6\overline{)48}$ = 8    20. $4\overline{)36}$ = 9    21. $6\overline{)12}$ = 2    22. $5\overline{)10}$ = 2

## Apply

Solve these problems.

23. Ruth earned $10 babysitting for 5 hours. How much did she earn per hour?
$2

24. Alicia bought 4 sweaters for $32. How much did each sweater cost?
$8

### EXCURSION

A number is divisible by 3 if the sum of its digits is divisible by 3. For example, 237 is divisible by three, because $2 + 3 + 7 = 12$, and 12 is divisible by 3. Find the sum of the digits for each number and check to see if it is divisible by 3.

| Number | Sum of the Digits | Divisible by 3 |
|---|---|---|
| 51 | $5 + 1 = 6$ | yes |
| 29 | $2 + 9 = 11$ | no |
| 234 | $2 + 3 + 4 = 9$ | yes |
| 1,633 | $1 + 6 + 3 + 3 = 13$ | no |
| 4,044 | $4 + 0 + 4 + 4 = 12$ | yes |

# Dividing by 7

pages 223-224

## Objective

To divide with 7 as the divisor

## Materials

## Mental Math

Ask students to find and label each sum or product:

1. 99 + 32 = (131, sum)
2. 9 × 5 = (45, product)
3. 6 × 2 = (12, product)
4. 50 + 25 + 25 = (100, sum)
5. 6 + 6 + 6 + 6 = (24, sum)
6. 6 × 4 = (24, product)
7. 2 × 2 × 3 = (12, product)

## Skill Review

Have the class skip count from 0 through 49, by sevens. (7, 14, 21, 28, 35, 42, 49) Have students come to the board and write one fact from the multiplication table for sevens. (1 × 7 = 7, through 9 × 7 = 63)

---

### Dividing by 7

Naomi is counting the days until summer vacation. She has 56 days to wait. How many weeks are there until Naomi's vacation begins?

We are looking for the number of weeks before Naomi's vacation starts.

There are ___56___ days until vacation begins.

A week is made up of ___7___ days.

To find the total number of weeks, we divide

___56___ by ___7___.

56 ÷ 7 = ___8___    ( 8 × 7 = 56 )

Naomi has ___8___ weeks to wait.

### Getting Started

Complete the number sentences.

1. 21 ÷ 7 = ___3___    2. 14 ÷ 7 = ___2___    3. 18 ÷ 6 = ___3___    4. 63 ÷ 7 = ___9___

5. 25 ÷ 5 = ___5___    6. 49 ÷ 7 = ___7___    7. 28 ÷ 4 = ___7___    8. 42 ÷ 7 = ___6___

Divide.

9. $7\overline{)28}$ = 4    10. $7\overline{)56}$ = 8    11. $3\overline{)27}$ = 9    12. $5\overline{)45}$ = 9

13. $2\overline{)18}$ = 9    14. $7\overline{)35}$ = 5    15. $4\overline{)36}$ = 9    16. $6\overline{)42}$ = 7

(two hundred twenty-three) **223**

---

## Teaching the Lesson

**Introducing the Problem**   Read the problem aloud and ask students to identify what is being asked. Ask students to explain where they can find the information to solve the problem. (some in the text, some they have to know) Have a student complete the information sentences. (56 days until vacation, A week is 7 days.) Read the plan aloud and have a student give the numbers required. (We divide 56 by 7.) Write the division on the board and ask a student to read the multiplication problem. (8 × 7 = 56) Have another student do the division on the board as the rest fill in their texts. (56 ÷ 7 = 8) Ask a student to read the solution sentence. (8 weeks)

**Developing the Skill**   Write these problems on the board:

14 ÷ 7 = ___        7 × ___ = 14

Ask a student to come up and fill in the blanks. Now write the next division and missing factor problems:

21 ÷ 7 = ___        7 × ___ = 21.

Have another student complete them. Ask the class to dictate to you the next problems in the series. (28 ÷ 7 = ___ and 7 × ___ = 28.) Have students come to the board and complete this table of problems through 63 ÷ 7 = ___, 7 × ___ = 63. Remind students of the division tables they have made for divisors 2 through 6, and have them make a similar table for sevens.

**223**

## Practice

Complete the number sentences.

1. $42 \div 6 = \underline{7}$  2. $32 \div 4 = \underline{8}$  3. $18 \div 3 = \underline{6}$  4. $36 \div 6 = \underline{6}$

5. $35 \div 7 = \underline{5}$  6. $21 \div 7 = \underline{3}$  7. $16 \div 4 = \underline{4}$  8. $40 \div 5 = \underline{8}$

9. $15 \div 3 = \underline{5}$  10. $63 \div 7 = \underline{9}$  11. $18 \div 2 = \underline{9}$  12. $21 \div 3 = \underline{7}$

13. $49 \div 7 = \underline{7}$  14. $24 \div 6 = \underline{4}$  15. $42 \div 7 = \underline{6}$  16. $20 \div 4 = \underline{5}$

Divide.

17. $3\overline{)15}$ = 5   18. $7\overline{)63}$ = 9   19. $5\overline{)10}$ = 2   20. $7\overline{)49}$ = 7   21. $4\overline{)24}$ = 6

22. $7\overline{)14}$ = 2   23. $2\overline{)8}$ = 4   24. $6\overline{)42}$ = 7   25. $5\overline{)35}$ = 7   26. $6\overline{)24}$ = 4

27. $5\overline{)40}$ = 8   28. $7\overline{)28}$ = 4   29. $7\overline{)56}$ = 8   30. $3\overline{)27}$ = 9   31. $7\overline{)21}$ = 3

32. $3\overline{)12}$ = 4   33. $6\overline{)54}$ = 9   34. $7\overline{)21}$ = 3   35. $4\overline{)36}$ = 9   36. $7\overline{)49}$ = 7

37. $3\overline{)9}$ = 3   38. $7\overline{)56}$ = 8   39. $7\overline{)63}$ = 9   40. $6\overline{)30}$ = 5   41. $4\overline{)28}$ = 7

42. $7\overline{)14}$ = 2   43. $7\overline{)35}$ = 5   44. $6\overline{)48}$ = 8   45. $5\overline{)25}$ = 5   46. $7\overline{)42}$ = 6

## Apply

Solve these problems.

47. Rachel's kitten is 49 days old. How many weeks old is her kitten?
7 weeks

48. Ben practiced piano 21 days in a row. How many weeks did Ben practice without missing a day?
3 weeks

49. Pat bought 9 pencils. Each pencil costs 7¢. How much did Pat pay for the pencils?
63¢

50. Vince paid 56¢ for 7 decals. How much did each decal cost?
8¢

## Correcting Common Errors

If students have difficulty dividing by 7, have them practice by writing fact families. Have them work in pairs. One at a time, give each pair index cards with three numbers belonging to a fact family for 7. The partners then work together to write two multiplication and two division sentences.
EXAMPLE: 2, 7, 14

$$2 \times 7 = 14 \qquad 14 \div 7 = 2$$
$$7 \times 2 = 14 \qquad 14 \div 2 = 7$$

## Enrichment

Introduce the idea of choice to the study of flow charts. Use this example: If a student rides a bus to school, they first walk to the stop, wait for the bus, then take the bus. If, however, it is raining, their parent drives them. Tell students that on flow charts, most steps are written in rectangles. The choice appears as a diamond. Have students draw a flow chart that starts with a choice diamond in the center and builds yes or no steps on either side. Tell them to use a choice they recently had to make.

## Practice

Have students complete the page. Remind them to write the quotient over the ones column in the dividend.

## Mixed Practice

1. $1{,}295 + 3{,}941$ (5,236)
2. $500 \times 2$ (1,000)
3. $8 \div 2$ (4)
4. $802 - 427$ (375)
5. $\$6.54 \times 9$ ($58.86)
6. $38 + 45 + 64$ (147)
7. $\$56.27 - 18.46$ ($37.81)
8. $14 \div 2$ (7)
9. $6{,}951 - 187$ (6,764)
10. $73 \times 4$ (292)

## Extra Credit  *Biography*

When we talk about temperature, we refer to degrees in Fahrenheit or Celsius. The Fahrenheit scale is named after its inventor, Gabriel Fahrenheit, a German scientist who was born in 1686. Fahrenheit's scale is based on two fixed temperatures. These are the freezing point of pure water, or 32°F, and the normal human body temperature, or 98.6°F. Fahrenheit later discovered that the boiling point of pure water is 212°F. Fahrenheit spent most of his life in Amsterdam, the Netherlands, as a manufacturer of weather instruments. He perfected the thermometer by using mercury in a glass tube, instead of the commonly used alcohol. The mercury provided a more accurate reading, and is the substance found in thermometers today. Fahrenheit is also remembered for his discovery of the hygrometer, which is used to measure the humidity or water content, of the air.

# Dividing by 8

## pages 225-226

### Objective

To divide with 8 as the divisor

### Materials

*division flash cards

### Mental Math

Have students solve and label difference or quotient in each:

1. $89 - 3 = (86, \text{difference})$
2. $21 \div 7 = (3, \text{quotient})$
3. $14 - 2 - 5 = (7, \text{difference})$
4. $42 \div 6 = (7, \text{quotient})$
5. $36 - 9 - 9 - 9 = (9, \text{difference})$
6. $36 \div 4 = (9, \text{quotient})$
7. $32 \div 4 = (8, \text{quotient})$

### Skill Review

Have students recite together the multiplication table for eights. ($1 \times 8 = 8$, $2 \times 8 = 16$, $3 \times 8 = 24$, etc.) Now use division flash cards with divisors 2 through 7, to review students' quick recognition of division facts. Repeat the facts they do not recognize quickly.

---

## Dividing by 8

Rhonda is making wooden plaques as gifts for her family. She wants to divide her piece of wood into 8 equal lengths. How long will each piece be?

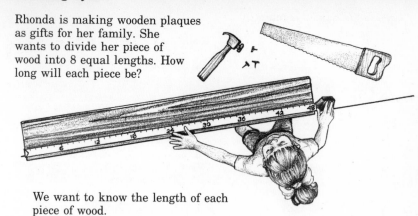

We want to know the length of each piece of wood.

The board is __48__ inches long.

Rhonda needs __8__ pieces for her plaques.

To find the length of each piece, we divide

__48__ by __8__.

$48 \div 8 =$ __6__  ($6 \times 8 = 48$)

Each plaque will be __6__ inches long.

### Getting Started

Complete the number sentences.

1. $24 \div 8 = \underline{3}$
2. $35 \div 7 = \underline{5}$
3. $48 \div 8 = \underline{6}$
4. $27 \div 3 = \underline{9}$
5. $32 \div 8 = \underline{4}$
6. $40 \div 8 = \underline{5}$
7. $36 \div 6 = \underline{6}$
8. $16 \div 8 = \underline{2}$

Divide.

9. $8\overline{)72}$ — 9
10. $5\overline{)45}$ — 9
11. $8\overline{)64}$ — 8
12. $6\overline{)42}$ — 7

13. $4\overline{)28}$ — 7
14. $6\overline{)48}$ — 8
15. $8\overline{)56}$ — 7
16. $3\overline{)24}$ — 8

(two hundred twenty-five) **225**

---

## Teaching the Lesson

**Introducing the Problem**  Have a student read the problem and tell what is being asked. Have students complete the information sentences. (Board is 48 inches long. Rhonda needs 8 pieces.) Have a student read the plan sentences, inserting the required numbers. (We divide 48 by 8.) Write the division problem on the board and ask someone to tell the multiplication problem suggested. ($6 \times 8 = 48$) Now have a student complete the division on the board and read the solution sentence, ($48 \div 8 = 6$, Each plaque will be 6 inches.) as students write the solution in their texts.

**Developing the Skill**  Students are familiar by now with the missing factor method for working out the division table. Write these two problems on the board and have students fill in the other sets: $16 \div 8 = \underline{\ \ }$ and $8 \times \underline{\ \ } = 16$, through $72 \div 8 = 9$ and $8 \times 9 = 72$. Have each student write out a division table for eights to keep as a reference, with the other tables they have done.

**225**

**Practice**

Complete the number sentences.

1. $40 \div 8 = \underline{5}$
2. $48 \div 6 = \underline{8}$
3. $35 \div 7 = \underline{5}$
4. $28 \div 7 = \underline{4}$

5. $56 \div 7 = \underline{8}$
6. $15 \div 5 = \underline{3}$
7. $32 \div 4 = \underline{8}$
8. $16 \div 8 = \underline{2}$

Divide.

9. $8\overline{)56}$ → 7
10. $8\overline{)24}$ → 3
11. $4\overline{)24}$ → 6
12. $8\overline{)32}$ → 4
13. $8\overline{)72}$ → 9

14. $7\overline{)49}$ → 7
15. $8\overline{)56}$ → 7
16. $8\overline{)16}$ → 2
17. $8\overline{)48}$ → 6
18. $6\overline{)12}$ → 2

19. $5\overline{)45}$ → 9
20. $8\overline{)72}$ → 9
21. $3\overline{)21}$ → 7
22. $8\overline{)32}$ → 4
23. $7\overline{)56}$ → 8

24. $8\overline{)40}$ → 5
25. $2\overline{)14}$ → 7
26. $7\overline{)42}$ → 6
27. $6\overline{)36}$ → 6
28. $8\overline{)64}$ → 8

**Apply**

Solve these problems.

29. Angie is making award badges from a piece of ribbon 64 centimeters long. She wants 8 badges. How long should she make each ribbon?
8 centimeters

30. A square has 4 equal sides. Each side of the square is 8 inches long. What is the perimeter of the square?
32 inches

31. Erasers cost 5¢ each. Amy bought 8 of them to use at home. How much did she pay?
40¢

32. Ricky earned $40 this fall raking leaves. He had 8 customers. How much did Ricky charge for each job?
$5

---

## Correcting Common Errors

Some students will continue to have difficulty dividing by 8. Have each student work with a partner, using counters to model the problem. To model $56 \div 8$, for example, the students use 56 counters and 8 paper cups. They deal out the counters into the cups until all counters have been distributed evenly. Then they count the number of counters in each cup. The answer is 7, the quotient.

## Enrichment

Explain that flow charts can involve a choice that sends the reader back to an earlier point. This is called a **loop**. Dictate this example: Mary is making valentines. She will be finished when she has made 20. She must count them after each is completed. Put the following statements and flow chart on the board:

**Make a Valentine.**
**Count Valentines.**
**Are there 20?**
**Mary is done.**

Discuss the flow chart. Tell students to copy the flow chart and insert the sentences. Then have students create a flow chart of their own that has a choice and a loop.

---

## Practice

Have students do all the problems on the page. Remind them to keep the quotient over the ones column in the dividend and to read the final four problems carefully.

## Mixed Practice

1. $3,070 - 2,472$ (598)
2. $\$3.27 \times 4$ ($13.08)
3. $21 \div 3$ (7)
4. $659 + 848$ (1,507)
5. $\$8 \times 30$ ($240)
6. $1,527 + 398$ (1,925)
7. $36 \div 4$ (9)
8. $\$51.02 - 35.39$ ($15.63)
9. $12 \div 2$ (6)
10. $560 - 283$ (277)

## Extra Credit   *Numeration*

Fill a box or bag with cards having the numbers 0-20 written on them. Tell students to draw 4 numbers. Using all 4 numbers, tell them to write an equation and solve it. Have them rewrite the equation on another paper, omitting all the signs, substituting a box instead. Tell them to trade papers with a classmate and have each student insert the correct signs. Tell them to give the papers back when they are finished to have them checked.

# Dividing by 9

pages 227-228

## Objective

To divide with 9 as the divisor

## Materials

## Mental Math

Ask students to find and label the factors or addends in each:

1. 47 + 91 = 138 (47, 91, addends)
2. 70 = 7 × 10 (7, 10, factors)
3. 4 + 5 + 3 = 12 (4, 5, 3, addends)
4. 24 = 8 + 8 + 8 (8, 8, 8, addends)
5. 24 = 8 × 3 (8, 3, factors)
6. 0 = 5 × 0 (5, 0, factors)
7. 300 + 900 = 1,200 (300, 900, addends)

## Skill Review

Dictate these missing factor problems and ask students to name the matching division problem:

1. 3 × __ = 24 (24 ÷ 3 = 8)
2. 5 × __ = 30 (30 ÷ 5 = 6)
3. 7 × __ = 56 (56 ÷ 7 = 8)
4. 4 × __ = 24 (24 ÷ 4 = 6)
5. 8 × __ = 64 (64 ÷ 8 = 8)
6. 6 × __ = 42 (42 ÷ 6 = 7)
7. 8 × __ = 40 (40 ÷ 8 = 5)

---

### Dividing by 9

Mr. Edward bought a transformer for each of his 9 grandchildren. He spent $72 in all. How much did each transformer cost?

We are looking for the cost of one transformer.

Mr. Edward has __9__ grandchildren.

He spent __$72__ for all the transformers.

To find the cost of one transformer, we divide

__$72__ by __9__.

$$\$72 \div 9 = \underline{\$8} \qquad (\$8 \times 9 = \$72)$$

Mr. Edward paid __$8__ for each transformer.

### Getting Started

Complete the number sentences.

1. 36 ÷ 9 = __4__
2. 45 ÷ 9 = __5__
3. 42 ÷ 7 = __6__
4. 27 ÷ 9 = __3__
5. 35 ÷ 5 = __7__
6. 72 ÷ 9 = __8__
7. 32 ÷ 8 = __4__
8. 36 ÷ 6 = __6__

Divide.

9. 9)54 → 6
10. 7)28 → 4
11. 9)18 → 2
12. 8)72 → 9
13. 9)63 → 7
14. 4)20 → 5
15. 7)56 → 8
16. 9)81 → 9

(two hundred twenty-seven) **227**

---

## Teaching the Lesson

**Introducing the Problem**  Read the problem aloud. Ask a student to read the information sentences, supplying the missing numbers. (9 grandchildren, spent $72 for transformers) Read the plan sentences aloud. Ask a student to supply the numbers in the second sentence and solve the problem on the board. (We divide $72 by 9, $72 ÷ 9 = 8.) Ask a student to give the multiplication problem that means the same thing. ($8 × 9 = $72) Remind students to label the answer with a dollar sign. Read the solution sentence and have a student fill in the amount paid. (paid $8 for each)

**Developing the Skill**  Have the class count from 0 through 81 by nines. Write these 9 missing factor problems on the board:

$$9 × \underline{\quad} = 18$$
$$9 × \underline{\quad} = 27, \text{ through}$$
$$9 × \underline{\quad} = 81$$

Have volunteers come to the board and supply the identical division problem:

$$18 ÷ 9 = 2$$
$$27 ÷ 9 = 3, \text{ through}$$
$$81 ÷ 9 = 9.$$

Have each student complete a division table for 9. Put the format on the board.

227

## Practice

Complete the number sentences.

| | | | |
|---|---|---|---|
| 1. 40 ÷ 5 = 8 | 2. 18 ÷ 9 = 2 | 3. 49 ÷ 7 = 7 | 4. 24 ÷ 6 = 4 |
| 5. 63 ÷ 9 = 7 | 6. 21 ÷ 3 = 7 | 7. 15 ÷ 5 = 3 | 8. 54 ÷ 6 = 9 |
| 9. 18 ÷ 6 = 3 | 10. 81 ÷ 9 = 9 | 11. 27 ÷ 9 = 3 | 12. 14 ÷ 7 = 2 |
| 13. 45 ÷ 9 = 5 | 14. 64 ÷ 8 = 8 | 15. 30 ÷ 6 = 5 | 16. 72 ÷ 9 = 8 |

Divide.

| | | | | |
|---|---|---|---|---|
| 17. $9\overline{)63}$ 7 | 18. $9\overline{)27}$ 3 | 19. $7\overline{)42}$ 6 | 20. $6\overline{)36}$ 6 | 21. $9\overline{)45}$ 5 |
| 22. $8\overline{)56}$ 7 | 23. $5\overline{)35}$ 7 | 24. $9\overline{)72}$ 8 | 25. $9\overline{)54}$ 6 | 26. $4\overline{)12}$ 3 |
| 27. $8\overline{)32}$ 4 | 28. $9\overline{)36}$ 4 | 29. $6\overline{)24}$ 4 | 30. $9\overline{)81}$ 9 | 31. $9\overline{)18}$ 2 |
| 32. $9\overline{)54}$ 6 | 33. $7\overline{)49}$ 7 | 34. $9\overline{)18}$ 2 | 35. $3\overline{)21}$ 7 | 36. $2\overline{)12}$ 6 |
| 37. $8\overline{)40}$ 5 | 38. $9\overline{)81}$ 9 | 39. $9\overline{)72}$ 8 | 40. $8\overline{)72}$ 9 | 41. $3\overline{)27}$ 9 |
| 42. $9\overline{)63}$ 7 | 43. $6\overline{)48}$ 8 | 44. $9\overline{)36}$ 4 | 45. $9\overline{)45}$ 5 | 46. $5\overline{)35}$ 7 |

## Apply

Solve these problems.

47. There are 8 baseball teams in the league. Each team has 9 players. How many people play in the league?
72 people

48. There are 36 children in the third grade who want to play volleyball. Each team has 9 players. How many teams can the third grade make up?
4 teams

49. Pretzels cost 9¢ each. Aaron spends 54¢ buying some for his friends. How many pretzels does he buy?
6 pretzels

50. Joan is buying 9 books that cost $5 each. What will she pay for all the books?
$45



## Correcting Common Errors

Some students may have difficulty with the facts for nine. Have them work with partners and, giving them the following number triples one at a time, have the partners write the four related number sentences in each fact family.

| | |
|---|---|
| 2, 9, 18 | 3, 9, 27 |
| 4, 9, 36 | 5, 9, 45 |
| 6, 9, 54 | 7, 9, 63 |
| 8, 9, 72 | 9, 9, 81 |

## Enrichment

Students learned how to incorporate a decision diamond into their flow charts in a previous lesson. Ask them to make a chart that requires two yes-no diamonds.

## Practice

Have students do all the problems on the page. Tell them to work problems as missing factor multiplication if they are unsure of a division fact. Remind them to write the quotient over the ones column in the dividend.

## Extra Credit *Applications*

Tell students their families are letting them decide where they should go for vacation. Ask where they would choose to go and why. Tell them they have a budget of $150.00, to buy all the clothes and supplies they would need for a week's vacation. Using a catalog or the newspaper, have students list each item they would buy, and its price, keeping a running total. Remind them not to go over their budget. Have students read their shopping lists, and discuss which students got the most for their money.

# Dividing by 1 and 0

**pages 229-230**

## Objective

To divide by 1 and 0

## Materials

paper cups
counters
10-inch string for loops

## Mental Math

Have students identify the minuend in each problem:

1. 92 − 3 = 89 (92)
2. 24 = 74 − 50 (74)
3. 0 = 20 − 10 − 10 (20)
4. 44 − 22 − 2 = 20 (44)
5. 200 = 500 − 300 (500)

## Skill Review

Review adding, subtracting and multiplying with 1 and 0. Dictate these problems:

1. 5 + 0 = (5)
2. 4 × 0 = (0)
3. 21 + 1 = (22)
4. 21 − 1 = (20)
5. 341 × 0 = (0)
6. 55 − 0 = (55)
7. 55 + 0 = (55)
8. 100 − 1 = (99)
9. 4 × 2 × 0 = (0)
10. 4 + 2 + 1 + 0 = (7)

## Dividing by 1 and 0

Study these important ideas about 1 and 0 in division.

Dividing a number by 1 does not change the number.

$$5 \div 1 = 5 \quad \text{or} \quad 1\overline{)5}^{\,5} \quad \text{because} \quad 5 \times 1 = \underline{5}$$

Dividing a number by itself equals 1.

$$8 \div 8 = 1 \quad \text{or} \quad 8\overline{)8}^{\,1} \quad \text{because} \quad 1 \times 8 = \underline{8}$$

Dividing 0 by a number always equals 0.

$$0 \div 7 = 0 \quad \text{or} \quad 7\overline{)0}^{\,0} \quad \text{because} \quad 0 \times 7 = \underline{0}$$

Dividing a number by 0 doesn't make sense.

$$6 \div 0 = ? \qquad \boxed{? \times 6 = 0}$$

There is no number that, multiplied by 0, would make 6.

**Never divide by zero.**

### Getting Started

Divide.

1. $6\overline{)6}^{\,1}$
2. $3\overline{)0}^{\,0}$
3. $1\overline{)4}^{\,4}$
4. $9\overline{)9}^{\,1}$
5. $1\overline{)1}^{\,1}$

6. $3\overline{)3}^{\,1}$
7. $7\overline{)0}^{\,0}$
8. $1\overline{)8}^{\,8}$
9. $2\overline{)0}^{\,0}$
10. $1\overline{)6}^{\,6}$

11. $7\overline{)7}^{\,1}$
12. $9\overline{)0}^{\,0}$
13. $5\overline{)5}^{\,1}$
14. $4\overline{)4}^{\,1}$
15. $5\overline{)0}^{\,0}$

(two hundred twenty-nine) **229**

---

## Teaching the Lesson

**Introducing the Problem**  Read the first and second sentences aloud. Explain that dividing a number by 1 is asking how many ones there are in that number. Because the number is made up of ones, any number divided by 1, has itself as a quotient. Write **5 ÷ 1 = 5** on the board and have students complete the multiplication in their books. (5 × 1 = 5) Read the next sentence aloud and explain that dividing a number by itself yields 1 as a quotient. This is like asking how many numbers, n, are there in n. Write on the board: **8 ÷ 8 = 1** and have students complete the multiplication in their books. (1 × 8 = 8) Read the third concept and explain that the quotient will always be zero because no matter what the divisor is, there can be none of that value in zero. Write **0 ÷ 7 = 0** and have students complete the multiplication in their books. (0 × 7 = 0). Read the final section and explain that it is not possible to divide a number by zero. Explain that there is no number which when multiplied by 0 would make 6.

**Developing the Skill**  Give each student 5 paper cups and 5 counters. Ask them to tell how many counters can be put evenly in each? (1) Write the problem: **5 ÷ 1 = 5**. Ask them to put all five in one cup. Write **5 ÷ 5 = 1**. Have each student hold an empty cup and ask how many fives are in it. (0) Write **0 ÷ 5 = 0**.

**229**

## Practicing Division Facts

Divide.

| | | | | | | | | |
|---|---|---|---|---|---|---|---|---|
| $\overset{3}{9\overline{)27}}$ | $\overset{6}{7\overline{)42}}$ | $\overset{5}{8\overline{)40}}$ | $\overset{7}{6\overline{)42}}$ | $\overset{0}{4\overline{)0}}$ | $\overset{9}{9\overline{)81}}$ | $\overset{9}{4\overline{)36}}$ | $\overset{0}{5\overline{)0}}$ | $\overset{1}{7\overline{)7}}$ |
| $\overset{6}{8\overline{)48}}$ | $\overset{4}{8\overline{)32}}$ | $\overset{2}{3\overline{)6}}$ | $\overset{4}{6\overline{)24}}$ | $\overset{8}{3\overline{)24}}$ | $\overset{1}{6\overline{)6}}$ | $\overset{3}{2\overline{)6}}$ | $\overset{6}{2\overline{)12}}$ | $\overset{2}{6\overline{)12}}$ |
| $\overset{5}{1\overline{)5}}$ | $\overset{9}{1\overline{)9}}$ | $\overset{0}{8\overline{)0}}$ | $\overset{4}{9\overline{)36}}$ | $\overset{3}{3\overline{)9}}$ | $\overset{7}{2\overline{)14}}$ | $\overset{6}{5\overline{)30}}$ | $\overset{6}{1\overline{)6}}$ | $\overset{3}{7\overline{)21}}$ |
| $\overset{7}{4\overline{)28}}$ | $\overset{0}{2\overline{)0}}$ | $\overset{8}{5\overline{)40}}$ | $\overset{0}{1\overline{)0}}$ | $\overset{1}{2\overline{)2}}$ | $\overset{8}{8\overline{)64}}$ | $\overset{6}{3\overline{)18}}$ | $\overset{7}{5\overline{)35}}$ | $\overset{9}{8\overline{)72}}$ |
| $\overset{5}{4\overline{)20}}$ | $\overset{2}{4\overline{)8}}$ | $\overset{7}{1\overline{)7}}$ | $\overset{1}{4\overline{)4}}$ | $\overset{9}{3\overline{)27}}$ | $\overset{8}{7\overline{)56}}$ | $\overset{2}{7\overline{)14}}$ | $\overset{4}{2\overline{)8}}$ | $\overset{2}{1\overline{)2}}$ |
| $\overset{1}{8\overline{)8}}$ | $\overset{2}{9\overline{)18}}$ | $\overset{6}{4\overline{)24}}$ | $\overset{9}{2\overline{)18}}$ | $\overset{7}{9\overline{)63}}$ | $\overset{5}{7\overline{)35}}$ | $\overset{9}{5\overline{)45}}$ | $\overset{5}{2\overline{)10}}$ | $\overset{1}{3\overline{)3}}$ |
| $\overset{8}{1\overline{)8}}$ | $\overset{3}{5\overline{)15}}$ | $\overset{7}{7\overline{)49}}$ | $\overset{2}{5\overline{)10}}$ | $\overset{5}{5\overline{)25}}$ | $\overset{0}{7\overline{)0}}$ | $\overset{9}{7\overline{)63}}$ | $\overset{4}{3\overline{)12}}$ | $\overset{8}{6\overline{)48}}$ |
| $\overset{4}{4\overline{)16}}$ | $\overset{2}{2\overline{)4}}$ | $\overset{3}{8\overline{)24}}$ | $\overset{6}{6\overline{)36}}$ | $\overset{2}{8\overline{)16}}$ | $\overset{5}{3\overline{)15}}$ | $\overset{1}{5\overline{)5}}$ | $\overset{7}{3\overline{)21}}$ | $\overset{5}{6\overline{)30}}$ |
| $\overset{9}{6\overline{)54}}$ | $\overset{6}{9\overline{)54}}$ | $\overset{4}{5\overline{)20}}$ | $\overset{3}{1\overline{)3}}$ | $\overset{8}{4\overline{)32}}$ | $\overset{0}{9\overline{)0}}$ | $\overset{4}{7\overline{)28}}$ | $\overset{0}{3\overline{)0}}$ | $\overset{8}{9\overline{)72}}$ |
| $\overset{8}{2\overline{)16}}$ | $\overset{0}{6\overline{)0}}$ | $\overset{3}{4\overline{)12}}$ | $\overset{4}{1\overline{)4}}$ | $\overset{7}{8\overline{)56}}$ | $\overset{5}{9\overline{)45}}$ | $\overset{3}{6\overline{)18}}$ | $\overset{1}{1\overline{)1}}$ | $\overset{1}{9\overline{)9}}$ |



## Correcting Common Errors

Some students may think the answer to both of these problems is 1.

| INCORRECT | CORRECT |
|---|---|
| $8 \div 1 = 1$ | $8 \div 8 = 1$ |

Correct by having each student work with a partner, using counters to model each problem. Have them deal out 8 counters into 8 cups to see that, when all the counters have been used, there is 1 counter in each cup. So, $8 \div 8 = 1$. Then have them deal out 8 counters into 1 cup to see that $8 \div 1 = 8$.

## Enrichment

Have students devise a flow chart that requires two decision diamonds and a loop, where the answer to a decision diamond sends the reader back to an earlier point in the chart. Have them review the flow charts they have made so far before they begin.

## Practice

Have students do all the problems on the page. Explain that the page consists of all the division facts they have learned. This page can be used to check for quick recognition by timing students as they work.

## Mixed Practice

1. $728 + 376 + 471$ (1,575)
2. $2,756 + 4,828$ (7,584)
3. $25 \div 5$ (5)
4. $300 - 152$ (148)
5. $326 \times 7$ (2,282)
6. $10 \div 2$ (5)
7. \$24.02 − 14.39 (\$9.63)
8. $36 \div 4$ (9)
9. \$9.78 + 19.23 (\$29.01)
10. $19 \times 9$ (171)

## Extra Credit *Numeration*

Divide students into groups. Tell each group to write three word problems using three different operations in each. Allow each group to read their word problems to the class, ask the class to name the 3 operations used, and then solve the problems. Have the group correct the class papers. Have students vote on which group created the most interesting problems.

# Estimating

pages 231-232

## Objective

To estimate as a check on division

## Materials

mail-order catalog

## Mental Math

Have students identify the subtrahend in each of these:

1. $40 = 95 - 55$ (55)
2. $9 - 4 = 5$ (4)
3. $50¢ - 30¢ = 20¢$ (30¢)
4. $14 + 13 = 27$ (no subtrahend, This problem is addition.)
5. $65 - 30 - 25 = 10$ (30, 25)
6. $12 - 12 = 0$ (12)
7. $(45 + 5) - 15 = 35$ (15)

## Skill Review

Remind students of the way to round a number. Explain that when rounding dollars to the nearest one dollar, they have to look at the cents. Anything below $.50 is rounded down, $.50 and over is rounded up. Have them round these amounts to the nearest dollar:

1. $2.67 ($3)    5. $7.99 ($8)
2. $45.50 ($46)    6. $57.29 ($57)
3. $29.23 ($29)    7. $88.89 ($89)
4. $5.51 ($6)    8. $12.45 ($12)

---

## Estimating

Towne Square Butcher Shop is having a sale. About how much does 1 pound of sirloin steak cost?

We want to know about how much 1 pound of steak costs.

Sirloin steak sells at 3 pounds for $8.75.

We need to round the amount to the nearest

dollar and divide by __3__.

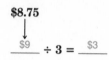

$8.75

__$9__ ÷ 3 = __$3__

One pound of sirloin steak costs about __$3__.

### Getting Started

Round the amounts to the nearest dollar and estimate your answers.

1. $8.25 ÷ 2    2. $15.95 ÷ 4    3. $4.36 × 5    4. $53.80 ÷ 9
   $4             $4               $20             $6
5. $21.25 ÷ 7    6. $6.27 + 3.48  7. $45.35 ÷ 5   8. $55.90 ÷ 8
   $3             $9               $9              $7
9. $34.23 × 3    10. $16.21 ÷ 8   11. $11.98 ÷ 3  12. $9.26 − 3.75
   $102           $2               $4              $5
13. $35.75 ÷ 6   14. $23.60 ÷ 3   15. $41.63 ÷ 7  16. $23.85 ÷ 6
    $6            $8               $6              $4

---

## Teaching the Lesson

**Introducing the Problem**   Read the problem aloud while students follow in their books. Have a student read the information sentence and find the data in the illustration, (3 pounds for $8.75) as students complete this sentence in their texts. Read the plan to the class and have a student supply the missing number. (Round the amount and divide by 3.) Have them round $8.75 as indicated in their books ($9) and complete the division. ($9 ÷ 3 = $3) Have a student work the problem on the board. Ask a student to read and complete the solution sentence while the rest of the class writes the answer. Remind students that they have found an estimated cost. (One pound costs $3.)

**Developing the Skill**   Remind students that estimates are very helpful in shopping because it is often necessary to estimate the cost of an item and not practical to use paper and pencil. Put the following amounts on the board:

**4 for $11.95     5 for $14.95     2 for $7.99**

Ask one student to come up and round each amount to the nearest dollar. Have three others come up and do the mental division, writing the price per item below the estimated figures. (4 for 12, $3 each; 5 for $15, $3 each; 2 for $8, $4 each) Remind students to label their answers with a dollar sign.

**231**

## Practicing Mixed Skills

Round the amounts to the nearest dollar
and estimate your answers.

1. $8.31 ÷ 4
$2

2. $7.38 × 5
$35

3. $35.19 ÷ 7
$5

4. $9.52 − 3.87
$6

5. $4.79 × 9
$45

6. $53.86 ÷ 9
$6

7. $9.95 ÷ 2
$5

8. $7.57 + 8.86
$17

9. $24.16 ÷ 8
$3

10. $23.59 ÷ 6
$4

11. $16.51 − 7.83
$9

12. $8.50 × 6
$54

13. $4.21 × 7
$28

14. $27.09 ÷ 3
$9

15. $48.75 ÷ 7
$7

16. $4.39 + 8.05
$12

17. $8.75 ÷ 9
$1

18. $14.25 − 8.21
$6

19. $5.68 − 1.39
$5

20. $21.12 ÷ 3
$7

21. $17.12 − 9.15
$8

22. $7.83 × 5
$40

23. $11.83 ÷ 4
$3

24. $32.19 ÷ 8
$4

25. $7.50 + 9.82
$18

26. $42.15 ÷ 6
$7

27. $10.20 ÷ 5
$2

28. $6.21 × 9
$54

29. $34.61 ÷ 7
$5

30. $12.37 ÷ 2
$6

31. $12.75 − 7.95
$5

32. $4.51 × 3
$15

## Apply

Solve these problems. Use estimation.

33. One plant stand costs $7.85. About how much will 5 plant stands cost?
$40

34. Four bicycle tires cost $27.65. About how much does 1 bicycle tire cost?
$7

35. Drinking glasses are on sale at 6 for $24.25. About how much does 1 glass cost?
$4

36. A beach towel costs $8.43. Sun tan lotion costs $5.65. About how much do they cost together?
$14

37. Tapes cost $8.98 each. Tad bought 6 tapes and Marcy bought 9 tapes. About how much more did Marcy spend?
$27

38. Ties cost $9.75 each. Walter bought 7 ties. He gave the clerk $100. About how much change did Walter receive?
$30

Some students may estimate incorrectly because they round incorrectly. Have them practice by working with partners. Give them the following dollar amounts and have them tell which round to $12 and which round to $13.

| | |
|---|---|
| $12.56 ($13) | $12.10 ($12) |
| $12.99 ($13) | $12.95 ($13) |
| $12.18 ($12) | $12.51 ($13) |
| $12.05 ($12) | $12.49 ($12) |

In each instance, be sure students verbalize the reason for their response.

## Enrichment

Explain that the flow charts they have previously written are similar to those in computer programming. Today they will add the start and stop commands. The first order in any flow chart is START, written as an oval:

The end of the program is signalled by a STOP written in the same type of long oval. Have students make up a flow chart for something they do after school which includes START and STOP and a decision diamond involving the weather.

## Practice

Have students complete the page. Point out that they must read the operation in each problem carefully, because this is a mixed practice page.

## Mixed Practice

1. 6,521 + 2,975 (9,226)
2. $5.03 × 4 ($20.12)
3. 56 ÷ 7 (8)
4. 4,080 − 2,621 (1,459)
5. 47 × 8 (376)
6. 591 − 43 (548)
7. 24 ÷ 6 (4)
8. 8,728 + 59 (8,787)
9. 7 × 60 (420)
10. 35 ÷ 5 (7)

## Extra Credit  *Geometry*

Provide students with drawing paper and patterns of geometric forms: circle, square, rectangle, triangle, half circle. Tell students to use the forms to draw buildings they might see in a city of the future. The geometric forms are to be traced in different combinations to design the fronts of the buildings. Remind students that the buildings will be of different heights and have different shapes for the roofs. When the city scapes are finished, have students describe their buildings, using the correct geometrical terms for each shape.

# Problem Solving, Making a Tally

pages 233-234

## Objective

To solve problems by making a tally

## Materials

## Mental Math

Have students give the mathematical name for the first number in each equation:

1. $18 \div 3 = 6$ (18 is a dividend.)
2. $100 \times 3 = 300$ (factor)
3. $27 = 3 \times 9$ (product)
4. $113 + 283 = 396$ (addend)
5. $9 = 3 + 6$ (sum)
6. $81 \div 9 = 9$ (dividend)
7. $5 = 45 \div 9$ (quotient)
8. $55 - 10 = 45$ (minuend)

## Making a Tally

How many times does a typist hit each key of a typewriter, when she types this sentence: Now is the time for all good men to come to the aid of their country.

★ SEE

We know the sentence that is being typed. We want to know the number of times the typist hits each key as she types this sentence.

★ PLAN

We make a list of all the letters of the alphabet. Then we make tally marks next to each letter in the list, when it occurs in the sentence.

To make the tallies easier to count, the fifth tally mark crosses the others to tie them together. So, ⅲ stands for 5 tally marks.

★ DO

A ‖     F ‖     K ‖     P ‖     U |
B        G |     L ‖     Q        V
C ‖     H ⦀    M ⦀    R ⦀    W |
D |     I ⦀⦀   N ⦀    S |     X
E ⅲ |   J        O ⅲ ⦀⦀  T ⅲ ‖   Y |
                                Z

| Letters | A | B | C | D | E | F | G | H | I | J | K | L | M | N | O | P | Q | R | S | T | U | V | W | X | Y | Z |
|---------|---|---|---|---|---|---|---|---|---|---|---|---|---|---|---|---|---|---|---|---|---|---|---|---|---|---|
| Times hit | 2 | 0 | 2 | 2 | 6 | 2 | 1 | 3 | 4 | 0 | 0 | 2 | 3 | 3 | 9 | 0 | 0 | 3 | 1 | 7 | 1 | 0 | 1 | 0 | 1 | 0 |

★ CHECK

Count the A's in the sentence and compare that with the number in your tally. Do this for each letter.

(two hundred thirty-three) **233**

## Teaching the Lesson

Have a student read the problem aloud. Ask students to describe different ways to solve the problem. Explain that they will be using a tally and the SEE-PLAN-DO-CHECK method. Have a student read the SEE section. Ask another to read the PLAN. Illustrate the cross tally on the board for students who are not familiar with this way of counting by fives. Direct the students' attention to the DO section of the model and work it through together at the board. Explain that the CHECK for this problem is simply going through the sentence and counting each letter without a tally. Have students work in pairs with one counting, and the other consulting the tallied answer to see that they match.

Tell the class that this kind of alphabet tally is useful to people who are trying to crack secret codes. In substitution codes, where one letter or symbol is replaced by another, it is possible to find the substitutions by comparing the code pattern to common English letter patterns.

**233**

## Apply

Make tallies to help you solve these problems.

1. Which letters are used 4 or more times in the word antidisestablishmentarianism?
A, I, S

2. How many times is a 2 used in the multiplication facts from 2 × 1 through 2 × 10?
11 times

3. How many times does a 9 appear in the years from 1900 through 1950?
56 times

4. How many even numbers are there between 2 and 100?
48 even numbers

5. How many birthdays of your classmates occur in each month?
Answers will vary.

6. Make a tally of what your classmates like to drink with their lunches.
Answers will vary.

7. Find the favorite color of your classmates.
Answers will vary.

8. Which school subject do your classmates like the best?
Answers will vary.

9. Use the tallies you gathered in Exercise 7 to help decide the 3 colors you would use in your classroom pennant.
Answers will vary.

10. Use the tallies you collected in Exercise 8 to help the teacher decide what subject to schedule at the end of the day. Explain your answer.
Answers will vary.

**234**  (two hundred thirty-four)

## Extra Credit  *Numeration*

Have the students draw a large tick-tack-toe chalk diagram on the floor, or school sidewalk. Ask students to prepare a list of multiplication problems that could be worked out mentally. Divide the class into two teams, one to be the O's and the other, the X's. One student from Team O reads a problem. The student on Team X has 5 seconds to answer. If the answer is correct the student walks to an empty square on the diagram. If the answer is incorrect, the turn passes to the other team, and no one is added to the diagram. The first team to place three people in a line, across, down or diagonally, will win a point. When all the problems have been used, the team with the most points wins.

# Solution Notes

1. This problem can be worked in the same way as the model problem.

2. Suggest that they write out all the problems before they start to tally.

3. Students should write out all the years from 1900 through 1950, before they begin the tally. Remind students to mark off each five to make the final count easier. Some students may see that there is a short-cut possible. They can find all the nines from 1900 through 1909 (11) and then realize that there will be the same number from 1910 through 1919 and so on.

4. Students should write out all the numbers 3 through 99 (the numbers between 2 and 100) and tally those that are even. There is a possible short-cut calculating the number of even numbers from 10 through 18, 20 through 28, etc., and then adding in the numbers 4, 6, and 8.

5. Conduct the poll yourself after each student has made a chart listing 12 months.

6. Make a list of possible drinks on the board and ask students to name any that are not included. Conduct the poll for the class. Have a student keep the tally on the board as other students keep it in their books.

7. Work this problem as problem 6, listing a variety of colors and then asking for additions from the class.

8. Do this problem as you have done problems 6 and 7.

## Higher-Order Thinking Skills

9. Synthesis: Answers will probably reflect the first three most-chosen colors.

10. Synthesis: Answers will depend on students' viewpoints on the adage; save the best until last.

# Using the Calculator, the Square Root Key

**pages 235-236**

## Objective

To understand the operation of the square root key on a calculator

## Materials

simple calculators

## Mental Math

Ask students to identify the divisor in each:

1. $45 \div 5 = 9$ (5)
2. $27 \div 9 = 3$ (9)
3. $8 \div 1 = 8$ (1)

and the dividend in these:

5. $56 \div 7 = 8$ (56)
6. $40 \div 5 = 8$ (40)
7. $32 \div 8 = 4$ (32)

## Skill Review

Draw the operation keys on the board:
$\boxed{+}$ $\boxed{-}$ $\boxed{\times}$ $\boxed{\div}$ $\boxed{CE}$ $\boxed{C}$ $\boxed{=}$
and ask students to identify each. (addition, subtraction, multiplication, division, clear last entry, clear last problem and equals) Dictate these problems for students to work on their calculators: $234 + 559$ (793), $14 \times 8$ (112), $\$45.50 \div 5$ ($9.10), and $4,522 - 2,145$ (2,377).

---

### Using the Calculator, the Square Root Key

I am thinking of a secret number. When I multiply the number by itself, the answer is 49. What is the secret number?

We can use trial-and-error to find the secret number. Complete these codes. Write the answers in the screens.

$5 \boxed{\times} 5 \boxed{=} \boxed{25}$

$6 \boxed{\times} 6 \boxed{=} \boxed{36}$

$7 \boxed{\times} 7 \boxed{=} \boxed{49}$

The secret number is ___7___.

We can find the answer on the calculator another way.

49 is called the **square** of 7. 7 is called the **square root** of 49.

✔ The symbol for square root is $\sqrt{\phantom{x}}$ . We write $\sqrt{49} = 7$ and read it as **the square root of 49 equals 7.**

✔ To find the square root of a number, we enter the number and the $\boxed{\sqrt{}}$ key. We do not need to enter the = sign after the $\boxed{\sqrt{}}$ key.

Enter these codes to find the square roots.

$225 \boxed{\sqrt{}} \boxed{15}$

$289 \boxed{\sqrt{}} \boxed{17}$

$3136 \boxed{\sqrt{}} \boxed{56}$

$7396 \boxed{\sqrt{}} \boxed{86}$

(two hundred thirty-five) **235**

---

## Teaching the Lesson

**Introducing the Problem** Read the problem aloud while students follow in their books. Ask students to look at the trial-and-error section below. Have them do the multiplication on their calculators. Tell them to write each product in the spaces provided. ($5 \times 5 = 25$, $6 \times 6 = 36$, $7 \times 7 = 49$) Read the solution sentence and ask a student for the secret number, while the others write it in their texts. (7) Explain that they could have found the number in a faster way. Read the section of the text in which squares and square roots are defined. Write the square root bracket on the board and have each student find the square root key on their calculators. Explain the use of the square root key on the calculator. To find a square root they need press only the number and the square root key. The calculator finds the square root without use of the equals key. Point out that this is different from any other operation.

**Developing the Skill** Reinforce the concept of squares and square roots by drawing a square array on the board, $6 \times 6$. Explain that the square number is 36, the square root is 6. Have a student come and draw an $8 \times 8$ array. Ask the class to give the square, and the square root for the array. (64, 8) Have them find the square roots of these numbers, using their calculators: 4 (2), 1 (1), and 81 (9).

## Practice

Complete these codes. Write the results in the screens.

1. $169$ $\boxed{\sqrt{}}$ $\boxed{13}$

2. $121$ $\boxed{\sqrt{}}$ $\boxed{11}$

3. $5$ $\boxed{+}$ $11$ $\boxed{=}$ $\boxed{\sqrt{}}$ $\boxed{4}$

4. $48$ $\boxed{-}$ $12$ $\boxed{=}$ $\boxed{\sqrt{}}$ $\boxed{6}$

5. $56$ $\boxed{+}$ $25$ $\boxed{=}$ $\boxed{\sqrt{}}$ $\boxed{9}$

6. $15$ $\boxed{\div}$ $3$ $\boxed{+}$ $44$ $\boxed{=}$ $\boxed{\sqrt{}}$ $\boxed{7}$

7. $5$ $\boxed{\times}$ $8$ $\boxed{+}$ $41$ $\boxed{=}$ $\boxed{\sqrt{}}$ $\boxed{9}$

8. $49$ $\boxed{\sqrt{}}$ $\boxed{+}$ $5$ $\boxed{\div}$ $6$ $\boxed{=}$ $\boxed{2}$

9. $169$ $\boxed{\sqrt{}}$ $\boxed{-}$ $8$ $\boxed{\times}$ $5$ $\boxed{=}$ $\boxed{25}$

10. $4$ $\boxed{\times}$ $16$ $\boxed{=}$ $\boxed{\sqrt{}}$ $\boxed{+}$ $2$ $\boxed{=}$ $\boxed{10}$

11. $52$ $\boxed{+}$ $86$ $\boxed{-}$ $137$ $\boxed{=}$ $\boxed{\sqrt{}}$ $\boxed{1}$

12. $48$ $\boxed{\div}$ $36$ $\boxed{\sqrt{}}$ $\boxed{\times}$ $5$ $\boxed{=}$ $\boxed{40}$

## Apply

Solve these problems. Use trial and error.

13. Tom has a secret number. He multiplied the number by 8 and subtracted 16. When he took the square root of the result, it was the same number he started with. Find the secret number.

4

14. Toni paid the same amount of money for 2 items. The sum of the two amounts is the same as the product of the two numbers. How much did Toni pay for each item?

$2

---

### EXCURSION

Complete this pattern.

1. $1 + 3$ $= 4$ $\quad \sqrt{4} = 2$

2. $1 + 3 + 5$ $= 9$ $\quad \sqrt{9} = 3$

3. $1 + 3 + 5 + \underline{7}$ $= \underline{16}$ $\quad \sqrt{16} = \underline{4}$

4. $1 + 3 + 5 + \underline{7} + \underline{9}$ $= \underline{25}$ $\quad \sqrt{25} = \underline{5}$

5. $1 + 3 + 5 + \underline{7} + \underline{9} + \underline{11} = \underline{36}$ $\quad \sqrt{36} = \underline{6}$

---

---

## Correcting Common Errors

Some students may have difficulty understanding square root. Have them work with partners, taking each of the numbers from 1 to 9, and multiplying them by themselves; that is, use each number as a factor twice. Have them write the result. Next, have them take these products one at a time, enter them into their calculator, and push the square-root key to find the square root. The number displayed will equal the number they used as a factor twice.

## Enrichment

Remind students that in flow charts START and STOP appear in long ovals, each ordinary step in a rectangle, and each choice in a diamond. Ask them to write a flow chart that shows how to find their way from home to school. Encourage them to include a choice diamond if they can.

---

## Practice

Have students complete the page. Explain that some of the codes tell them to do one problem before or after they find a square root. Ask them to read the sequence of codes carefully before they begin.

## Excursion

Tell students to pay attention to square roots and patterns. Have them read the first problem and sum (4), and verify the square root of the sum (2) on their calculators. Tell them to look at the next addition, and calculate the square root of the sum. (3) Ask a student to fill in the next addition (7), give the sum (16) and calculate the square root. (4) Now, have all students complete the excursion and describe the two patterns that emerge. (They are adding successive odd numbers. The resulting square roots are successive even numbers.)

## Extra Credit  *Numeration*

| Arabic Numeral | Roman | Egyptian | Greek | Mayan |
|---|---|---|---|---|
| 1 | I | ı | A | • |
| 2 | II | ıı | B | •• |
| 3 | III | ııı | Γ | ••• |
| 4 | IV | ıııı | Δ | •••• |
| 5 | V | ııııı | E | — |
| 6 | VI | ııı ııı | F | ⊥ |
| 7 | VII | ııı ıııı | Z | ⊥⊥ |
| 8 | VIII | ıııı ıııı | H | ⊥⊥⊥ |
| 9 | IX | ııı ıı ıııı | Θ | ⊥⊥⊥⊥ |
| 10 | X | ∩ | I | ═ |
| 11 | XI | ∩ı | IA | ⊥ |
| 12 | XII | ∩ıı | IB | ⊥⊥ |
| 13 | XIII | ∩ııı | IΓ | ⊥⊥⊥ |
| 14 | XIV | ∩ıııı | IΔ | ⊥⊥⊥⊥ |
| 15 | XV | ∩ııııı | IE | ═ |

Tell the students that in this chart, the Arabic numerals are shown in the first column. The Roman, Egyptian, Greek and Mayan numerals are next to them. Instruct the students to study the way the numerals are written and complete the missing elements.

**236**

# Chapter Test

page 237

| Item | Objective |
|------|-----------|
| 1-40 | Recall division facts (See pages 201-214, 221-230) |
| 41-44 | Solve word problems involving division facts (See pages 222, 224, 226, 228) |

Divide.

1. $12 \div 6 = \underline{2}$     2. $40 \div 8 = \underline{5}$     3. $28 \div 4 = \underline{7}$     4. $10 \div 5 = \underline{2}$

5. $9 \div 9 = \underline{1}$     6. $42 \div 7 = \underline{6}$     7. $16 \div 2 = \underline{8}$     8. $18 \div 3 = \underline{6}$

9. $64 \div 8 = \underline{8}$     10. $18 \div 6 = \underline{3}$     11. $27 \div 9 = \underline{3}$     12. $6 \div 1 = \underline{6}$

13. $0 \div 3 = \underline{0}$     14. $14 \div 2 = \underline{7}$     15. $72 \div 8 = \underline{9}$     16. $56 \div 7 = \underline{8}$

17. $24 \div 3 = \underline{8}$     18. $32 \div 4 = \underline{8}$     19. $30 \div 5 = \underline{6}$     20. $81 \div 9 = \underline{9}$

21. $6\overline{)48}$ = 8     22. $7\overline{)49}$ = 7     23. $2\overline{)6}$ = 3     24. $3\overline{)21}$ = 7

25. $4\overline{)4}$ = 1     26. $4\overline{)16}$ = 4     27. $5\overline{)45}$ = 9     28. $9\overline{)72}$ = 8

29. $8\overline{)24}$ = 3     30. $6\overline{)42}$ = 7     31. $3\overline{)27}$ = 9     32. $4\overline{)32}$ = 8

33. $1\overline{)9}$ = 9     34. $5\overline{)35}$ = 7     35. $9\overline{)63}$ = 7     36. $4\overline{)28}$ = 7

37. $2\overline{)18}$ = 9     38. $4\overline{)36}$ = 9     39. $8\overline{)0}$ = 0     40. $6\overline{)54}$ = 9

Solve these problems.

41. Jean buys 3 boxes of stationery as gifts for her teachers. If she pays $2.74 for each box, about how much money does she need?
$9

42. Manuel spent 15 hours this week working on his computer. If he worked 5 days, how long did he work each day?
3 hours

43. Scott bought 5 computer games for $34.75. About how much did he pav for each game?
$7

44. Sally is reading a book that is 81 pages long. How long will it take her to finish the book if she reads 9 pages a day?
9 days

Circle the letter of the correct answer.

**1** 912 ◯ 921
   ⓐ <
   b >

**2** What is the value of the 5 in 320,510?
   a tens
   b ones
   ⓒ hundreds
   d NG

**3**
  5,396
 + 2,085
   a 7,381
   b 7,371
   ⓒ 7,481
   d NG

**4**
  2,365
     86
 +  194
   a 2,545
   b 2,635
   c 2,745
   ⓓ NG

**5**
  703
 − 285
   a 988
   b 582
   ⓒ 418
   d NG

**6**
  $43.20
 −  8.98
   a $34.38
   b $45.78
   c $52.18
   ⓓ NG

**7**
   a 3:40
   b 3:45
   c 10:15
   ⓓ NG

**8** Find the perimeter.
12 m, 12 m, 12 m, 12 m
   ⓐ 48 m
   b 24 m
   c 144 m
   d NG

**9** Choose the better estimate.
   a 1 oz
   ⓑ 1 lb

**10**
  48
 × 7
   a 334
   ⓑ 336
   c 2,856
   d NG

**11**
  $6.37
 ×   4
   a $24.28
   b $25.28
   ⓒ $25.48
   d NG

**12** Find the area.
   a 7 units
   b 7 sq units
   ⓒ 14 sq units
   d NG

**13** Find the volume.
   a 4 cu units
   b 6 cu units
   ⓒ 12 cu units
   d NG

☐ score

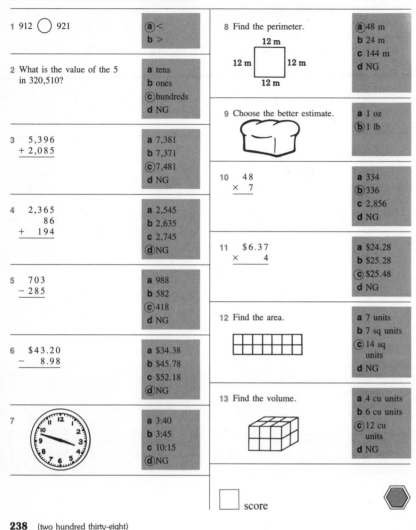

## Cumulative Review

**page 238**

| Item | Objective |
|------|-----------|
| 1 | Compare numbers less than 1,000 (See pages 27-28) |
| 2 | Identify the value of a digit in a number less than 1,000,000 (See pages 35-36) |
| 3 | Add two 4-digit numbers (See pages 47-48) |
| 4 | Add three or four numbers (See pages 49-50) |
| 5 | Subtract two 3-digit numbers with two regroupings (See pages 67-68, 170) |
| 6 | Subtract dollars, cents with regrouping (See pages 75-76, 170) |
| 7 | Read the time to the minute (See pages 87-88) |
| 8 | Add to find perimeter (See pages 95-96) |
| 9 | Choose the appropriate unit of weight (See pages 93-94) |
| 10 | Multiply 2-digit number by 1-digit number with regrouping (See pages 163-164) |
| 11 | Multiply dollars and cents with regrouping (See pages 167-168) |
| 12 | Find area of plane figure in square units (See pages 181-182) |
| 13 | Find the volume of a space figure in cubic units (See pages 185-186) |

## Alternate Cumulative Review

Circle the letter of the correct answer.

**1** 648 ◯ 684
   a >
   ⓑ <
   c =

**2** What is the value of the 3 in 621,543?
   a thousands
   b hundreds
   c tens
   ⓓ NG

**3**
  7,475
 + 2,187
   a 5,288
   ⓑ 9,662
   c 9,552
   d NG

**4**
  6,494
     28
 +  332
   ⓐ 6,854
   b 6,744
   c 6,754
   d NG

**5**
  406
 − 238
   ⓐ 168
   b 232
   c 278
   d NG

**6**
  $38.40
 −  9.86
   a $38.53
   b $28.53
   ⓒ $28.54
   d NG

**7** What time is it? (Show a clock.)
   a 5:10
   b 5:12
   ⓒ 2:27
   d NG

**8** Find the perimeter of an 11 cm square.
   a 31 cm
   ⓑ 44 cm
   c 26 cm
   d NG

**9** What would you use to measure your notebook?
   ⓐ inches
   b feet
   c miles
   d NG

**10**
  54
 ×8
   ⓐ 432
   b 4,032
   c 142
   d NG

**11**
  $7.65
 ×6
   ⓐ $45.90
   b $45.63
   c $14.31
   d NG

**12** Find the area of a rectangle 7 units by 5 units.
   a 35 units
   b 30 sq units
   c 24 sq units
   ⓓ NG

**13** Find the volume of a solid figure 2 units by 3 units by 5 units.
   a 30 sq units
   b 31 cu units
   ⓒ 30 cu units
   d NG

**238**

# Understanding Division

## pages 239-240

### Objective

To divide, quotients with remainders

### Materials

paper cups and counters
assorted buttons
*multiplication and division flash cards

### Mental Math

Have students find these totals:

1. $12 + 25 ($37)
2. $1.50 + 1.50 ($3)
3. $.47 + .53 ($1.00)
4. $36 + 27 ($63)
5. $1.20 + 5.45 ($6.65)
6. $130 + 200 ($330)

### Skill Review

Make a sheet of 100 basic multiplication facts (0 × 1 through 9 × 9) arranged in random order and another of 90 basic division facts (1 ÷ 1 through 81 ÷ 9). Give students the multiplication page and allow them 3 minutes to complete as many problems as they can. Now give them the division page with the same time limit. Adjust the time allowed depending on student abilities.

---

## Understanding Division

Ed works in a nursery. His job today is to fill flats with 25 begonias. Each flat must contain the same number of plants. How many begonias will go into each flat? How many plants will Ed have left over?

We want to know the number of plants in each flat and the number left over.

Ed has __4__ flats to fill.

He has __25__ begonias to put into the flats. To find the number of begonias in each flat,

we separate the __25__ plants into __4__ equal groups.

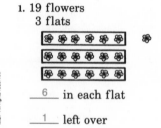

He divides 25 by 4 and gets __6__, with __1__ left over.

Ed can put __6__ plants into each flat and have __1__ left over.

### Getting Started

Use the pictures to help you solve the problems.

1. 19 flowers
   3 flats

   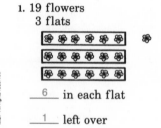

   __6__ in each flat

   __1__ left over

2. 27 packs of seeds
   5 rows planted

   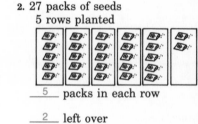

   __5__ packs in each row

   __2__ left over

(two hundred thirty-nine) **239**

---

## Teaching the Lesson

**Introducing the Problem**  Read the problem aloud and ask students to identify the questions being asked. Have a student read and complete the information sentences. (4 flats to fill, 25 begonias to put in) Read the plan sentences aloud, allowing students to provide the numbers required. (We separate 25 plants into 4 equal groups.) Now ask them to look at the four equal groups in the text and have a student explain how many plants were left over. (1) Have another read the solution sentences while the class writes the answer in their books. (divides 25 by 4, 1 left over; 6 plants in each flat, 1 left over)

**Developing the Skill**  Give each student 5 cups and 17 counters. Tell them to divide the counters among the cups as evenly as they can. They are to put the extra counters aside. After they have finished, work through the problem aloud. Draw five large circles on the board and fill them with small circles one by one, counting aloud as you fill them. When you get to 16 and 17 point out that there are not enough counters to go around once more. Explain that 17 divided by 5 gives 3 with 2 left over. Do another example using 4 cups, 18 counters.

**239**

## Practice

Use the pictures to help you solve the problems.

**1.** 11 books
   2 shelves

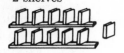

   __5__ books on a shelf

   __1__ left over

**2.** 17 sheets of paper
   4 paper clips

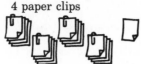

   __4__ sheets clipped together

   __1__ left over

**3.** 19 tennis balls
   3 balls to a can

   __6__ cans

   __1__ ball left over

**4.** $15 to spend
   $4 for each kite

   __3__ kites bought

   __$3__ left over

### EXCURSION

If a number is divisible by 2, then 2 divides into that number equally, with no leftovers. We say the number is **even**. If there is a leftover of 1, then the number is **odd**.

Add the two addends and write below each number **odd** or **even**.

| | Addend | Addend | Sum |
|---|---|---|---|
| 1. | 7 | 9 | 16 |
| | odd | odd | even |
| 3. | 6 | 5 | 11 |
| | even | odd | odd |
| 5. | 8 | 6 | 14 |
| | even | even | even |

| | Addend | Addend | Sum |
|---|---|---|---|
| 2. | 3 | 4 | 7 |
| | odd | even | odd |
| 4. | 7 | 5 | 12 |
| | odd | odd | even |
| 6. | 4 | 8 | 12 |
| | even | even | even |

**240** (two hundred forty)

---

## Correcting Common Errors

Some students will have difficulty understanding the idea of a remainder. Have them work in cooperative-learning groups of three. Give each group 26 counters and ask them to share the counters so that each member of the group has the same number of counters. Ask, "How many counters does each person have?" (8) "How many counters are left over?" (2) Write the following on the chalkboard.
PROBLEM: 26 counters in all
           3 sharers
ANSWER: 8 counters each
          2 counters left over
Repeat with 15 counters and other numbers for which there would be a remainder when divided by three.

## Enrichment

Explain that a set is a group of objects that have something in common. Give each pair of students a pile of assorted buttons and have them divide the buttons into sets. They may group them by size, color, shape, or any other criterion. When they are done they will have sets of buttons. Ask students to describe the ways in which they grouped the buttons. (Answers will vary.)

---

## Practice

Have students complete the page.

## Excursion

Read the paragraph with the students and have them complete the tables. Ask students what happens to the leftovers when 2 odd numbers are added together. (They create another group of 2.) Help students formulate rules for determining if a sum of 2 addends will be odd or even. (odd + odd = even, even + even = even, odd + even = odd) Have students test the rules with more sums of 2 addends.

## Extra Credit *Geometry*

Give students a sheet of drawing paper. Ask them to make a jigsaw puzzle using only squares, rectangles and triangles of different sizes. Explain that all of the paper must be used and all of the shapes must fit together. Tell them to use a ruler to keep the lines straight. When they have a design they find works, have them trace the pieces onto tagboard and cut them out. Have students exchange puzzles with others in the class and try to assemble the original rectangle again.

**240**

# Dividing, 1-digit Quotients

## pages 241-242

### Objective

To divide, 1-digit quotients with remainders

### Materials

multiplication fact sheets

### Mental Math

Dictate the following problems:

1. $4.25 − 3.00 ($1.25)
2. $10.00 − 5.50 ($4.50)
3. $.69 − .25 ($.44)
4. $.73 − .39 ($.34)
5. $56 − 48 ($8)

### Skill Review

Give each student a multiplication fact sheet and allow them three minutes to complete the page. Explain that they should work as quickly as possible, but not worry if they can't finish. Point out that accuracy is more important than speed.

Review division using an array. Put 34 dots on the board and have a student divide it into six groups. Show that the remainder is made up of the 4 uncircled dots.

## Dividing, 1-digit Quotients

Lana helps her father in the produce department of his grocery store. He tells her to put 6 apples into each plastic bag. How many bags of apples can she pack? How many apples will be left over?

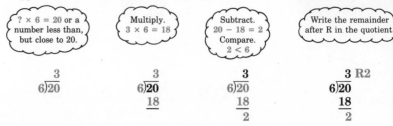

We want to know the number of bags Lana packs and how many apples are left over.

Lana has __20__ apples to pack.

She packs __6__ apples in each bag.
To see how many bags can be packed, we

need to divide __20__ by __6__. The number of apples left over is called the **remainder.**

| ? × 6 = 20 or a number less than, but close to 20. | Multiply. 3 × 6 = 18 | Subtract. 20 − 18 = 2 Compare. 2 < 6 | Write the remainder after R in the quotient. |

$$\begin{array}{r} 3 \\ 6\overline{)20} \end{array} \qquad \begin{array}{r} 3 \\ 6\overline{)20} \\ \underline{18} \end{array} \qquad \begin{array}{r} 3 \\ 6\overline{)20} \\ \underline{18} \\ 2 \end{array} \qquad \begin{array}{r} 3\ \text{R2} \\ 6\overline{)20} \\ \underline{18} \\ 2 \end{array}$$

20 divided by 6 is __3__ with a remainder of __2__.

Lana will pack __3__ bags of apples with __2__ apples left over.

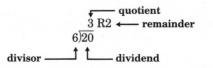

### Getting Started

Divide. Show the work.

1. 5)27  5 R2
2. 3)19  6 R1
3. 7)25  3 R4
4. 6)34  5 R4
5. 8)40  5

(two hundred forty-one) **241**

---

## Teaching the Lesson

**Introducing the Problem**  Have a student read the problem aloud. Ask a student to read and complete the information sentences. (has 20 apples to pack, packs 6 apples in each bag) Read the plan sentences aloud, asking one student to provide the numbers. (We need to divide 20 by 6.) Emphasize that the apples left over are the remainder in the division. Put the division shown in the model on the board and ask students to follow in their books. Point out that the first step is to estimate the number of sixes in 20, remembering that 3 multiplied by 6 gives a product close to 20. (18) Explain that the 3 becomes the quotient and is written over the ones place in the dividend. Explain that to find the remainder they will multiply the quotient, 3, by the divisor, 6 and write the product, 18, below the dividend. Subtract, showing students how to find the remainder. Compare it to the divisor so they can see that they have the largest possible quotient. Have them look at the fourth stage to see how to write the remainder. Label the four parts of a division

problem. Have students complete the solution sentences. (20 divided by 6 is 3 with a remainder of 2. Lana will pack 3 bags of apples with 2 left.)

**Developing the Skill**  Work at least one more problem with the class in the pattern of four steps used in the model.

**241**

## Practice

Divide. Show the work.

1. $6\overline{)19}$    3 R1
2. $4\overline{)25}$    6 R1
3. $7\overline{)32}$    4 R4
4. $8\overline{)27}$    3 R3
5. $2\overline{)9}$    4 R1

6. $5\overline{)40}$    8
7. $9\overline{)43}$    4 R7
8. $3\overline{)17}$    5 R2
9. $4\overline{)19}$    4 R3
10. $7\overline{)56}$    8

11. $8\overline{)44}$    5 R4
12. $9\overline{)59}$    6 R5
13. $2\overline{)15}$    7 R1
14. $5\overline{)43}$    8 R3
15. $6\overline{)46}$    7 R4

16. $4\overline{)25}$    6 R1
17. $3\overline{)27}$    9
18. $8\overline{)31}$    3 R7
19. $6\overline{)45}$    7 R3
20. $2\overline{)13}$    6 R1

21. $9\overline{)35}$    3 R8
22. $7\overline{)50}$    7 R1
23. $5\overline{)45}$    9
24. $3\overline{)22}$    7 R1
25. $4\overline{)15}$    3 R3

26. $8\overline{)43}$    5 R3
27. $9\overline{)72}$    8
28. $6\overline{)29}$    4 R5
29. $2\overline{)17}$    8 R1
30. $5\overline{)34}$    6 R4

## Apply

Solve these problems.

31. Tom has 56 empty bottles to put into cases. Each case holds 6 bottles. How many full cases will he have? How many bottles will be left over?
    9 cases    2 bottles

32. Rhoda takes stickers to school to give to her 23 classmates. Rhoda gives each student 3 stickers. How many stickers does she give away?
    69 stickers

242   (two hundred forty-two)

242

# Checking Division

## Objective

To check division by multiplying quotient by divisor, and adding the remainder

## Materials

division fact sheets
counters

## Mental Math

Dictate these problems:

1. What is the price of 3 apples if each costs $.15? ($.45)
2. If packs of gum are advertised at 3 for $.99, how much will 6 packs cost? ($1.98)
3. Simone's mother is buying a jacket for her and one for each of her twin brothers. Each costs $25. How much will her mother spend altogether? ($75)

## Skill Review

Begin with the 3-minute division test. Encourage students to work as quickly as they can, but not to give up accuracy for speed. Review 1-digit division. Put these problems on the board for students to solve on paper. Remind them of the form for expressing the remainder.

1. **23 ÷ 7** (3 R2)   3. **46 ÷ 9** (5 R1)
2. **17 ÷ 3** (5 R2)   4. **28 ÷ 3** (9 R1)

---

## Checking Division

Roy is making necklaces for gifts. He is stringing 5 beads on each necklace. How many necklaces can he make? How many beads will he have left over?

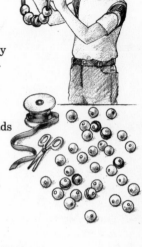

We want to find the number of necklaces Roy can make and the number of beads left over.

Roy has __37__ beads.

Each necklace needs __5__ beads.
To find the number of necklaces and the beads

left over, we divide __37__ by __5__.

$$
\begin{array}{r}
7 \text{ R2} \\
5\overline{)37} \\
35 \\
\hline
2
\end{array}
$$

> To check division, we multiply the divisor by the quotient and then add any remainder. The sum should be the same as the dividend.

$$
\begin{array}{r}
7 \\
\times 5 \\
\hline
35
\end{array}
\qquad
\begin{array}{r}
35 \\
+ 2 \\
\hline
37
\end{array}
$$

Roy can make __7__ necklaces.

He will have __2__ beads left over.

### Getting Started

Divide and check the problems.

1. $\overset{4 \text{ R1}}{4\overline{)17}}$        2. $\overset{8 \text{ R4}}{7\overline{)60}}$        3. $\overset{9 \text{ R5}}{9\overline{)86}}$

---

## Teaching the Lesson

**Introducing the Problem**   Read the problem aloud. Have a student read and complete the information sentences. (has 37 beads, Each necklace needs 5.) Read the plan aloud (We divide 37 by 5.) while students fill in these blanks. Emphasize that in this problem it is not the quotient they are interested in, but the remainder. Put the division on the board and ask a student to work it. Read the section of the text which explains the check process. Label the parts of the division problem and point out that when the divisor is multiplied by the quotient and the remainder added in, the answer should match the dividend. Ask a student to explain why this is so. (You are adding where you subtracted, multiplying where you divided.) Complete the check on the board with the class. Have a student complete the solution sentences while the others write the answers in the blanks. (7 necklaces, 2 beads left over)

**Developing the Skill**   Work back and forth between division and a check to show students why the check works. On the board divide 30 by 4. Write 7 above the dividend. Now to the side, multiply 7 by 4. In the problem, multiply quotient by divisor and subtract. (2) On the side add the product, 28, and the remainder, 2. (30) Ask students if the answer to the check matches the dividend in the original problem. (30, yes)

## Practice

Divide and check the problems.

1. $\overset{6\ R2}{7\overline{)44}}$     2. $\overset{8\ R5}{6\overline{)53}}$     3. $\overset{6\ R1}{8\overline{)49}}$     4. $\overset{4\ R4}{9\overline{)40}}$

5. $\overset{8\ R1}{5\overline{)41}}$     6. $\overset{3\ R2}{4\overline{)14}}$     7. $\overset{7\ R4}{7\overline{)53}}$     8. $\overset{8\ R6}{8\overline{)70}}$

9. $\overset{5\ R4}{9\overline{)49}}$     10. $\overset{7\ R3}{4\overline{)31}}$     11. $\overset{3\ R3}{5\overline{)18}}$     12. $\overset{8\ R2}{6\overline{)50}}$

## Apply

Solve these problems.

13. In your school, 26 students sign up for the chess tournament. There will be 4 players on each team. How many teams will there be? How many extra players will there be?
    6 teams    2 extra players

14. The principal wants to write directions. He knows there are 6 teams with 4 players on each team. He knows that there are also 2 extra players. Show how he knows that he needs 26 copies of directions.
    $(6 \times 4) + 2 = 26$

**EXCURSION**

That's 12 white, 12 red and 12 black squares in all.

I'm going to pick 1 square. What are the chances it will be red?

My chances are 12 in 36 that I have a red square in my hand.

What are the chances that the chosen square will be

white? __12__ in __36__

black? __12__ in __36__ .

black or white? __24__ in __36__

black, white or red? __36__ in __36__

**244** (two hundred forty-four)

# Dividing, 2-digit Quotients

**pages 245-246**

## Objective

To divide, 2-digit quotients

## Materials

multiplication fact sheets
ten-strips and single counters
paper cups

## Mental Math

Dictate these problems to the class:

1. Pencils are 3 for $.15. How much does each cost? ($.05)
2. Oranges are $.20 each or 3 for $.50. Which is the better buy? (3 for $.50)
3. Ribbon is $.75 for 3 yards. How much is it per yard? ($.25)

## Skill Review

Continue to give students timed practice using the multiplication sheet. Give them 3 minutes, stressing speed and accuracy. Help students pinpoint facts they miss repeatedly. Review division with remainders. Dictate these problems for students to work on paper: 37 ÷ 5 (7 R2), 28 ÷ 6 (4 R4), and 13 ÷ 2 (6 R1).

---

### Dividing, 2-digit Quotients

Rolando has 48¢ left in the club treasury. He wants to divide it equally among all the club members. How much will each receive?

We want to know the amount of money each member will receive if the treasury is divided equally.
The club treasury has ___48¢___ in it.

The club has ___3___ members.
To find the amount in one share, we divide

___48¢___ by ___3___.

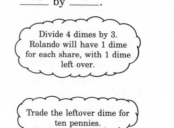

> Divide 4 dimes by 3. Rolando will have 1 dime for each share, with 1 dime left over.

$$\begin{array}{r} 1 \\ 3\overline{)48¢} \\ 3 \\ \hline 1 \end{array}$$

> Divide. $3\overline{)4}$
> Multiply. $3 \times 1 = 3$
> Subtract. $4 - 3 = 1$
> Compare. $1 < 3$

> Trade the leftover dime for ten pennies.

$$\begin{array}{r} 1 \\ 3\overline{)48¢} \\ 3 \\ \hline 18 \end{array}$$

> Bring down the ones digit. There are now 18 pennies.

> Divide 18 pennies by 3. Rolando will put 6 pennies in each share. There is 1 dime and 6 pennies or 16¢ in each share.

$$\begin{array}{r} 16¢ \\ 3\overline{)48¢} \\ 3 \\ \hline 18 \\ 18 \\ \hline 0 \end{array}$$

> Divide. $3\overline{)18}$
> Multiply. $3 \times 6 = 18$
> Subtract. $18 - 18 = 0$
> Compare. $0 < 3$
> No remainder

Each member will receive ___16¢___.

### Getting Started

Divide. Show the work.

1. $2\overline{)36}$    18
2. $4\overline{)92}$    23
3. $8\overline{)80}$    10
4. $2\overline{)78}$    39
5. $7\overline{)84}$    12

---

## Teaching the Lesson

**Introducing the Problem**  Ask a student to read the problem aloud and another to complete the information sentences. (48¢, 3 members) Have a student read and complete the plan sentences. (We divide 48¢ by 3.) Explain that the quotient will have more than 1 digit because the highest single digit, 9, multiplied by 3 gives 27, which is much less than the dividend, 48. Explain that they will divide 3 into tens in the dividend and then into ones. Ask students to follow carefully in their books while you work the problem on the board with them. Have a student read the quotient from the problem on the board (16¢) and complete solution sentence.

**Developing the Skill**  Give each student 3 ten-strips, 4 single counters, and two cups. Ask them to divide the strips equally between the cups. They will distribute two ten-strips and 4 singles first. Have them distribute the left-over ten. (Trade it for 10 singles to be divided equally.) Ask how many are in each cup. (17) On the board write:

$$2\overline{)34}$$

Work through the division problem with students, arriving at the same solution as above. (17)

## Practice

Divide. Show the work.

1. $\overset{16}{3\overline{)48}}$    2. $\overset{13}{5\overline{)65}}$    3. $\overset{12}{8\overline{)96}}$    4. $\overset{24}{4\overline{)96}}$    5. $\overset{10}{7\overline{)70}}$

6. $\overset{11}{9\overline{)99}}$    7. $\overset{14}{6\overline{)84}}$    8. $\overset{28}{2\overline{)56}}$    9. $\overset{24}{3\overline{)72}}$    10. $\overset{12}{8\overline{)96}}$

11. $\overset{14}{5\overline{)70}}$    12. $\overset{22}{4\overline{)88}}$    13. $\overset{10}{9\overline{)90}}$    14. $\overset{38}{2\overline{)76}}$    15. $\overset{29}{3\overline{)87}}$

16. $\overset{13}{7\overline{)91}}$    17. $\overset{15}{5\overline{)75}}$    18. $\overset{11}{8\overline{)88}}$    19. $\overset{12}{6\overline{)72}}$    20. $\overset{28}{2\overline{)56}}$

21. $\overset{27}{3\overline{)81}}$    22. $\overset{24}{2\overline{)48}}$    23. $\overset{12}{5\overline{)60}}$    24. $\overset{23}{2\overline{)46}}$    25. $\overset{30}{3\overline{)90}}$

26. $\overset{17}{5\overline{)85}}$    27. $\overset{11}{7\overline{)77}}$    28. $\overset{45}{2\overline{)90}}$    29. $\overset{13}{6\overline{)78}}$    30. $\overset{20}{4\overline{)80}}$

## Apply

Solve these problems.

31. Quan has 98¢. He wants to divide the money among his 7 brothers and sisters. How much will each person get?

    14¢

32. Toni bought a top for 79¢. Lois bought one for 87¢. How much more did Lois pay for her top?

    8¢

33. Alexi collected 95 pine cones to make fall wreaths. Each wreath takes 5 pine cones. How many wreaths can he make?

    19 wreaths

34. Corey bought 3 birthday cards. Each card cost 25¢. How much did Corey pay for the cards?

    75¢

# Dividing, 2-digit Quotients with Remainders

pages 247-248

## Objective

To divide, 2-digit quotients with remainders

## Materials

ten-strips and single counters
15-inch strings for loops
division fact sheets

## Mental Math

Tell students to start at 2:00 PM, and tell what time it will be:

1. in 30 minutes. (2:30 PM)
2. in 3 hours. (5:00 PM)
3. in 12 hours. (2:00 AM)
4. in 65 minutes. (3:05 PM)
5. in 90 minutes. (3:30 PM)
6. in 16 hours. (6:00 AM)

## Skill Review

Review those division facts which students find troublesome. Have the students do the timed division test, allowing 3 minutes. Use any remaining time to review division with 2-digit quotients.

1. 48 ÷ 4 (12)   3. 56 ÷ 2 (28)
2. 93 ÷ 3 (31)   4. 85 ÷ 5 (17)

---

### Dividing, 2-digit Quotients with Remainders

Jill baked 71 gingerbread men to give her 3 neighbors as gifts. She wants to give each neighbor the same number of cookies. How many cookies will each neighbor receive? How many cookies will be left over?

We are looking for the number of cookies each neighbor will receive, and the number left over.

Jill baked __71__ gingerbread men.

She wants to give gift boxes to __3__ neighbors. To find how many cookies go in each gift box,

we divide __71__ by __3__.
The remainder is the number of leftovers.

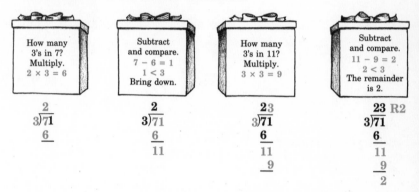

| How many 3's in 7? Multiply. $2 \times 3 = 6$ | Subtract and compare. $7 - 6 = 1$ $1 < 3$ Bring down. | How many 3's in 11? Multiply. $3 \times 3 = 9$ | Subtract and compare. $11 - 9 = 2$ $2 < 3$ The remainder is 2. |
|---|---|---|---|

$$\begin{array}{r} 2 \\ 3\overline{)71} \\ 6 \end{array} \qquad \begin{array}{r} 2 \\ 3\overline{)71} \\ 6 \\ \hline 11 \end{array} \qquad \begin{array}{r} 23 \\ 3\overline{)71} \\ 6 \\ \hline 11 \\ 9 \end{array} \qquad \begin{array}{r} 23 \text{ R2} \\ 3\overline{)71} \\ 6 \\ \hline 11 \\ 9 \\ \hline 2 \end{array}$$

Jill can put __23__ gingerbread cookies in each gift box.

She will have __2__ cookies left over to eat.

### Getting Started

Divide. Show the work.

1. $4\overline{)65}$ — 16 R1   2. $6\overline{)81}$ — 13 R3   3. $7\overline{)90}$ — 12 R6   4. $5\overline{)43}$ — 8 R3   5. $9\overline{)97}$ — 10 R7

---

## Teaching the Lesson

**Introducing the Problem**   Read the problem aloud. Have a student read and complete the information sentences. (baked 71, to 3 neighbors) Read the plan aloud while students complete the plan sentences in their texts. (We divide 71 by 3.) Start the 4-step division. Work through each of the four steps of the model with the students having one work it at the board. Have them follow in their books, filling in the numbers as each step is completed. Read the solution sentences aloud and have students complete them. (23 cookies in each box, 2 left over.)

**Developing the Skill**   Give each student 5 ten-strips, 17 ones, and four strings for loops. Tell them to divide 57 by 4. Demonstrate on the board as they use the counters to work the problem. Start with 5 tens, 7 ones. Divide the tens (1), trade the left-over ten for ones, divide the ones (4) and have students hold up the remainder. (1)

## Practice

Divide. Show the work.

1. $\overset{13\ R3}{5)\overline{68}}$  2. $\overset{13\ R2}{7)\overline{93}}$  3. $\overset{14\ R3}{6)\overline{87}}$  4. $\overset{18\ R1}{3)\overline{55}}$  5. $\overset{12\ R2}{8)\overline{98}}$

6. $\overset{10\ R5}{7)\overline{75}}$  7. $\overset{17\ R3}{5)\overline{88}}$  8. $\overset{10\ R3}{8)\overline{83}}$  9. $\overset{18\ R2}{4)\overline{74}}$  10. $\overset{28\ R2}{3)\overline{86}}$

11. $\overset{45\ R1}{2)\overline{91}}$  12. $\overset{10\ R3}{9)\overline{93}}$  13. $\overset{16}{4)\overline{64}}$  14. $\overset{11\ R5}{6)\overline{71}}$  15. $\overset{16\ R1}{3)\overline{49}}$

16. $\overset{13}{6)\overline{78}}$  17. $\overset{33\ R1}{2)\overline{67}}$  18. $\overset{10\ R3}{5)\overline{53}}$  19. $\overset{12\ R1}{8)\overline{97}}$  20. $\overset{20\ R3}{4)\overline{83}}$

21. $\overset{23\ R2}{3)\overline{71}}$  22. $\overset{12}{7)\overline{84}}$  23. $\overset{9\ R5}{9)\overline{86}}$  24. $\overset{19\ R4}{5)\overline{99}}$  25. $\overset{31\ R1}{2)\overline{63}}$

26. $\overset{11\ R2}{6)\overline{68}}$  27. $\overset{32}{3)\overline{96}}$  28. $\overset{11}{8)\overline{88}}$  29. $\overset{11\ R2}{7)\overline{79}}$  30. $\overset{23\ R2}{4)\overline{94}}$

## Apply

Solve these problems.

31. The 8 pandas at the zoo were fed 48 pounds of food in one week. How many pounds were eaten by each panda?
6 pounds

32. Each of the school buses can carry 72 children. How many can ride in 4 buses?
288 children

33. The school bus holds 72 passengers. Each seat holds 2 people. How many seats are in the bus?
36 seats

34. There are 58 shirts to be put into boxes. Only 4 of them fit in a box. How many boxes are needed? How many leftover shirts are there?
14 boxes    2 leftover shirts

## Correcting Common Errors

If students have difficulty understanding the division procedure, have them practice with partners using the method shown below.

$$\begin{array}{r} 7 \\ 10 \\ 3)\overline{52} \\ \underline{30} \leftarrow 10 \times 3 \\ 22 \\ \underline{21} \leftarrow 7 \times 3 \\ 1 \end{array}$$

The quotient is 17 R1.

## Enrichment

Have students identify each as a union, ∪, or an intersection, ∩:
1. One subset of children with blue eyes (BE); one subset of children with brown hair (BH). What are the children with blue eyes and brown hair? (BE ∩ BH) What are the children with blue eyes or brown hair? (BE ∪ BH)
2. One subset of houses with peaked roofs (PR); one of white houses (WH). What are the houses which have peaked roofs or are white? (WH ∪ PR) What are the houses which are white and have peaked roofs? (WH ∩ PR)

## Practice

Have students complete all the problems on the page. Remind them to keep their columns straight, and to bring each remainder up and write it after the quotient.

## Mixed Practice

1. $158 \times 5$ (790)
2. $65 \div 8$ (8 R1)
3. $2,379 + 28$ (2,407)
4. $7 \times 800$ (5,600)
5. $702 - 378$ (324)
6. $4,738 + 3,295$ (8,033)
7. $35 \div 4$ (8 R3)
8. $4 \times \$2.58$ ($10.32)
9. $7,341 - 4,178$ (3,163)
10. $45 \div 7$ (6 R3)

## Extra Credit   *Applications*

Tell students the highest mountain on earth is Mt. Everest, which is 29,028 feet above sea level.
The deepest trench is the Mariana Trench, in the Pacific Ocean, which is 38,635 feet below sea level. Ask students if Mt. Everest were placed at the bottom of the Mariana Trench, how many feet of water would be above its peak? (9,607 feet)
There are 8 other trenches in the Pacific deeper than Everest's height. Have students use an Almanac to find and list their names and depths.

**248**

# Understanding Remainders

## pages 249-250

### Objective

To review remainders and to use division and remainders in problem solving

### Materials

several 8-oz juice glasses
container with 47 oz of water

### Mental Math

Tell students to start at 9 AM. Have them tell what the time was:

1. half an hour ago. (8:30 AM)
2. 20 minutes ago. (8:40 AM)
3. 3 hours ago. (6:00 AM)
4. 12 hours ago. (9 PM)
5. 24 hours ago. (9 AM, yesterday)
6. 90 minutes ago. (7:30 AM)
7. 65 minutes ago. (7:55 AM)

### Skill Review

Review 2-digit division with remainders by putting these problems on the board for students to solve at their desks:

1. **47 ÷ 2** (23 R1)
2. **73 ÷ 3** (24 R1)
3. **84 ÷ 5** (16 R4)
4. **31 ÷ 2** (15 R1)

---

## Understanding Remainders

Stacey has 71¢ to spend on hair barettes at the variety store. Each cost 5¢. How many barettes can she buy?

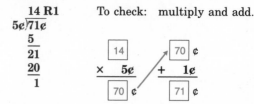

We want to know how many barettes Stacey can buy.

Stacey has ___71¢___ to spend on barettes.

One barette costs ___5¢___.
To find the number she can buy, we divide ___71¢___ by ___5¢___.

$$\begin{array}{r} 14\ \text{R}1 \\ 5¢\overline{)71¢} \\ 5\phantom{¢} \\ \hline 21 \\ 20 \\ \hline 1 \end{array}$$

To check:   multiply and add.

$$\times\ \boxed{14}\ \ \ \boxed{5¢} \qquad + \ \boxed{70}¢ \ \ \boxed{1¢}$$
$$\boxed{70}¢ \qquad\qquad \boxed{71}¢$$

Stacey can buy ___14___ barettes. The remaining 1¢ is not enough to buy another barette, so the remainder does not affect the answer.

✔ Remember, sometimes the remainder will affect the answer.

### Getting Started

Divide and check the problems.

1. $\overset{23\ \text{R}1}{4)93}$    2. $\overset{12\ \text{R}3}{6)75}$    3. $\overset{13}{7)91}$    4. $\overset{17\ \text{R}2}{5)87}$

Solve these problems.

5. Susan has 92 oranges to put into bags. Each bag holds 8 oranges. How many bags will Susan need?
12 bags

6. There are 53 children riding floats in the parade. Only 4 children can ride on each float. How many floats will be needed to hold all the children?
14 floats

(two hundred forty-nine)   **249**

---

## Teaching the Lesson

**Introducing the Problem**   Read the problem aloud. Have students find the required data and complete the information sentences. (has 71¢ to spend; barette costs 5¢.) Have a student work the problem on the board. Have another complete the check while the rest follow in their books. Remind students that the first step is to find the number of fives in 70. Explain that the answer (10) is written as a one in the tens column of the quotient. The remainder (70 − 50 = 20) is added to the other ones in the dividend (1). Ask how many fives are in 21. The answer, 4, is written in the ones column of the quotient. Have them subtract and write the remainder after the quotient. (R1) Explain that they multiply and add to check. Read the solution sentence aloud and explain that the problem asks only how many Stacey can buy; (14) the remainder is not needed to answer the question.

**Developing the Skill**   Show students 47 oz of water and an 8 oz glass. Ask them to guess how many glasses will have to be filled to empty the larger container. Pour water from the large container into the glass and have a student keep a tally on the board, one mark for each glass filled. When the last of the water has been poured ask students to identify the quotient (5), the dividend (47), the divisor (8), and the remainder (7). Write the problem on the board.

**Practice**

Divide and check the problems.

1. $5\overline{)63}$   12 R3

2. $4\overline{)97}$   24 R1

3. $2\overline{)83}$   41 R1

4. $7\overline{)84}$   12

5. $6\overline{)88}$   14 R4

6. $3\overline{)76}$   25 R1

7. $9\overline{)95}$   10 R5

8. $2\overline{)57}$   28 R1

9. $8\overline{)80}$   10

10. $3\overline{)91}$   30 R1

11. $5\overline{)79}$   15 R4

12. $4\overline{)95}$   23 R3

13. $6\overline{)76}$   12 R4

14. $2\overline{)89}$   44 R1

15. $5\overline{)97}$   19 R2

**Apply**

Solve these problems.

16. Mr. La Frank is building a split-rail fence around his yard. He has 39 split rails. It takes 4 rails for each section. How many sections can Mr. La Frank build?
9 sections

17. Mrs. Grabski's class of 23 students is going on a field trip. A school rule allows only 4 students in a car. How many cars will be needed?
6 cars

18. Thomas is making sandwiches for the class picnic. He has 35 slices of bread. How many full sandwiches can he make?
17 sandwiches

19. Roberta bought 80 ounces of juice for the picnic. Each paper cup holds 6 ounces. How many cups will she need to use all the juice?
14 cups

**250** (two hundred fifty)

## Correcting Common Errors

Some students will have difficulty seeing that sometimes the remainder tells them to use just the quotient without the remainder for the answer and sometimes it tells them to increase the quotient by 1. Discuss with students how in Exercise 16 the 3 rails left over are not enough for another whole section, so the answer is the quotient without the remainder, or 9 sections. In Exercise 17, however, the 3 students left over also must go on the trip, so the quotient must be increased by 1 and that, instead of needing 5 cars, the class will need 6.

## Enrichment

Explain that the intersection of two subsets can produce an empty set. For example: one subset is girls with curly hair and the other girls with straight hair. Ask students to describe the intersection of these sets. (girls with straight and curly hair) Ask if this makes sense. (no) Explain we would write the intersection: $S \cap C = /$, an empty set. Ask students to think of another intersection of 2 subsets which produces an empty set.

## Practice

Have students complete the page. Remind them to bring the remainder up next to the quotient.

## Mixed Practice

1. $727 + 493$ (1,220)
2. $39 \times 9$ (351)
3. $93 \div 3$ (31)
4. $512 \times 8$ (4,096)
5. $627 - 39$ (588)
6. $39 \div 7$ (5 R4)
7. $5,408 + 2,793$ (8,201)
8. $738 - 429$ (309)
9. $84 \div 4$ (21)
10. $6 \times 40$ (240)

## Extra Credit   *Biography*

Tell students that the names of these famous mathematicians are hidden in the following puzzle. Tell students to circle the names, which may be found forward, up, down, or on the diagonal. As an extension, ask students to select one of the famous mathematicians and find out more facts about that person's life and accomplishments.

Archimedes   Hippias
Archytas   Hypatia
Conon   Menelaus
Diocles   Pappus
Diophantus   Pythagoras
Euclid   Thales
Eudoxus   Theon
Heron   Zeno

**250**

# Finding Averages

**pages 251-252**

## Objective

To find averages

## Materials

counters

## Mental Math

Dictate these problems:

1. It takes 20 minutes to walk to the store. How long will two round-trips take? (20 min × 4 = 80 minutes or 1 hr 20 min)
2. It takes 12 minutes to bake cookies. How long will it take to make 3 batches? (12 min × 3 = 36 min)
3. Joanne watches T.V. for 30 min every night. How much time does she spend watching over a period of 5 days? (30 min × 5 = 150 min = 2 hr 30 min)

## Skill Review

Write these problems on the board. Work the first one with students and ask them to do the rest independently.

1. **64 ÷ 4** (16)
2. **73 ÷ 5** (14 R3)
3. **92 ÷ 3** (30 R2)
4. **33 ÷ 4** (8 R1)
5. **99 ÷ 3** (33)
6. **71 ÷ 4** (17 R3)

---

## Finding Averages

Miss Fischer keeps a chart of math test scores for her class. What is Mark's average score for the week?

| Pupil | M | T | W | T | F | Average |
|-------|----|----|----|----|----|---------|
| Mark | 15 | 12 | 18 | 16 | 14 | |
| Yang | 20 | 15 | 18 | 15 | 12 | |
| Kay | 18 | 20 | 20 | 12 | 20 | |

We want to know Mark's average math test score.

Mark's test scores were ___15___, ___12___, ___18___, ___16___ and ___14___.

He took ___5___ tests this week.

To find the average score, we add ___15___, ___12___, ___18___, ___16___ and ___14___, and then divide by ___5___.

Add the numbers.

$$
\begin{array}{r}
15 \\
\boxed{12} \\
18 \\
\boxed{16} \\
+\ 14 \\
\hline
\boxed{75}
\end{array}
$$

Divide by the number of addends.

$$
5\overline{)75}\ ^{15}
$$

Mark's average score is ___15___.

### Getting Started

1. Write Yang's average score.

___16___

2. Write Kay's average score.

___18___

Write the average of each set of numbers.

3. 16, 23, 42 ___27___

4. 31, 26, 42 ___33___

5. 23, 19, 31, 15 ___22___

(two hundred fifty-one) **251**

---

## Teaching the Lesson

**Introducing the Problem**   Read the problem aloud. Ask students to find the information needed and write it in their texts. (15, 12, 18, 16, 14; He took 5 tests.) Explain that the average tells you about how well he did on all the tests. Ask students to complete the plan sentences. (We add 15, 12, 18, 16 and 14 and then divide by 5.) Explain that you divide by 5 because that is the number of scores Mark has to be averaged. If he had taken 4 tests, you would divide by 4. Have a student put the addition on the board. Have another divide the sum (75) by 5, and write the quotient above. (15) Explain that his average score was 15. Point out that the average is not always one of the numbers given, though in this case he did actually have a score of 15 one day. Have students complete the solution sentence. (Average score is 15.)

## Developing the Skill   Write on the board:

**MILES WALKED BY RAMON**
**Friday: 4   Saturday: 5   Sunday: 6**

Ask how far he walked in three days. (15 miles) Ask how far he would have walked each day, if he had walked exactly the same distance. (5) Explain that he walked an average of 5 miles each day, although he only actually walked 5 miles one day and on the others walked more or less. Have students think of times when averages are used: batting average, average car speed or bowling average.

**251**

## Practice

Write the average of each set of numbers.

**1.** 24, 48

36

**2.** 15, 29, 19, 21

21

**3.** 40, 25, 31

32

**4.** 18, 22, 24, 20

21

**5.** 13, 7, 5, 17, 15, 9

11

**6.** 25, 14, 16, 21, 19

19

## Apply

Solve these problems.

**7.** Sandi works part time at an ice cream store. Find the average number of hours Sandi works each day.

| Day | Mon. | Tues. | Wed. | Thurs. | Fri. |
|-----|------|-------|------|--------|------|
| Hours | 2 | 3 | 2 | 4 | 4 |

3 hours

**8.** Beverly, Karen and Leah played 3 rounds of darts. Complete the score card to show their average scores.

| | Round 1 | Round 2 | Round 3 | Average |
|---|---------|---------|---------|---------|
| Beverly | 17 | 14 | 8 | 13 |
| Karen | 12 | 14 | 16 | 14 |
| Leah | 19 | 19 | 13 | 17 |

Use the bar graph to solve problems 9–12.

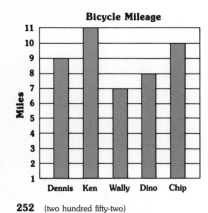

**Bicycle Mileage**

**9.** How much farther did Dennis ride than Wally? ___2 miles___

**10.** Dino wanted to ride 15 miles. How much farther does he need to ride? ___7 miles___

**11.** How far did the boys ride altogether? ___45 miles___

**12.** Find the average distance the boys rode. ___9 miles___

# Problem Solving, Making a Table

pages 253-254

## Objective

To use a data table to solve problems

## Materials

calendar

## Mental Math

Ask students to tell how many minutes are:

1. in a half-hour. (30 minutes)
2. in a quarter hour. (15 minutes)
3. in one hour. (60 minutes)
4. between the 3 and the 5 on a clock face. (10 minutes)
5. in three quarters of an hour. (45 minutes)
6. between 12 and 6 on a clock. (30 minutes)
7. between 6 and 9 on a clock. (15 minutes)

## Making a Table

Eric's mother was 30 when he was born. How old will Eric be when his mother is 4 times his age?

★ SEE

We want to find Eric's age when his mother's age is 4 times his.
When Eric was 0 years old, his mother was 30.

★ PLAN

We can make a table comparing Eric's age with his mother's, beginning with his birth.

★ DO

| ERIC'S AGE | 0 | 1 | 2 | 3 | 4 | 5 | 6 | 7 | 8 | 9 | 10 |
|---|---|---|---|---|---|---|---|---|---|---|---|
| MOTHER'S AGE | 30 | 31 | 32 | 33 | 34 | 35 | 36 | 37 | 38 | 39 | 40 |

When Eric is __10__, his mother will be __40__.
She will be 4 times his age.

★ CHECK

$4 \times 10 = 40$
This is the first age combination that solves the problem.

(two hundred fifty-three) **253**

## Teaching the Lesson

Read the problem aloud to the class. Remind them of the SEE-PLAN-DO-CHECK problem solving method and ask a student to read the SEE section aloud. Read the PLAN section and explain that a table resembles the lists they have made in earlier lessons. The table will allow them to tabulate information in a logical way. Direct their attention to the table below. Explain that it has been constructed in chronological order, starting from the year in which Eric was born. Ask a student to explain the increments between one entry and the next. (There is one year between entries.) Copy the table on the board, then have a student multiply Eric's age by four. Put these products in a column on the board. ($0 \times 4 = 0$, $1 \times 4 = 4$, $2 \times 4 = 8$, etc) This will help students see that $10 \times 40$ is the first possible solution. Ask the students if there will ever be another time in Eric's life when his mother is four times as old as he is. (no) Have students complete the solution sentence. (Eric is 10 and his mother 40.)

Point out that tables are really a way of organizing information and a way of working problems in an orderly way.

**253**

**Apply**

Make tables to help you solve these problems.

1. How many months have only 30 days? How many have a total of 31?
   4 have only 30 days. 7 have 31 days.

2. How many brothers and sisters of your classmates are between 0 and 5 years of age? How many are between 6 and 10?
   Answers will vary.

3. What numbers between 75 and 100 are evenly divisible by both 2 and 3?
   78, 84, 90, 96

4. What numbers between 20 and 40 can be divided by 3, 6 and 9?
   36

5. Ask each of your classmates their favorite color, day and season. Record the answers for each student.
   Answers will vary.

6. Make up 3 questions that can be answered by yes or no. Ask these questions of each of your classmates and record the answers for each student.
   Answers will vary.

7. There are 9 equal groups of birds in a tree watching a baseball game. The total number of birds is less than 100 and greater than 9. What is the greatest number of birds possible in each group, and what is the least number of birds possible in each group?
   See Solution Notes.

8. Molly is the manager for the Blue Birds Baseball Team. She tries to put the bats in equal rows. When she makes 3 equal rows, she has 1 bat left over. When she makes 4 equal rows, she has 1 bat left over. If she has fewer than 20 bats, exactly how many bats does she have?
   13 bats

9. Suppose a stationery store sells a package of 4 notepads for $1.68. Explain how to find the cost of 24 notepads.
   See Solution Notes.

**254**  (two hundred fifty-four)

---

---

# Solution Notes

1. Pass out calendars or use one as a demonstration. Spell the months of the year on the board for the class and have them make up a table of months.

2. Suggest that students start with a tally. List ages on the board: 0 through 5 and 6 through 10. Ask students to come up one by one and make a mark for each sibling. Now ask students to make a table from the tallies and then answer the questions.

3. Suggest a table with three columns: one for numbers between 75 and 100, another for the number divided by 2, and another when divided by 3. Tell students the three's trick. If the sum of the digits in a number is divisible by 3, then the number itself is divisible by 3: Ex. 78, 7 + 8 = 15, 15 can be divided by 3, so 78 can be divided by 3.

4. Suggest that students work this problem like problem 3, adding a fourth column for the extra divisor.

5. This activity can be simplified by having students tell the form of the table and put it on the board. Have students vote for their favorite color, day, and season.

6. Suggest that students make up the table they will use before they begin to poll their classmates.

## Higher-Order Thinking Skills

7. Analysis: The greatest number possible in each group is $99 \div 9$, or 11 birds; the least number possible is $18 \div 9$, or 2 birds in each group. Some students may arrive at these conclusions by constructing a table.

8. Synthesis: Make two tables—one of the numbers less than 20 that have 1 as a remainder when divided by 3 (4, 7, 10, 13, 16, 19) and one of the numbers less than 20 that a number divided by 4 and have a remainder of 1 (5, 9, 13, 17). The only number common to both is 13.

9. Synthesis: Some students will make a table of numbers of notepads and use multiplication.

# Using a Calculator, Find the Best Buy

**pages 255-256**

## Objective

To use the calculator to find unit prices

## Materials

* three toothpaste boxes
simple calculators

## Mental Math

Dictate these problems:

1. It takes an hour and a half to do 3 math assignments. About how long does it take to do each one? (90 min ÷ 3 = 30 min)
2. Jane read five chapters of a book, in 40 min. How long did it take her to read each chapter, on the average? (40 min ÷ 5 = 8 min)
3. Dana runs 2 miles in 12 min. How long does each mile take? (12 min ÷ 2 = 6 min)

## Skill Review

Write these calculator codes on the board for students to complete.

1. 45 $+$ 63 $=$ (108)
2. 82 $-$ 29 $=$ (53)
3. 84 $\times$ 14 $=$ (1,176)
4. 4,560 $-$ 554 = (4,006)
5. 91 $\div$ 13 $=$ (7)

---

## Using Calculators, Find the Best Buy

Marcie wants to buy her dog some dog food. She finds 4 choices on the store shelf. Which bag of dog food is the best buy for Marcie?

We want to know which bag of dog food is the best buy.

We know the cost of Puppy Dog

Food in the 5- and 8-pound bags.

We also know the cost of the Happy

Dog Food in the 3- and 7-pound bags.

To find the best buy, we need to find the **unit price** for each item. We divide the total cost of each bag of dog food by the number of pounds in each bag.

| Puppy Dog Food | | | Unit Price |
|---|---|---|---|
| 5 pounds | 6.95 $\div$ 5 $=$ | | 1.39 |
| 8 pounds | 9.52 $\div$ 8 $=$ | | 1.19 |
| **Happy Dog Food** | | | |
| 3 pounds | 4.23 $\div$ 3 $=$ | | 1.41 |
| 7 pounds | 8.19 $\div$ 7 $=$ | | 1.17 |

The best buy is ___7___ pounds of __Happy__ Dog Food, for $__8.19__.

Find the unit price.

1. 8 pounds for $11.12
$1.39

2. 7 grams for $2.45
$0.35

3. 6 ounces for 96¢
$0.16

Circle the better buy.

4. 6 pounds of apples for $2.94

(9 pounds of apples for $3.87)

5. (T-bone steak 3 pounds for $6.57)

porterhouse 4 pounds for $8.92

(two hundred fifty-five) **255**

## Teaching the Lesson

**Introducing the Problem** Read the problem aloud while class studies illustration. Have a student read the information sentences. Read the plan sentences, explaining that the unit price, in this case, will be the price per pound for each type of dog food in each type of package. Have students complete the calculator codes for each of the four divisions and then work the problems on their calculators. Have a student put each problem and its solution on the board. (unit prices: $1.39, $1.19, $1.41, $1.17) Ask a student to explain which bag is the best value. (Happy Dog Food in 7-pound bags averages $1.17 a pound.) Have students complete the solution sentence. (7 lb Happy Dog Food for $8.19)

**Developing the Skill** Explain that unit prices are important when comparing items packaged in unequal amounts. They can help a shopper decide whether a small or large package, or which brand is a better buy. Point out that some stores list unit prices along the shelves. Ask your students to look for this the next time they go to the store. Now help them figure the unit prices for this item, using their calculators: instant coffee is sold in 2-, 4-, and 8-oz jars at $2.49, $3.79, and $5.89. Ask for the price per oz and the best buy. ($1.25, $.95, and $.74; The 8 oz is best.)

**255**

## Practice

Find the unit price.

1. 6 ounces for $5.10
   $0.85
2. 8 pairs for $8.40
   $1.05
3. 3 pieces for $6.87
   $2.29
4. 5 pounds for $9.75
   $1.95
5. 2 kilograms for $4.12
   $2.06
6. 9 liters for $19.44
   $2.16
7. 7 feet for $8.75
   $1.25
8. 4 ounces for $1.48
   $0.37
9. 5 quarts for $9.25
   $1.85

Circle the better buy.

10. (5 ice bars for $4.80)
    7 ice bars for $6.86
11. (6 pounds hamburger for $18.90)
    4 pounds hamburger for $12.72

12. (8 ties for $18.96)
    3 ties for $7.68
13. 2 baseballs for $9.48
    (3 baseballs for $14.10)

14. 4 hats for $5.00
    (3 hats for $3.60)
15. 6 plants for $5.70
    (9 plants for $8.01)

16. (9 pounds apples for $4.05)
    6 pounds of apples for $2.88
17. 8 cups for $6.40
    (5 cups for $3.80)

## Apply

Solve these problems.

18. One store is selling Good Glassware at 6 glasses for $43.50. Another store is selling the same brand at 8 glasses for $57.20. Which is the better buy?
    8 glasses for $57.20

19. Mr. Harris is buying tires for his car. The tires he wants to buy are priced at 4 for $508. Another store will sell Mr. Harris 5 tires for $595. Which is the better buy?
    5 tires for $595

**256**  (two hundred fifty-six)

**256**

# Chapter Test

page 257

| Item | Objective |
|------|-----------|
| 1-20 | Divide 2-digit by 1-digit number with and without remainders (See pages 241-250) |
| 21-24 | Solve word problems involving division facts of 2-digit number (See pages 242, 244, 246, 248, 250) |

Divide. Show the work.

1. $7\overline{)71}$   10 R1

2. $5\overline{)86}$   17 R1

3. $9\overline{)81}$   9

4. $2\overline{)57}$   28 R1

5. $3\overline{)72}$   24

6. $6\overline{)53}$   8 R5

7. $8\overline{)98}$   12 R2

8. $4\overline{)83}$   20 R3

9. $5\overline{)35}$   7

10. $7\overline{)86}$   12 R2

11. $5\overline{)82}$   16 R2

12. $4\overline{)76}$   19

13. $7\overline{)99}$   14 R1

14. $3\overline{)97}$   32 R1

15. $2\overline{)80}$   40

16. $7\overline{)43}$   6 R1

17. $9\overline{)99}$   11

18. $6\overline{)87}$   14 R3

19. $5\overline{)88}$   17 R3

20. $3\overline{)71}$   23 R2

Solve these problems.

21. Rodney is sewing 26 badges on his scout uniform. How many badges will be on each sleeve?
13 badges

22. Mr. Springer has 50 extra math worksheets to hand out to 8 students. How many worksheets will he have left over if he gives each student the same number?
2 worksheets

23. Mr. Fraser is keeping track of phone calls coming into his office. He recorded 16 on Monday, 30 on Tuesday, 21 on Wednesday and 9 on Thursday. What is his average number of calls each day?
19 phone calls

24. Bruce has the following scores:

Test 1    17
Test 2    20
Test 3    18
Test 4    17
What is Bruce's average score?
18

**257**

Circle the letter of the correct answer.

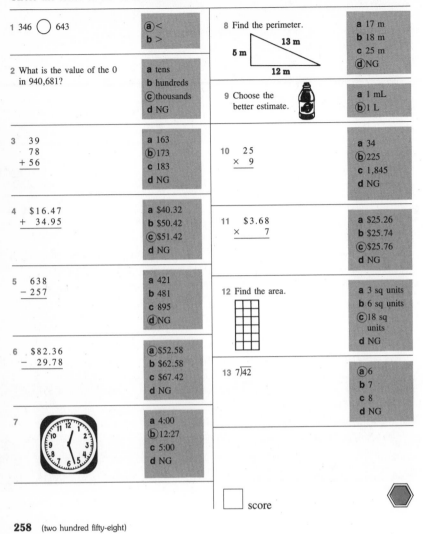

1  346 ◯ 643
  (a) <
  b >

2  What is the value of the 0 in 940,681?
  a tens
  b hundreds
  (c) thousands
  d NG

3   39
    78
  + 56
  a 163
  (b) 173
  c 183
  d NG

4  $16.47
  + 34.95
  a $40.32
  b $50.42
  (c) $51.42
  d NG

5   638
  − 257
  a 421
  b 481
  c 895
  (d) NG

6  $82.36
  − 29.78
  (a) $52.58
  b $62.58
  c $67.42
  d NG

7
  a 4:00
  (b) 12:27
  c 5:00
  d NG

8  Find the perimeter.
  13 m
  5 m
  12 m
  a 17 m
  b 18 m
  c 25 m
  (d) NG

9  Choose the better estimate.
  a 1 mL
  (b) 1 L

10   25
   ×  9
  a 34
  (b) 225
  c 1,845
  d NG

11   $3.68
   ×    7
  a $25.26
  b $25.74
  (c) $25.76
  d NG

12  Find the area.
  a 3 sq units
  b 6 sq units
  (c) 18 sq units
  d NG

13  7)42
  (a) 6
  b 7
  c 8
  d NG

☐ score

## Cumulative Review
page 258

| Item | Objective |
|---|---|
| 1 | Compare numbers less than 1,000 (See pages 27-28) |
| 2 | Identify the value of a digit in a number less than 1,000,000 (See pages 35-36) |
| 3 | Add three or four numbers (See pages 49-50) |
| 4 | Add dollars, cents with regrouping (See pages 51-52) |
| 5 | Subtract two 3-digit numbers with two regroupings (See pages 67-68) |
| 6 | Subtract dollars, cents with regrouping (See pages 75-76) |
| 7 | Read the time to the minute (See pages 87-88) |
| 8 | Add to find the perimeter (See pages 95-96) |
| 9 | Choose the appropriate metric unit of capacity (See pages 109-110) |
| 10 | Multiply 2-digit number by 1-digit number with regrouping (See pages 163-164) |
| 11 | Multiply dollars and cents by 1-digit number with regrouping (See pages 167-168) |
| 12 | Find area of plane figure in square units (See pages 181-182) |
| 13 | Find a quotient in a division fact (See pages 201-218) |

## Alternate Cumulative Review
Circle the letter of the correct answer.

1  472 ◯ 742
  a >
  (b) <
  c =

2  What is the value of 7 in 432,721?
  (a) hundreds
  b thousands
  c tens
  d NG

3   46
    27
  + 63
  (a) 136
  b 126
  c 146
  d NG

4  $27.46
  + 63.87
  a $81.23
  (b) $91.33
  c $81.33
  d NG

5   726
  − 368
  (a) 358
  b 442
  c 1094
  d NG

6  $74.25
  − 27.86
  a $53.61
  (b) $46.39
  c $56.39
  d NG

7  What time is it? (Show a clock.)
  a 12:00
  b 10:56
  c 11:50
  (d) NG

8  Find the perimeter of a triangle 15 m by 20 m by 5 m.
  (a) 40 m
  b 21 m
  c 19 m
  d NG

9  What unit would you use to measure water?
  a gram
  (b) liter
  c kilogram
  d NG

10   37
   × 6
  a 204
  (b) 222
  c 182
  d NG

11  $6.78
  × 8
  a $4856.64
  b $54.04
  (c) $54.24
  d NG

12  Find the area of a 3 ft by 8 ft rectangle.
  a 24 ft
  (b) 24 square feet
  c 24 cu ft
  d NG

13  9)72
  (a) 8
  b 7
  c 9
  d NG

# Understanding Fractions

## pages 259-260

## Objective

To understand fractions

## Materials

*sheet of 8 postage stamps
*piece of string
paper (8½ × 11 inches)
scissors

## Mental Math

Ask students to put these numbers in increasing order as you dictate them:

1. 20, 18, 19 (18, 19, 20)
2. 435, 413, 422 (413, 422, 435)
3. 37, 29, 58 (29, 37, 58)

Have them put these in decreasing order:

4. 67, 77, 64 (77, 67, 64)
5. 134, 152, 155 (155, 152, 134)

## Skill Review

Review shapes with the class. Have students draw a rectangle, square, triangle, pentagon and hexagon on the board. Show students how to draw a circle. Tie a string to a piece of chalk and have a student hold the end of the string in the center while you circle that spot with the chalk.

---

## Understanding Fractions

Art and Phil are helping their dad pour concrete for their new driveway. They have finished one section. What part of the job have the boys finished?

When an object is separated into equal parts, each part is called a fraction.

____2____ equal parts
Each is $\frac{1}{2}$.

____3____ equal parts
Each is $\frac{1}{3}$.

____4____ equal parts
Each is $\frac{1}{4}$.

____5____ equal parts
Each is $\frac{1}{5}$.

____6____ equal parts
Each is $\frac{1}{6}$.

____7____ equal parts
Each is $\frac{1}{7}$.

Art and Phil have finished  $\frac{1}{4}$ of the driveway.

## Getting Started

Write the number of equal parts. Write the fraction for one part.

1. ____4____ parts

Each is ___$\frac{1}{4}$___.

2. ____12____ parts

Each is ___$\frac{1}{12}$___.

(two hundred fifty-nine) **259**

---

## Teaching the Lesson

**Introducing the Problem** Read the problem aloud and ask students to look at the picture. Direct their attention to the divided rectangles in the model. Read the introduction and have students tell the number of parts they see in each rectangle. Read the name of each fraction represented and ask students to fill in the number of equal parts. Ask the class to match the drawing of the driveway with one of the rectangles in the model. Have a student explain how much of the driveway they have finished. (¼) Have them complete the solution sentence.

**Developing the Skill** Have each student fold a piece of paper in half. Ask them to open the sheet and explain that the two equal parts are halves. Draw the paper on the board both flat and folded. Label the drawings **whole** and **halves**. Now have them fold another sheet of paper in half twice. Explain that they have made fourths. Ask how many fourths there are in the whole sheet (4); how many halves (2). Have them repeat this activity for eighths. Ask them to draw lines along the fold lines and label the parts halves (½), fourths (¼) and eighths. (⅛)

**259**

## Practice

Write the number of equal parts. Write the fraction for one part.

1.
   _3_ parts

   Each is _1/3_ .

2.
   _5_ parts

   Each is _1/5_ .

3.
   _6_ parts

   Each is _1/6_ .

4.
   _8_ parts

   Each is _1/8_ .

5.
   _12_ parts

   Each is _1/12_ .

6.
   _8_ parts

   Each is _1/8_ .

7.
   _7_ parts

   Each is _1/7_ .

8.
   _10_ parts

   Each is _1/10_ .

---

**EXCURSION**

1. Divide each square into 4 equal parts a different way.

2. Divide each square into 6 equal parts a different way.

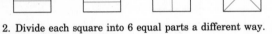

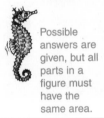

Possible answers are given, but all parts in a figure must have the same area.

**260**

# Naming Parts of a Whole

pages 261-262

## Objective

To name fractional parts of a whole

## Materials

*red chalk
*tagboard unit circle and wedge-shaped paper cutouts for halves and thirds

## Mental Math

Have students arrange these units in increasing order:

1. foot, mile, inch (inch, foot, mile)
2. hour, second, minute (second, minute, hour)
3. cup, gallon, quart (cup, quart, gallon)
4. pint, quart, cup (cup, pint, quart)
5. week, day, month (day, week, month)

## Skill Review

Draw rectangles on the board. Divide them into halves, thirds, fourths, fifths and sixths but do not put them in any order. Ask students to label the fractional parts of each. (½, ⅓, ¼, ⅕ and ⅙)

---

**Naming Parts of a Whole**

Rosita is making a quilt for her bed.
She has finished 3 of the quilt squares.
What part of the quilt has Rosita completed?

We want to write a number that shows the part of the quilt that is finished.

Rosita has finished __3__ squares of the quilt.

The finished quilt will have __4__ squares.
We use a fraction to show what part is finished.

finished parts  ⟶  3  ⟵  **numerator**
parts in the  ⟶  4  ⟵  **denominator**
whole quilt

Three-fourths or $\frac{3}{4}$ of the quilt is finished.

### Getting Started

Write the fractions.

1. five twelfths $\frac{5}{12}$    2. one eighth $\frac{1}{8}$    3. three fourths $\frac{3}{4}$

Write the fraction that tells what part is red.

4. 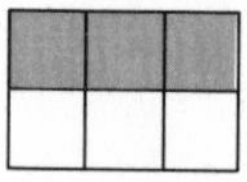  $\frac{3}{6}$    5. 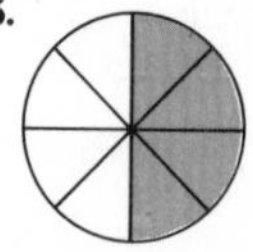  $\frac{4}{8}$    6. 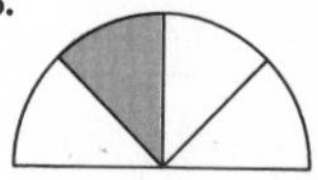  $\frac{1}{4}$

Write the fraction that tells what part is *not* red.

7. 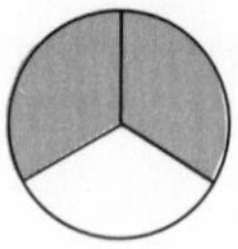  $\frac{1}{3}$    8. 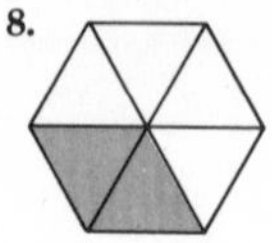  $\frac{4}{6}$    9. 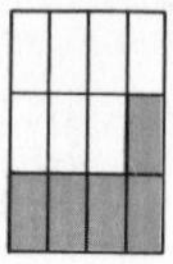  $\frac{7}{12}$

(two hundred sixty-one) **261**

---

## Teaching the Lesson

**Introducing the Problem**   Read the problem aloud and ask students to examine the picture. Have a student read and complete the information sentences. (has finished 3 squares, will have 4 squares) Read the plan sentence aloud. Point out that the quilt will have four parts, each of which will be a fourth. Explain that a fraction has a numerator which identifies a portion of the region or set and a denominator which identifies the total number of parts. On the board have a student write the number of quilt pieces finished. (3) Draw a line and have another write the number of parts the quilt will have. (4) Label the parts of the fraction **numerator** and **denominator** on the board. Read the solution sentence aloud, explaining that ¾ is read three-fourths.

**Developing the Skill**   Draw a rectangle on the board. Divide it in half and color one half red. Label the red part ½. Ask students to identify the numerator (1) and the denominator (2). Hold up the unit circle and cover it with the paper halves. Now hold up the thirds and show that 3 thirds cover the whole. Ask a student to write the fraction for one-third and for two-thirds on the board. (⅓, ⅔) Point to the two and the three in ⅔. Have a student explain what they mean. (2 means a portion of the region; 3 means the number of total parts.)

**261**

## Practice

Write the fractions.

1. two eighths $\frac{2}{8}$
2. three fourths $\frac{3}{4}$
3. five eighths $\frac{5}{8}$
4. ten twelfths $\frac{10}{12}$
5. four fifths $\frac{4}{5}$
6. seven tenths $\frac{7}{10}$

Write the fraction that tells what part is red.

7.  $\frac{3}{4}$

8.  $\frac{4}{8}$

9.  $\frac{4}{6}$

10.  $\frac{5}{10}$

11.  $\frac{3}{8}$

12.  $\frac{7}{12}$

Write the fraction that tells what part is *not* red.

13.  $\frac{1}{6}$

14.  $\frac{5}{8}$

15.  $\frac{5}{8}$

16.  $\frac{5}{12}$

17.  $\frac{1}{2}$

18.  $\frac{6}{12}$

## Apply

Solve these problems.

19. Shade $\frac{5}{6}$ of the circle.
    What part is not shaded? $\frac{1}{6}$

20. Shade $\frac{1}{8}$ of the figure.
    Shade another $\frac{3}{8}$.
    What part is not shaded? $\frac{4}{8}$

**262** (two hundred sixty-two)

## Practice

Have students complete the problems on the page. Remind them that the total number of parts is the denominator. The shaded area represents the numerator.

## Mixed Practice

1. $274 \times 8$ (2,192)
2. $795 + 438$ (1,233)
3. $68 \div 4$ (17)
4. $6,409 - 2,807$ (3,602)
5. $7 \times 56$ (392)
6. $\$58.27 - 43.36$ ($14.91)
7. $38 \div 4$ (9R2)
8. $5,727 + 88$ (5,815)
9. $\$3.25 \times 4$ ($13.00)
10. $77 \div 2$ (38R1)

## Extra Credit  *Applications*

Ask students who they would invite to a dinner, if they could ask anyone in the world. Offer them suggestions such as the President of the United States, a television star, or perhaps a favorite rock star. Then ask what they would serve for dinner for this special person, and have each student write the menu. Next, have students make a grocery list for everything they will need to make dinner. This activity can be spaced over several days. Have them use the ad section of the newspaper or visit the grocery store, and write down the prices of each item on their lists. Tell students to total their grocery bills. Ask them how much money they would have left if their grocery budget was $75.

# Naming Parts of a Set

pages 263-264

## Objective

To name fractional parts of a set

## Materials

paper squares
*four glasses and sand

## Mental Math

Have students continue these series:

1. 2, 4, 6, . . . (8, 10, 12)
2. 10, 20, 30, . . . (40, 50, 60)
3. 1, 5, 2, 6, . . . (3, 7, 4, 8)
4. 1, 2, 4, . . . (8, 16, 32)
5. 1, ½, ¼, . . . (⅛, 1/16, 1/32)
6. 10, 8, 6, . . . (4, 2, 0)
7. 1, 4, 7, . . . (10, 13, 16)

## Skill Review

Dictate the following to the class and have them write the fractions on paper:

1. one-half (½)
2. two-thirds (⅔)
3. one-fourth (¼)
4. four-fifths (⅘)
5. seven-eighths (⅞)
6. three-sixths (³⁄₆)
7. three-tenths (³⁄₁₀)

---

## Naming Parts of a Set

Tina fills 3 of the glasses in the set with milk. What part of all the glasses is filled with milk?

We want to know what part of all the glasses contains milk.

Tina pours milk into ___3___ glasses.

There are ___5___ glasses in the set.

We use a fraction to show what part of the set of glasses is filled.

glasses filled  ⟶  3  ⟵  **numerator**
number in  ⟶  5  ⟵  **denominator**
the set

Tina fills $\dfrac{3}{5}$ of the set with milk.

### Getting Started

Write the fractions that answer the questions.

1. What part of all the cars is red?

$\dfrac{2}{5}$

2. What part of all the pets is puppies?

$\dfrac{3}{4}$

3. What part of the set of coins is pennies?

$\dfrac{4}{9}$

4. What part of the set of figures is *not* squares?

$\dfrac{3}{10}$

(two hundred sixty-three) **263**

---

## Teaching the Lesson

**Introducing the Problem**   Read the problem aloud. Tell students to consider the glasses pictured as one set. Have students read and complete the information sentences. (pours milk into 3 glasses, 5 glasses in the set) Continue to read the model aloud. Explain that a fraction can be used to describe part of a set. Have a student read the number of glasses filled (3) and the number in the set. (5) Have another write them on the board as numerator and denominator of a fraction. Read the fraction *three-fifths* and have the class repeat it aloud. Ask a student to fill in the solution sentence.

**Developing the Skill**   Put four glasses on your desk and have a student fill three with sand. Ask the class how many glasses are in the set (4) and how many are filled. (3) Have a student write the fraction on the board that represents the filled glasses. (¾) Have another write the fraction that describes the empty glass. (¼) Ask a student to empty one glass and then write the fractions for the full and empty glasses. (²⁄₄, ²⁄₄) Now draw three triangles and four squares on the board. Ask how many figures are in the set (7), how many are triangles (3), and how many squares. (4) Have students write the fraction that is triangles (³⁄₇), and the fraction that is squares (⁴⁄₇) on the board.

263

## Practice

Write the fractions that answer the questions.

**1.** What fraction of all the triangles is red?

$\dfrac{5}{8}$

**2.** What fraction of all the squares is *not* red?

$\dfrac{3}{7}$

**3.** What fraction of all the bowls is full?

$\dfrac{2}{10}$

**4.** What fraction of all the vases is full?

$\dfrac{5}{6}$

**5.** What fraction of the set of dishes is *not* broken?

$\dfrac{9}{12}$

**6.** What fraction of the set of coins is quarters?

$\dfrac{5}{8}$

**7.** What fraction of the week has already passed?

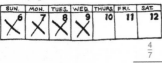

$\dfrac{4}{7}$

**8.** What fraction of the set of candles is lit?

$\dfrac{10}{12}$

## Apply

Solve these problems.

**9.** What fraction of all of the days of the week starts with the letter S?

$\dfrac{2}{7}$

**10.** What fraction of all of the months of the year starts with the letter J?

$\dfrac{3}{12}$

**264**  (two hundred sixty-four)

**264**

# Finding a Fraction of a Number

**pages 265-266**

## Objective

To find a fraction of a 1- or 2-digit number

## Materials

counters
15-inch strings
*overhead projector
*tagboard unit circle with paper cutouts for halves, thirds and fourths

## Mental Math

Have students tell whether the middle number is closer to the first or last number in each set:

1. 121, 130, 175 (first)
2. 100, 151, 200 (last)
3. 4, 8, 11 (last)
4. 15, 25, 36 (first)
5. 0, 5, 10 (same distance)

## Skill Review

Dictate these fractions to the class. Have them write and illustrate each:

1. two-thirds ($\frac{2}{3}$)
2. five-tenths ($\frac{5}{10}$)
3. three-fourths ($\frac{3}{4}$)
4. seven-eighths ($\frac{7}{8}$)
5. seven-ninths ($\frac{7}{9}$)

---

### Finding a Fraction of a Number

Martina has to polish her mother's shoes to earn her allowance this week. She has shined $\frac{1}{4}$ of them so far. How many shoes has she polished?

We want to know the number of shoes Martina has polished.

Martina has ___12___ shoes to polish.

She has shined $\frac{1}{4}$ of them.

To find the number of shoes, we find $\frac{1}{4}$ of 12. This is the same as dividing 12 by 4.

$$12 \div \underline{\ \ 4\ \ } = \underline{\ \ 3\ \ }$$

Martina has polished ___3___ shoes so far.

### Getting Started

Find the fraction of each number.

1. $\frac{1}{3}$ of 6 = ___2___
2. $\frac{1}{2}$ of 8 = ___4___
3. $\frac{1}{5}$ of 10 = ___2___
4. $\frac{1}{3}$ of 12 = ___4___
5. $\frac{1}{6}$ of 18 = ___3___
6. $\frac{1}{9}$ of 27 = ___3___
7. $\frac{1}{7}$ of 49 = ___7___
8. $\frac{1}{4}$ of 64 = ___16___

Solve these problems.

9. Pat has 60¢. She gave her brother $\frac{1}{4}$ of the money. How much money did Pat give her brother?
15¢

10. Dick has 85 marbles. He gave $\frac{1}{5}$ of the marbles to Jim. How many marbles does Dick still have?
68 marbles

(two hundred sixty-five) **265**

---

## Teaching the Lesson

**Introducing the Problem**   Read the problem aloud. Have students read and complete the information sentences. (has 12 shoes to polish, has shined ¼ of them.) Read the plan section of the model aloud. Explain that finding a fraction of a larger number involves division. In this case they will divide the number of shoes into four groups. On the board, write **12 ÷ ___ = ___**. Have one student complete the problem while others write the answers in their books. (4, 3) Have the class read and complete the solution sentence. (has polished 3 shoes so far)

**Developing the Skill**   Put 12 counters on the overhead projector and explain that you want to divide them into thirds. Have a student come up and divide the 12 evenly with string loops.
Ask how many counters are in each loop. (4) Now ask a volunteer to explain what we mean by a third of the counters. (4 counters) On the board write, **12 ÷ 3 = 4**. Have students use the counters and string at their desks to find half of 12 (6), one-fourth of 12 (3), and one-sixth of 12 (2).

## Practice

Find the fraction of each number.

1. $\frac{1}{2}$ of 16 = __8__  2. $\frac{1}{3}$ of 18 = __6__  3. $\frac{1}{5}$ of 25 = __5__  4. $\frac{1}{7}$ of 28 = __4__

5. $\frac{1}{4}$ of 32 = __8__  6. $\frac{1}{6}$ of 30 = __5__  7. $\frac{1}{8}$ of 64 = __8__  8. $\frac{1}{9}$ of 72 = __8__

9. $\frac{1}{7}$ of 56 = __8__  10. $\frac{1}{4}$ of 60 = __15__  11. $\frac{1}{3}$ of 69 = __23__  12. $\frac{1}{8}$ of 72 = __9__

13. $\frac{1}{2}$ of 76 = __38__  14. $\frac{1}{6}$ of 72 = __12__  15. $\frac{1}{5}$ of 85 = __17__  16. $\frac{1}{9}$ of 27 = __3__

17. $\frac{1}{6}$ of 36 = __6__  18. $\frac{1}{4}$ of 96 = __24__  19. $\frac{1}{3}$ of 81 = __27__  20. $\frac{1}{8}$ of 40 = __5__

## Apply

Solve these problems.

21. Rene buys 18 cans of cat food. She wants $\frac{1}{2}$ of the cans to be tuna. How many cans of tuna does she buy?
9 cans

22. Mr. Campana buys 48 cans of vegetables. He wants $\frac{1}{4}$ of the cans to be corn. How many cans of corn does Mr. Campana buy?
12 cans

23. Hal has 36 fish in his tank. He says $\frac{1}{3}$ of them are goldfish. How many of Hal's fish are goldfish?
12 fish

24. Lori has 75¢. She gives $\frac{1}{5}$ of her money to her best friend Jo. How much does Lori give Jo?
15¢

25. Ellen has 24 stamps. She uses $\frac{1}{4}$ of them to mail a package. How many stamps does Ellen have left?
18 stamps

26. Eduardo buys a jacket for $96. His father agrees to pay $\frac{1}{6}$ of the price. How much does Eduardo pay?
$80

# Writing Equivalent Fractions

pages 267-268

## Objective

To understand equivalent fractions

## Materials

*tagboard unit circle
three paper circles, same size as unit
circle

## Mental Math

Have students round to the nearest
dollar before they add:

1. $1.32 + 1.99 ($3)
2. $29.00 + 41.95 ($71)
3. $14.95 + 14.95 ($30)
4. $10.50 + 2.50 ($14)
5. Erin wants to buy a baby doll that
   costs $14.95 and a doll bonnet for
   $3.95. About how much will these
   items cost? ($19)

## Skill Review

Remind students that to find the number of objects in a fraction of a whole
set, they have to divide by the number of fractional parts. For example, to
find one-third of 12 they divide 12
into three parts. (12 ÷ 3 = 4) Have
them find:

1. ¼ of 16 (4)
2. ⅕ of 20 (4)
3. ½ of 32 (16)
4. ⅓ of 30 (10)

## Writing Equivalent Fractions

Jeff and Nadia are cutting pies to serve
at the PTA social. Jeff cuts his pies into
thirds, and serves $\frac{1}{3}$ of a pie to each person.
Nadia cuts her pies into sixths. How many
sixths does Nadia have to serve to each
person to equal Jeff's serving?

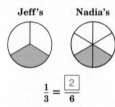

We want to know how many of Nadia's pieces
equal one of Jeff's.

Each of Jeff's pieces is $\frac{\boxed{1}}{\boxed{3}}$ of a pie.

Nadia cuts her pie into __6__ equal pieces.
We can draw a picture and compare the pies.

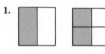

Jeff's    Nadia's

$$\frac{1}{3} = \frac{\boxed{2}}{6}$$

One-third of Jeff's pie equals $\frac{\boxed{2}}{6}$ of Nadia's pie.

Fractions that are equal are called **equivalent fractions.**

### Getting Started

Write the equivalent fractions.

1.

$\frac{1}{2} = \frac{2}{4}$

2.

$\frac{1}{3} = \frac{2}{6}$

Draw a picture to help you find the equivalent fractions.

3. $\frac{1}{2} = \frac{3}{6}$           4. $\frac{3}{4} = \frac{6}{8}$

(two hundred sixty-seven) **267**

## Teaching the Lesson

**Introducing the Problem**  Read the problem aloud and
have students look carefully at the picture. Have students
read and complete the information sentences. (Jeff's pieces,
⅓ of a pie; Nadia cuts 6 pieces.) Read the plan sentences
and direct their attention to the pies illustrated. Ask how
many pieces of Nadia's pie it would take to make one piece
of Jeff's. (2) Ask how many pieces Jeff would have to cut
each of his wedges into in order to match Nadia's. (2) Read
the solution sentence aloud and have a student supply the
answer. (one-third of Jeff's equals ⅔ of Nadia's) Explain
that when fractions have different denominators but are
equal in value, they are called **equivalent fractions.**

**Developing the Skill**  Use the tagboard unit circle and
three 10-inch paper circles. Cut the paper circles into pie-
shaped wedges: halves, thirds and sixths. Hold up the tagboard unit circle and put a half circle on it. Ask a student to
place fourths on the half until it is completely covered. Ask
how many fourths it took to cover the half. (2) Write on the
board: ½ = ²⁄₄. Now hold up the unit circle covered with
the half and have a student cover the half with sixths. When
it is completely covered ask how many sixths it took to
cover the half. (3) Write: ½ = ²⁄₄ = ³⁄₆.

**267**

## Practice

Write the equivalent fractions.

1.
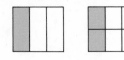

$$\frac{1}{3} = \frac{2}{6}$$

2.

$$\frac{1}{4} = \frac{2}{8}$$

3.

$$\frac{2}{6} = \frac{1}{3}$$

4.

$$\frac{2}{5} = \frac{4}{10}$$

5.
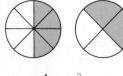

$$\frac{3}{6} = \frac{6}{12}$$

6.

$$\frac{3}{4} = \frac{6}{8}$$

7.

$$\frac{4}{8} = \frac{2}{4}$$

8.

$$\frac{2}{10} = \frac{1}{5}$$

Draw a picture to help you find the equivalent fractions.

9. $\frac{8}{10} = \frac{4}{5}$       10. $\frac{3}{9} = \frac{1}{3}$

11. $\frac{3}{6} = \frac{6}{12}$       12. $\frac{4}{8} = \frac{1}{2}$

**268**   (two hundred sixty-eight)

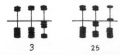
**268**

# Comparing Fractions

## Objective

To compare fractions with different denominators

## Materials

*tagboard unit circle and paper cutouts for fifths and tenths

## Mental Math

Have students round to the nearest $10 and subtract:

1. $34 − 19 ($10)
2. $75 − 25 ($50)
3. $110 − 105 ($0)
4. $423 − 399 ($20)
5. $885 − 780 ($110)
6. Ray had a twenty dollar bill and bought a snow shovel for $8.95. About how much change should he expect? ($11)

## Skill Review

Illustrate these equivalent fractions on the board with rectangles or circles. Have students write the equivalent fractions:

1. $\frac{1}{2} = \frac{3}{6}$
2. $\frac{4}{8} = \frac{2}{4}$
3. $\frac{1}{3} = \frac{4}{12}$
4. $\frac{3}{4} = \frac{6}{8}$

---

## Comparing Fractions

Carlos and Ivan each ordered the same size cheese pizza. Neither boy can finish, so they save part to take home. Does Carlos have more or less pizza left over than Ivan?

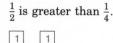

We want to know if the pizza Carlos has left over is greater or less than Ivan's.

Carlos saves $\frac{1}{4}$ of his pizza.

Ivan saves $\frac{1}{2}$ of his.

We can draw a picture and compare the pieces.

$\frac{1}{4}$ for Carlos  $\frac{1}{2}$ for Ivan

$\frac{1}{4}$ is less than $\frac{1}{2}$.  $\frac{1}{2}$ is greater than $\frac{1}{4}$.

$\frac{1}{4} < \frac{1}{2}$  $\frac{1}{2} > \frac{1}{4}$

The pizza Carlos has left over is ___less___ than Ivan's.

### Getting Started

Compare these numbers. Write <, > or = in the circle.

1.

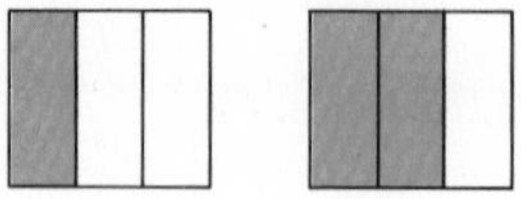

$\frac{1}{3}$ ⊙< $\frac{2}{3}$

2.

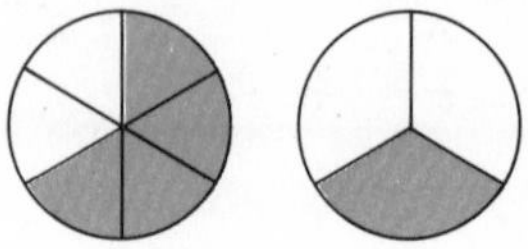

$\frac{4}{6}$ ⊙> $\frac{1}{3}$

---

## Teaching the Lesson

**Introducing the Problem**   Read the problem aloud and have students examine the illustration carefully. Ask students to complete the information sentences. (Carlos saves ¼. Ivan saves ½.) Direct the students' attention to the pizza diagrams. Ask students to complete the comparisons. (¼ is less than ½. ½ is greater than ¼. Illustrate the use of the < and > symbols on the board. Have a student read and complete the solution sentence.

**Developing the Skill**   Explain that they will compare unequal fractions. Hold up the unit circle and all the fifths. Show that five-fifths completely cover the unit circle. Now ask one student to hold one-fifth and another student to hold two. Ask the class who is holding the greater amount. (⅖) Write the comparison on the board: **⅖ > ⅕.** Now hold up the unit circle and one-fifth. Have a volunteer come up and cover the fifth with tenths. Ask how many tenths cover one-fifth. (2) Write on the board: **⅕ = ²/₁₀.** Now have one student hold up one fifth and another ³/₁₀. Ask which is holding more. (³/₁₀) Write **⅕ < ³/₁₀.** Have two students compare ⅖ and ⁵/₁₀. Ask one of them to write the comparison on the board. (⅖ < ⁵/₁₀)

**269**

## Practice

Compare these numbers. Write <, > or = in the circle.

1.

$$\frac{1}{4} \;\bigcirc<\; \frac{3}{4}$$

2.

$$\frac{5}{8} \;\bigcirc>\; \frac{3}{8}$$

3.

$$\frac{1}{2} \;\bigcirc<\; \frac{7}{10}$$

4.

$$\frac{3}{5} \;\bigcirc=\; \frac{6}{10}$$

5.

$$\frac{5}{8} \;\bigcirc>\; \frac{2}{4}$$

6.

$$\frac{2}{6} \;\bigcirc<\; \frac{2}{3}$$

### EXCURSION

Use the picture to help you answer the questions.

1. What part of the whole figure is each square? $\frac{1}{16}$

2. What part of the figure is each column? $\frac{4}{16}$

3. What part is each row? $\frac{4}{16}$    4. What part is each half-row? $\frac{2}{16}$

5. What part is 2 rows? $\frac{8}{16}$    6. What part is 2 columns? $\frac{8}{16}$

7. Why is it easy to compare all these fractions?

   They all have the same denominator.

**270** (two hundred seventy)

---

## Correcting Common Errors

Some students may compare just the numerators when comparing fractions. For problems like those in Exercises 3–6, have students look at the diagrams first and point to the one with the greater part shaded. Then have them look at the corresponding fractions and write the correct symbol.

## Enrichment

Have students use the abacus for addition. Explain that they are to make the first number in each sum, pushing the required beads to the divider. Starting with the ones they add each digit of the second number. When they reach ten in any row, they push ten away in that row and move one bead in the next row. Give them several practice problems. Have them check their answers with a calculator.

## Practice

Have students complete the problems on the page. Write **< means less than, > means more than** on the board as a reminder.

## Excursion

Give 3 sheets of paper to one student and several identical books to another student. Ask if we can compare what the 2 students have. (No, one has papers and the other has books.) Replace the student's books with 2 sheets of paper and ask if we can now make a comparison. (Yes, one has 3 sheets and the other has 2.) Tell students that just as we can compare what each student has when both have papers, we can easily compare 2 fractions when both have the same denominator. Have students answer the questions.

## Extra Credit  *Measurement*

Bring necessary ingredients to class for students to make the play dough recipe. Include measuring cups, etc. Divide stu-

dents into small groups. Write the following recipe on the board:

> ***Edible Playdough***
> ⅓ **cup peanut butter**
> ¼ **cup honey**
> ⅔ **cup powdered milk**

Mix all ingredients to the consistency of playdough. Refrigerate after use.

Tell students that they will be making the playdough for a first-grade class, but that to make enough, each group must double the recipe. Have them make the necessary calculations to adjust the recipe. Then allow students to get the necessary utensils, measure the ingredients and make the play dough. Remind them to work carefully and clean up after they have finished. Refrigerate the playdough overnight, and allow the class to present it to the younger students the next day.

# Adding Fractions

## pages 271-272

### Objective

To add fractions with like denominators

### Materials

one-inch graph paper cut into 5- and
  6-inch strips
*tagboard unit circle and paper
  cutouts for fourths and sixths

### Mental Math

Have students round to the nearest
dollar and multiply:

1. $4.50 × 3 ($15)
2. $12.25 × 2 ($24)
3. $99.95 × 2 ($200)
4. $235.50 × 1 ($236)
5. $9.75 × 12 ($120)
6. $8.29 × 7 ($56)
7. $1,429 × 0 ($0)

### Skill Review

Illustrate these sets of fractions on the
board. Ask students to copy the drawings, color the appropriate segments,
and compare each pair.

1. ⅔ and ⅚ (⅔ < ⅚)
2. ½ and ¾ (½ < ¾)
3. 3/6 and ⅓ (3/6 > ⅓)

---

## Adding Fractions

On Monday, Beth's father told
her he had worked $\frac{1}{5}$ of his
workweek already. On Wednesday,
he said he had worked another
$\frac{2}{5}$ of his week. What part of the
week had her father worked?

We want to find the part of the week Beth's
father had worked so far.

By Monday evening he had worked $\boxed{\frac{1}{5}}$ of a week.

Tuesday and Wednesday he had worked another $\boxed{\frac{2}{5}}$ of a week.

To find the part of the week that he had worked,
we add $\frac{1}{5}$ and $\frac{2}{5}$.

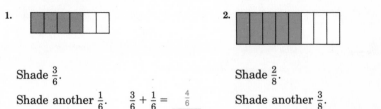

$\frac{1}{5} + \frac{2}{5} = \boxed{\frac{3}{5}}$

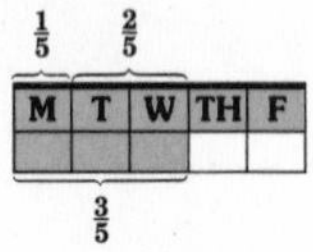

$\frac{1}{5}$ Monday

$+ \frac{2}{5}$ Tuesday and Wednesday

$\boxed{\frac{3}{5}}$ Monday through Wednesday

Beth's father had worked $\boxed{\frac{3}{5}}$ of his workweek.

✔ Remember that when the denominators are the same, only the
numerators are added. The denominator remains the same.

### Getting Started

Use the pictures to help you add these fractions.

1.

Shade $\frac{3}{6}$.

Shade another $\frac{1}{6}$.    $\frac{3}{6} + \frac{1}{6} = \underline{\frac{4}{6}}$

2.

Shade $\frac{2}{8}$.

Shade another $\frac{3}{8}$.

$\frac{2}{8}$
$+ \frac{3}{8}$
$\overline{\frac{5}{8}}$

(two hundred seventy-one) **271**

---

## Teaching the Lesson

**Introducing the Problem** Read the problem aloud.
Have students read and complete the information sentences.
(by Monday he had worked ⅕ of a week, Tuesday and
Wednesday he had worked another ⅖) Read the plan
aloud, explaining that in order to find the total they will

have to add ⅕ and ⅖. Write **⅕ + ⅖ = $\frac{\square}{5}$** on the board.

Direct their attention to the week's calendar. Ask how many
days there are in the work week. (5) Ask how many days
her father has worked. (3) Have a student tell how many
fifths of a week he has worked. (⅗) Write the problem
again in vertical form. Have students complete the addition
problems in their books. (⅕ + ⅖ = ⅗) Have students read
and complete the solution sentence. (⅗ of his work week)
Explain that because all fifths are the same size, they can
simply add the number of fifths in the numerator of the
fractions: 1 + 2 = 3 fifths.

**Developing the Skill** Hold up the unit circle and cover
part with one-fourth. Now add another fourth. Ask how
many fourths you have all together. (2) Write ¼ + ¼ = 2/4
on the board. Hold up still another fourth and have a student write the addition. (2/4 + ¼ = ¾) Repeat showing different combinations of fourths and of sixths. Have students
write the addition on the board.

**271**

**Practice**

Use the pictures to help you add these fractions.

1.

Shade $\frac{1}{6}$.

Shade another $\frac{2}{6}$. $\qquad \frac{1}{6} + \frac{2}{6} = \underline{\frac{3}{6}}$

2.
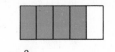

Shade $\frac{2}{5}$.

Shade another $\frac{2}{5}$. $\quad \begin{array}{r} \frac{2}{5} \\ + \frac{2}{5} \\ \hline \frac{4}{5} \end{array}$

3.

Shade $\frac{3}{8}$.

Shade another $\frac{2}{8}$. $\qquad \frac{3}{8} + \frac{2}{8} = \underline{\frac{5}{8}}$

4.

Shade $\frac{3}{10}$.

Shade another $\frac{2}{10}$. $\quad \begin{array}{r} \frac{3}{10} \\ + \frac{2}{10} \\ \hline \frac{5}{10} \end{array}$

5.

Shade $\frac{1}{4}$.

Shade another $\frac{2}{4}$. $\qquad \frac{1}{4} + \frac{2}{4} = \underline{\frac{3}{4}}$

6.
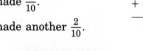

Shade $\frac{3}{7}$.

Shade another $\frac{4}{7}$. $\quad \begin{array}{r} \frac{3}{7} \\ + \frac{4}{7} \\ \hline \frac{7}{7} \end{array}$

7.

Shade $\frac{4}{9}$.

Shade another $\frac{3}{9}$. $\qquad \frac{4}{9} + \frac{3}{9} = \underline{\frac{7}{9}}$

8.

Shade $\frac{5}{8}$.

Shade another $\frac{2}{8}$. $\quad \begin{array}{r} \frac{5}{8} \\ + \frac{2}{8} \\ \hline \frac{7}{8} \end{array}$

9.

Shade $\frac{5}{10}$.

Shade another $\frac{3}{10}$. $\qquad \frac{5}{10} + \frac{3}{10} = \underline{\frac{8}{10}}$

10.

Shade $\frac{2}{6}$.

Shade another $\frac{3}{6}$. $\quad \begin{array}{r} \frac{2}{6} \\ + \frac{3}{6} \\ \hline \frac{5}{6} \end{array}$

## Correcting Common Errors

Some students may have difficulty associating the drawing with the addition problem. Have them work with partners with a strip of paper separated into 8 equal parts. Tell them to color ³⁄₈ of the paper and then write the fraction to describe what they have done. Next, tell them that they are going to add, so they should write an addition sign next to the ³⁄₈. Tell them to color another ²⁄₈ of the paper strip and write the fraction for what they did next to the addition sign. Have them write an equals sign and then ask, "How much of the paper is colored?" (⁵⁄₈) Have students write ⁵⁄₈ next to the equals sign.

## Enrichment

Give students several subtraction problems to work on the abacus. Ask them to push the beads away from the divider then register the minuend by pushing the appropriate number of beads to the center. To subtract they remove beads from the center. See if they notice that to trade for a ten, they have to push a ten away in the tens row, adding 2 fives in the ones row.

## Practice

Have students work all the problems on the page. Tell them to shade the pictures to help them add fractional parts.

### Mixed Practice

1. $701 - 38$ (663)
2. $6,790 + 2,532$ (9,322)
3. $\frac{4}{10} = \frac{}{5}$ (2)
4. $\frac{1}{9}$ of 27 (3)
5. $\frac{1}{5} + \frac{3}{5}$ $\left(\frac{4}{5}\right)$
6. $62 \div 2$ (31)
7. $\frac{}{12} = \frac{1}{4}$ (3)
8. $\$3.76 \times 3$ (\$11.28)
9. $71 \div 4$ (17 R3)
10. $\$63.00 - 24.38$ (\$38.62)

## Extra Credit  *Numeration*

Have students test their knowledge of some well-known children's stories by following these directions:

1. Write your age.
2. Multiply it by the number of letters in Pinocchio. (9)
3. Divide by the number of pigs who built houses. (3)
4. Add the number of kittens that lost their mittens. (3)
5. Multiply by the number of children who found the witch's house of cake and candy. (2)
6. Divide by the number of letters in the second name of the horse, whose first name was *Black*. (6)
7. Subtract the number of children in the story of *The Three Bears.* (1)

If completed correctly, the students will arrive at their age, or the number they started with.

# Subtracting Fractions

## pages 273-274

### Objective

To subtract fractions with like denominators

### Materials

strips of one-inch graph paper
*tagboard unit circle with paper
  cutouts for fifths
*transparent container

### Mental Math

Have students round each amount to the nearest dollar and divide:

1. $25.15 \div 5 = ($5)
2. $21.20 \div 7 = ($3)
3. $25.34 \div 4 = ($6 R$1)
4. $8.95 \div 4 = ($2 R$1)
5. $48.91 \div 8 = ($6 R$1)
6. $55.01 \div 10 = ($5 R$5)

### Skill Review

Remind students to add fractions with like denominators by adding the numerators. Put this example on the board: $2/5 + 1/5 = 3/5$. Then dictate the following problems to the class:

1. $1/3 + 1/3 = (2/3)$
2. $3/6 + 1/6 = (4/6)$
3. $4/9 + 4/9 = (8/9)$
4. $5/12 + 3/12 = (8/12)$
5. $1/2 + 1/2 = (2/2)$
6. $2/3 + 1/3 = (3/3)$

## Subtracting Fractions

Daphne is cooking rice for dinner. She uses $\frac{2}{4}$ cup of water. How much water does she have left over in her measuring cup?

We want to know the part of the cup of water Daphne has left over.

Daphne starts with $\frac{3}{4}$ cup of water.

She uses $\frac{2}{4}$ cup of water to make the rice.

To find the part left over, we subtract $\frac{2}{4}$ from $\frac{3}{4}$.

$$\frac{3}{4} - \frac{2}{4} = \frac{1}{4}$$

$\frac{3}{4}$ to start

$- \frac{2}{4}$ used

$\frac{1}{4}$ left

Daphne has $\frac{1}{4}$ of a cup of water left over.

✔ Remember that when the denominators are the same, only the numerators are subtracted. The denominator remains the same.

### Getting Started

Use the pictures to help you subtract these fractions.

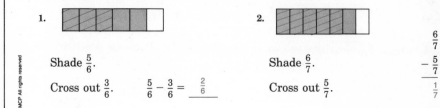

1. Shade $\frac{5}{6}$.

Cross out $\frac{3}{6}$.

$\frac{5}{6} - \frac{3}{6} = \frac{2}{6}$

2. Shade $\frac{6}{7}$.

Cross out $\frac{5}{7}$.

$$\begin{aligned}&\frac{6}{7}\\-\,&\frac{5}{7}\\\hline&\frac{1}{7}\end{aligned}$$

(two hundred seventy-three) **273**

---

## Teaching the Lesson

**Introducing the Problem**   Read the problem aloud. Have students read and complete the information sentences. (starts with ¾ cup water, uses ²⁄₄ cup to make rice) Read the plan sentence aloud. Copy the subtraction in horizontal and vertical forms on the board and ask a student to supply the missing numerators. (¾ − ²⁄₄ = ¼; ¾ to start − ²⁄₄ used = ¼ left) Reproduce the illustration on the board, shading the original ¾ in one way and the ²⁄₄ in another. Ask a student to point to the fraction that remains after ²⁄₄ has been removed. (¼) Have students complete the solution sentence. (¼) Read the final note to the class, explaining that the denominators merely label the type of fraction. During subtraction, the denominators stay the same, while the numerators are subtracted.

**Developing the Skill**   Hold up the unit circle and put three-fifths on it. Ask students to identify the fraction. (³⁄₅) Now put the fifths in a transparent container and have a student remove one of the fifths. Ask how many remain in the container. (²⁄₅) Write the subtraction on the board: $3/5 − 1/5 = 2/5$.

**273**

**Practice**

Use the pictures to help you subtract these fractions.

**1.**

Shade $\frac{3}{8}$.

Cross out $\frac{1}{8}$.  $\frac{3}{8} - \frac{1}{8} = \underline{\frac{2}{8}}$

**2.**

Shade $\frac{5}{6}$.

Cross out $\frac{3}{6}$.

$$\frac{5}{6}$$
$$-\frac{3}{6}$$
$$\overline{\frac{2}{6}}$$

**3.**

Shade $\frac{5}{7}$.

Cross out $\frac{2}{7}$.  $\frac{5}{7} - \frac{2}{7} = \underline{\frac{3}{7}}$

**4.**

Shade $\frac{2}{3}$.

Cross out $\frac{1}{3}$.

$$\frac{2}{3}$$
$$-\frac{1}{3}$$
$$\overline{\frac{1}{3}}$$

**5.**

Shade $\frac{3}{4}$.

Cross out $\frac{1}{4}$.  $\frac{3}{4} - \frac{1}{4} = \underline{\frac{2}{4}}$

**6.**

Shade $\frac{7}{10}$.

Cross out $\frac{5}{10}$.

$$\frac{7}{10}$$
$$-\frac{5}{10}$$
$$\overline{\frac{2}{10}}$$

**7.**

Shade $\frac{9}{10}$.

Cross out $\frac{6}{10}$.  $\frac{9}{10} - \frac{6}{10} = \underline{\frac{3}{10}}$

**8.**

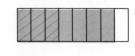

Shade $\frac{4}{5}$.

Cross out $\frac{3}{5}$.

$$\frac{4}{5}$$
$$-\frac{3}{5}$$
$$\overline{\frac{1}{5}}$$

**9.**

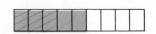

Shade $\frac{5}{9}$.

Cross out $\frac{3}{9}$.  $\frac{5}{9} - \frac{3}{9} = \underline{\frac{2}{9}}$

**10.**

Shade $\frac{7}{8}$.

Cross out $\frac{3}{8}$.

$$\frac{7}{8}$$
$$-\frac{3}{8}$$
$$\overline{\frac{4}{8}}$$

**274** (two hundred seventy-four)

## Correcting Common Errors

Students may have difficulty visualizing subtraction of fractions. Give each student a one-by-six inch strip of one-inch graph paper. Ask what part of the whole strip does each square represent. (⅙) Have them shade 5 squares and ask what part of the whole strip do the shaded squares represent. (⅚) Have them cut apart all the squares and work with the shaded ones. Tell them to remove 2 shaded squares and ask how many shaded squares remain. (3) Ask what part of the whole do these squares represent. (³⁄₆) Write on the chalkboard:

$$⅚ - ²⁄₆ = ³⁄₆$$

## Enrichment

Bring in a book on sign language for the group. *Signing: How to Speak with Your Hands* by Elaine Costello is one possibility. Have students study the section on signing numbers one through twenty. Point out that like Roman numerals and the Chinese system, sign language is based on fives. Ask the group why they think this is so. (It uses one hand, or five fingers.) Have students practice the numbers through 20.

## Practice

Have students complete the problems on the page. Remind them that when they subtract fractions with like denominators, they subtract only the numerators.

## Extra Credit  *Applications*

Tell students you know some birthday mathematical magic. Tell them they can guess the age of a person and also the month of their birthday. Tell them to follow this procedure: Tell another student to write the number of their birthday month, without letting you see it. (January is 1, February is 2, etc.) Then have that student multiply the number of their birthday month by 2, and add 5 to their answer. Next, tell them to multiply that answer by 50, and add their age. Next, tell them to subtract 365 (the number of days in a year) from that answer, and add 115. Have them give you their answer. The first number of their answer will be the number of the birthday month, and the second number will be their age. (If the number is 510, their birthday is in May and they are 10 years old.)

# Problem Solving, Making a Graph

## pages 275-276

### Objective

To use graphs in problem solving

### Materials

graph paper with one inch squares

### Mental Math

Ask students to suggest how these numbers should be rounded. Then have them round and add:

1. 23 + 49 (to nearest 10, 70)
2. 338 + 921 (to nearest 100, 1,200)
3. $.56 + .88 (to nearest $.10, $1.50)
4. 5 + 129 (to nearest 10, 140)
5. 338 + 2,459 (to nearest 100, 2,800)
6. $59.50 + 3.49 (to nearest dollar, $63)
7. $159 + 304 (to nearest $100, $500)

---

## Making a Graph

Lisa puts 10¢ in her piggy bank. Next week she will put in double that amount. The week after that, she will double that amount. If she continues this pattern, how many weeks will it take before Lisa is putting over a dollar at a time in her bank?

★ **SEE**

We want to know how long it will take before Lisa is saving over a dollar a week.
Lisa saves 10¢ the first week.
She always doubles the amount she saves from the week before.

★ **PLAN**

We can make a bar graph of her savings.

★ **DO**

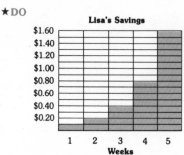

**Lisa's Savings**

In week number __5__, Lisa will save __$1.60__. This will be the first week her savings will be more than a dollar.

★ **CHECK**

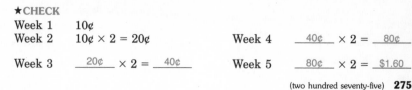

| | | | | |
|---|---|---|---|---|
| Week 1 | 10¢ | | | |
| Week 2 | 10¢ × 2 = 20¢ | | Week 4 | __40¢__ × 2 = __80¢__ |
| Week 3 | __20¢__ × 2 = __40¢__ | | Week 5 | __80¢__ × 2 = __$1.60__ |

(two hundred seventy-five) **275**

---

## Teaching the Lesson

Read the problem aloud. Explain that using the SEE-PLAN-DO-CHECK method, students will learn to use graphs to solve word problems. Point out that graphs are like the tables they made in the last chapter. Have one student read the SEE section aloud. You read the PLAN section, explaining that a bar graph is like a picture of the information given in the problem. Direct their attention to the bar graph outlined in the space below. Put the bar graph on the board and work through the problem with the class. Read the solution sentences and ask students to provide the information required from their graphs. (week number 5, will save $1.60) Ask students to complete the check in their books. Hold up one graph and ask students what they can see from a distance. (The amount being saved is increasing rapidly.) Point out that this is the function of graphs. They allow us to get number information at a glance.

**275**

**Apply**

Complete the graphs to help you solve these problems.

1. Fritz thinks about his day. He spends 8 hours sleeping, 2 hours eating, 6 hours studying, 4 hours playing, 1 hour reading, 2 hours working and 1 hour watching television. Help Fritz finish the graph of his day.

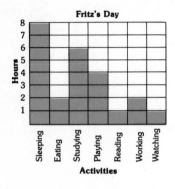

2. In 1970, 25,000 people lived in Grover City. By 1980 the population had doubled. If this pattern continues, how many people will live in Grover City in the year 2000?

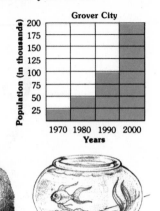

Make graphs to help you solve these problems.

3. In your class, what color eyes do most of the students have?
   Answers will vary.

4. In your class, what kind of pet is the most popular and what kind is the least popular?
   Answers will vary.

Explain how you got your answer to these problems.

5. Paula's Pizza Parlor serves a group of friends two and four-sixths pizzas. Is this closer to two pizzas or to three pizzas?
   Closer to 3 pizzas

6. Using only 1-digit numbers, what is the largest fraction less than 1 that you can write and what is the smallest?
   $\frac{8}{9}$ and $\frac{1}{9}$

7. To make a fraction larger, do you increase the numerator or the denominator?
   The numerator

8. To make a fraction smaller, do you decrease the numerator or the denominator?
   The numerator

**276** (two hundred seventy-six)

---

## Solution Notes

1. Because the graph has already been laid out, have students simply shade in columns. Ask students to tell you at a glance what Fritz spends the most time doing. (sleeping)

2. Explain to students that the graph shown does not start at one the way many graphs do. If they look at the vertical axis, they will see that the first number is 25,000. Each line after that increases by 25,000.

3. Give each student a piece of graph paper. Suggest to students that this problem could first be done as a tally. The squares can then be shaded one by one on a bar graph. Have students agree on what colors they will list before they begin.

4. Give students graph paper. Then determine the kinds of pets they will list before students start their bar graphs.

### Higher-Order Thinking Skills

5. Analysis: The student can visualize this comparison by making a bar graph representing 3 pizzas, 2 pizzas, and two and four-sixths pizzas.

6. Analysis: Explanations will vary, but the greatest 1-digit whole number is 9. This should be used for the "whole," or the denominator. The numerators, then, can be chosen accordingly. A bar graph of each of the ninths from ⅑ to ⅛ will help the students visualize these numbers.

7. Analysis: The denominator tells how many pieces are in the whole. The numerator tells how many of these pieces you are considering. Encourage students to prove this in a bar graph.

8. Analysis: The denominator tells how many pieces are in the whole. The numerator tells how many of these pieces you are considering; so, the fewer of these pieces, the smaller the amount. Encourage students to prove this in a bar graph.

---

**Extra Credit**  *Measurement*

Have students measure their height in meters. Tell students to use strips of construction paper and glue them together to make models of their heights. For example: white strips = 1 meter, green strips = 1 decimeter, orange strips = 1 centimeter. Give students a yellow circle to place between the meter and decimeters to stand for the decimal point. Lastly, tell students to label the white strip with their actual height.

# Using Calculators, Finding a Fractional Part

**pages 277-278**

## Objective

To use calculators to find a fractional part

## Materials

calculators

## Mental Math

Explain that **n** is a number half-way between two other numbers. Ask students to identify **n**:

1. between 35 and 55. (45)
2. between 0 and 100. (50)
3. between 5¢ and 15¢. (10¢)
4. between $1.50 and $2.00. ($1.75)
5. between 2 and 6. (4)
6. between 12 and 24. (18)
7. between 30 and 36. (33)

## Skill Review

Remind students that to find a single fractional part of a number, they divide by the denominator. Ask students to find:

1. ½ of 10. (5)
2. ⅕ of 15. (3)
3. ¹⁄₁₀ of 40. (4)
4. ⅙ of 12. (2)
5. ⅓ of 24. (8)
6. ⅐ of 49. (7)

---

**Using Calculators, Finding a Fractional Part**

Marty is buying a new shirt at a sale. The sale price is hidden. Help Marty figure how much he will save.

We want to know how much Marty will save.

We know the original price was ___$27.75___.

Marty will save $\frac{2}{3}$ of the original price.

To find the amount he will save, we need to multiply

___$27.75___ by $\frac{2}{3}$.

We already know that $\$27.75 \times \frac{1}{3}$
  is the same as 27 $\boxed{\cdot}$ 75 $\boxed{\div}$ 3.

Now we learn that $\$27.75 \times \frac{2}{3}$
  is the same as 27 $\boxed{\cdot}$ 75 $\boxed{\div}$ 3 $\boxed{\times}$ 2.

Marty will save ___$18.50___ on the original price.

Use your calculator to solve these problems.

1. $\frac{3}{4}$ of 16 = ___12___
2. $\frac{5}{8}$ of $64 = ___$40___
3. $\frac{5}{6}$ of $30.60 = ___$25.50___
4. original price = $128
   $\frac{1}{4}$ of original price = ___$32___
5. original price = $156.64
   $\frac{7}{8}$ of original price = ___$137.06___

(two hundred seventy-seven) **277**

---

## Teaching the Lesson

**Introducing the Problem**   Read the problem aloud. Have students complete the information sentences in the model. ($27.75, ⅔) Ask students what the fraction two-thirds means. (If the price could be divided into thirds, this would identify two of the parts.) Read the plan sentences with the students. (Multiply $27.75 by ⅔.) Work through the procedure with the class. Ask students to do the problem on their calculators. ($27.75 ÷ 3 × 2 = $18.50) Have a student read the solution sentence while the others complete it in their texts. ($18.50)

**Developing the Skill**   Help students complete the five problems at the bottom of the page. Have them identify the denominator and divide; then identify the numerator and multiply. Ask students to provide answers and let them compare their results.

**277**

## Practice

Use your calculator to solve these problems.

1. $\frac{1}{6}$ of 96 = __16__   2. $\frac{4}{5}$ of \$10.50 = __\$8.40__   3. $\frac{2}{3}$ of 126 = __84__

4. $\frac{5}{8}$ of \$16.48 = __\$10.30__   5. $\frac{5}{9}$ of 99 = __55__   6. $\frac{7}{8}$ of \$112 = __\$98__

7. original price = \$120

$\frac{7}{8}$ of original price = __\$105__

8. original price = \$225

$\frac{7}{9}$ of original price = __\$175__

9. original price = \$2.48

$\frac{3}{4}$ of original price = __\$1.86__

10. original price = \$87.50

$\frac{5}{7}$ of original price = __\$62.50__

## Apply

Solve these problems.

11. Suits are on sale for $\frac{2}{3}$ of the original price. The original price is \$150. What is the sale price?
$100

12. A pair of slacks is on sale for $\frac{4}{5}$ of its original price. The original price of the slacks is \$84.50. What is the sale price?
$67.60

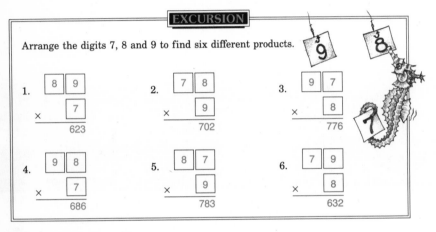

EXCURSION

Arrange the digits 7, 8 and 9 to find six different products.

1. 
```
  8 9
×   7
─────
  623
```

2. 
```
  7 8
×   9
─────
  702
```

3. 
```
  9 7
×   8
─────
  776
```

4. 
```
  9 8
×   7
─────
  686
```

5. 
```
  8 7
×   9
─────
  783
```

6. 
```
  7 9
×   8
─────
  632
```

**278** (two hundred seventy-eight)

# Chapter Test

page 279

| Item | Objective |
|---|---|
| 1-3 | Write a fraction for a part of a whole (See pages 259-262) |
| 4-6 | Write a fraction for a part of a set (See pages 263-264) |
| 7-9 | Find the fractional part of a number (See pages 265-266) |
| 10-11 | Write the equivalent fraction (See pages 267-268) |
| 12-13 | Use a picture to add two fractions with common denominators (See pages 271-272) |

Write the fraction that tells what part is red.

1.   $\frac{1}{5}$

2.   $\frac{6}{8}$

3.   $\frac{4}{10}$

Write the fraction that tells what part is squares.

4.   $\frac{1}{3}$

5.   $\frac{3}{6}$

6.   $\frac{4}{8}$

Find the fraction of each number.

7. $\frac{1}{3}$ of 12 ___4___   8. $\frac{1}{5}$ of 60 = ___12___   9. $\frac{1}{8}$ of 56 = ___7___

Write the missing fractions.

10.

$\frac{2}{3} = \frac{4}{6}$

11.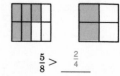

$\frac{5}{8} > \frac{2}{4}$

Use the pictures to help you add or subtract these fractions.

12.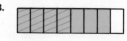

Shade $\frac{2}{5}$.   $\frac{2}{5} + \frac{1}{5} = \frac{3}{5}$

Shade another $\frac{1}{5}$.

13.

Shade $\frac{7}{8}$.

Cross out $\frac{4}{8}$.

$\begin{array}{r} \frac{7}{8} \\ - \frac{4}{8} \\ \hline \frac{3}{8} \end{array}$

**279**

Circle the letter of the correct answer.

**1** What is the value of the 3 in 536,296?
a thousands
(b) ten thousands
c hundred thousands
d NG

**2**
```
  42
  78
+ 57
```
a 167
(b) 177
c 187
d NG

**3**
```
$27.48
+ 58.18
```
(a) $85.66
b $85.67
c $75.66
d NG

**4**
```
  803
- 658
```
a 157
b 252
c 1,461
(d) NG

**5**
```
$17.46
-  2.99
```
(a) $14.47
b $15.53
c $20.45
d NG

**6**
a 5:45
(b) 9:25
c 9:38
d NG

**7** Find the perimeter.
2 m
3 m   3 m
5 m
a 6 m
b 7 m
(c) 13 m
d NG

**8**
```
  36
×  8
```
a 248
(b) 288
c 2,448
d NG

**9**
```
$4.50
×    9
```
a $5.05
b $36.50
(c) $40.50
d NG

**10** Find the area.
a 3 sq units
b 5 sq units
c 16 sq units
(d) NG

**11** 3)48
a 12
b 14
(c) 16
d NG

**12** 4)97
a 20 R1
b 24
(c) 24 R1
d NG

☐ score

**280** (two hundred eighty)

## Cumulative Review
**page 280**

| Item | Objective |
|---|---|
| 1 | Identify value of a digit in a number less than 10,000 (See pages 33-34) |
| 2 | Add three or four numbers (See pages 49-50) |
| 3 | Add dollars, cents with regrouping (See pages 51-52, 170) |
| 4 | Subtract two 3-digit numbers with two regroupings (See pages 67-68, 170) |
| 5 | Subtract dollars, cents with regrouping (See pages 75-76, 170) |
| 6 | Read the time to the minute (See pages 87-88) |
| 7 | Add to find perimeter (See pages 95-96) |
| 8 | Multiply 2-digit number by 1-digit number with regrouping (See pages 163-164) |
| 9 | Multiply dollars, cents by 1-digit number with regrouping (See pages 167-168) |
| 10 | Find area of plane figure in square units (See pages 181-182) |
| 11 | Divide 2-digit number by 1-digit number for 2-digit quotient without remainder (See pages 245-246) |
| 12 | Divide 2-digit number by 1-digit number for 2-digit quotient with remainder (See pages 247-248) |

---

## Alternate Cumulative Review

**Circle the letter of the correct answer.**

**1** What is the value of 7 in 27,964?
a hundreds
(b) thousands
c ten thousands
d NG

**2**
```
  59
  87
+ 43
```
(a) 189
b 187
c 199
d NG

**3**
```
$36.25
+ 19.26
```
a $16.99
b $55.41
c $55.31
(d) NG

**4**
```
  702
- 358
```
a 354
(b) 344
c 456
d NG

**5**
```
$16.27
-  9.48
```
(a) $6.79
b $25.75
c $13.21
d NG

**6** What time is it? (Show a clock.)
(a) 2:25
b 3:25
c 5:10

**7** Find the perimeter of a rectangle 2 cm by 4 cm.
a 8 cm
b 16 sq cm
c 8 sq cm
(d) NG

**8**
```
 27
× 8
```
a 225
(b) 216
c 1,656
d NG

**9**
```
$3.70
×    4
```
a $13.14
b $122.80
(c) $14.80
d NG

**10** Find the area of a rectangle 2 in. by 6 in.
a 16 sq in.
(b) 12 sq in.
c 12 in.
d NG

**11** 6)72
a 10 R12
b 10 R2
(c) 12
d NG

**12** 5)83
a 1 R3
b 16
(c) 16 R3
d NG

# Understanding Tenths

## pages 281-282

### Objective

To understand decimal place value to tenths

### Materials

one-inch graph paper
scissors
unit circle and tenth wedges

### Mental Math

Explain that the two numbers you dictate represent two sides of a rectangle. Ask students to find each perimeter.

1. 3 in and 5 in (16 in)
2. 1 ft and 1/2 ft (3 ft)
3. 10 in and 4 in (28 in)
4. 6 cm and 8 cm (28 cm)
5. 2 m and 20 m (44 m)

### Skill Review

Write ½ on the board and ask a student to explain what it means. (A fraction is made up of a denominator, the total number of equal pieces in each whole and a numerator, the number of these pieces the fraction represents. One half means one piece out of two.) Dictate these fractions for students to write: ⅔, ¹⁄₁₀ ⅖, ⁴⁄₉, ¹⁄₁₂, ⁵⁄₁₀, ⁹⁄₁₀, ¼, ³⁄₇.

## Understanding Tenths

Lorinda's job is to paint the fence on the east side of Mayfield Street. It started to rain before she could finish it. What decimal part of the fence did she get painted?

We want to write the part of the fence Lorinda has painted.
She has painted ___2___ sections of the fence.

The fence is ___10___ sections long.
We can write this part as a fraction.
Lorinda has painted **two tenths** or $\frac{2}{10}$ of the fence.

We can also write two tenths as a decimal.

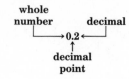

Study this place value chart.

| ones | tenths |
|------|--------|
| 0 | 2 |

Lorinda has painted ___0.2___ of the fence.

✔ Remember that the decimal point always separates the ones place from the tenths place.

### Getting Started

Write the decimals.

1. five tenths ___0.5___
2. $\frac{1}{10}$ ___0.1___
3. seven tenths ___0.7___

## Teaching the Lesson

**Introducing the Problem** Have students read the problem silently while you read it aloud. Direct their attention to the illustration while one student reads the information sentences. (has painted 2 sections, fence is 10 sections long) Read the plan sentences aloud and the section of the model which defines a decimal. Explain that decimals are used to describe fractional units in tenths by giving tenths a place value column of their own. Put the place value chart on the board and explain that tenths will be written to the right of the ones column. Point out that in order to distinguish between tenths and ones, a decimal point is put between ones and tenths. Write two tenths as a decimal on the board **0.2** and have students complete the solution sentence. (0.2 of the fence.)

**Developing the Skill** Give each student graph paper, and scissors. Ask them to cut out a strip of paper 10 squares long. Now have them color 2 tenths red, 3 tenths green, and 5 tenths blue. Ask a student to come to the board and write the decimal describing the red squares (0.2), the green squares (0.3), and the blue squares (0.5). Have students cut out another 10-square strip, color one square orange and nine squares black. Ask them to write the decimal parts on the reverse side. (0.1, 0.9) Repeat these activities, varying the decimal units and colors.

## Practice

Write the decimals.

1. $\frac{3}{10}$ __0.3__

2. four tenths __0.4__

3. nine tenths __0.9__

4. $\frac{5}{10}$ __0.5__

5. two tenths __0.2__

6. $\frac{8}{10}$ __0.8__

7. six tenths __0.6__

8. one tenth __0.1__

9. $\frac{7}{10}$ __0.7__

10. What part is painted? __0.3__

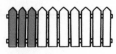

11. What part is *not* painted? __0.3__

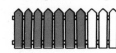

12. What part is *not* painted? __0.4__

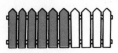

13. What part is painted? __0.2__

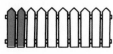

14. What part is painted? __0.5__

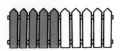

15. What part is painted? __0.8__

16. What part is *not* painted? __0.6__

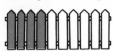

17. What part is painted? __0.9__

18. What part is painted? __0.6__

19. What part is *not* painted? __0.9__

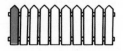

## Practice

Have students complete the page. Remind them to put a decimal point in each answer and a zero in the ones column.

## Mixed Practice

1. $26 \div 8$ (3 R2)
2. $376 \times 7$ (2,632)
3. $\frac{7}{8} - \frac{2}{8}$ $\left(\frac{5}{8}\right)$
4. $87 \div 7$ (12 R3)
5. $492 + 395 + 178$ (1,065)
6. $\frac{5}{9} + \frac{3}{9}$ $\left(\frac{8}{9}\right)$
7. $3{,}070 - 1{,}256$ (1,814)
8. $\frac{1}{6} + \frac{4}{6}$ $\left(\frac{5}{6}\right)$
9. $38 \times 5$ (190)
10. $\frac{1}{6}$ of 24 (4)

## Extra Credit  *Applications*

Tell the class that although all stairways seem the same, each one is slightly different. There are two measurements that are important in building a set of stairs: the height of each **riser** and the width of each **tread.** Illustrate on the board a model step in the same proportion of the riser being 7½ in. high and the tread, 10 in. wide.

Carpenters decide how to build the stairs, by making the product of the height of the riser and the depth of the tread equal to about 75. Explain that for a riser that is 7 1/2 inches high, the tread would be 10 inches deep. Have students check the multiplication by doing the problem on their calculators. (7.5 x 10 = 75) Tell students to measure the height of the riser and the depth of the tread of at least two different staircases. Have students bring their measurements to class and use calculators to see if the product for each staircase is about 75. Compare to see if any two staircases measured were exactly alike.

# Understanding Mixed Decimals

pages 283-284

## Objective

To understand mixed decimals

## Materials

one-inch graph paper
scissors

## Mental Math

Explain that the number you dictate represents one side of a square. Ask students to find the perimeter of each figure:

1. 1 meter (4 meters)
2. 3 in (12 in)
3. 10 cm (40 cm)
4. 3 ft (12 ft)
5. 12 in (48 in)
6. ¼ m (1 m)

## Skill Review

Ask a student to come to the board and write the decimal for ⁴⁄₁₀ (0.4). Now dictate the following and have students write them in decimal form: ¹⁄₁₀ (0.1), ⁵⁄₁₀ (0.5), ²⁄₁₀ (0.2), ⁹⁄₁₀ (0.9), and ⁷⁄₁₀ (0.7)

---

### Understanding Mixed Decimals

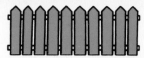

Lorinda is still painting fences at the end of the week. How many fences has she completed?

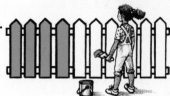

We want to write a decimal number that tells the number of fences Lorinda has painted.

She has painted __2__ complete fences

and __4__ sections of another fence.

There are __10__ sections in a fence.

We can write this as a **mixed number.**

two full fences → four tenths of another fence →

2 . 4

We write this as **two and four tenths.**
Study this place value chart.

| ones | tenths |
|------|--------|
| 2 | 4 |

Lorinda has painted __2.4__ fences.

### Getting Started

Write the mixed decimals.

1. three and six tenths __3.6__
2. four and eight tenths __4.8__
3. twelve and one tenth __12.1__
4. thirty-six and two tenths __36.2__
5. How many fences are painted?

__1.4__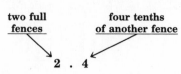

6. How many fences are *not* painted?

__1.7__

(two hundred eighty-three) **283**

---

## Teaching the Lesson

**Introducing the Problem**  Have students read the problem silently while you read it aloud. Have one student complete each information sentence. (Has painted 2 fences and 4 sections of another fence. There are 10 sections in a fence.) Put a place value chart on the board showing ones and tenths. Explain that the ones represent whole objects, in this case each completed fence. Read aloud the section defining mixed numbers. Show the class that 2 is written in the ones column, 4 in the tenths column on the place value chart. Ask a student to write the mixed number on the board. (2.4) Have the class complete the solution sentence in their texts. (has painted 2.4 fences)

**Developing the Skill**  Have students cut out several strips of the inch graph paper, each 10 squares long. Explain that each strip is a whole unit and ask what each square represents. (one tenth) Ask them to color and cut out 1 whole and 5 tenths. Have one student hold up the finished pieces and have another write the mixed decimal on the board. (1.5) Ask them to color and cut out 3 and ⁸⁄₁₀; and again have one hold up the pieces and another write the decimal on the board. (3.8) Repeat for several mixed decimals.

**283**

## Practice

Write the mixed decimals.

1. five and six tenths __5.6__

2. nine and five tenths __9.5__

3. three and one tenth __3.1__

4. fifteen and three tenths __15.3__

5. twenty-nine and seven tenths
__29.7__

6. seventy-five and two tenths
__75.2__

7. How many fences are painted?
__2.1__

8. How many fences are *not* painted?
__1.1__

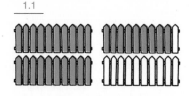

9. How many fences are painted?
__5.9__

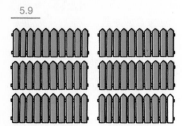

10. How many fences are *not* painted?
__3.9__

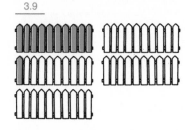

11. How many fences are painted?
__4.8__

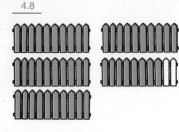

12. How many fences are painted?
__5.4__

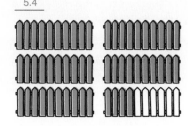

**284** (two hundred eighty-four)

**284**

# Comparing Decimals

### pages 285-286

## Objective

To compare mixed decimals

## Materials

blank ten-strips

## Mental Math

Dictate lengths of the sides of a triangle. Ask students to find the perimeter.

1. 3, 7, and 2 in. (12 in.)
2. 8, 8, and 4 m (20 m)
3. 10, 12, 15 cm (37 cm)
4. ⅓, ⅓, and ⅓ yd (1 yd)
5. 20, 25, 20 in. (65 in.)
6. ²⁄₁₀, ²⁄₁₀, and ⁵⁄₁₀ m (⁹⁄₁₀ m)

## Skill Review

Put this 3-digit place value chart on the board:

**tens   ones . tenths**

Ask students to write the following mixed decimals in the correct columns. Check for the decimal point: 41.3, 80.4, 9.0, 15.1, 32.9 and 6.2.

---

## Comparing Decimals

The third grade class raised money for charity in a walk-a-thon. Those who walked the farthest also earned prizes. Who won the top prize?

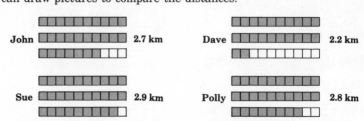

| John | 2.7 km |
| Dave | 2.2 km |
| Sue | 2.9 km |
| Polly | 2.8 km |

We want to know which third grader won the prize for walking the farthest.

John walked ___2.7___ kilometers, Dave

___2.2___ kilometers, Sue ___2.9___ kilometers

and Polly ___2.8___ kilometers.
To find which student went the farthest, we can draw pictures to compare the distances.

John  2.7 km     Dave  2.2 km

Sue  2.9 km      Polly  2.8 km

We can also compare the distances on a number line.

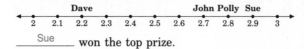

        Dave              John Polly Sue
2   2.1   2.2   2.3   2.4   2.5   2.6   2.7   2.8   2.9   3

___Sue___ won the top prize.

### Getting Started

1. Use the number line to help you circle the least number.

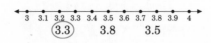

3   3.1  3.2  3.3  3.4  3.5  3.6  3.7  3.8  3.9   4
      (3.3)        3.8        3.5

2. Circle the greater number.

    1.6      (1.9)

Compare these numbers. Write < or > in the circle.

3. 5.7 (<) 5.9          4. 0.7 (>) 0.3          5. 12.3 (<) 15.3

(two hundred eighty-five) **285**

---

## Teaching the Lesson

**Introducing the Problem**   Read the problem aloud. Have a student read the information sentence and interpret the drawing to identify required numbers. (John, 2.7 km; Dave, 2.2 km; Sue, 2.9; Polly, 2.8 km) Point out to students the ten-strips drawn in their books. Reproduce the first set of three strips on the board and shade two whole strips and the first seven tenths of the third. Ask students to do the same and then shade strips illustrating the distances each student walked. Ask if they can tell who walked farthest by looking at the pictures they have made. (Yes; Sue) Put the number line on the board from 1 through 3, divided in tenths, and have a student point to John's, Dave's, Sue's and Polly's position. Ask a student to complete the solution sentence. (Sue won top prize.)

**Developing the Skill**   Draw two ten-strips on the board and shade one to represent ⁴⁄₁₀ and the other, ⁷⁄₁₀. Write the decimal below each drawing. (0.4, 0.7) Ask students to explain which is the larger fraction. (⁷⁄₁₀ or 0.7) Put a number line on the board from 0 through 1, marked in tenths. Have volunteers come up and show which decimal is larger: 0.5 or 0.2 (0.5); 0.6 or 0.1 (0.6); 0.9 or 0.8 (0.9), 0.4 or 0.6 (0.6). Write the same number pairs on the board and have students come and put < and > symbols between the numbers. (0.5 > 0.2; 0.6 > 0.1; 0.9 > 0.8; 0.4 < 0.6)

## Getting Started   *Error Pattern Analysis*

place value errors 18, 22; mechanical errors 24, 26, 29; language errors 31; computational errors 49; misunderstanding definitions 74

1. Use the number line to help you circle the least number.

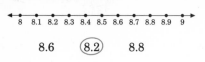

8.6    (8.2)    8.8

2. Use the picture to help you circle the greater number.

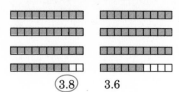

(3.8)    3.6

Circle the greater number.

| | | | | | |
|---|---|---|---|---|---|
| 3. 6.4 | (6.8) | 4. (9.1) | 9.0 | 5. 1.6 | (1.7) |
| 6. (2.7) | 2.4 | 7. (4.3) | 4.2 | 8. 9.5 | (9.6) |

Compare these numbers. Write < or > in the circle.

9. 6.4 (<) 6.7     10. 8.8 (<) 8.9     11. 2.5 (>) 2.3

12. 0.6 (<) 0.8     13. 9.3 (<) 9.6     14. 12.2 (<) 12.3

15. 28.5 (>) 28.1     16. 17.6 (<) 17.8     17. 30.2 (<) 30.4

18. 94.8 (>) 94.6     19. 27.3 (<) 72.3     20. 48.4 (<) 48.5

**Apply**

21. Jan ran 4.2 kilometers. Sid ran 4.7 kilometers. Who ran farther? Sid

22. Roberto weighs 68.6 kilograms. Raul weighs 68.7 kilograms. Who is lighter? Roberto

**EXCURSION**

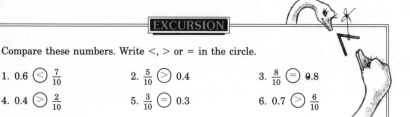

Compare these numbers. Write <, > or = in the circle.

1. 0.6 (<) $\frac{7}{10}$     2. $\frac{5}{10}$ (>) 0.4     3. $\frac{8}{10}$ (=) 0.8

4. 0.4 (>) $\frac{2}{10}$     5. $\frac{3}{10}$ (=) 0.3     6. 0.7 (>) $\frac{6}{10}$

## Correcting Common Errors

Some students may have difficulty comparing decimals. Have them work with partners with a number line marked off in tenths from 6.0 to 6.9. For each of the following problems, have them locate both points on the number line and then determine which is the larger number.

1. 6.0 6.5    2. 6.9 6.1
3. 6.4 6.5    4. 6.3 6.8
5. 6.7 6.4    6. 6.6 6.5

## Enrichment

Explain that a substitution code is a cipher in which the letters are changed, but the order remains the same.

A B C D E F G H I J K L M
↓ ↓ ↓ ↓ ↓ ↓ ↓ ↓ ↓ ↓ ↓ ↓ ↓
Z Y X W V U T S R Q P O N

N O P Q R S T U V W X Y Z
↓ ↓ ↓ ↓ ↓ ↓ ↓ ↓ ↓ ↓ ↓ ↓ ↓
M L K J I H G F E D C B A

To write in this code they substitute the letter in the second row for each in the first; Z for A, Y for B, and so on. Have students write and decipher messages using this cipher.

## Practice

Have students complete the page. Write < **means less than**, > **means more than** on the board as a reminder.

## Excursion

Write ⁴/₁₀ ○ ⁶/₁₀ on the board. Have a student read and compare the numbers and then write >, < or = in the circle. (<) Repeat for **0.4** ○ **0.6** (<) Tell students we could also write **0.4 < 0.6** as ⁴/₁₀ < ⁶/₁₀ since 0.4 and ⁴/₁₀ are both ways of writing the same number. Now write **0.4** ○ ⁶/₁₀ on the board and have students rewrite the decimal as a fraction or the fraction as a decimal, to more easily compare the numbers. Have students write 0.0, 0.6 and 0.2 as fractions and ¹/₁₀, ⁸/₁₀ and ⁵/₁₀ as decimals.

Remind students to rewrite each problem so that its numbers are in the same form before comparing the numbers.

## Extra Credit   *Logic*

Introduce the concept of **syllogisms** by asking students what new fact they can discover by putting the two given facts together in the following:

     Bob is shorter than Mark. Sue is shorter than Bob.
         (Sue is shorter than Mark.)

Give them 2 more syllogisms to complete, such as:

   Bob walks 1 kilometer to school.
   1 kilometer equals 0.62 mile.
   (Bob walks 0.62 mile to school.)

   All rectangles are parallelograms.
   A square is a rectangle.
   (A square is a parallelogram.)

Then have students create two, 3-step syllogisms on any subject, and exchange to have other students complete them. Display finished syllogisms on the bulletin board. Warn students that if no one can complete their syllogism, it probably isn't logical. Have them rework their statements.

**286**

# Understanding Hundredths

## pages 287-288

## Objective

To understand decimal place value to hundredths

## Materials

graph paper, squares smaller than one inch
*overhead projector
*transparency showing array of one hundred squares

## Mental Math

Name an object. Ask students to identify its two-dimensional geometric shape:

1. clock face (circle)
2. cover of a book (rectangle)
3. paper napkin (square)
4. paper plate (circle)
5. sail on a boat (triangle)
6. door (rectangle)

## Skill Review

Write these number pairs on the board and have students copy each pair, inserting the correct sign: <, >, or =.

1. **21.3  23.1**  (<)
2. **1.7  1.2**  (>)
3. **15.0  15.1**  (<)
4. **2.0  2.0**  (=)
5. **44.9  45.0**  (<)

---

## Understanding Hundredths

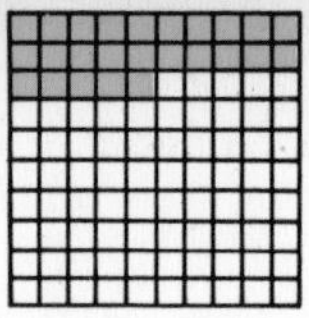

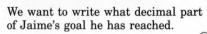

Jaime's goal is to do 100 situps at a time. He charts his progress on a grid with 100 squares. Each square stands for a situp. The shaded squares show the highest number of situps Jaime has done at one time. What decimal part of his goal has he reached?

We want to write what decimal part of Jaime's goal he has reached.

Jaime wants to do __100__ situps.

So far he can do __25__ situps at one time. We can write this as the fraction **twenty-five hundredths** or $\frac{25}{100}$.

As a decimal, $\frac{25}{100}$ is written as **0.25.**

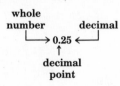

Study this place value chart.

| ones | tenths | hundredths |
|:----:|:------:|:----------:|
| **0** | **2** | **5** |

Jaime has reached __0.25__ of his goal.

### Getting Started

Write the decimals.

1. fourteen hundredths __0.14__    2. $\frac{19}{100}$ __0.19__    3. five hundredths __0.05__

4. What part is red?    5. What part is *not* red?

__0.80__     __0.38__

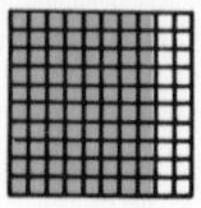

(two hundred eighty-seven) **287**

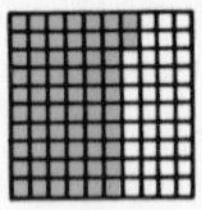

---

## Teaching the Lesson

**Introducing the Problem**  Read the problem aloud. Have a student read and complete the information sentences. (wants to do 100 situps; can do 25 situps) Explain that Jaime's goal is to do 100 situps and he can do 25 now. Write the fraction **25/100** on the board and have a student explain what it means. (That the whole has 100 parts; this particular fraction, 25 of the 100.) Write this on the board as a decimal **(0.25)** while the students write the decimal in their books. Explain that this is read "twenty-five hundredths." Put a place value chart on the board:

### ones | tenths | hundredths.

Explain that 25 hundredths is the same as 2 tenths and 5 hundredths, and write it on the place value chart in that way. Have a student read and complete the solution sentence. (has reached 0.25 of his goal)

**Developing the Skill**  Give each student a piece of graph paper. With the overhead projector, show students a 10 by 10 array of squares and ask them to cut out several such arrays from the graph paper. Ask how many small squares are in each. (100) Have them color ten squares while you demonstrate on the overhead. Ask how many hundredths are shaded. (10) Write this as **0.10** on the board. Have them illustrate these numbers, writing the decimal on the back: 47 squares (0.47), 20 squares (0.20), and 84 squares (0.84).

**287**

## Practice

Write the decimals.

1. twelve hundredths __0.12__

2. six hundredths __0.06__

3. $\frac{14}{100}$ __0.14__

4. sixteen hundredths __0.16__

5. $\frac{3}{100}$ __0.03__

6. thirty-six hundredths __0.36__

7. ninety-nine hundredths __0.99__

8. $\frac{1}{100}$ __0.01__

9. four hundredths __0.04__

10. $\frac{25}{100}$ __0.25__

What part is red?

11.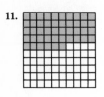

12.

13.

__0.46__          __0.75__          __0.50__

14.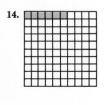

15.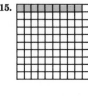

16.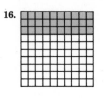

__0.06__          __0.09__          __0.30__

What part is *not* red?

17.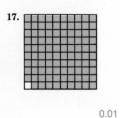

18.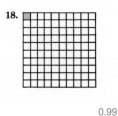

19.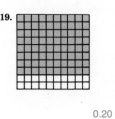

__0.01__          __0.99__          __0.20__

## Correcting Common Errors

Some students may omit zero as a placeholder and write seven hundredths as 0.7. Have them work with partners and write the decimals for one tenth through nine tenths and then for one hundredth through nine hundredths on a place-value chart.

## Enrichment

Explain that a shift substitution cipher involves using a letter further along in the alphabet. In this example each letter is represented by the letter two places away.
A B C K E F G H I J
↓ ↓ ↓ ↓ ↓ ↓ ↓ ↓ ↓ ↓
C D E F G H I J K L and so on. Have each student devise a shift substitution code and write a message.

## Practice

Have students complete the page. Remind them that when there are 2-digit hundredths, it is the last digit that goes in the hundredths column, the first will be in the tenths column.

## Extra Credit    *Numeration*

Ask students to select a short page in their reading book. Have them write the letters of the alphabet on a sheet of paper. Ask them to count and tally the number of times each letter appears on that one page. Have them identify which letters appear most often. Have students repeat the activity using another page of a different book. Have them make a bar graph for each page, and compare. Have them prepare a list of questions that could be answered with their graphs, such as: Are there any letters that seem to be used more often than others? Are there any letters never used?

### 288

# Adding Decimals

pages 289-290

## Objective

To add mixed decimals

## Materials

## Mental Math

Name these objects and ask students to name their 3-dimensional geometric shapes:

1. ping pong ball (sphere)
2. shoe box (rectangular prism)
3. sugar cube (cube)
4. soup can (cylinder)
5. sponge (rectangular prism)
6. coffee mug; minus the handle (cylinder)
7. spool of thread (cylinder)

## Skill Review

Remind students that they have written 2-place decimals and ask a volunteer to describe the value of each place. (tenths, hundredths) Now dictate these decimal values for students to write on paper while a volunteer puts each on the board.

| | | |
|---|---|---|
| 1. 0.4 | 4. 10.25 | 7. 21.6 |
| 2. 2.5 | 5. 0.41 | 8. 50.50 |
| 3. 1.1 | 6. 0.9 | 9. 8.98 |

---

## Adding Decimals

Pablo, the weatherman, will report the amount of rain that fell on Thursday and Friday in his weekly wrap-up. How much rain fell on those two days?

| Rainfall for the Week | |
|---|---|
| Monday | None |
| Tuesday | 2.08 cm |
| Wednesday | None |
| Thursday | 4.57 cm |
| Friday | 2.36 cm |

We want the total amount of rainfall for both days.

On Thursday, __4.57__ centimeters of rain fell.

The rainfall for Friday was __2.36__ centimeters.

To find the total rainfall, we add __4.57__ and __2.36__.

✔ Remember, always line up the decimal points in the addends.

Add the hundredths. Trade if needed.

$$\begin{array}{r} \overset{1}{4.5\,7} \\ + 2.3\,6 \\ \hline 3 \end{array}$$

Add the tenths. Trade if needed. Line up the decimal point.

$$\begin{array}{r} \overset{1}{4.5\,7} \\ + 2.3\,6 \\ \hline .9\,3 \end{array}$$

Add the ones.

$$\begin{array}{r} 4.5\,7 \\ + 2.3\,6 \\ \hline 6.9\,3 \end{array}$$

It rained __6.93__ centimeters on Thursday and Friday.

### Getting Started

Add.

1.
$$\begin{array}{r} 3.6 \\ + 5.9 \\ \hline 9.5 \end{array}$$

2.
$$\begin{array}{r} 7.85 \\ + 8.60 \\ \hline 16.45 \end{array}$$

3.
$$\begin{array}{r} 0.87 \\ + 5.39 \\ \hline 6.26 \end{array}$$

4.
$$\begin{array}{r} 2.08 \\ 4.57 \\ + 2.36 \\ \hline 9.01 \end{array}$$

Copy and add.

5. 2.08 + 4.57
6.65

6. 3.24 + 6.93
10.17

7. 7.4 + 8.9
16.3

(two hundred eighty-nine) **289**

---

## Teaching the Lesson

**Introducing the Problem** Read the problem aloud while students follow in their books. Ask a volunteer to read and complete the information sentences. (Thursday, 4.57 cm; Friday, 2.36 cm) Read the plan aloud while students complete the sentence in their texts. (We add 4.57 and 2.36.) Direct students' attention to the problem worked below. Remind them that they must align the decimals before adding. Ask a student to begin the problem, adding hundredths on the board. Explain that they will trade hundredths for tenths and that there are 10 hundredths in every tenth. (7 + 6 = 13; 3 in hundredths column, 1 over the tenths) Have another student add the tenths. (1 + 5 + 3 = 9; write 9 in tenths column.) Finish the problem on the board, adding ones. (4 + 2 = 6; write 6 in ones column.) Have a student read the solution sentence. (6.93 cm)

**Developing the Skill** Remind students that there are 10 hundredths in 1 tenth, and 10 tenths in one. Explain that when they add decimals, they will line up the decimal points and add just like other multi-place numbers. They will trade when necessary: hundredths for tenths, tenths for ones, and ones for tens. Work these problems on the board while students follow on paper: **52.34 + 13.91** (66.25); **19.05 + 8.97** (28.02).

**289**

## Practice

Add.

| | | | |
|---|---|---|---|
| **1.** 4.6 <br> + 2.3 <br> 6.9 | **2.** 6.6 <br> + 1.2 <br> 7.8 | **3.** 8.4 <br> + 3.3 <br> 11.7 | **4.** 7.3 <br> + 6.5 <br> 13.8 |
| **5.** 5.6 <br> + 4.7 <br> 10.3 | **6.** 9.7 <br> + 3.8 <br> 13.5 | **7.** 6.4 <br> + 8.9 <br> 15.3 | **8.** 4.8 <br> + 0.6 <br> 5.4 |
| **9.** 2.43 <br> + 3.16 <br> 5.59 | **10.** 5.18 <br> + 1.30 <br> 6.48 | **11.** 2.48 <br> + 7.35 <br> 9.83 | **12.** 4.27 <br> + 5.76 <br> 10.03 |
| **13.** 1.6 <br> 4.3 <br> + 5.9 <br> 11.8 | **14.** 4.7 <br> 8.2 <br> + 7.5 <br> 20.4 | **15.** 2.39 <br> 1.64 <br> + 0.86 <br> 4.89 | **16.** 5.48 <br> 3.25 <br> + 1.07 <br> 9.80 |

### Copy and Do

**17.** 2.35 + 9.16
11.51

**18.** 8.06 + 7.28
15.34

**19.** 3.79 + 0.85
4.64

**20.** 9.39 + 6.87
16.26

**21.** 4.52 + 7.79
12.31

**22.** 8.56 + 9.70
18.26

### Apply

Solve these problems.

**23.** It is 3.5 kilometers from Steve's house to the market. It is 2.3 kilometers farther to the library. What is the distance from Steve's house to the library?
5.8 kilometers

**24.** One jar holds 1.45 liters of juice. Another jar holds 3.76 liters. How many liters will both jars hold?
5.21 liters

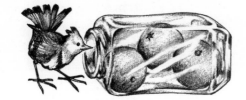

**290** (two hundred ninety)

# Subtracting Decimals

pages 291-292

### Objective

To subtract mixed decimals

### Materials

### Mental Math

Ask students to imagine a tiled floor. Explain that you are going to tell them how many tiles are along the short and long sides of the floor. Ask how many tiles all together are on each floor:

1. 2 tiles by 4 tiles (8 tiles)
2. 4 tiles by 10 tiles (40 tiles)
3. 1 tile by 15 tiles (15 tiles)
4. 3 tiles by 3 tiles (9 tiles)
5. 2 tiles by 5 tiles (10 tiles)
6. 3 tiles by 5 tiles (15 tiles)

### Skill Review

Put the following problems on the board for students to do on paper.

1. 2.39 + 1.55 (3.94)
2. 5.50 + 1.28 (6.78)
3. 6.02 + 9.34 (15.36)
4. 1.80 + 1.80 (3.60)
5. 4.00 + 3.56 (7.56)
6. 7.70 + 1.54 (9.24)

---

## Subtracting Decimals

Pablo's reports of snowfall are of special interest to the weekend skiers. How much more snow fell on Friday than on Thursday?

| Snowfall for the Week | |
|---|---|
| Monday | none |
| Tuesday | none |
| Wednesday | 1.11 cm |
| Thursday | 2.45 cm |
| Friday | 6.73 cm |

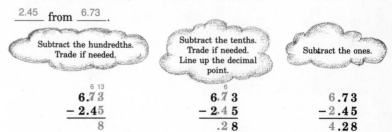

We want to know how much more snow fell on Friday than on Thursday.

On Thursday, 2.45 centimeters of snow fell.

Friday's snowfall was 6.73 centimeters.

To compare the amount of snowfall, we subtract

2.45 from 6.73 .

Subtract the hundredths. Trade if needed.

Subtract the tenths. Trade if needed. Line up the decimal point.

Subtract the ones.

$$
\begin{array}{r} 6.\overset{6\ 13}{7\ 3} \\ -\ 2.45 \\ \hline 8 \end{array}
\qquad
\begin{array}{r} 6.\overset{6}{7}3 \\ -\ 2.45 \\ \hline .28 \end{array}
\qquad
\begin{array}{r} 6.73 \\ -\ 2.45 \\ \hline 4.28 \end{array}
$$

It snowed 4.28 centimeters more on Friday.

### Getting Started

Subtract.

1.  $\begin{array}{r} 6.9 \\ -\ 2.5 \\ \hline 4.4 \end{array}$
2.  $\begin{array}{r} 7.36 \\ -\ 2.56 \\ \hline 4.80 \end{array}$
3.  $\begin{array}{r} 8.02 \\ -\ 5.46 \\ \hline 2.56 \end{array}$
4.  $\begin{array}{r} 6.30 \\ -\ 2.52 \\ \hline 3.78 \end{array}$

Copy and subtract.

5. 5.21 − 2.57   2.64
6. 9.20 − 5.84   3.36
7. 6.24 − 5.88   0.36

(two hundred ninety-one) **291**

---

## Teaching the Lesson

**Introducing the Problem** Have one student read the problem aloud. Ask another student to complete the information sentences. (Thursday 6.73 cm; Friday's was 2.45 cm.) Read the plan sentences aloud, having students follow along in their texts. (We subtract 2.45 from 6.73.) Ask students how they know which number is smaller, 2.45 or 6.73. (by comparing the numbers in the ones column: 2 and 6) Direct their attention to the problem worked in the model. Copy the problem on the board, have a student work each step. Point out that they start at the right-hand side of the problem, just as they do with any other subtraction. Have a volunteer read the solution sentence. (snowed 4.28 cm more)

**Developing the Skill** Put these two place value charts on the board:

**ones. tenths | hundredths    dollars. dimes | pennies**

Explain that when they subtract mixed decimals, they will use the same process they use to subtract dollars and cents. Ask volunteers to explain how many pennies are in a dime (10) and hundredths in a tenth (10); dimes in a dollar (10) and tenths in one (10). Dictate several sets of problems, for example: 3.78 − 1.82 and $3.78 − 1.82 (1.96, $1.96). Have students work the problems on paper while you do them on the board.

**291**

## Practice

Subtract.

| | | | |
|---|---|---|---|
| 1.   7.4<br>− 2.3<br>5.1 | 2.   8.7<br>− 5.6<br>3.1 | 3.   9.2<br>− 3.2<br>6.0 | 4.   8.3<br>− 8.1<br>0.2 |
| 5.   5.3<br>− 2.6<br>2.7 | 6.   7.2<br>− 3.7<br>3.5 | 7.   8.1<br>− 4.8<br>3.3 | 8.   9.3<br>− 2.9<br>6.4 |
| 9.   4.64<br>− 2.32<br>2.32 | 10.   7.75<br>− 5.61<br>2.14 | 11.   8.57<br>− 1.53<br>7.04 | 12.   6.68<br>− 2.48<br>4.20 |
| 13.   7.96<br>− 4.58<br>3.38 | 14.   8.15<br>− 2.58<br>5.57 | 15.   6.21<br>− 5.96<br>0.25 | 16.   9.85<br>− 2.86<br>6.99 |

### Copy and Do

17. 8.06 − 2.88
5.18

18. 9.00 − 5.29
3.71

19. 6.18 − 2.09
4.09

20. 3.89 − 2.96
0.93

21. 7.08 − 3.65
3.43

22. 6.24 − 3.86
2.38

### Apply

Solve these problems.

23. Keith pours 2.6 liters of milk from a new jug which holds 4.0 liters. How much milk is left in the jug?
1.4 liters

24. The American record for the women's indoor high hurdles is 8.07 seconds. The world record is 7.86 seconds. How much difference is there between the two records?
0.21 seconds

**292** (two hundred ninety-two)

**292**

# Estimating

## Objective

To estimate using decimals

## Materials

## Mental Math

Ask students to tell if the following objects are congruent. Remind them that congruent figures have the same size and shape.

1. two identical text books (congruent)
2. a window and a door (probably not congruent)
3. a pencil and an eraser (not congruent)
4. two pieces of paper, different colors, same size (congruent)

## Skill Review

Put these problems on the board for students to work on paper:

1. Which is greater: 4.5 or 5.4? (5.4)
2. Which is smaller: 0.92 or 0.58? (0.58)
3. 4.52 − 2.39 (2.13)
4. 0.38 − 0.18 (0.20)
5. 3.05 − 3.01 (0.04)

---

### Estimating

Barry and Peter ran their turtles in the Memorial Day Race for Slow Pokes. About how far did Barry's turtle go in the race?

We want to know how far Barry's turtle raced altogether.

It ran heats of __32.4__ , __43.3__ and __31.5__ centimeters. To find how far Barry's turtle went, we can add the length of each heat. We can check by rounding the distance of each heat to a whole number, and adding.

| The Memorial Day Race for Slowpokes | | |
|---|---|---|
| | Barry's | Peter's |
| Heat 1 | 32.4 cm | 28.9 cm |
| Heat 2 | 43.3 cm | 35.2 cm |
| Heat 3 | 31.5 cm | 39.6 cm |

> To round a decimal number to the nearest whole number, look at the tenths digit.

If the tenths digit is 0, 1, 2, 3 or 4, the ones digit remains the same and all the digits to the right are dropped.

**32.4 is rounded to 32.**

If the tenths digit is 5, 6, 7, 8 or 9, the ones digit is raised one and all the digits to the right are dropped.

**31.5 is rounded to 32.**

$$\underset{\underset{\textbf{32.4}}{\uparrow}}{32} + \underset{\underset{\textbf{43.3}}{\uparrow}}{43} + \underset{\underset{\textbf{31.5}}{\uparrow}}{32} = 107$$

Barry's turtle raced about ___107___ centimeters.

### Getting Started

Round each decimal number to the nearest whole number.

1. 4.6 __5__     2. 7.2 __7__     3. 1.46 __1__     4. 18.9 __19__

Add or subtract. Round the numbers to check the answers.

5.  16.4
  + 12.7
   29.1

6.  5.91
  − 2.57
   3.34

7.  42.3
   18.6
  +  5.5
   66.4

---

## Teaching the Lesson

**Introducing the Problem**  Have a student read the problem aloud. Read the information sentence and ask a student to supply the numbers from the illustration. (heats of 32.4, 43.3 and 31.5 cm) Point out the rule, explaining that decimals can be rounded just as whole numbers can be rounded. Point out how similar this is to rounding whole numbers to the nearest ten or rounding cents to the nearest dollar. Put each of the numbers on the board and ask students to identify the nearest whole number for each: 32.4 (32); 43.3 (43); 31.5 (32) Ask one student to do the addition on the board while the others do it in their books. (107) Have students complete the solution sentence. (raced about 107 cm)

**Developing the Skill**  Put this number line on the board:

2.0  2.1  2.2  2.3  2.4  2.5  2.6  2.7  2.8  2.9  3.0

Ask a student to come to the board and point to the very middle of the line. (2.5) Explain that although this number is equally close to 2.0 and to 3.0, it is rounded up to 3.0. This is called a **convention** and is probably something they remember from earlier lessons. Dictate numbers between 2.0 and 3.0 to the class. Have students come find the number and explain whether it is closer to 2.0 or 3.0.

**293**

## Practice

Round each decimal number to the nearest whole number.

1. 5.3 ___5___  2. 4.9 ___5___  3. 2.16 ___2___  4. 3.87 ___4___

5. 12.5 ___13___  6. 19.7 ___20___  7. 3.56 ___4___  8. 4.39 ___4___

9. 17.6 ___18___  10. 18.1 ___18___  11. 88.9 ___89___  12. 1.25 ___1___

Add or subtract. Round the numbers to check the answers.

13.  9.63
    − 2.47
    ‾‾‾‾‾‾
     7.16

14.  4.27
    + 3.16
    ‾‾‾‾‾‾
     7.43

15.  34.6
    + 18.4
    ‾‾‾‾‾‾
     53.0

16.  26.8
    − 10.9
    ‾‾‾‾‾‾
     15.9

17.  4.27
    − 2.35
    ‾‾‾‾‾‾
     1.92

18.  25.9
    + 18.9
    ‾‾‾‾‾‾
     44.8

### Copy and Do

19. 26.5 + 7.3 + 8.2
    42.0

20. 49.7 − 28.9
    20.8

21. 8.54 − 1.87
    6.67

22. 6.91 − 5.95
    0.96

23. 2.56 + 4.29
    6.85

24. 5.77 + 1.89 + 2.01
    9.67

---

### EXCURSION

Zero can be written at the end of a decimal number without changing its value. For example, 3.7 = 3.70. Use this idea to help find a number between the two given numbers.

The middle number can be from:

1. 2.5 < 2.6    2.50 < 2.55 < 2.60

2. 1.9 < 2.0    1.90 < (1.91 to 1.99) < 2.00

3. 1.3 < 1.4    1.30 < (1.31 to 1.39) < 1.40

4. 3.2 < 3.3    3.20 < (3.21 to 3.29) < 3.30

5. 3.1 < 3.2    3.10 < (3.11 to 3.19) < 3.20

6. 2.05 < 2.1   2.05 < (2.06 to 2.09) < 2.10

**294** (two hundred ninety-four)

---

## Practice

Have students complete the page. Explain that in problems 13 through 18 they will round each of the addends to the nearest whole number and then add them in the space to the right of each problem. In problems 19 through 24 they are not expected to round the numbers, but only to do the addition.

## Excursion

Draw a number line on the board and write **1** at one end and **2** at the other. Ask students how many hundredths make 1 whole. (100) Remind students that if the space between 1 and 2 were marked in hundredths, the number line would represent the numbers from 1.00 through 2.00. Ask students to tell the halfway mark on this number line. (1.50 or 1 and 50 hundredths or 1 50/100) Have students name numbers between 1.00 and 1.50. Repeat for numbers between 1.50 and 2.00. Have students complete the activity.

## Extra Credit  *Biography*

Leonardo daVinci is probably best known for his art work, such as the *Mona Lisa,* but he was also a scientist and inventor. DaVinci's art and science were not separate interests, because as he observed something in nature, he tried to find out how it worked. DaVinci was born near Florence, Italy, in 1452. During his early career, daVinci served as a military engineer, civil engineer, and court sculptor in Milan. He designed everything from weapons, to sculptures. DaVinci spent his last years in France, until he died in 1519. There, daVinci spent more time on his experiments and inventions. His scientific inventions dealt with the problems of his day, such as grinding lenses for eyeglasses, and building canals and fortresses. But he also examined future possibilities by designing things like flying machines. He wrote his ideas in notebooks, all curiously written backwards, so that a mirror must be used to read them.

# Problem Solving, Review

pages 295-296

## Objective

To review problem-solving strategies

## Materials

cup, pint, and 2-quart containers
5 × 8 inch cards
yardstick
map of the United States
red, yellow, blue and green blocks

## Mental Math

Ask students to imagine a point moving along the following paths, and name the figure formed by a line:

1. from your desk to the teacher's desk and out to your neighbor's desk. (an angle)
2. from the tip of the minute hand on the clock, starting at 12 and moving once around the edge of the clock. (circle)
3. from the desk in one corner of the room to the desk in the opposite corner. (a line)
4. from your desk, to the teacher's desk, out to your neighbor's desk and back to your own. (triangle)
5. around the perimeter of a paper napkin. (square)

## Review

The 4-step plan can help us to be better problem solvers. A review of this plan can remind us of ways to use it.

★ SEE

We decide what we are looking for. We state all the facts we know.

★ PLAN

We think about the important facts and choose a plan to solve the problem.

Among the plans that will help us solve a problem are:

**Drawing a picture**

**Acting it out**

**Making a list**

**Making a tally**

**Making a table**

**Making a graph**

★ DO

We carry out the plan and reach a solution to the problem.

★ CHECK

We check the problem for careless errors.
We see if the solution makes sense.
We look for another way to work the problem.

(two hundred ninety-five) **295**

## Teaching the Lesson

Have a student read aloud the introductory explanation. Then have different students read the SEE, PLAN, DO, and CHECK sections. Remind students of the ways they have used each of the problem-solving strategies: for example, they drew pictures to show various ways of cutting a cake into eight equal pieces; they acted out the six ways that four people could shake hands; they made a list of the ways that jeans in three colors and three sizes could be arranged; they made a tally of the letters in a sentence; they made a table of all their classmates' brothers and sisters; and they made a graph of the number of hours they watched T.V. in a week.

1. How many cups are there all together in 2 quarts and 1 pint?
   10 cups

2. How many different outfits would you have if you had 5 shirts and 3 pairs of slacks?
   See Solution Notes.

3. How many 5-inch by 8-inch notecards do you need to cover a rectangle that is 15 inches by 32 inches?
   12 notecards

4. How many times is each letter of the alphabet used in the sentence: The quick brown fox jumped over the lazy dog?
   See Solution Notes.

5. There are 8 girls and 8 boys sitting around a table. No 2 boys are sitting next to each other. Each boy is directly across from a girl. How are the children arranged at the table?
   See Solution Notes.

6. Make a tally of the number of times each letter of the alphabet is used in naming the fifty states of the United States. What letter is never used?
   See Solution Notes.

7. There are eight blocks with the digits 0, 1, 2, 5, 6, 7, 9, and a decimal point painted on them. How would you arrange 3 of the blocks to show the largest decimal and how would you arrange 3 to show the smallest decimal?
   See Solution Notes.

8. Last week, Larry bought a pound of birdseed for 65¢. This week he saw a sign that said a pound of birdseed is on sale for 0.49¢. Do you think this sign is correct or incorrect? Why?
   Incorrect

9. Two birds share a cracker which is broken into the two parts, 0.5 of a cracker and 0.50 of a cracker. Which part is larger? Explain your answer.
   See Solution Notes.

  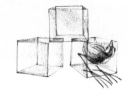

**296** (two hundred ninety-six)

## Solution Notes

1. Encourage groups of students to act this problem out. Provide the containers and water.

2. Suggest that students identify the shirts and slacks in a way that distinguishes one from another. For example, the shirts could be S1, S2, S3, S4, S5; and the slacks SL1, SL2, SL3. Ask students if S1 with SL2 is the same as SL2 with S1. (Yes, that would be the same outfit.)

3. Provide yardsticks, large sheets of paper, and $5 \times 8$ notecards and let students act the problem out. Have them work in pairs to make the large rectangle and then cover it with cards.

4. Have students work in groups. Tell one student to dictate the letters while the other keeps the tally.

5. Choose 8 girls and 8 boys to act this problem out. It may not be possible to actually seat that many children around a classroom table, but have them arrange themselves, standing, in the way described. Have a student diagram the arrangement on the board.

6. As in problem 4, it is better to have students work in groups. See that each group has a map of the United States.

### Higher-Order Thinking Skills

7. Synthesis and Evaluation: The largest possible number is 9.7 and the smallest is 0.1.

8. Synthesis: The sign is incorrect because by combining the two forms of writing money the birdseed would cost less than ½ cent a pound, a totally unreasonable amount. The signwriter intended to say either 49¢ a pound or $0.49 a pound.

9. Evaluation: 0.5 and 0.50 are equivalent decimals for one-half; so the birds will get fair shares no matter which part each gets.

## Extra Credit   *Applications*

Tell students they will work in groups to design their own financial game. Divide the students. Tell the first group to design a gameboard, using the format of a path of at least 20 squares for the players to move around. Tell them each square must tell an adding or subtracting money story, using amounts of $3.00 or less such as: find 15¢; break a window, pay $1.00; get allowance, 75¢; etc. (some squares can be repeated). Tell another group to make play coins, another to design paper dollars and five-dollar bills, and another group to design the moving pieces. Have students write the rules to play the game, and allow groups to try them out. One suggested method of play is to choose one player to be banker, give each player $20, and use a spinner to determine how many spaces each player moves around the board. Taking turns, players must follow the directions on each square, using their $20. The game ends when the first player goes broke. The player with the most money wins.

# Calculator Review

## pages 297-298

### Objective

To review calculator skills using the four basic operations

### Materials

calculators

### Mental Math

Ask students to name the 2-dimensional geometric figure that has:

1. five straight sides and five corners. (pentagon)
2. four right angles. (square or rectangle)
3. no straight sides, no corners. (circle)
4. three straight sides and one right angle. (triangle)
5. six straight sides. (hexagon)

### Skill Review

Ask a student to write 354 plus 188 on the board, as they would do it on a calculator. (354 $+$ 188 $=$) Have students do the problem with calculators. (542) Dictate these problems, having students write the calculator codes on the board, then work them:

1. 938 − 445 (493)
2. 174 × 8 (1,392)
3. 894 + 6 (900)

---

## Calculator Review

You have learned to use your calculator to add, subtract, multiply and divide. You can also find square roots and work with money. Now let's use your calculator to have some fun.

### Activity 1   Reading Your Calculator

Complete each code. Turn the display screen upside down and find the answer to the clue.

1. 8 $\times$ 132 $-$ 351 $=$ 705

   Another name for the sun ___SOL___

2. 4271 $-$ 231 $\div$ 5 $=$ 808

   What you do with apples ___BOB___

3. 839 $-$ 582 $\times$ 2 $=$ 514

   The opposite of hers ___HIS___

4. 215 $\times$ 9 $+$ 3,172 $=$ 5107

   Superman's friend ___LOIS___

### Activity 2   Finding the Pattern

Multiply to find the first three products. Predict the next three. Use your calculator to check.

1. 1 $\times$ 142,857 $=$ ___142,857___
2. 2 $\times$ 142,857 $=$ ___285,714___
3. 3 $\times$ 142,857 $=$ ___428,571___
4. 4 $\times$ 142,857 $=$ ___571,428___
5. 5 $\times$ 142,857 $=$ ___714,285___
6. 6 $\times$ 142,857 $=$ ___857,142___

(two hundred ninety-seven) **297**

---

## Teaching the Lesson

Work through the first two activities with students. Have them look at Activity 1. Remind them that they enter multi-digit numbers from left to right, just as they read them. Have a student point out and explain the operation keys. Ask students to do the problems. As they finish each one show them how to turn the calculator upside down, to read the hidden message. Have them fill in each numerical answer and the resulting word.

Help students work the first three problems in Activity 2. Point out that accuracy in entering each number is very important. When they have completed the first three problems, ask them to examine the sequences. Have them write their predictions of the next three products to the right of the spaces provided. Now have them work the problems and compare the predictions with the actual answers.

## Getting Started   *Error Pattern Analysis*

mechanical errors 26, 27, 29; language errors 31

**Practice**

**Activity 3**  Finding the Value of a Name

Use this chart.

| | | | | | | |
|---|---|---|---|---|---|---|
| A = 1 | B = 2 | C = 3 | D = 4 | E = 5 | F = 6 | G = 7 |
| H = 8 | I = 9 | J = 10 | K = 11 | L = 12 | M = 13 | N = 14 |
| O = 15 | P = 16 | Q = 17 | R = 18 | S = 19 | T = 20 | U = 21 |
| V = 22 | W = 23 | X = 24 | Y = 25 | Z = 26 | | |

The value of Richard is 18 $+$ 9 $+$ 3 $+$ 8 $+$ 1 $+$ 18 $+$ 4 $=$ 61

Find the value of each name.

1. Ron   _18_ $+$ _15_ $+$ _14_ $=$ _47_

2. Alicia  _1_ $+$ _12_ $+$ _9_ $+$ _3_ $+$ _9_ $+$ _1_ $=$ _35_

3. Chen   _3_ $+$ _8_ $+$ _5_ $+$ _14_ $=$ _30_

4. Jose   _10_ $+$ _15_ $+$ _19_ $+$ _5_ $=$ _49_

5. Find the value of your own name.
   Answers will vary.

6. What name will give you the greatest value?
   Answers will vary.

**Activity 4**
Playing with Numbers

1. Enter a number between 1 and 10.
2. Multiply by 2.
3. Add 7.
4. Multiply by 5.
5. Subtract 15.
6. Divide by 10.
7. Subtract 2.
8. Enter $=$.

What happens? We get the number
             we started with.

**Activity 5**
More Playing with Numbers

1. Enter a 3 digit number.
2. Enter the same 3 digits again.
3. Divide by 7.
4. Divide by 11.
5. Divide by 13.
6. Enter $=$.

What happens? We get the number
             we started with.

**298**  (two hundred ninety-eight)

**Practice**

Have students complete Activities 3 and 4. Remind them to read each set of directions carefully. Point out that in Activity 3, each letter stands for a number and each name represents the sum of its letters.

**Correcting Common Errors**

Some students may need practice with single operation sentences before they can do those with 2, 3, and 4 operations. Have students work with partners to perform the following, checking to see that they enter each number and operation sign correctly.

1. 12 $+$ 45 $=$ (57)
2. 100 $-$ 42 $=$ (58)
3. 338 $\times$ 9 $=$ (3,042)
4. 502 $\div$ 2 $=$ (251)

**Enrichment**

Have students use a changeable substitution cipher. Explain that they will decide which letter of the alphabet begins the substitution by the date. If it is the third of the month then the substitution begins with the third letter, C, For example: ABCDEF . . .
            CDEFGH . . . etc.
Have them write a message in code using today's date as the key.

**Extra Credit**  *Applications*

As a final activity for the study of equivalent fractions have your class plan a Fraction Festival. Write down half as many different fractions as there are students in the class, and then write an equivalent fraction for each one. Assign each student one of the fractions. On the day of the party, tell students to bring in an object showing his fraction as part of a whole. (For ¼, they could bring in a whole apple and also ¼ of an apple.) Each student must also display his fraction. To begin the festival, have everyone find the person who has his matching equivalent fraction. The matching pairs could then be partners for such activities as a fractional term word search, fraction bingo or solving fraction word problems. Perhaps have a special lunch, and center the menu around something that can be cut into fractions (pizza or gelatin squares etc.) Also, serve a beverage in cups marked with each student's fraction and fill each cup to its mark.

**298**

# Chapter Test

| Item | Objective |
|------|-----------|
| 1-2 | Write a decimal to match a picture (See pages 281-288) |
| 3-8 | Compare decimals through tenths (See pages 285-286) |
| 9-14 | Add decimals and round numbers to check the answers (See pages 289-294) |
| 15-20 | Subtract decimals and round numbers to check the answers (See pages 289-294) |

Write decimals for the parts that are red.

1.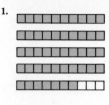

2.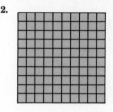

4.7

1.32

Compare these numbers. Write < or > in the circle.

3. 0.3 ⊙< 0.6    4. 15.1 ⊙< 15.6    5. 4.7 ⊙> 4.3

6. 5.9 ⊙< 7.9    7. 9.5 ⊙> 9.2    8. 27.8 ⊙> 27.7

Add. Round the numbers to check the answers.

9.  $\begin{array}{r} 13.3 \\ + 26.5 \\ \hline 39.8 \end{array}$    10.  $\begin{array}{r} 27.5 \\ + 14.8 \\ \hline 42.3 \end{array}$    11.  $\begin{array}{r} 39.7 \\ + 11.9 \\ \hline 51.6 \end{array}$

12.  $\begin{array}{r} 7.24 \\ + 1.18 \\ \hline 8.42 \end{array}$    13.  $\begin{array}{r} 4.96 \\ + 2.37 \\ \hline 7.33 \end{array}$    14.  $\begin{array}{r} 3.26 \\ + 5.84 \\ \hline 9.10 \end{array}$

Subtract. Round the numbers to check the answers.

15.  $\begin{array}{r} 7.6 \\ - 1.4 \\ \hline 6.2 \end{array}$    16.  $\begin{array}{r} 86.8 \\ - 43.9 \\ \hline 42.9 \end{array}$    17.  $\begin{array}{r} 73.2 \\ - 36.8 \\ \hline 36.4 \end{array}$

18.  $\begin{array}{r} 8.46 \\ - 2.29 \\ \hline 6.17 \end{array}$    19.  $\begin{array}{r} 6.17 \\ - 4.38 \\ \hline 1.79 \end{array}$    20.  $\begin{array}{r} 9.41 \\ - 8.65 \\ \hline 0.76 \end{array}$

(two hundred ninety-nine) **299**

Circle the letter of the correct answer.

**1** What is the value of the 4 in 932,450?
- a tens
- (b) hundreds
- c thousands
- d NG

**2**
$$38 \\ 47 \\ +76$$
- a 141
- b 151
- (c) 161
- d NG

**3**
$$\$38.42 \\ +\ 46.59$$
- a $75.01
- b $84.01
- (c) $85.01
- d NG

**4**
$$627 \\ -428$$
- a 201
- b 209
- c 1,055
- (d) NG

**5**
$$8,246 \\ -3,198$$
- a 4,048
- (b) 5,048
- c 5,148
- d NG

**6** Find the perimeter.

18 cm    18 cm
18 cm
- a 36 cm
- b 54 sq cm
- (c) 54 cm
- d NG

**7**
$$42 \\ \times\ 9$$
- a 368
- (b) 378
- c 3,618
- d NG

**8**
$$\$3.75 \\ \times\quad 4$$
- a $13.00
- b $14.00
- c $14.80
- (d) NG

**9** Find the area.
- a 20 units
- b 20 sq units
- (c) 21 sq units
- d NG

**10** 4)72
- a 13
- b 15
- c 17
- (d) NG

**11** 6)70
- a 11
- (b) 11 R4
- c 12
- d NG

**12** $\frac{1}{3}$ of 54
- (a) 18
- b 19
- c 20
- d NG

score

**300** (three hundred)

---

## Alternate Cumulative Review
Circle the letter of the correct answer.

**1** What is the value of 9 in 693,874?
- a thousands
- (b) ten thousands
- c hundred thousands
- d NG

**2**
$$27 \\ 64 \\ +81$$
- (a) 172
- b 162
- c 271
- d NG

**3**
$$\$26.87 \\ +\ 19.36$$
- (a) $46.23
- b $7.51
- c $45.13
- d NG

**4**
$$832 \\ -347$$
- a 1179
- b 515
- (c) 485
- d NG

**5**
$$6,832 \\ -4,786$$
- (a) 2,046
- b 2,154
- c 2,146
- d NG

**6** Find the perimeter of a 17 cm square.
- (a) 68 cm
- b 77 sq. cm
- c 68 sq. cm
- d NG

**7**
$$36 \\ \times 8$$
- a 2,448
- (b) 288
- c 324
- d NG

**8**
$$\$6.27 \\ \times 5$$
- a $310.35
- b $30.35
- (c) $31.35
- d NG

**9** Find the area of a rectangle 2 m by 11 m.
- (a) 22 sq m
- b 22 m
- c 24 m
- d NG

**10** 7)84
- (a) 12
- b 12 R2
- c 13
- d NG

**11** 5)77
- a 15
- (b) 15 R2
- c 15 R4
- d NG

**12** Find ⅕ of 85.
- a 16
- (b) 17
- c 18
- d NG

---

# Cumulative Review
page 300

| Item | Objective |
|------|-----------|
| 1 | Identify the value of a digit in a number less than 1,000,000 (See pages 35-36) |
| 2 | Add three or four numbers (See pages 49-50) |
| 3 | Add dollars, cents with regrouping (See pages 51-52) |
| 4 | Subtract two 3-digit numbers with two regroupings (See pages 67-68) |
| 5 | Subtract two 4-digit numbers with regrouping (See pages 73-74) |
| 6 | Add to find the perimeter (See pages 95-96) |
| 7 | Multiply 2-digit number by 1-digit number with regrouping (See pages 163-164) |
| 8 | Multiply dollars, cents by 1-digit number with regrouping (See pages 167-168) |
| 9 | Find area of plane figure in square units (See pages 181-182) |
| 10 | Divide 2-digit number by 1-digit number for 2-digit quotient without remainder (See pages 245-246) |
| 11 | Divide 2-digit number by 1-digit number for 2-digit quotient with remainder (See pages 247-248) |
| 12 | Find the fractional part of a number (See pages 265-266) |

# Alternate Chapter Test

**for page 37**

| Item | Objective |
|------|-----------|
| 1-6 | Read and write numbers and money (See pages 17-22, 25-26, 33-34) |
| 7-10 | Compare and order numbers less than 1,000 (See pages 23-24, 27-28) |
| 11-14 | Round to nearest 10 or 10¢ (See pages 29-30) |
| 15-18 | Round to the nearest 100 or dollar (See pages 31-32) |
| 19-22 | Identify the value of a digit in a number less than 1,000,000 (See pages 33-36) |
| 23-26 | Order numbers less than 100 (See pages 23-24) |

How much?

1.  _4,056_

2.  _$2.33_

Write the numbers.

3. ninety-seven _97_

4. fifty-five _55_

5. six hundred four _604_

6. seven thousand, one _7,001_

Compare these numbers. Write < or > in the circle.

7. 18 ⟨<⟩ 25

8. 327 ⟨>⟩ 227

9. 545 ⟨<⟩ 554

10. 737 ⟨<⟩ 773

Round to the nearest ten.

11. 79 _80_

12. 32¢ _30¢_

13. 74 _70_

14. 15¢ _20¢_

Round to the nearest hundred or dollar.

15. $6.81 _$7_

16. 465 _500_

17. 186 _200_

18. $3.26 _$3_

Give the place value of the 6 in each number.

19. 576,321 _thousands_

20. 340,627 _hundreds_

21. 862,391 _ten thousands_

22. 697,225 _hundred thousands_

Complete the sequences.

23. 21, _23_, 25, 27, _29_, _31_

24. 50, _45_, 40, 35, _30_, _25_, 20

25. 75, 76, _77_, _78_, _79_, 80

26. 98, 96, _94_, 92, _90_, _88_

Add.

1.  47
    + 23
    ――――
    70

2.  68
    + 14
    ――――
    82

3.  56
    + 19
    ――――
    75

4.  66
    + 28
    ――――
    94

5.  368
    + 295
    ――――
    663

6.  372
    + 248
    ――――
    620

7.  148
    + 492
    ――――
    640

8.  173
    + 598
    ――――
    771

9.  1,369
    + 1,558
    ――――
    2,927

10. 2,689
    + 6,586
    ――――
    9,275

11. 2,364
    + 1,976
    ――――
    4,340

12. 6,035
    + 2,896
    ――――
    8,931

13. 76
    415
    + 3,539
    ――――
    4,030

14. 5,468
    302
    + 641
    ――――
    6,411

15. $24.75
    13.25
    + 33.21
    ――――
    $71.21

16. $37.98
    23.75
    + 15.45
    ――――
    $77.18

Round each addend to the nearest ten and add.

17. 45   50
    + 63  + 60
    ―――― ――――
         110

18. 59   60
    + 32  + 30
    ―――― ――――
         90

19. 57   60
    + 21  + 20
    ―――― ――――
         80

20. 73   70
    + 26  + 30
    ―――― ――――
         100

Round each addend to the nearest hundred and add.

21. 849   800
    + 325  + 300
    ――――  ――――
          1,100

22. 374   400
    + 651  + 700
    ――――  ――――
          1,100

23. 238   200
    + 918  + 900
    ――――  ――――
          1,100

Round each addend to the nearest dollar and add.

24. $14.76  $15
    + 8.31  + 8
    ――――   ――――
           $23

25. $16.22  $16
    + 8.69  + 9
    ――――   ――――
           $25

26. $37.25  $37
    + 21.83  + 22
    ――――   ――――
           $59

27. $19.41  $19
    + 84.99  + 85
    ――――   ――――
           $104

28. $75.46  $75
    + 13.98  + 14
    ――――   ――――
           $89

29. $16.97  $17
    + 7.46  + 7
    ――――   ――――
           $24

# Alternate Chapter Test

**for page 59**

| Item | Objective |
|---|---|
| 1-4 | Add two 2-digit addends with one regrouping (See pages 39-40) |
| 5-8 | Add two 3-digit addends with two regroupings (See pages 41-42) |
| 9-12 | Add two 4-digit addends (See pages 47-48) |
| 13-16 | Add three numbers or amounts of money (See pages 49-52) |
| 17-20 | Round addends to the nearest 10 and add (See pages 53-56) |
| 21-23 | Round addends to the nearest 100 and add (See pages 53-56) |
| 24-29 | Round each addend to the nearest dollar and add (See pages 53-56) |

# Alternate Chapter Test

for page 83

| Item | Objective |
|------|-----------|
| 1-4 | Subtract 2-digit numbers with one regrouping (See pages 63-64) |
| 5-12 | Subtract 3-digit numbers with one or two regroupings (See pages 65-68) |
| 13-16 | Subtract 4-digit numbers (See pages 73-74) |
| 17-20 | Round numbers to the nearest 10 and subtract (See pages 77-78) |
| 21-23 | Round numbers to the nearest 100 and subtract (See pages 77-78) |
| 24-26 | Round addends to the nearest dollar and subtract (See pages 77-78) |

Subtract.

1.
$$86$$
$$-29$$
$$57$$

2.
$$52$$
$$-19$$
$$33$$

3.
$$31$$
$$-12$$
$$19$$

4.
$$92$$
$$-27$$
$$65$$

5.
$$278$$
$$-129$$
$$149$$

6.
$$653$$
$$-427$$
$$226$$

7.
$$727$$
$$-189$$
$$538$$

8.
$$823$$
$$-646$$
$$177$$

9.
$$708$$
$$-247$$
$$461$$

10.
$$500$$
$$-327$$
$$173$$

11.
$$306$$
$$-109$$
$$197$$

12.
$$606$$
$$-368$$
$$238$$

13.
$$7,874$$
$$-3,439$$
$$4,435$$

14.
$$3,122$$
$$-1,764$$
$$1,358$$

15.
$$8,412$$
$$-6,543$$
$$1,869$$

16.
$$5,678$$
$$-2,389$$
$$3,289$$

Estimate the difference by rounding each number to the nearest ten.

17.
$$84$$
$$-65$$
  $$80$$
$$-70$$
$$10$$

18.
$$71$$
$$-38$$
  $$70$$
$$-40$$
$$30$$

19.
$$53$$
$$-19$$
  $$50$$
$$-20$$
$$30$$

20.
$$75$$
$$-29$$
  $$80$$
$$-30$$
$$50$$

Estimate the difference by rounding each number to the nearest hundred.

21.
$$515$$
$$-138$$
  $$500$$
$$-100$$
$$400$$

22.
$$297$$
$$-116$$
  $$300$$
$$-100$$
$$200$$

23.
$$624$$
$$-478$$
  $$600$$
$$-500$$
$$100$$

Estimate the difference by rounding each number to the nearest dollar.

24.
$$\$86.25$$
$$-29.74$$
  $$\$86$$
$$-30$$
$$\$56$$

25.
$$\$36.26$$
$$-17.38$$
  $$\$36$$
$$-17$$
$$\$19$$

26.
$$\$74.29$$
$$-36.34$$
  $$\$74$$
$$-36$$
$$\$38$$

# Alternate Chapter Test

**for page 103**

| Item | Objective |
|------|-----------|
| 1-4 | Read the time to one minute (See pages 87-88) |
| 5-6 | Choose the appropriate unit of length (See pages 93-94) |
| 7-8 | Add to find perimeter (See pages 95-96) |
| 9 | Choose the appropriate unit of capacity (See pages 97-98) |
| 10 | Choose the appropriate temperature reading (See pages 101-102) |

Write the time as you would see it on a digital clock.

1.

2.

3.

4.

| 6:12 | 9:37 | 4:45 | 12:38 |

Circle the better estimate.

5. the distance you can ride a bike in thirty minutes

2 feet    (2 miles)

6. the height of your house

20 inches    (20 feet)

Find the perimeter.

7.

6 in.    5 in.
8 in.

19 in.

8.

47 ft
25 ft    25 ft
47 ft

144 ft

Circle the better estimate.

9.

2 ounces    (2 quarts)

10.

(25°F)    65°F

**304**    (three hundred four)

# Alternate Chapter Test

**for page 115**

| Item | Objective |
|------|-----------|
| 1-3 | Measure objects to the nearest centimeter (See pages 105-106) |
| 4-5 | Choose the appropriate metric unit of length (See pages 107-108) |
| 6-7 | Find the perimeter in metric units (See pages 107-108) |
| 8-9 | Choose the appropriate metric unit of capacity (See pages 109-110) |
| 10 | Choose the appropriate metric unit of weight (See pages 111-112) |
| 11-13 | Write the temperature reading of a Celsius thermometer (See pages 113-114) |

Measure each item to the nearest centimeter.

1. 5 cm

2. 2 cm

3. 9 cm

Would you measure these in centimeters, meters, or kilometers?

4. a drive to the city

kilometers

5. your height

centimeters

Find the perimeter.

6. 28 m  32 m  47 m

107 m

7. 567 km  432 km  432 km  567 km

1,998 km

Circle the unit you would use to measure these items.

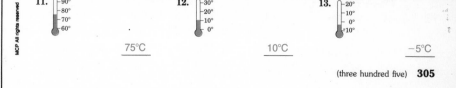

8. mL  (L)

9. (mL)  L

10. (g)  kg

Write the temperature reading for each Celsius thermometer.

11. -90° -80° -70° -60°

75°C

12. -30° -20° -10° -0°

10°C

13. -20° -10° -0° -10°

-5°C

(three hundred five) **305**

| Item | Objective |
|------|-----------|
| 1-75 | Recall multiplication facts through 9 (See pages 119-129, 137-144, 147) |
| 76-78 | Understand the terms factor and product (See page 117) |

Multiply.

|  | | | | | | | | | |
|---|---|---|---|---|---|---|---|---|---|
| 4<br>× 3<br>—<br>12 | 2<br>× 9<br>—<br>18 | 7<br>× 0<br>—<br>0 | 4<br>× 8<br>—<br>32 | 9<br>× 3<br>—<br>27 | 8<br>× 3<br>—<br>24 | 6<br>× 5<br>—<br>30 | 5<br>× 5<br>—<br>25 | 0<br>× 3<br>—<br>0 | 8<br>× 2<br>—<br>16 |
| 1<br>× 7<br>—<br>7 | 4<br>× 4<br>—<br>16 | 8<br>× 0<br>—<br>0 | 5<br>× 9<br>—<br>45 | 2<br>× 6<br>—<br>12 | 0<br>× 9<br>—<br>0 | 1<br>× 1<br>—<br>1 | 2<br>× 7<br>—<br>14 | 3<br>× 3<br>—<br>9 | 4<br>× 5<br>—<br>20 |
| 2<br>× 5<br>—<br>10 | 9<br>× 5<br>—<br>45 | 1<br>× 4<br>—<br>4 | 3<br>× 2<br>—<br>6 | 4<br>× 9<br>—<br>36 | 5<br>× 3<br>—<br>15 | 3<br>× 8<br>—<br>24 | 0<br>× 7<br>—<br>0 | 5<br>× 5<br>—<br>25 | 3<br>× 9<br>—<br>27 |
| 2<br>× 2<br>—<br>4 | 6<br>× 3<br>—<br>18 | 1<br>× 3<br>—<br>3 | 8<br>× 1<br>—<br>8 | 3<br>× 4<br>—<br>12 | 1<br>× 0<br>—<br>0 | 7<br>× 3<br>—<br>21 | 9<br>× 2<br>—<br>18 | 9<br>× 0<br>—<br>0 | 4<br>× 2<br>—<br>8 |
| 8<br>× 4<br>—<br>32 | 6<br>× 4<br>—<br>24 | 1<br>× 5<br>—<br>5 | 3<br>× 0<br>—<br>0 | 3<br>× 7<br>—<br>21 | 4<br>× 8<br>—<br>32 | 2<br>× 9<br>—<br>18 | 5<br>× 8<br>—<br>40 | 6<br>× 0<br>—<br>0 | 2<br>× 8<br>—<br>16 |
| 4<br>× 1<br>—<br>4 | 5<br>× 8<br>—<br>40 | 1<br>× 6<br>—<br>6 | 0<br>× 0<br>—<br>0 | 3<br>× 6<br>—<br>18 | 3<br>× 1<br>—<br>3 | 5<br>× 6<br>—<br>30 | 4<br>× 0<br>—<br>0 | 6<br>× 1<br>—<br>6 | 5<br>× 2<br>—<br>10 |

$1 \times 9 = \underline{9}$   $7 \times 4 = \underline{28}$   $5 \times 0 = \underline{0}$   $9 \times 6 = \underline{54}$   $7 \times 2 = \underline{14}$

$0 \times 6 = \underline{0}$   $9 \times 4 = \underline{36}$   $6 \times 2 = \underline{12}$   $0 \times 2 = \underline{0}$   $8 \times 7 = \underline{56}$

$2 \times 6 = \underline{12}$   $4 \times 6 = \underline{24}$   $4 \times 7 = \underline{28}$   $9 \times 1 = \underline{9}$   $9 \times 7 = \underline{63}$

In the problem $6 \times 3 = 18$,

the 6 is called a ___factor___,

the 3 is called a ___factor___,

and the 18 is called a ___product___.

# Alternate Chapter Test

**for page 153**

| Item | Objective |
|------|-----------|
| 1-33 | Recall multiplication facts through 9 (See pages 119-129, 137-144, 147) |
| 34-36 | Solve word problems involving multiplication facts (See pages 119-129, 137-144, 147) |

Multiply.

1. $\begin{array}{r} 7 \\ \times 5 \\ \hline 35 \end{array}$
2. $\begin{array}{r} 8 \\ \times 7 \\ \hline 56 \end{array}$
3. $\begin{array}{r} 6 \\ \times 6 \\ \hline 36 \end{array}$
4. $\begin{array}{r} 9 \\ \times 8 \\ \hline 72 \end{array}$
5. $\begin{array}{r} 7 \\ \times 8 \\ \hline 56 \end{array}$
6. $\begin{array}{r} 8 \\ \times 7 \\ \hline 56 \end{array}$
7. $\begin{array}{r} 7 \\ \times 7 \\ \hline 49 \end{array}$

8. $\begin{array}{r} 7 \\ \times 9 \\ \hline 63 \end{array}$
9. $\begin{array}{r} 8 \\ \times 5 \\ \hline 40 \end{array}$
10. $\begin{array}{r} 0 \\ \times 7 \\ \hline 0 \end{array}$
11. $\begin{array}{r} 3 \\ \times 8 \\ \hline 24 \end{array}$
12. $\begin{array}{r} 7 \\ \times 4 \\ \hline 28 \end{array}$
13. $\begin{array}{r} 0 \\ \times 5 \\ \hline 0 \end{array}$
14. $\begin{array}{r} 9 \\ \times 6 \\ \hline 54 \end{array}$

15. $\begin{array}{r} 4 \\ \times 5 \\ \hline 20 \end{array}$
16. $\begin{array}{r} 8 \\ \times 8 \\ \hline 64 \end{array}$
17. $\begin{array}{r} 9 \\ \times 8 \\ \hline 72 \end{array}$
18. $\begin{array}{r} 7 \\ \times 3 \\ \hline 21 \end{array}$
19. $\begin{array}{r} 3 \\ \times 7 \\ \hline 21 \end{array}$
20. $\begin{array}{r} 7 \\ \times 6 \\ \hline 42 \end{array}$
21. $\begin{array}{r} 9 \\ \times 7 \\ \hline 63 \end{array}$

22. $4 \times 6 = \underline{24}$   23. $8 \times 6 = \underline{48}$   24. $0 \times 8 = \underline{0}$   25. $4 \times 9 = \underline{36}$

26. $8 \times 4 = \underline{32}$   27. $9 \times 1 = \underline{9}$   28. $9 \times 9 = \underline{81}$   29. $9 \times 5 = \underline{45}$

30. $6 \times 4 = \underline{24}$   31. $9 \times 2 = \underline{18}$   32. $5 \times 7 = \underline{35}$   33. $9 \times 3 = \underline{27}$

Solve these problems.

34. There are 5 rows of trees. Each row has 9 trees in it. How many trees are there?
45 trees

35. Balloons are sold in packages of 8. Rhonda bought 6 packages. How many balloons did Rhonda buy?
48 balloons

36. Use your calculator to find the total cost of this order.

| Number | Item | Cost | Total |
|--------|------|------|-------|
| 4 | Hammers | $9 | $36 |
| 5 | Wrenches | $3 | $15 |
| 8 | Pliers | $7 | $56 |
| | | Total Cost | $107 |

| SALE | |
|------|---|
| Washers | $1 |
| Hammers | $9 |
| Screwdrivers | $4 |
| Wrenches | $3 |
| Pliers | $7 |

(three hundred seven) **307**

**307**

Multiply.

| | | | |
|---|---|---|---|
| 1. $\begin{array}{r} 42 \\ \times\ 3 \\ \hline 126 \end{array}$ | 2. $\begin{array}{r} 26 \\ \times\ 4 \\ \hline 104 \end{array}$ | 3. $\begin{array}{r} 34 \\ \times\ 2 \\ \hline 68 \end{array}$ | 4. $\begin{array}{r} 21 \\ \times\ 6 \\ \hline 126 \end{array}$ |
| 5. $\begin{array}{r} 132 \\ \times\ 3 \\ \hline 396 \end{array}$ | 6. $\begin{array}{r} 212 \\ \times\ 4 \\ \hline 848 \end{array}$ | 7. $\begin{array}{r} 344 \\ \times\ 2 \\ \hline 688 \end{array}$ | 8. $\begin{array}{r} 312 \\ \times\ 3 \\ \hline 936 \end{array}$ |
| 9. $\begin{array}{r} 86 \\ \times\ 5 \\ \hline 430 \end{array}$ | 10. $\begin{array}{r} 29 \\ \times\ 4 \\ \hline 116 \end{array}$ | 11. $\begin{array}{r} 43 \\ \times\ 7 \\ \hline 301 \end{array}$ | 12. $\begin{array}{r} 96 \\ \times\ 8 \\ \hline 768 \end{array}$ |
| 13. $\begin{array}{r} 423 \\ \times\ 6 \\ \hline 2{,}538 \end{array}$ | 14. $\begin{array}{r} 288 \\ \times\ 5 \\ \hline 1{,}440 \end{array}$ | 15. $\begin{array}{r} 537 \\ \times\ 3 \\ \hline 1{,}611 \end{array}$ | 16. $\begin{array}{r} 763 \\ \times\ 4 \\ \hline 3{,}052 \end{array}$ |
| 17. $\begin{array}{r} \$3.27 \\ \times\ 6 \\ \hline \$19.62 \end{array}$ | 18. $\begin{array}{r} \$9.02 \\ \times\ 5 \\ \hline \$45.10 \end{array}$ | 19. $\begin{array}{r} \$6.58 \\ \times\ 8 \\ \hline \$52.64 \end{array}$ | 20. $\begin{array}{r} \$7.26 \\ \times\ 4 \\ \hline \$29.04 \end{array}$ |

Solve these problems.

21. Penny worked out in the gym for 40 minutes every day. How many minutes did Penny work out each week?
280 minutes

22. Jack fills 49 crates of apples each day. He works 5 days. How many crates of apples does Jack fill?
245 crates

23. Ted works 6 hours on Saturday. He earns $5.35 each hour. How much does Ted make?
$32.10

24. $6.75 × 4 = $27.00

$6.75 is a ___factor___ and

$27.00 is a ___product___.

| Item | Objective |
|---|---|
| 1-4 | Multiply 2-digit number by 1-digit number (See pages 159-160) |
| 5-8 | Multiply 1-digit number by 3-digit number (See pages 161-162) |
| 9-12 | Multiply 1-digit number by 2-digit number with regrouping (See pages 163-164) |
| 13-16 | Multiply 1-digit number by 3-digit number with two regroupings (See pages 165-166) |
| 17-20 | Multiply dollars and cents by 1-digit number with regrouping (See pages 167-168) |
| 21-23 | Solve word problems involving multiplication (See pages 158, 160, 164, 166) |
| 24 | Identify the terms of a multiplication problem (See pages 155-176) |

# Alternate Chapter Test

**for page 199**

| Item | Objective |
|---|---|
| 1-3 | Find the area of a plane figure in square units (See pages 181-182) |
| 4-6 | Identify solid figures (See pages 183-184) |
| 7-9 | Find the volume of space figures in cubic units (See pages 185-186) |
| 10 | Tell when two plane figures are congruent (See pages 189-190) |
| 11 | Make a bar graph (See pages 191-192) |
| 12 | Identify a number pair for a point on a graph (See pages 195-196) |



## ALTERNATE CHAPTER TEST

Write the number of square units in each figure.

1. 

18 square units

2. 

12 square units

3. 

4 square units

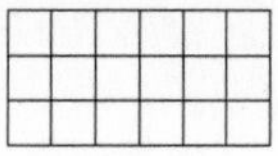

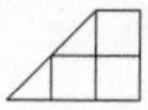

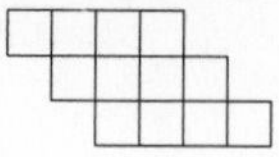

Write the name of each solid figure.

4. 

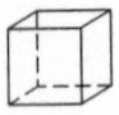

cube

5. 

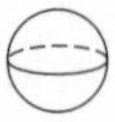

sphere

6. 

rectangular prism

Write the number of cubic units in each figure.

7. 

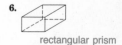

32 cubic units

8. 

15 cubic units

9. 

24 cubic units

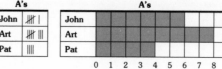

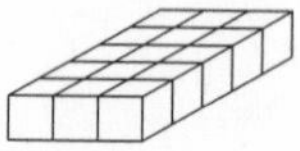

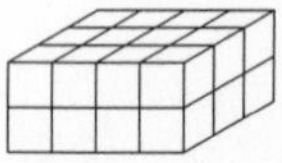

10. Circle the letters of the congruent figures.

A
B
C
D

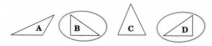

11. Make a bar graph to show the number of A's each student received on spelling tests.

| A's | |
|---|---|
| John | 卌 I |
| Art | 卌 III |
| Pat | IIII |

A's
John
Art
Pat
0 1 2 3 4 5 6 7 8 9

12. Write the number pair for A. 2, 4

A
4
3
2
1
Start
1 2 3 4 5

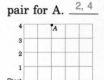

Divide.

1. $12 \div 3 = \underline{4}$　　2. $5\overline{)20}^{\,4}$　　3. $3\overline{)9}^{\,3}$　　4. $21 \div 3 = \underline{7}$

5. $3\overline{)18}^{\,6}$　　6. $4\overline{)24}^{\,6}$　　7. $24 \div 3 = \underline{8}$　　8. $4\overline{)12}^{\,3}$

9. $3\overline{)15}^{\,5}$　　10. $16 \div 4 = \underline{4}$　　11. $10 \div 5 = \underline{2}$　　12. $14 \div 2 = \underline{7}$

13. $3\overline{)27}^{\,9}$　　14. $18 \div 2 = \underline{9}$　　15. $2\overline{)16}^{\,8}$　　16. $3\overline{)12}^{\,4}$

17. $8 \div 2 = \underline{4}$　　18. $12 \div 2 = \underline{6}$　　19. $21 \div 3 = \underline{7}$　　20. $5\overline{)15}^{\,3}$

21. $5\overline{)25}^{\,5}$　　22. $4\overline{)28}^{\,7}$　　23. $4\overline{)32}^{\,8}$　　24. $4\overline{)20}^{\,5}$

Write the missing numbers. Check your answers
with multiplication or division.

25. $24 \div 4 = \underline{6}$　　26. $8 \times 4 = \underline{32}$　　27. $5\overline{)45}^{\,9}$　　28. $5 \times \underline{4} = 20$

29. $5\overline{)30}^{\,6}$　　30. $\underline{9} \times 3 = 27$　　31. $16 \div 2 = \underline{8}$　　32. $4 \times \underline{7} = 28$

33. $\underline{1} \times 8 = 8$　　34. $0 \times 6 = \underline{0}$　　35. $9 \times \underline{4} = 36$　　36. $24 \div 3 = \underline{8}$

37. $15 \div 3 = \underline{5}$　　38. $8\overline{)56}^{\,7}$　　39. $5\overline{)40}^{\,8}$　　40. $30 \div 5 = \underline{6}$

41. $6\overline{)36}^{\,6}$　　42. $32 \div 4 = \underline{8}$　　43. $7\overline{)49}^{\,7}$　　44. $9\overline{)81}^{\,9}$

# Alternate Chapter Test
**for page 219**

| Item | Objective |
|------|-----------|
| 1-24 | Recall division facts (See pages 203-212) |
| 25-44 | Find missing numbers in multiplication and division facts by using inverse operations (See pages 213-214) |

# Alternate Chapter Test

for page 237

**Item** | **Objective**

1-40 | Recall division facts (See pages 201-214, 221-230)

41-44 | Solve word problems involving division facts (See pages 222, 224, 226, 228)

Divide.

1. $12 \div 2 = \underline{6}$  2. $40 \div 8 = \underline{5}$  3. $18 \div 3 = \underline{6}$  4. $12 \div 2 = \underline{6}$

5. $30 \div 6 = \underline{5}$  6. $54 \div 9 = \underline{6}$  7. $32 \div 8 = \underline{4}$  8. $36 \div 6 = \underline{6}$

9. $81 \div 9 = \underline{9}$  10. $72 \div 8 = \underline{9}$  11. $42 \div 7 = \underline{6}$  12. $30 \div 5 = \underline{6}$

13. $8 \div 4 = \underline{2}$  14. $36 \div 6 = \underline{6}$  15. $27 \div 3 = \underline{9}$  16. $9 \div 1 = \underline{9}$

17. $8 \div 8 = \underline{1}$  18. $42 \div 6 = \underline{7}$  19. $48 \div 6 = \underline{8}$  20. $49 \div 7 = \underline{7}$

21. $4\overline{)36}$ — 9     22. $7\overline{)56}$ — 8     23. $6\overline{)54}$ — 9     24. $7\overline{)21}$ — 3

25. $5\overline{)25}$ — 5     26. $7\overline{)49}$ — 7     27. $6\overline{)24}$ — 4     28. $6\overline{)30}$ — 5

29. $7\overline{)0}$ — 0     30. $7\overline{)56}$ — 8     31. $3\overline{)18}$ — 6     32. $9\overline{)45}$ — 5

33. $9\overline{)63}$ — 7     34. $4\overline{)36}$ — 9     35. $8\overline{)48}$ — 6     36. $8\overline{)72}$ — 9

37. $4\overline{)28}$ — 7     38. $8\overline{)56}$ — 7     39. $4\overline{)32}$ — 8     40. $6\overline{)36}$ — 6

Solve these problems.

41. Jean buys 4 boxes of stationery as gifts for her teachers. If she pays $3.59 for each box, about how much money does she need?
$16

42. Manuel spent 16 hours this week working on his computer. If he worked 4 days, how long did he work each day?
4 hours

43. Scott bought 3 computer games for $45.39. About how much did he pay for each game?
$15

44. Sally is reading a book that is 96 pages long. How long will it take her to finish the book if she reads 12 pages a day?
8 days

Divide. Show the work.

1. 6)25    4 R1
2. 4)97    24 R1
3. 8)72    9
4. 4)69    17 R1
5. 4)95    23 R3

6. 3)86    28 R2
7. 4)76    19
8. 8)58    7 R2
9. 5)78    15 R3
10. 7)37    5 R2

11. 2)47    23 R1
12. 6)62    10 R2
13. 2)72    36
14. 3)75    25
15. 9)68    7 R5

16. 5)73    14 R3
17. 6)92    15 R2
18. 5)65    13
19. 7)96    13 R5
20. 6)66    11

Solve these problems.

21. Rodney is sewing 14 badges on his scout uniform. How many badges will be on each sleeve?
7 badges

22. Mr. Springer has 50 extra math worksheets to hand out to 6 students. How many worksheets will he have left over if he gives each student the same number?
2 worksheets

23. Mr. Fraser is keeping track of phone calls coming into his office. He recorded 17 on Monday, 14 on Tuesday, 10 on Wednesday, and 11 on Thursday. What is his average number of calls each day?
13 phone calls

24. Bruce has the following scores:
Test 1   15
Test 2   18
Test 3   21
Test 4   10
What is Bruce's average score?
16

| Item | Objective |
| --- | --- |
| 1-20 | Divide 2-digit by 1-digit numbers with and without remainders (See pages 241-250) |
| 21-24 | Solve word problems involving division of 2-digit numbers (See pages 242, 244, 246, 248, 250) |

# Alternate Chapter Test

**for page 279**

| Item | Objective |
|------|-----------|
| 1-3 | Write a fraction for a part of a whole (See pages 259-262) |
| 4-6 | Write a fraction for a part of a set (See pages 263-264) |
| 7-9 | Find the fractional part of a number (See pages 265-266) |
| 10-11 | Write the equivalent fraction (See pages 267-268) |
| 12-13 | Use a picture to add two fractions with common denominators (See pages 271-272) |

Write the fraction that tells what part is red.

**1.** 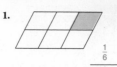 $\frac{1}{6}$

**2.** 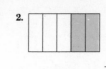 $\frac{2}{5}$

**3.** $\frac{5}{8}$

Write the fraction that tells what part is squares.

**4.**  $\frac{2}{3}$

**5.** $\frac{4}{8}$

**6.**  $\frac{4}{6}$

Find the fraction of each number.

**7.** $\frac{1}{4}$ of 48 __12__

**8.** $\frac{1}{2}$ of 92 = __46__

**9.** $\frac{1}{3}$ of 36 = __12__

Write the missing fractions.

**10.**

$\frac{3}{4} = \frac{6}{8}$

**11.**

$\frac{2}{5} > \frac{2}{8}$

Use the pictures to help you add or subtract these fractions.

**12.**

Shade $\frac{1}{4}$.   $\frac{1}{4} + \frac{1}{4} = \frac{2}{4}$

Shade another $\frac{1}{4}$.

**13.**

Shade $\frac{5}{6}$.   $\frac{5}{6}$

Cross out $\frac{1}{6}$.   $-\frac{1}{6}$ $\frac{4}{6}$

**313**

Write decimals for the parts that are red.

1.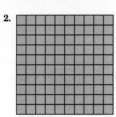

2.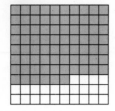

_____3.5_____          _____1.76_____

Compare these numbers. Write < or > in the circle.

**3.** 3.6 ⊙> 3.3     **4.** 4.5 ⊙< 4.8     **5.** 0.9 ⊙> 0.7

**6.** 2.7 ⊙> 2.2     **7.** 4.4 ⊙< 6.1     **8.** 5.9 ⊙< 6.8

Add. Round the numbers to check the answers.

**9.**
$$\begin{array}{r} 21.6 \\ +\,12.2 \\ \hline 33.8 \end{array}$$

**10.**
$$\begin{array}{r} 36.9 \\ +\,15.2 \\ \hline 52.1 \end{array}$$

**11.**
$$\begin{array}{r} 54.7 \\ +\,25.4 \\ \hline 80.1 \end{array}$$

**12.**
$$\begin{array}{r} 6.27 \\ +\,2.67 \\ \hline 8.94 \end{array}$$

**13.**
$$\begin{array}{r} 8.95 \\ +\,1.87 \\ \hline 10.82 \end{array}$$

**14.**
$$\begin{array}{r} 2.49 \\ +\,6.73 \\ \hline 9.22 \end{array}$$

Subtract. Round the numbers to check the answers.

**15.**
$$\begin{array}{r} 6.7 \\ -\,2.1 \\ \hline 4.6 \end{array}$$

**16.**
$$\begin{array}{r} 75.7 \\ -\,32.8 \\ \hline 42.9 \end{array}$$

**17.**
$$\begin{array}{r} 58.1 \\ -\,39.7 \\ \hline 18.4 \end{array}$$

**18.**
$$\begin{array}{r} 6.43 \\ -\,4.27 \\ \hline 2.16 \end{array}$$

**19.**
$$\begin{array}{r} 8.04 \\ -\,4.47 \\ \hline 3.57 \end{array}$$

**20.**
$$\begin{array}{r} 9.73 \\ -\,4.86 \\ \hline 4.87 \end{array}$$

# Alternate Chapter Test
**for page 299**

| Item | Objective |
|------|-----------|
| 1-2 | Write a decimal to match a picture (See pages 281-288) |
| 3-8 | Compare decimals through tenths (See pages 285-286) |
| 9-14 | Add decimals and round numbers to check the answers (See pages 289-294) |
| 15-20 | Subtract decimals and round numbers to check the answers (See pages 289-294) |

# Glossary

**Addend**   A number that is added to another number.

3 + 4 = 7, 3 and 4 are both addends.

**Angle**   The figure made by two straight lines that meet at one endpoint, or vertex.

**Area**   The measure of a surface surrounded by a boundary.

The shaded part of the square is its area.

**Average**   The number obtained by adding two or more quantities and dividing by the number of quantities added.

The average of 2, 5 and 11 is 6;
2 + 5 + 11 = 18; 18 ÷ 3 = 6

**Bar graph**   A way to picture numbers and amounts using columns or bars.

**Calculator codes**   Symbols that name the keys to be pressed on a calculator.

**Celsius scale**   A metric temperature scale naming 0 degrees as the freezing point of water and 100 degrees as its boiling point.

**Circle**   A plane figure whose border is a single curved line with every point equally distant from the center of the figure.

**Composite number**   A number that can be divided evenly by some number other than itself and one.

12 is a composite number because it can be divided by 2, 3, 4 and 6 without a remainder.

**Congruent figures**   Figures of exactly the same size and shape.

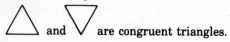 and are congruent triangles.

**Cube**   A solid figure with six equal, square sides.

**Cubic units**   Units used to measure the volume of solid figures.

   There are 8 cubic units in this cube.

**Cylinder**   A solid figure with two bases that are congruent circles.

**Decimal**   A fractional part that uses place value and a decimal point to show tenths, hundredths and so on.

0.6 is the decimal equivalent for the fraction $\frac{3}{5}$.

**Decimal point**   A point or dot that separates ones place value from tenths place value.

**Denominator**   The number below the line in a fraction.

In $\frac{3}{5}$, 5 is the denominator.

**Difference**   The answer in a subtraction problem.

In 14 − 2 = 12, 12 is the difference.

**Diagonal**   A straight line from one vertex to another vertex that is not next to it in a plane figure.

**Digit**   Any one of the ten number symbols: 0, 1, 2, 3, 4, 5, 6, 7, 8 and 9.

**Dividend**   The number that is being divided in a division problem.

In 42 ÷ 7 = 6, 42 is the dividend.

**Divisor**   The number that is being divided into the dividend.

In 42 ÷ 7 = 6, 7 is the divisor.

**Equivalent fractions**   Fractions that name the same number.

$\frac{3}{4}$ and $\frac{9}{12}$ are equivalent fractions because both name $\frac{3}{4}$.

**Estimating**   Using one of various ways to name answers that are close to correct answers.

**Even number**   A whole number with 0, 2, 4, 6 or 8 in the ones place.

**Factor**   A number to be multiplied.
In 2 × 3 = 6, both 2 and 3 are factors.

**Fahrenheit scale**   A temperature scale naming 32 degrees as the freezing point of water and 212 degrees as its boiling point.

**Fraction**   A number that names a part of a whole.

$\frac{1}{2}$ is a fraction.

**Geometry**   The branch of mathematics that studies points, lines, plane figures, and solid figures.

**Graphing**   Drawing a picture of relationships among numbers and quantities.

**Hexagon**   A plane figure with six straight sides.

**Minuend**   A number or quantity from which another is subtracted.
   In 18 − 5 = 13, 18 is the minuend.

**Mixed decimal**   A number containing both a whole number and a decimal.
   3.4 is a mixed decimal.

**Multiple**   A product of two counting numbers.
   In 5 × 7 = 35, 35 is a multiple of 5 and a multiple of 7.

**Number pair**   Two numbers that define one point on a graph; The first number names the distance across, and the second names the distance up.
   The number pair naming point A is (3, 1).

**Numerator**   The number above the line in a fraction.
   In $\frac{3}{5}$, 3 is the numerator.

**Odd number**   A whole number with 1, 3, 5, 7 or 9 in the ones place.

**Pentagon**   A plane figure with five straight sides.

**Perimeter**   The distance around a shape that is the sum of the lengths of all of its sides.

   The perimeter of this rectangle is in red, and is equal to 10 units.
   4 + 1 + 4 + 1 = 10 units

**Picture graph**   A way to show numbers or amounts using symbols or pictures.

**Place value**   The value of the place where a digit appears in a number.
   In 137,510, the **7** is in thousands place and stands for 7,000.

**Plane figure**   A shape that appears on a flat surface.
   Circle, square, triangle, and so on

**Prime number**   A whole number greater than one that has only two divisors, 1 and itself.
   7, 11, 19 and 101 are all prime numbers.

**Product**   The answer to a multiplication problem.
   In 4 × 5 = 20, 20 is the product.

**Quotient**   The answer to a division problem.
   In 7)$\overline{63}$, 9 is the quotient.

**Rectangle**   A four-sided plane figure with four right angles.

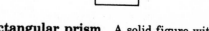

**Rectangular prism**   A solid figure with six sides that are rectangles.

**Remainder**   The number left over in a division problem.
   In 6)$\overline{100}$   4 is the remainder.

$$
\begin{array}{r}
16 \text{ R4} \\
6\overline{)100} \\
\underline{6} \\
40 \\
\underline{36} \\
4
\end{array}
$$

**Right angle**   An angle with the same shape as the vertex of a square; 90 degrees.
   In this square, all angles are right angles.

**Rounding**   Estimating a number's value by raising or lowering any of its place values.
   To round to the nearest ten, look at the ones digit. If it is 4 or less, the tens digit stays the same, and the ones digit is replaced by zero. If the ones digit is 5 or more, the tens digit is raised by one, and the ones digit is replaced by zero. **35** rounded to the nearest 10 is **40**.

**Sequence**   Numbers following a pattern.
   3, 6, 9, 12, 15 and so on.

**Series**   Numbers listed in sequence.
   5, 6, 7 and so on.

**Side**   One border of a plane or space figure.
   A triangle has three sides.

**Solid figure**   A solid shape.
   Sphere, rectangular prism, cube and so on

**Sphere**   A solid with all points the same distance from a center point.

**Square**   A plane figure with four sides of equal length and four right angles.

**Square root**   A number which, when multiplied by itself, produces a given number.

3 is the square root of 9 because $3 \times 3 = 9$.

The square root of $9 = 3$ is written $\sqrt[3]{9}$.

**Subtrahend**   The number that is subtracted from the minuend.

In $18 - 5 = 13$, 5 is the subtrahend.

**Sum**   The answer to an addition problem.

In $8 + 9 = 17$, 17 is the sum.

**Symmetry**   A characteristic of a figure in which, if cut in half, both sides would be the same shape.

**Tally**   Marks used to count by fives.

卌 卌 ||| = 13

**Trading**   The regrouping or renaming of a number value so that an operation can be performed.

**Triangle**   A plane figure with three straight sides.

 are both triangles.

**Unit cost**   The price per unit found by dividing the total cost by the number of units.

If one dozen eggs cost \$1.20, the unit cost per egg is 10¢; $\$1.20 \div 12 = \$0.10$.

**Vertex** (pl. vertices)   The point at which two sides of an angle, two sides of a plane figure, or three or more sides of a solid figure meet.

**Volume**   The number of cubic units needed to fill a solid figure.

The volume of this cube is 8 cubic units.

**Whole numbers**   Those numbers used in counting and zero.

# Index

## A

Addends
  decimals, 289–290
  grouping, 11–12

Addition
  and multiplication, 117–126,
    137–144
  calculator, 57–58, 81–82,
    133–134
  checking, 5–6, 11–12
  column, 5–6, 12, 49–54
  decimals, 289–290
  estimating, 53–56, 293–294
  facts, 1–4, 11–12
  four-digit, 47–52
  fractions, 271–272
  in checking subtraction, 9–12,
    71–72
  money, 51–54
  order, 11–12
  properties, 11–12
  sums through 18, 1–4
  tables, 4
  three-digit numbers, 43–46
  trading, 39–52, 170
  two-digit numbers, 39–42
  zero, 11–12

Angles, 187–188

Area, 181–182

Averages, 251–252

## B

Bar graphs, 191–192

## C

Calculator
  addition key, 57–58, 81–82,
    133–134
  best buy, 255–256
  codes, 57–58, 81–82, 152
  division key, 217–218
  equal key, 133–134
  fractional part, 277–278
  money, 175–176, 231–232,
    255–256
  multiplication key, 151–152
  special keys, 57–58
  square root key, 235–236
  subtraction key, 81–82, 134

Calendar, 89–90

Celsius scale, 113–114

Centimeter, 105–108

Checking
  addition, 5–6, 11–12
  division, 243–244
  subtraction, 9–12, 71–72

Choosing the operation, 13–14,
  79–80

Circle, 179–180, 190

Comparing
  decimals, 285–286
  fractions, 269–270
  numbers, 27–28, 30

Congruent figures, 189–190

Counting
  money, 25–26, 197
  numbers, 23–24

Cube, 183–186

Cubic units, 185–186

Customary measurement
  length, 91–96
  liquid, 97–98
  temperature, 101–102
  weight, 99–100
  volume, 97–98

Cylinder, 183–184

## D

Decimals
  adding, 289–290
  averages, 251–252
  checking, 243–244
  comparing, 285–286, 294
  estimating, 293–294
  mixed, 283–284
  place value, 281, 283, 287
  rounding, 293–294
  subtracting, 291–292
  writing, 281–284, 287–288

Diagonals, 180

Division
  by one, 229–230
  by zero, 229–230
  calculator, 217–218
  checking, 213–214, 243–244
  dividend, 211
  divisor, 211
  facts, 201–218, 221–230
  estimating, 231–232
  quotient, 211
    one digit, 239–244
    remainders, 239–244,
      247–250
    two digits, 245–250

## E

Estimating
  decimals, 293–294
  differences, 77–78
  length, 93–94, 107–108
  money, 171–172, 231–232

products, 171–172
quotients, 231–232
rounding, 29–32, 53–56, 77–78
sums, 53–56
volume, 97–98
weight, 99–100

## F

Fahrenheit scale, 101–102

Feet, 93–96

Fractions
  adding, 271–272
  calculator, 277–278
  comparing, 269–270
  equivalent, 267–268
  naming, 259–264
  of a number, 265–266,
    277–278
  subtracting, 273–274

## G

Gallon, 97–98

Geometry
  angles, 187–188
  plane figures, 179–182,
    187–190
  solid figures, 183–186

Gram, 111–112

Graphs
  bar, 55–56, 191–192, 275–276
  making, 275–276
  number pairs, 195–196
  picture, 193–194

## H

Hexagon, 179–180

## I

Inch, 91–96

## K

Kilogram, 111–112

Kilometer, 107–108

## L

Liter, 109–110

## M

Measuring
  area, 181–182
  customary, 91–102
  length, 91–96, 105–108
  metric, 105–114, 185–186
  perimeter, 95–96

temperature, 101–102,
113–114
volume, 97–98, 109–110,
185–186
weight, 99–100, 111–112

Meter, 107–108

Metric measurement
length, 105–108
liquid, 109–110
temperature, 113–114
weight, 111–112
volume, 109–110, 185–186

Milliliter, 109–110

Miles, 93–96

Money
addition, 51–54
calculator, 175–176, 231–232,
255–256
counting, 21–22, 25–26, 197
division, 231–232, 255–256
multiplication, 167–172
rounding, 29–32, 77–78
subtraction, 75–78

Multiplication
by multiples of ten and one
hundred, 157–158
by one, 127–130
by ten and one hundred, 135–
136
by one-digit multipliers, 155–
172
by zero, 127–130, 145–146
calculator, 151–152
facts, 117–130, 137–148
in checking division, 243–244
money, 167–172
properties, 145–146
trading, 161–170

# N

Number pairs, 195–196
Numbers
comparing, 27–28, 30
composite, 168
even or odd, 240
larger, 35–36
prime, 168
rounding, 29–32, 53–56, 77–
78, 293–294
series, 23–24
writing, 17–20, 33–36

# O

Ordinal numbers, 23–24

Ordering numbers, 23–24

Ounces, 99–100

# P

Pentagon, 179–180

Perimeter, 95–96, 107–108

Picture graphs, 193–194

Pint, 97–98

Place value
decimals, 281–284, 287–288
hundreds, 19–20
larger numbers, 35–36
ones, tens, 17–18
thousands, 33–36

Plane figures, 179–182, 187–190

Pound, 99–100

Predictions, 32, 244

Problem solving
acting it out, 197–198
choosing operation, 13–14,
79–80
drawing a picture, 149–150,
173–174
estimating, 171–172
making a graph, 275–276
making a list, 215–216
making a table, 253–254
making a tally, 233–234
using a plan, 131–132
using estimation, 55–56

# Q

Quart, 97–98

# R

Rectangle, 179–182

Rectangular prism, 183–186

Remainders, 239–244, 247–250

Right angles, 187–188

Roman numerals, 36

Rounding
decimals, 293–294
nearest dollar, 31–32, 53–54,
171–172
nearest hundred, 31–32
nearest ten, 29–30, 53–54

# S

Solid figures, 183–186

Sphere, 183–184

Square, 179–180, 182

Square root, 235–236

Subtraction
calculator, 81–82, 134
checking, 9–12, 71–72

decimals, 291–292
difference, 7
estimating, 77–78, 293–294
facts, 7–12
four-digit numbers, 73–78
fractions, 273–274
minuend, 7
money, 75–78
properties, 11–12
subtrahend, 7
three-digit numbers, 65–72
trading, 61–76, 170
two-digit numbers, 63–64
wheels, 8
zero, 11–12, 69–70

Symmetry, 184

# T

Temperature, 101–102, 113–114

Time
understanding calendars, 89–
90
to the half-hour, 85–86
to the hour, 85–86
to the minute, 87–88
to the quarter-hour, 85–86

Trading
addition, 39–52, 170
multiplication, 161–170
subtraction, 61–76, 170

Triangle, 179–180, 182

# U

Unit cost, 255–256

# V

Volume, 97–98, 109–110,
185–186

# W

Weight, 99–100, 111–112

# Y

Yards, 93–96

# Z

Zero
in addition, 11–12
in division, 229–230
in multiplication, 127–128,
145–146
in subtraction, 11–12, 69–70